Matrix Analysis
and
Computations

Matrix Analysis and Computations

Zhong-Zhi Bai

Academy of Mathematics and Systems Science
Chinese Academy of Sciences
Beijing, China

Jian-Yu Pan

East China Normal University
Shanghai, China

Society for Industrial and Applied Mathematics
Philadelphia

Publications Director	Kivmars H. Bowling
Executive Editor	Elizabeth Greenspan
Developmental Editor	Mellisa Pascale
Managing Editor	Kelly Thomas
Production Editor	Ann Manning Allen
Copy Editor	Claudine Dugan
Production Manager	Donna Witzleben
Production Coordinator	Cally A. Shrader
Compositor	Cheryl Hufnagle
Graphic Designer	Doug Smock

Library of Congress Cataloging-in-Publication Data
Names: Bai, Zhong-Zhi, author. | Pan, Jian-Yu, author.
Title: Matrix analysis and computations / Zhong-Zhi Bai, Jian-Yu Pan.
Description: Philadelphia : Society for Industrial and Applied Mathematics,
  [2021] | Includes bibliographical references and index. | Summary: "This
  book introduces the basics of matrix analysis and presents
  representative methods and their corresponding theories in matrix
  computations"-- Provided by publisher.
Identifiers: LCCN 2021011456 (print) | LCCN 2021011457 (ebook) | ISBN
  9781611976625 (paperback) | ISBN 9781611976632 (ebook)
Subjects: LCSH: Matrices. | Numerical analysis.
Classification: LCC QA188 .B324 2021 (print) | LCC QA188 (ebook) | DDC
  512.9/434--dc23
LC record available at *https://lccn.loc.gov/2021011456*
LC ebook record available at *https://lccn.loc.gov/2021011457*

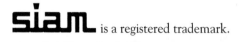 is a registered trademark.

Contents

Preface

Analysis and computation, the most important and indispensable methods for processing matrices, are closely related but two significantly different areas. The former focuses more on theoretical analysis and belongs to the category of pure linear algebra, while the latter concentrates more on practical applications and is classified as numerical linear algebra, although both of them are located at the core bases of pure and computational mathematics. Moreover, matrix theory is the kernel and foundation of matrix computations, while matrix computations are the extensions and applications of matrix theory. Therefore, these two kinds of knowledge are absolute requirements for matrix analysts, computational scientists, and algorithmic practitioners.

This book provides graduate students, scientific researchers, and engineering technicians a judicious combination and organic whole of the knowledge on matrix analysis and matrix computations. It can be used as a standard textbook as well as a self-study tool and reference. One of the key features of the book is the worked-out exercise section at the end of each chapter.

The first part of the book introduces basics in matrix analysis that are necessary for matrix computations. In this part, we chiefly focus on exploring, probing, and extracting various geometric and algebraic structures and properties of matrices, which are useful for theoretical understanding and practical applications of such matrices. The second part of the book presents representative methods and the corresponding theories in matrix computations. In this part, we mainly concentrate on algorithmically designing and theoretically analyzing fast, accurate, and robust computational methods for various matrix problems, which are often fundamental parts of many areas associated with computational sciences and engineering applications.

This book consists of eight chapters. In Chapter 1, we introduce some basic knowledge in linear algebra, such as matrix norms, canonical forms, and Kronecker product. In Chapter 2, we introduce some useful decompositions of matrices, which play a very important role in matrix computations. Chapter 3 is about the numerical ranges, including the standard numerical range and its generalizations. Chapter 4 is about the nonnegative matrices and the M-matrices; some basic but important properties are discussed in detail. Chapter 5 is for the iteration methods and their convergence results for solving systems of linear equations, which are based on matrix splittings. Chapter 6 is for the Krylov subspace iteration methods, including the popular ones such as CG, MINRES, GMRES, BiCGSTAB, etc. In Chapter 7, we discuss preconditioning, which is the key ingredient for successful use of the Krylov subspace iteration methods. Finally, in Chapter 8, we introduce some popular iteration methods and elementary preconditioning techniques for solving structured linear systems of the saddle-point type, which frequently arise in a wide variety of real-world applications.

This content is essentially based on the lectures, handouts, and manuscripts I delivered in many numerical linear algebra summer schools, short-term courses, and long-term seminars since 2000, for graduate students and young scholars, and at a number of Chinese institutions and universities such as Academy of Mathematics and Systems Science of Chinese Academy of Sciences (Beijing: September 2008), Guizhou Normal University (Guiyang: July 2011), Lanzhou University (Lanzhou: May 2000 and July–August 2007), Shanghai University

(Shanghai: December 2013–January 2014), South China Normal University (Guangzhou: July 2006), and Zhejiang University (Hangzhou: July–August 2007). I would like to take this opportunity to thank the main local organizers of these academic activities, including Professors Raymond H. Chan, Chuan-Qing Gu, Zheng-Da Huang, Wen Li, Lin-Zhang Lu, Ping Sun, and Yu-Jiang Wu. I also thank the second author of this book, Professor Jian-Yu Pan, for his efforts in re-typesetting and re-arranging these materials, which yielded part of the initial and workable draft of this book, for me; that is also exactly the only reason that he is my co-author of this book.

Lastly, I thank Professors Kuniyoshi Abe, Ljiljana Cvetkovic, Hua Dai, Walter Gander, Apostolos Hadjidimos, Ken Hayami, Yu-Mei Huang, Ilse C.F. Ipsen, Lev A. Krukier, Xin-Guo Liu, Galina V. Muratova, Maya G. Neytcheva, Min Tao, Zeng-Qi Wang, Yu-Jiang Wu, and many other friends and colleagues for providing helpful advice, suggestions, and comments. In particular, I thank Drs. Fang Chen, Tian-Yi Li, Yao-Ning Liu, Kang-Ya Lu, Lu Wang, and Wen-Ting Wu for carefully reading the original version of this book and finding typos and errors in it; and the three reviewers of this book for strongly supporting its publication and expertly suggesting some modifications to its draft version. Last but not least, I would like to extend my thanks to the SIAM (Society for Industrial and Applied Mathematics) publisher, especially the Executive Editor, Elizabeth Greenspan, who made the publication of this book possible, and Mellisa Pascale, who patiently and competently dealt with all of my typesetting requests. In addition, I am indebted very much to Cheryl Hufnagle and Ann Manning Allen for their exquisite composition, meticulous proofreading, and elaborate correction.

I would also like to take the opportunity to thank my two lovely sons, Ge-Qi Bai and Ge-Yang Bai, for their understanding and support during a reasonably long period while I wrote this book!

Zhong-Zhi Bai
Zhong-Guan-Cun, Beijing, China
June 28, 2020
(Revised and extended on
June 30, 2021)

List of Symbols

$\mathcal{O}(n)$	A quantity of order n
$\lfloor r \rfloor$	The floor of r: The nearest integer not less than the real number r
$\lceil r \rceil$	The ceiling of r: The nearest integer not larger than the real number r
i	Imaginary unit
$\mathbb{R}$	Domain of real numbers
$\mathbb{C}$	Domain of complex numbers
$\mathbb{R}^n$ (or $\mathbb{R}^{n \times n}$)	Linear space of all real n-vectors (or $n \times n$-matrices)
$\mathbb{C}^n$ (or $\mathbb{C}^{n \times n}$)	Linear space of all complex n-vectors (or $n \times n$-matrices)
x^T (or A^T)	Transpose of vector x (or matrix A)
x^* (or A^*)	Conjugate transpose of vector x (or matrix A)
$\text{length}(x)$	Dimension of vector x
$\Re(z)$	Real part of $z \in \mathbb{C}$
$\Im(z)$	Imaginary part of $z \in \mathbb{C}$
$\langle x, y \rangle$	Inner product of vectors x and y
$x \perp y$	Vector x is orthogonal to vector y
$\overline{z}$	Conjugacy of $z \in \mathbb{C}$
$|z|$	Absolute value or modulus of $z \in \mathbb{C}$
$\text{sign}(z)$	Sign function of $z \in \mathbb{C}$, which equals 0 if $z = 0$ and $\frac{z}{|z|}$ if $z \neq 0$
$\|x\|_p$ (or $\|A\|_p$)	p-norm of vector x (or matrix A)
$\|x\|_A$	A-norm or energy norm of vector x
$a_{ij}, a_{i,j}$	The (i, j)-th entry of the matrix $A = [a_{ij}]$
$A(i, j), [A]_{ij}, [A]_{i,j}$	The (i, j)-th entry of the matrix A
I	The identity matrix
I_n	The identity matrix of dimension n
e_i	The i-th column vector of the identity matrix I
e	The vector of all components equal to 1, i.e., $e = [1, 1, \ldots, 1]^\mathsf{T}$
$\mathscr{H}(A), \mathscr{S}(A)$	The Hermitian and the skew-Hermitian part of matrix A
$\text{diag}(\cdot)$	$\text{diag}(a_{11}, a_{22}, \ldots, a_{mm})$ is the diagonal matrix with a_{ii} being the i-th diagonal entry
$\text{Diag}(\cdot)$	$\text{Diag}(A_{11}, A_{22}, \ldots, A_{mm})$ is the block-diagonal matrix with A_{ii} being the i-th block-diagonal entry
$\|A\|_F$	Frobenius norm of matrix A
$\rho(A)$	Spectral radius of matrix A
$\det(A)$	Determinant of matrix A
A^{-1}	Inverse of matrix A

$P_A(\lambda)$	Characteristic polynomial of matrix A
$\mathrm{tr}(A)$	Trace of matrix A
$\mathrm{rank}(A)$	Rank of matrix A
$\kappa(A), \kappa_p(A), \kappa_F(A)$	Condition number of matrix A in 2-norm, p-norm, F-norm
$\lambda(A)$	Any eigenvalue of matrix A
$\lambda_{\min}(A), \lambda_{\max}(A)$	Largest and smallest eigenvalues of a Hermitian matrix A
$\sigma_{\min}(A), \sigma_{\max}(A)$	Largest and smallest singular values of matrix A
$\mathrm{diag}(x)$	Diagonal matrix with the main diagonal elements equal to the elements of the vector x
$\mathrm{Ker}(A)$	Null space or kernel of matrix A
$\mathrm{Ran}(A)$	Range space or range of matrix A
$A \circ B$	Hadamard product of matrices A and B
$A \oplus B$	Direct sum of matrices A and B
$A \otimes B$	Kronecker (direct or tensor) product of matrices A and B
$\mathcal{F}(A)$	Numerical range, or field of values, of matrix A
$\mathcal{F}_k(A), \mathcal{F}_c(A), \mathcal{F}_C(A)$	k-numerical range, c-numerical range, C-numerical range of matrix A
$r(A), r_C(A)$	Numerical radius, C-numerical radius of matrix A
$\sigma(A), \sigma_C(A), \rho_C(A)$	Spectrum, C-spectrum, C-spectral radius of matrix A
$\|A\|_C$	C-spectral norm of matrix A
$\mathrm{span}(G)$	Vector space spanned by the columns of matrix G
$\mathrm{span}\{x_1, x_2, \ldots, x_n\}$	Vector space spanned by $\{x_1, x_2, \ldots, x_n\}$, where $x_1, x_2, \ldots, x_n$ are vectors of the same size
$\mathrm{span}\{x\}^\perp$	The vertical space, or the orthogonal complement space, of the space spanned by vector x
$\mathcal{K}_m(A, v)$	Krylov subspace with respect to the matrix A and the vector v, that is, $\mathcal{K}_m(A, v) = \mathrm{span}\{v, Av, \ldots, A^{m-1}v\}$
$\dim(V)$	Dimension of vector space V
$\mathrm{Co}(S)$	Convex hull of set S
$\mathcal{C}(c, r)$	The disc centered at c with radius r
$\deg(p)$	The degree of the real polynomial $p(t)$
$\mathcal{P}_n$	The set of all real polynomials $p(t)$ with $\deg(p) \le n$
$\mathcal{E}(c, d, a)$	The ellipse centered at c with the focal distance d and the semi-major axis a

Chapter 1

Basic Concepts and Properties

This chapter gives basic concepts and some corresponding properties in linear algebra that are useful in the subsequent chapters.

1.1 ▪ Vectors and Vector Norms

Let $\mathbb{C}^n$ and $\mathbb{R}^n$ be the vector spaces of all complex and all real n-dimensional vectors, respectively. For $x \in \mathbb{C}^n$, i.e.,

$$x = \begin{bmatrix} x_1 \\ x_2 \\ \vdots \\ x_n \end{bmatrix}, \quad \text{with} \quad x_i \in \mathbb{C} \text{ the } i\text{-th component,}$$

we use x^T and x^* to denote its **transpose** and **conjugate transpose**, respectively. For two vectors $x, y \in \mathbb{C}^n$, we define their (*Euclidean*) **inner product** as

$$\langle x, y \rangle = y^* x = \sum_{i=1}^{n} \bar{y}_i x_i,$$

where $\bar{y}_i$ denotes the complex conjugacy of y_i.

Definition 1.1. *A **vector norm** on $\mathbb{C}^n$ is a function $f : \mathbb{C}^n \to \mathbb{R}$ satisfying the following properties:*

> (1) (nonnegativity) $f(x) \geq 0$, *and* $f(x) = 0$ *if and only if* $x = 0$, $\quad \forall x \in \mathbb{C}^n$;
> (2) (triangle inequality) $f(x+y) \leq f(x) + f(y)$, $\quad \forall x, y \in \mathbb{C}^n$;
> (3) (positive homogeneity) $f(\alpha x) = |\alpha| f(x)$, $\quad \forall x \in \mathbb{C}^n, \forall \alpha \in \mathbb{C}$.

Such a function with respect to the vector x is briefly denoted as $\|x\|$.

In particular, the **p-norms** of vectors in $\mathbb{C}^n$ are defined as

$$\|x\|_p = (|x_1|^p + |x_2|^p + \cdots + |x_n|^p)^{\frac{1}{p}}, \quad p \geq 1.$$

Among them, the **1-norm**, the **2-norm**, and the **∞-norm** given below are the most important norms:

$$\|x\|_1 = |x_1| + |x_2| + \cdots + |x_n|,$$
$$\|x\|_2 = \left(|x_1|^2 + |x_2|^2 + \cdots + |x_n|^2\right)^{\frac{1}{2}},$$
$$\|x\|_\infty = \max\left\{|x_1|, |x_2|, \ldots, |x_n|\right\}.$$

The 2-norm is also called the **Euclidean norm**, as it can be equivalently defined through the inner product

$$\|x\|_2 = \sqrt{\langle x, x \rangle}, \quad \forall\, x \in \mathbb{C}^n.$$

The **angle** θ between two nonzero vectors $x, y \in \mathbb{C}^n$ is defined as

$$\cos\theta = \frac{|\langle x, y \rangle|}{\|x\|_2 \|y\|_2}, \quad 0 \leq \theta \leq \frac{\pi}{2}.$$

An essential property of the p-norm is the **Hölder inequality**:

$$|\langle x, y \rangle| \leq \|x\|_p \|y\|_q, \quad \frac{1}{p} + \frac{1}{q} = 1, \ p > 0, \ q > 0.$$

When $p = q = 2$, as a special case, we obtain the **Cauchy–Schwarz inequality**:

$$|\langle x, y \rangle| \leq \|x\|_2 \|y\|_2.$$

Two given norms, say, α-norm and β-norm, in $\mathbb{C}^n$, are called **equivalent** if there exist two positive constants c_1 and c_2 such that

$$c_1 \|x\|_\alpha \leq \|x\|_\beta \leq c_2 \|x\|_\alpha, \quad \forall\, x \in \mathbb{C}^n.$$

We can easily verify that the 1-norm, the 2-norm, and the ∞-norm are equivalent in $\mathbb{C}^n$, as it holds that

$$\|x\|_2 \leq \|x\|_1 \leq \sqrt{n}\, \|x\|_2, \tag{1.1}$$
$$\|x\|_\infty \leq \|x\|_2 \leq \sqrt{n}\, \|x\|_\infty, \tag{1.2}$$
$$\|x\|_\infty \leq \|x\|_1 \leq n\, \|x\|_\infty. \tag{1.3}$$

Actually, for any two vector norms we have the following theorem.

Theorem 1.2. [257] *Let $\|\cdot\|_\alpha$ and $\|\cdot\|_\beta$ be two vector norms defined on $\mathbb{C}^n$. Then there exist constants $c_2 \geq c_1 > 0$ such that*

$$c_1 \|x\|_\alpha \leq \|x\|_\beta \leq c_2 \|x\|_\alpha, \quad \forall\, x \in \mathbb{C}^n.$$

A **unit vector** with respect to a norm $\|\cdot\|$ is a vector x that satisfies $\|x\| = 1$. Two vectors $x, y \in \mathbb{C}^n$ are said to be **orthogonal**, denoted by $x \perp y$, if $\langle x, y \rangle = 0$. We say that the vectors $x_1, x_2, \ldots, x_n \in \mathbb{C}^n$ form an **orthogonal set** if $\langle x_i, x_j \rangle = 0$ hold for all $i \neq j$. If, in addition, the vectors are normalized, i.e., $\|x_i\|_2 = 1$, $i = 1, 2, \ldots, n$, then the set of these vectors is called **orthonormal**.

Proposition 1.3. *If the vectors $x_1, x_2, \ldots, x_n \in \mathbb{C}^n$ form an orthogonal set, then it holds that*

$$\|x_1 + x_2 + \cdots + x_n\|_2^2 = \|x_1\|_2^2 + \|x_2\|_2^2 + \cdots + \|x_n\|_2^2.$$

A set of **vectors** $\{x_1, x_2, \ldots, x_k\} \subseteq \mathbb{C}^n$ is called **linearly dependent** if there exist scalars $\alpha_1, \alpha_2, \ldots, \alpha_k \in \mathbb{C}$ such that

$$\alpha_1 x_1 + \alpha_2 x_2 + \cdots + \alpha_k x_k = 0$$

holds true with at least one $\alpha_i \neq 0$, $i \in \{1, 2, \ldots, k\}$. Otherwise, it is called **linearly independent**.

A linearly independent **subset** $\mathcal{S}$ of a **vector space** $\mathbb{V}$ is called a **basis** of $\mathbb{V}$ if every element of the vector space $\mathbb{V}$ can be represented as a unique **linear combination** of the elements of the subset $\mathcal{S}$. If, in addition, the subset $\mathcal{S}$ is orthonormal, then it is called an **orthonormal basis** of the vector space $\mathbb{V}$.

If a basis of the vector space $\mathbb{V}$ consists of a finite number of elements, then all bases of $\mathbb{V}$ have the same number of elements. This number is called the **dimension** of the vector space $\mathbb{V}$ and is denoted by $\dim(\mathbb{V})$. In this case, the vector space $\mathbb{V}$ is said to be of finite dimension. Otherwise, $\mathbb{V}$ is said to be a vector space of infinite dimension.

Any linearly independent subset in a vector space $\mathbb{V}$ can be extended to a basis of $\mathbb{V}$. That is to say, for a given linearly independent set $\{x_1, x_2, \ldots, x_m\} \subseteq \mathbb{V}$, there exist additional vectors $x_{m+1}, x_{m+2}, \ldots \in \mathbb{V}$ such that $\{x_1, \ldots, x_m, x_{m+1}, \ldots\}$ is a basis of the vector space $\mathbb{V}$.

The basis $\{e_1, e_2, \ldots, e_n\}$, with e_i having 1 as its i-th component and 0 elsewhere, is called the **standard basis** of $\mathbb{C}^n$ or $\mathbb{R}^n$.

For a set of vectors $\mathcal{G} = \{x_1, x_2, \ldots, x_k\}$, with $x_i \in \mathbb{C}^n$, $i = 1, 2, \ldots, k$, the set

$$\text{span}(\mathcal{G}) = \left\{ z \,:\, z = \sum_{i=1}^{k} \alpha_i x_i, \ \alpha_i \in \mathbb{C}, \quad i = 1, 2, \ldots, k \right\}$$

is a subspace of $\mathbb{C}^n$, which is called the **space spanned by** $\mathcal{G}$. If the vectors $x_1, x_2, \ldots, x_k$ are linearly independent, each vector of $\text{span}(\mathcal{G})$ admits a unique expression as a linear combination of these vectors $x_1, x_2, \ldots, x_k$. Therefore, $\{x_1, x_2, \ldots, x_k\}$ forms a **basis** of the linear subspace $\text{span}(\mathcal{G})$.

Given a set of linearly independent vectors, say, $\{v_1, v_2, \ldots, v_m\}$, we can construct an orthonormal set, say, $\{u_1, u_2, \ldots, u_m\}$, by using the **Gram–Schmidt** (GS) procedure:

$$\begin{cases} u_1 = \dfrac{v_1}{\|v_1\|_2}, \\[2mm] u_k = \dfrac{\tilde{u}_k}{\|\tilde{u}_k\|_2}, & \text{with } \tilde{u}_k = v_k - \displaystyle\sum_{i=1}^{k-1} (v_k^* u_i) u_i, \quad k = 2, 3, \ldots, m. \end{cases}$$

In practical computations, a mathematically equivalent but more stable one, called the **modified Gram–Schmidt** (MGS) procedure, is often used. The MGS algorithm is described as follows.

Algorithm 1.1: The MGS Algorithm

1: $u_1 = \dfrac{v_1}{\|v_1\|_2}$
2: **for** $k = 2, 3, \ldots, m$ **do**
3: $\quad u_k = v_k$
4: $\quad$ **for** $i = 1, 2, \ldots, k-1$ **do**
5: $\quad\quad u_k = u_k - (u_k^* u_i) u_i$
6: $\quad$ **end for**
7: $\quad u_k = \dfrac{u_k}{\|u_k\|_2}$
8: **end for**

The MGS procedure forms the core of many iterative methods for solving systems of linear equations.

Theorem 1.4. *Let k be a positive integer such that $1 \leq k \leq n$, and $u_1, u_2, \ldots, u_k \in \mathbb{C}^n$ form an orthonormal set. Then there exist vectors $u_{k+1}, u_{k+2}, \ldots, u_n \in \mathbb{C}^n$ such that*

$$\{u_1, \ldots, u_k, u_{k+1}, \ldots, u_n\}$$

forms an orthonormal basis of $\mathbb{C}^n$.

At the end of this section, we define the convergence of a vector sequence in terms of a vector norm.

Definition 1.5. *Let $\| \cdot \|$ be any vector norm in $\mathbb{C}^n$ (or $\mathbb{R}^n$). Then the vector sequence $\{x_k\}_{k=0}^{\infty} \subset \mathbb{C}^n$ (or $\mathbb{R}^n$) **converges** to $x_* \in \mathbb{C}^n$ (or $\mathbb{R}^n$) if and only if*

$$\lim_{k \to \infty} \|x_k - x_*\| = 0.$$

That is to say, all entries of the error vector $x_k - x_*$ tend to zero. Alternatively, this fact is written as

$$\lim_{k \to \infty} x_k = x_*,$$

or

$$x_k \to x_*, \quad as \ k \to \infty.$$

A sequence that is not convergent is called **divergent**.

1.2 ▪ Matrices

A complex (real) $m \times n$ matrix A is an $m \times n$ array of complex (real) numbers arranged in the form

$$A = [a_{ij}] = \begin{bmatrix} a_{11} & a_{12} & \cdots & a_{1n} \\ a_{21} & a_{22} & \cdots & a_{2n} \\ \vdots & \vdots & \ddots & \vdots \\ a_{m1} & a_{m2} & \cdots & a_{mn} \end{bmatrix}.$$

We denote the set of all complex (or real) $m \times n$ matrices by $\mathbb{C}^{m \times n}$ (or $\mathbb{R}^{m \times n}$). A matrix is said to be **square** if $m = n$. A **submatrix** of a given matrix A is obtained by deleting some specified rows and columns. A **principal submatrix** is a square submatrix obtained by deleting some rows and columns of the same numbers, and the j-th **leading principal submatrix** of a given square matrix A is a square submatrix obtained by deleting the last $n - j$ rows and columns.

The **transpose** and the **conjugate transpose** of a matrix A are denoted by A^{T} and A^*, respectively. If A is a real matrix, then $A^* = A^{\mathsf{T}}$. We use 0 and I to denote the zero and the identity matrices, respectively. For a square matrix $A = [a_{ij}] \in \mathbb{C}^{n \times n}$ (or $\mathbb{R}^{n \times n}$), its **trace**, denoted by $\mathrm{tr}(A)$, is defined as the sum of its diagonal entries, i.e.,

$$\mathrm{tr}(A) \triangleq \sum_{i=1}^{n} a_{ii}.$$

A few elementary properties for the trace are

(1) $\operatorname{tr}(A^*) = \operatorname{tr}(\overline{A}) = \overline{\operatorname{tr}(A)}$,

(2) $\operatorname{tr}(cA) = c \operatorname{tr}(A)$,

(3) $\operatorname{tr}(A + B) = \operatorname{tr}(A) + \operatorname{tr}(B)$,

(4) $\operatorname{tr}(AB) = \operatorname{tr}(BA)$,

where $A, B \in \mathbb{C}^{n \times n}$ and $c \in \mathbb{C}$.

The last statement holds true even when A and B are not square matrices, but they are conformable for multiplication in the order given, that is, the number of columns of the first matrix is the same as the number of rows of the second.

Any matrix $A \in \mathbb{C}^{m \times n}$ (or $\mathbb{R}^{m \times n}$) can be regarded as a linear mapping from $\mathbb{C}^n$ to $\mathbb{C}^m$ (or $\mathbb{R}^n$ to $\mathbb{R}^m$). The **range** of the matrix $A \in \mathbb{C}^{m \times n}$ is defined by

$$\operatorname{Ran}(A) \triangleq \{z = Ax : x \in \mathbb{C}^n\},$$

which is a subspace of $\mathbb{C}^m$. The **kernel** (or **null space**) of the matrix $A \in \mathbb{C}^{m \times n}$ is defined by

$$\operatorname{Ker}(A) \triangleq \{x \in \mathbb{C}^n : Ax = 0\},$$

which is a subspace of $\mathbb{C}^n$.

Proposition 1.6. *Let $A \in \mathbb{C}^{n \times n}$. Then it holds that*

- $\operatorname{Ran}(A)$ *is the space spanned by the columns of the matrix A, denoted by* $\operatorname{span}(A)$;
- $\dim(\operatorname{Ran}(A)) = \dim(\operatorname{Ran}(A^*))$;
- $\dim\big(\operatorname{Ran}(A)\big) + \dim\big(\operatorname{Ker}(A)\big) = n$.

We remark that, in general, $\dim(\operatorname{Ker}(A)) \neq \dim(\operatorname{Ker}(A^*))$ for $A \in \mathbb{C}^{m \times n}$.

Example 1.7. Let

$$A = \begin{bmatrix} 1 & 1 & 0 \\ -1 & 1 & 1 \end{bmatrix}.$$

Then $\dim(\operatorname{Ran}(A)) = \dim(\operatorname{Ran}(A^*)) = 2$, $\dim(\operatorname{Ker}(A)) = 1$ and $\dim(\operatorname{Ker}(A^*)) = 0$.

Proposition 1.8. *Let $A \in \mathbb{C}^{n \times n}$. Then it holds that*

$$\operatorname{Ker}(A^*) = \operatorname{Ran}(A)^\perp.$$

Proof. If $y \in \operatorname{Ker}(A^*)$, then $A^*y = 0$. For any vector $z \in \operatorname{Ran}(A)$, there exists a vector $x \in \mathbb{C}^n$ such that $z = Ax$. Hence, we have

$$z^*y = (Ax)^*y = x^*(A^*y) = 0,$$

which implies that $y \in \operatorname{Ran}(A)^\perp$. Therefore,

$$\operatorname{Ker}(A^*) \subseteq \operatorname{Ran}(A)^\perp. \tag{1.4}$$

On the other hand, if $y \in \operatorname{Ran}(A)^\perp$, then for any vector $z \in \operatorname{Ran}(A)$ we have $z^*y = 0$. As $AA^*y \in \operatorname{Ran}(A)$, it holds that

$$(A^*y)^*(A^*y) = y^*AA^*y = (AA^*y)^*y = 0,$$

which implies $A^*y = 0$, i.e., $y \in \mathrm{Ker}(A^*)$. Therefore,

$$\mathrm{Ran}(A)^\perp \subseteq \mathrm{Ker}(A^*). \tag{1.5}$$

It follows from (1.4) and (1.5) that

$$\mathrm{Ker}(A^*) = \mathrm{Ran}(A)^\perp. \qquad \Box$$

1.2.1 ▪ Special Types of Matrices

For $A = [a_{ij}] \in \mathbb{C}^{n \times n}$, $T = [t_{ij}] \in \mathbb{C}^{n \times n}$, $C = [c_{ij}] \in \mathbb{C}^{n \times n}$ and $H = [h_{ij}] \in \mathbb{C}^{n \times n}$, in the following we list several types of matrices that play an important role in numerical analysis and scientific computing:

- symmetric matrix: A is real and $A^\mathsf{T} = A$;
- Hermitian matrix: $A^* = A$;
- skew-symmetric matrix: A is real and $A^\mathsf{T} = -A$;
- skew-Hermitian matrix: $A^* = -A$;
- normal matrix: $A^*A = AA^*$;
- orthogonal matrix: A is real and $A^\mathsf{T}A = AA^\mathsf{T} = I$;
- unitary matrix: $A^*A = AA^* = I$;
- diagonal matrix: $a_{ij} = 0$ for all i, j such that $i \neq j$ (notation: $A = \mathrm{diag}(a_{11}, a_{22}, \ldots, a_{nn})$);
- tridiagonal matrix: $a_{ij} = 0$ for all i, j such that $|i - j| > 1$ (notation: $A = \mathrm{tridiag}(a_{i,i-1}, a_{i,i}, a_{i,i+1})$);
- strictly upper-triangular matrix: $a_{ij} = 0$ for all i, j such that $i \geq j$;
- strictly lower-triangular matrix: $a_{ij} = 0$ for all i, j such that $i \leq j$;
- banded matrix: $a_{ij} \neq 0$ only for those i, j such that $-b_u \leq i - j \leq b_l$, where b_l and b_u are nonnegative integers called the lower- and upper-half bandwidths, respectively, and the number $b_u + b_l + 1$ is called the *bandwidth* of the banded matrix A;
- permutation matrix: the columns of A are a permutation of the columns of I;
- upper Hessenberg matrix: $a_{ij} = 0$ for those i, j such that $i - j > 1$;
- lower Hessenberg matrix: $a_{ij} = 0$ for those i, j such that $j - i > 1$;
- block-diagonal matrix: replacing the diagonal entries of a diagonal matrix by square submatrices (notation: $A = \mathrm{Diag}(A_{11}, A_{22}, \ldots, A_{kk})$);
- block-tridiagonal matrix can be defined similarly (notation: $A = \mathrm{Tridiag}(A_{i,t-1}, A_{i,i}, A_{i,i+1})$);
- Toeplitz matrix: the elements are the same along each diagonals, i.e.,

$$T = \begin{bmatrix} t_0 & t_{-1} & \cdots & t_{-n+1} \\ t_1 & \ddots & \ddots & \vdots \\ \vdots & \ddots & \ddots & t_{-1} \\ t_{n-1} & \cdots & t_1 & t_0 \end{bmatrix},$$

so that $t_{ij} = t_{i-j}$ for all i, j;
- circulant matrix: the rows are composed of cyclically shifted versions of a vector, say, e.g.,

$[c_0, c_1, \ldots, c_{n-1}]^\mathsf{T}$, i.e.,

$$C = \begin{bmatrix} c_0 & c_{n-1} & c_{n-2} & \cdots & c_1 \\ c_1 & c_0 & c_{n-1} & \cdots & c_2 \\ c_2 & c_1 & c_0 & \cdots & c_3 \\ \vdots & \vdots & \vdots & \ddots & \vdots \\ c_{n-1} & c_{n-2} & c_{n-3} & \cdots & c_0 \end{bmatrix};$$

- skew-circulant matrix: a circulant matrix $C = [c_{ij}]$ satisfying $c_{ij} = -c_{i-j}$ for all i, j such that $i > j$, i.e.,

$$C = \begin{bmatrix} c_0 & c_{n-1} & c_{n-2} & \cdots & c_1 \\ -c_1 & c_0 & c_{n-1} & \cdots & c_2 \\ -c_2 & -c_1 & c_0 & \cdots & c_3 \\ \vdots & \vdots & \vdots & \ddots & \vdots \\ -c_{n-1} & -c_{n-2} & -c_{n-3} & \cdots & c_0 \end{bmatrix};$$

- Hankel matrix: the elements are the same along each counterdiagonal, i.e.,

$$H = \begin{bmatrix} h_0 & h_1 & \cdots & h_{n-2} & h_{n-1} \\ h_1 & \iddots & \iddots & \iddots & h_n \\ \vdots & \iddots & \iddots & \iddots & \vdots \\ h_{n-2} & \iddots & \iddots & \iddots & h_{2n-2} \\ h_{n-1} & h_n & \cdots & h_{2n-2} & h_{2n-1} \end{bmatrix}.$$

Remark 1.1. *A block-diagonal matrix $A = \mathrm{Diag}(A_{11}, A_{22}, \ldots, A_{kk})$ is often indicated as $A = A_{11} \oplus A_{22} \oplus \cdots \oplus A_{kk}$, more briefly, $A = \oplus_{i=1}^{k} A_{ii}$. So the matrix A is also said to be the **direct sum** of the matrices $A_{11}, A_{22}, \ldots, A_{kk}$.*

Remark 1.2. *The Toeplitz matrix is persymmetric [167], that is, the matrix T is symmetric with respect to its counterdiagonal or northeast-southwest diagonal. Circulant and skew-circulant matrices are special Toeplitz matrices.*

1.2.2 ▪ Determinant and Rank

For a square matrix $A = [a_{i,j}] \in \mathbb{C}^{n \times n}$, we define its **determinant** as the scalar

$$\det(A) = \sum_{\pi} \mathrm{sign}(\pi)\, a_{1,\pi(1)} a_{2,\pi(2)} \cdots a_{n,\pi(n)},$$

where the sum runs over all $n!$ permutations π of the n items $\{1, 2, \ldots, n\}$ and $\mathrm{sign}(\pi)$ is equal to 1 or -1 according to whether the number of exchanges necessarily obtaining from $\{1, 2, \ldots, n\}$ is even or odd.

Another way for defining the determinant of a matrix A is by recursion. Let the determinant of a 1×1 matrix $A = (a)$ be the scalar a. Then the determinant of an $n \times n$ matrix $A = [a_{ij}]_{n \times n}$ is defined as

$$\det(A) = \sum_{j=1}^{n} (-1)^{j+1} a_{1j} \det(A_{1j}),$$

where A_{1j} is an $(n-1) \times (n-1)$ submatrix obtained by deleting the first row and the j-th column of the matrix A.

Let $A \in \mathbb{C}^{n \times n}$ be a square matrix. If there exists a square matrix B such that

$$AB = BA = I,$$

then the matrix B is called the **inverse** of the matrix A, denoted by $B = A^{-1}$. The matrix A is said to be **nonsingular** if A^{-1} exists; otherwise, it is called **singular**.

For two square matrices A and B, the following equations hold true:

- $\det(AB) = \det(A) \det(B)$;
- $\det(A^{\mathsf{T}}) = \det(A)$;
- $\det(A^*) = \overline{\det(A)}$;
- $\det(\alpha A) = \alpha^n \det(A)$, $\forall \alpha \in \mathbb{C}$;
- $\det(A^{-1}) = \frac{1}{\det(A)}$;
- $\det(I) = 1$;
- $\det\left(\begin{bmatrix} A_{11} & A_{12} \\ 0 & A_{22} \end{bmatrix} \right) = \det\left(\begin{bmatrix} A_{11} & 0 \\ A_{21} & A_{22} \end{bmatrix} \right) = \det(A_{11}) \det(A_{22})$.

The **column rank** of a matrix $A \in \mathbb{C}^{m \times n}$ is the maximum number of linearly independent columns of the matrix A, and the **row rank** of a matrix A is the maximum number of linearly independent rows of the matrix A. It is a remarkable fact that "column rank = row rank." So, we call either the column rank or the row rank just the **rank** and, for the matrix A, we briefly denote it by $\mathrm{rank}(A)$.

The following are several fundamental properties with respect to the rank:

- $\mathrm{rank}(A) \le \min\{m, n\}$, $\forall A \in \mathbb{C}^{m \times n}$;
- $\mathrm{rank}(A^*) = \mathrm{rank}(A)$, $\forall A \in \mathbb{C}^{m \times n}$;
- $\mathrm{rank}(A^*A) = \mathrm{rank}(AA^*) = \mathrm{rank}(A)$, $\forall A \in \mathbb{C}^{m \times n}$;
- for nonsingular matrices $P \in \mathbb{C}^{m \times m}$ and $Q \in \mathbb{C}^{n \times n}$,

$$\mathrm{rank}(PA) = \mathrm{rank}(AQ) = \mathrm{rank}(A) = \mathrm{rank}(PAQ), \quad \forall A \in \mathbb{C}^{m \times n};$$

- for $A, B \in \mathbb{C}^{m \times n}$, $\mathrm{rank}(A) = \mathrm{rank}(B)$ if and only if there exist nonsingular matrices $P \in \mathbb{C}^{m \times m}$ and $Q \in \mathbb{C}^{n \times n}$ such that $A = PBQ$;
- for $A, B \in \mathbb{C}^{m \times n}$, $|\mathrm{rank}(A) - \mathrm{rank}(B)| \le \mathrm{rank}(A + B) \le \mathrm{rank}(A) + \mathrm{rank}(B)$;
- for $A \in \mathbb{C}^{m \times k}$ and $B \in \mathbb{C}^{k \times n}$,

$$\mathrm{rank}(A) + \mathrm{rank}(B) - k \le \mathrm{rank}(AB) \le \min\{\mathrm{rank}(A), \ \mathrm{rank}(B)\}.$$

The left-hand side of the last inequality is called the **Sylvester law** of nullity.

Proposition 1.9. *For a matrix $A \in \mathbb{C}^{m \times n}$, the following properties are equivalent:*

- $\mathrm{rank}(A) = k$;
- *there is a $k \times k$ submatrix of the matrix A with nonzero determinant, but all $(k+1) \times (k+1)$ submatrices of the matrix A have determinant 0;*
- $\dim(\mathrm{Ran}(A)) = k$;
- *there exist k, and no more than k, columns (rows) of the matrix A that constitute a linearly independent set.*

Proposition 1.10. *For a matrix $A \in \mathbb{C}^{n \times n}$, the following properties are equivalent:*

- *the matrix A is nonsingular,*
- $\det(A) \ne 0$,

- $\dim(\mathrm{Ker}(A)) = 0$,
- $\mathrm{rank}(A) = n$,
- *the columns (rows) of the matrix A are linearly independent.*

Proposition 1.11. *Let $U \in \mathbb{C}^{n \times n}$. If U is a unitary matrix, then the columns of the matrix U form an orthonormal basis of $\mathbb{C}^n$. Conversely, if the columns of the matrix U form an orthonormal basis of $\mathbb{C}^n$, then the matrix U is unitary.*

1.2.3 ▪ Eigenvalue and Eigenvector

Let $A \in \mathbb{C}^{n \times n}$ be a square matrix. A complex scalar λ is said to be an **eigenvalue** of the matrix A if there exists a nonzero vector $x \in \mathbb{C}^n$ such that

$$Ax = \lambda x.$$

The vector x is called an **eigenvector** of the matrix A associated with the eigenvalue λ, and (λ, x) is called an **eigenpair** of the matrix A. The set of all eigenvalues of the matrix A is said to be the **spectrum** of the matrix A, denoted by $\sigma(A)$.

The maximum module of the eigenvalues of the matrix A is said to be the **spectral radius** of the matrix A, denoted by

$$\rho(A) = \max_{\lambda \in \sigma(A)} |\lambda|.$$

The equation $Ax = \lambda x$ is equivalent to the equation $(\lambda I - A)x = 0$. The latter has a nonzero solution if and only if its coefficient matrix $\lambda I - A$ is singular. Therefore, the eigenvalues λ of the matrix A are the scalars such that

$$\det(\lambda I - A) = 0.$$

Let

$$P_A(\lambda) = \det(\lambda I - A).$$

Then $P_A(\lambda)$ is a polynomial of degree n in λ and is called the **characteristic polynomial** of the matrix A. According to the fundamental theorem in linear algebra, there exist exactly n eigenvalues of the matrix A, counting multiplicities. If the matrix A is real, then $P_A(\lambda)$ is a polynomial of real coefficients, so that the complex eigenvalues of the matrix A, if exist, should occur in complex conjugate pairs.

It is easy to see that the eigenvalues of a diagonal or a triangular matrix are just its diagonal elements.

For $A \in \mathbb{C}^{n \times n}$ with $\sigma(A) = \{\lambda_1, \lambda_2, \ldots, \lambda_n\}$, the following properties hold true:

$$\det(A) = \prod_{i=1}^{n} \lambda_i, \quad \mathrm{tr}(A) = \sum_{i=1}^{n} \lambda_i.$$

Proposition 1.12. *Let $A \in \mathbb{C}^{n \times n}$. Then*

(1) *λ is an eigenvalue of the matrix A if and only if $P_A(\lambda) = 0$;*

(2) *the matrix A is singular if and only if $0 \in \sigma(A)$;*

(3) *when the matrix A is nonsingular, $\lambda \in \sigma(A)$ if and only if $\frac{1}{\lambda} \in \sigma(A^{-1})$.*

It follows from Proposition 1.12 (1) that if λ is an eigenvalue of the matrix A, then $\overline{\lambda}$ is an eigenvalue of the matrix A^*. An eigenvector v of the matrix A^* associated with the eigenvalue $\overline{\lambda}$ is called a **left-eigenvector** of the matrix A associated with the eigenvalue λ, i.e., $A^*v = \overline{\lambda}v$ and, thus,

$$v^*A = \lambda v^*.$$

If there exists a nonsingular matrix $X \in \mathbb{C}^{n \times n}$ such that

$$A = XBX^{-1},$$

then the two matrices A and B are called **similar**. If, in addition, the matrix X is unitary, then the matrices A and B are called **unitarily similar**. If the matrix A is similar to a diagonal matrix, then A is said to be **diagonalizable**.

The mapping $A \to X^{-1}AX$ is called a **similarity transformation** with respect to the similarity matrix X. Similar matrices have the same characteristic polynomial and, thus, have the same spectrum. That is to say, similarity transformations preserve the eigenvalues of matrices. More precisely, if λ is an eigenvalue of the matrix A with the associated eigenvector u, then λ is also an eigenvalue of the matrix B and $X^{-1}u$ is the associated eigenvector. In particular, if the matrix B is a diagonal matrix, then the diagonal entries of B are the eigenvalues of the matrix A and the columns of the matrix X are the associated eigenvectors.

Proposition 1.13. *Let $\lambda_1, \lambda_2, \ldots, \lambda_k$ be distinct eigenvalues of the matrix A, and x_i be an eigenvector associated with λ_i, $i = 1, 2, \ldots, k$. Then $\{x_1, x_2, \ldots, x_k\}$ is a linearly independent set.*

From Proposition 1.13, we see that the eigenvectors corresponding to distinct eigenvalues must be linearly independent.

Let λ be an eigenvalue of the matrix A. Then $\mathrm{Ker}(\lambda I - A)$ is the set of all eigenvectors corresponding to the eigenvalue λ together with the zero vector; it is called the **eigenspace** belonging to the eigenvalue λ.

The eigenspace associated with an eigenvalue of the matrix A is invariant with respect to the matrix A (or an invariant subspace of the matrix A) in the sense of the following definition.

Definition 1.14. *A subspace $\mathcal{S} \subseteq \mathbb{C}^n$ is called **invariant** with respect to a square matrix $A \in \mathbb{C}^{n \times n}$, if $x \in \mathcal{S}$ implies $Ax \in \mathcal{S}$. This property is also written as $A\mathcal{S} \subseteq \mathcal{S}$.*

Obviously, if x_1 is an eigenvector of the matrix A, then $\mathrm{span}\{x_1\}$ is invariant with respect to the matrix A. Let $x_1, x_2, \ldots, x_m$ be independent eigenvectors of the matrix A. Then $\mathrm{span}\{x_1, x_2, \ldots, x_m\}$ is an m-dimensional **invariant subspace** of the matrix A. Moreover, we have the following statement.

Theorem 1.15. *Let $A \in \mathbb{C}^{n \times n}$ and $X = [x_1, x_2, \ldots, x_m] \in \mathbb{C}^{n \times m}$ with $\mathrm{rank}(X) = m$. Then $\mathrm{span}(X) \triangleq \mathrm{span}\{x_1, x_2, \ldots, x_m\}$ is invariant with respect to the matrix A if and only if there exists a matrix $B \in \mathbb{C}^{m \times m}$ such that*

$$AX = XB.$$

In this case, the eigenvalues of the matrix B are also the eigenvalues of the matrix A.

Proof. We first suppose that $\mathrm{span}(X)$ is invariant with respect to the matrix A. Then $Ax_j \in \mathrm{span}(X)$. As the vectors $x_1, x_2, \ldots, x_m$ are linearly independent, they constitute a basis of the subspace span(X). Hence, we have

$$Ax_j = b_{1j}x_1 + b_{2j}x_2 + \cdots + b_{mj}x_m, \quad j = 1, 2, \ldots, m.$$

In matrix form, it can be written as $AX = XB$, where $B = [b_{ij}] \in \mathbb{C}^{m \times m}$.

Conversely, if there exists a matrix $B \in \mathbb{C}^{m \times m}$ such that $AX = XB$, then the vector Ax_j is a linear combination of the vectors $x_1, x_2, \ldots, x_m$. This implies that span(X) is an invariant subspace of the matrix A.

Now we prove that the eigenvalues of the matrix B are also eigenvalues of the matrix A. Let $\tilde{X} \in \mathbb{C}^{n \times (n-m)}$ be a matrix such that the matrix $Y = [X, \tilde{X}] \in \mathbb{C}^{n \times n}$ is nonsingular and write $Y^{-1} = \begin{bmatrix} Z_1 \\ Z_2 \end{bmatrix}$, where $Z_1 \in \mathbb{C}^{m \times n}$ and $Z_2 \in \mathbb{C}^{(n-m) \times n}$. It follows from $Y^{-1}Y = I_{n \times n}$ that $Z_1 X = I_{m \times m}$ and $Z_2 X = 0$. As $AX = XB$, we have

$$Y^{-1}AY = \begin{bmatrix} Z_1 \\ Z_2 \end{bmatrix} A[X, \tilde{X}] = \begin{bmatrix} Z_1 AX & Z_1 A\tilde{X} \\ Z_2 AX & Z_2 A\tilde{X} \end{bmatrix} = \begin{bmatrix} Z_1 XB & Z_1 A\tilde{X} \\ Z_2 XB & Z_2 A\tilde{X} \end{bmatrix} = \begin{bmatrix} B & Z_1 A\tilde{X} \\ 0 & Z_2 A\tilde{X} \end{bmatrix}.$$

Therefore, the eigenvalues of the matrix B are also eigenvalues of the matrix $Y^{-1}AY$; see Exercise 1.33. As the matrices A and $Y^{-1}AY$ are similar, they have the same eigenvalues. Consequently, the eigenvalues of the matrix B are also the eigenvalues of the matrix A. $\qquad$ □

In the following, we give some terminologies associated with eigenvalue and eigenvector:

(1) An eigenvalue λ of the matrix A has **algebraic multiplicity** μ if it is a root of multiplicity μ of the characteristic polynomial. (In this book, if not specified, the *multiplicity* of an eigenvalue refers to the algebraic multiplicity.)

(2) If an eigenvalue is of algebraic multiplicity 1, then it is **simple**; a nonsimple eigenvalue is **multiple**.

(3) The **geometric multiplicity** ν of an eigenvalue λ of the matrix A is the maximum number of independent eigenvectors associated with λ, or, in other words, ν is the dimension of the eigenspace Ker($\lambda I - A$); it always holds that $1 \leq \nu \leq \mu$.

(4) A matrix is **derogatory** if the geometric multiplicity of one of its eigenvalues is larger than 1.

(5) An eigenvalue is **semi-simple** if its algebraic multiplicity is equal to its geometric multiplicity; an eigenvalue that is not semi-simple is called **defective**; a matrix having at least one defective eigenvalue is called a **defective matrix**.

The simplest form that a matrix can be reduced to is undoubtedly the diagonal form. Unfortunately, such a reduction is not always possible.

Theorem 1.16. *A matrix of order n is diagonalizable if and only if it has n linearly independent eigenvectors.*

An immediate corollary of Theorem 1.16 is as follows.

Corollary 1.17. *A matrix of order n is diagonalizable if and only if all of its eigenvalues are semi-simple. In particular, if a matrix of order n has n distinct eigenvalues, then it is diagonalizable.*

Two diagonalizable matrices $A, B \in \mathbb{C}^{n \times n}$ are said to be **simultaneously diagonalizable** if there exists a nonsingular matrix $X \in \mathbb{C}^{n \times n}$ such that both matrices $X^{-1}AX$ and $X^{-1}BX$ are diagonal.

Theorem 1.18. [199] *Let $A, B \in \mathbb{C}^{n \times n}$ be diagonalizable matrices. Then the matrices A and B commute, i.e., $AB = BA$, if and only if they are simultaneously diagonalizable.*

Proof. Suppose that the matrix A has k distinct eigenvalues $\lambda_1, \lambda_2, \ldots, \lambda_k$. Since the matrix A is diagonalizable, there exists a nonsingular matrix S such that $A = S\Lambda S^{-1}$, where Λ is a diagonal matrix. Without loss of generality, we assume that any multiple eigenvalue of the matrix A occurs continuously on the diagonal of the matrix Λ, that is,

$$\Lambda = \begin{bmatrix} \lambda_1 I & & & \\ & \lambda_2 I & & \\ & & \ddots & \\ & & & \lambda_k I \end{bmatrix},$$

where each scalar matrix $\lambda_i I$ has the same size as the multiplicity of λ_i.

Assume $AB = BA$ and let $\tilde{B} = S^{-1} B S$. Then we have

$$\Lambda \tilde{B} = S^{-1} A S \cdot S^{-1} B S = S^{-1} A B S = S^{-1} B A S = S^{-1} B S \cdot S^{-1} A S = \tilde{B} \Lambda.$$

Now we partition the matrix $\tilde{B}$ into blocks as

$$\tilde{B} = \begin{bmatrix} \tilde{B}_{11} & \tilde{B}_{12} & \cdots & \tilde{B}_{1k} \\ \tilde{B}_{21} & \tilde{B}_{22} & \cdots & \tilde{B}_{2k} \\ \vdots & \vdots & \ddots & \vdots \\ \tilde{B}_{k1} & \tilde{B}_{k2} & \cdots & \tilde{B}_{kk} \end{bmatrix},$$

where the submatrix $\tilde{B}_{ii}$ has the same size as $\lambda_i I$. As $\Lambda \tilde{B} = \tilde{B} \Lambda$, we have

$$\lambda_i \tilde{B}_{ij} = \lambda_j \tilde{B}_{ij}, \quad i, j = 1, 2, \ldots, k.$$

It follows that $\tilde{B}_{ij} = 0$ for $i \neq j$ and, hence, $\tilde{B}$ is a block-diagonal matrix. Because the matrix B is diagonalizable, so are the matrices $\tilde{B}$ and $\tilde{B}_{ii}$. Let T_i be the nonsingular matrix such that $T_i^{-1} \tilde{B}_{ii} T_i$ is diagonal, represented by

$$T = \begin{bmatrix} T_1 & & & \\ & T_2 & & \\ & & \ddots & \\ & & & T_k \end{bmatrix}.$$

Because $T_i^{-1}(\lambda_i I) T_i = \lambda_i I$, we have $T^{-1} \Lambda T = \Lambda$. If we further define $X = ST$, then both matrices $X^{-1} A X$ and $X^{-1} B X$ are diagonal.

The converse can be demonstrated in an analogous fashion. $\quad\square$

Let $A \in \mathbb{C}^{m \times n}$ and $B \in \mathbb{C}^{n \times m}$. By direct computations, we have

$$\begin{bmatrix} AB & 0 \\ B & 0 \end{bmatrix} \begin{bmatrix} I & A \\ 0 & I \end{bmatrix} = \begin{bmatrix} I & A \\ 0 & I \end{bmatrix} \begin{bmatrix} 0 & 0 \\ B & BA \end{bmatrix},$$

which results in

$$\begin{bmatrix} AB & 0 \\ B & 0 \end{bmatrix} = \begin{bmatrix} I & A \\ 0 & I \end{bmatrix} \begin{bmatrix} 0 & 0 \\ B & BA \end{bmatrix} \begin{bmatrix} I & A \\ 0 & I \end{bmatrix}^{-1}.$$

This shows that the two $(m + n) \times (m + n)$ matrices

$$C_1 = \begin{bmatrix} AB & 0 \\ B & 0 \end{bmatrix} \quad \text{and} \quad C_2 = \begin{bmatrix} 0 & 0 \\ B & BA \end{bmatrix}$$

are similar. Note that the eigenvalues of the matrix C_1 are the eigenvalues of the matrix AB together with n zeros, and the eigenvalues of the matrix C_2 are the eigenvalues of the matrix BA together with m zeros. Hence, we can get the following conclusion.

Theorem 1.19. *Let $A \in \mathbb{C}^{m \times n}$ and $B \in \mathbb{C}^{n \times m}$. Then the matrix BA has the same nonzero eigenvalues as the matrix AB (counting multiplicities). More precisely, if $\lambda \neq 0$ is an eigenvalue of the matrix AB with the associated eigenvector u, then λ is an eigenvalue of the matrix BA with the associated eigenvector Bu. Conversely, if $\lambda \neq 0$ is an eigenvalue of the matrix BA with the associated eigenvector v, then λ is an eigenvalue of the matrix AB with the associated eigenvector Av.*

1.2.4 ▪ Minimal Polynomial

Let $A \in \mathbb{C}^{n \times n}$ be a square matrix and

$$p(t) = a_k t^k + a_{k-1} t^{k-1} + \cdots + a_1 t + a_0$$

be a given **polynomial**. Then we can define the **matrix polynomial** with respect to the matrix A as

$$p(A) = a_k A^k + a_{k-1} A^{k-1} + \cdots + a_1 A + a_0 I.$$

Theorem 1.20. [199] *Let $p(t)$ be a polynomial with respect to $t \in \mathbb{C}$. If λ is an eigenvalue of the matrix $A \in \mathbb{C}^{n \times n}$ with the associated eigenvector x, then $p(\lambda)$ is an eigenvalue of the matrix $p(A)$ and x is an eigenvector of $p(A)$ associated with $p(\lambda)$.*

Theorem 1.20 shows that a matrix obtained by acting a polynomial on the matrix A has the same eigenvectors as the matrix A and its eigenvalues are also linked to those of the matrix A in a simple way.

Theorem 1.21 (Cayley–Hamilton Theorem). *Let $P_A(\lambda)$ be the **characteristic polynomial** of the matrix $A \in \mathbb{C}^{n \times n}$. Then $P_A(A) = 0$.*

Proof. See [199] or [8]. □

Theorem 1.22. *Let $f(t)$ be a **monic polynomial** of degree n with respect to $t \in \mathbb{C}$, that is, its highest-order term has the coefficient 1. Then there exists a matrix $A \in \mathbb{C}^{n \times n}$ such that $f(t)$ is the characteristic polynomial of the matrix A. In particular, if*

$$f(t) = t^n + a_{n-1} t^{n-1} + \cdots + a_1 t + a_0,$$

then $f(t)$ is the characteristic polynomial of the matrix

$$A = \begin{bmatrix} 0 & 1 & 0 & \cdots & 0 & 0 \\ 0 & 0 & 1 & \cdots & 0 & 0 \\ \vdots & \vdots & \vdots & \ddots & \vdots & \vdots \\ 0 & 0 & 0 & \cdots & 0 & 1 \\ -a_0 & -a_1 & -a_2 & \cdots & -a_{n-2} & -a_{n-1} \end{bmatrix}.$$

*This matrix A is called the **companion matrix** of $f(t)$.*

Proof. Multiplying the matrix $tI - A$ from right by the matrix

$$B = \begin{bmatrix} 1 & 0 & 0 & \cdots & 0 & 0 \\ t & 1 & 0 & \cdots & 0 & 0 \\ \vdots & \vdots & \vdots & \ddots & \vdots & \vdots \\ t^{n-2} & t^{n-3} & t^{n-4} & \cdots & 1 & 0 \\ t^{n-1} & t^{n-2} & t^{n-3} & \cdots & t & 1 \end{bmatrix},$$

we obtain

$$C \triangleq (tI - A)B = \begin{bmatrix} 0 & -1 & 0 & \cdots & 0 & 0 \\ 0 & 0 & -1 & \cdots & 0 & 0 \\ \vdots & \vdots & \vdots & \ddots & \vdots & \vdots \\ 0 & 0 & 0 & \cdots & 0 & -1 \\ f(t) & \star & \star & \cdots & \star & \star \end{bmatrix},$$

where the symbol "$\star$" denotes some unspecified entry. Therefore, it holds that

$$\det(tI - A) = \det(C) = f(t).$$

Here we have used the fact that $\det(B) = 1$. $\qquad \square$

The Cayley–Hamilton theorem guarantees that for any matrix $A \in \mathbb{C}^{n \times n}$ there is a polynomial $p(t)$ of degree n such that $p(A) = 0$. A polynomial whose value is zero at the matrix A is said to be an **annihilating polynomial** of the matrix A; see [199]. There may be a polynomial of degree less than n which annihilates the matrix A. Obviously, if $p(A) = 0$, then $\alpha\, p(A) = 0$ for any $\alpha \in \mathbb{C}$. So, it is clear that we may always normalize a nontrivial annihilating polynomial so that the coefficient of its highest-order term is 1.

Again, we emphasize that a polynomial whose highest-order term has coefficient 1 is said to be monic. Note that a monic polynomial cannot be identically zero.

Theorem 1.23. [199] *For $A \in \mathbb{C}^{n \times n}$, there exists a unique monic polynomial $q_A(t)$ of **minimum degree** that annihilates the matrix A. The degree of $q_A(t)$ is at most n. If $p(t)$ is any polynomial such that $p(A) = 0$, then $q_A(t)$ divides $p(t)$.*

The unique monic polynomial $q_A(t)$ of minimum degree that annihilates the matrix A is called the **minimal polynomial** of the matrix A.

Proposition 1.24. *Similar matrices have the same minimal polynomial.*

Proposition 1.25. *For $A \in \mathbb{C}^{n \times n}$, the minimal polynomial $q_A(t)$ divides the characteristic polynomial $P_A(t)$. Moreover, $q_A(\lambda) = 0$ if and only if λ is an eigenvalue of the matrix A; so every root of $P_A(t) = 0$ is a root of $q_A(t) = 0$.*

Proposition 1.25 shows that if the characteristic polynomial $P_A(t)$ is completely factorized as

$$P_A(t) = \prod_{i=1}^{k} (t - \lambda_i)^{s_i}, \quad 1 \le s_i \le n \text{ and } s_1 + s_2 + \cdots + s_k = n,$$

with $\lambda_1, \lambda_2, \ldots, \lambda_k$ being distinct, then the minimal polynomial $q_A(t)$ must have the form

$$q_A(t) = \prod_{i=1}^{k} (t - \lambda_i)^{r_i}, \quad 1 \le r_i \le s_i.$$

In fact, an important connection exists between the **Jordan canonical form** and the minimal polynomial, which is precisely described in the following theorem.

Theorem 1.26. *For $A \in \mathbb{C}^{n \times n}$ with distinct eigenvalues $\lambda_1, \lambda_2, \ldots, \lambda_k$, the minimal polynomial of the matrix A is given by*

$$q_A(t) = \prod_{i=1}^{k} (t - \lambda_i)^{r_i}, \tag{1.6}$$

*where r_i is the order of the largest **Jordan block** of the matrix A corresponding to the eigenvalue λ_i.*

In practice, Theorem 1.26 is not very helpful in computing the minimal polynomial, since it is usually harder to determine the Jordan canonical form than to determine the minimal polynomial. However, because a matrix is diagonalizable if and only if all of its Jordan blocks have order 1, from Theorem 1.26 we know that a necessary and sufficient condition for a matrix to be diagonalizable is that all $r_i = 1$ in (1.6). This result is precisely stated in the following corollary.

Corollary 1.27. *Let $A \in \mathbb{C}^{n \times n}$ with the distinct eigenvalues $\lambda_1, \lambda_2, \ldots, \lambda_k$. Then the matrix A is diagonalizable if and only if $q(A) = 0$, where*

$$q(t) = (t - \lambda_1)(t - \lambda_2) \cdots (t - \lambda_k).$$

This criterion is useful for determining whether a given matrix is diagonalizable, provided one knows the distinct eigenvalues of that matrix.

1.3 ▪ Matrix Norms

Definition 1.28. *A **matrix norm** on $A \in \mathbb{C}^{m \times n}$ is a function $f : \mathbb{C}^{m \times n} \to \mathbb{R}$ satisfying the following properties:*

(1) *(nonnegativity) $f(A) \geq 0$, and $f(A) = 0$ if and only if $A = 0$, $\quad \forall A \in \mathbb{C}^{m \times n}$;*
(2) *(triangle inequality) $f(A + B) \leq f(A) + f(B)$, $\quad \forall A, B \in \mathbb{C}^{m \times n}$;*
(3) *(positive homogeneity) $f(\alpha A) = |\alpha| \, f(A)$, $\quad \forall A \in \mathbb{C}^{m \times n}, \forall \alpha \in \mathbb{C}$.*

Such a function for the matrix A is briefly denoted as $f(A) = \|A\|$.

Note that if $m = 1$ or $n = 1$, then the matrix norm is reduced to the vector norm. It then follows that all properties of the matrix norm are valid for the vector norm, too.

Let $A \in \mathbb{C}^{m \times n}$ be a complex matrix. Then the **p-norms** of the matrix A are defined as

$$\|A\|_p = \sup_{x \in \mathbb{C}^n \setminus \{0\}} \frac{\|Ax\|_p}{\|x\|_p} = \max_{\|x\|_p = 1} \|Ax\|_p, \quad p \geq 1. \tag{1.7}$$

Note that these norms are **induced** by the vector norms $\|\cdot\|_p$, and that they satisfy those properties in Definition 1.1. A fundamental property of the p-norms is that

$$\|AB\|_p \leq \|A\|_p \|B\|_p, \tag{1.8}$$

whenever the matrices A and B are conformable for multiplication. Matrix norms that satisfy the **sub-multiplicative property** (1.8) are called **consistent matrix norms** [288]. A direct result of a consistent matrix norm is that

$$\|A^k\| \leq \|A\|^k, \quad \forall A \in \mathbb{C}^{n \times n}.$$

It follows directly from the definition of the matrix p-norms in (1.7) that

$$\|Ax\|_p \leq \|A\|_p \|x\|_p$$

holds for any $A \in \mathbb{C}^{m \times n}$ and $x \in \mathbb{C}^n$.

Another frequently used matrix norm is the **Frobenius norm** defined as

$$\|A\|_F = \left(\sum_{j=1}^{n} \sum_{i=1}^{m} |a_{ij}|^2 \right)^{\frac{1}{2}},$$

where $A = [a_{ij}] \in \mathbb{C}^{m \times n}$. We can easily verify that the Frobenius norm is also consistent in the sense that it satisfies

$$\|Ax\|_2 \leq \|A\|_F \|x\|_2, \quad \text{for any } A \in \mathbb{C}^{m \times n} \text{ and } x \in \mathbb{C}^n.$$

Alternatively, the **Frobenius norm** can be defined through the inner product of matrices $A, B \in \mathbb{C}^{m \times n}$ as follows:

$$\langle A, B \rangle \triangleq \operatorname{tr}(A^* B),$$

so that

$$\|A\|_F \triangleq \sqrt{\langle A, A \rangle} = \sqrt{\operatorname{tr}(A^* A)}.$$

Note that

$$\langle A, B \rangle = \langle B^*, A^* \rangle,$$

so that $\|A^*\|_F = \|A\|_F$. Also, the **Cauchy–Schwarz inequality** is true for this **matrix inner product**, that is, it holds that

$$|\langle A, B \rangle| \leq \langle A, A \rangle^{\frac{1}{2}} \langle B, B \rangle^{\frac{1}{2}},$$

with equality holding only if $A = 0$ or $B = \alpha A$ for some scalar α.

Similar to defining the angle between two vectors in terms of the inner product and the norm arising from the inner product, for two matrices $A, B \in \mathbb{C}^{m \times n}$ we define the **angle** θ between them as

$$\cos \theta = \frac{|\langle A, B \rangle|}{\|A\|_F \|B\|_F}.$$

Theorem 1.29. *The following statements hold true:*

(1) *if $Q \in \mathbb{C}^{m \times n}$ is a unitary matrix, then $\|Q\|_F = \sqrt{n}$;*

(2) *if $A, B \in \mathbb{C}^{n \times n}$ are unitarily similar, then $\|A\|_F = \|B\|_F$.*

Proof. As $Q^* Q = I_n$, it holds that

$$\|Q\|_F = \sqrt{\operatorname{tr}(Q^* Q)} = \sqrt{\operatorname{tr}(I_n)} = \sqrt{n}.$$

When $A, B \in \mathbb{C}^{n \times n}$ are unitarily similar, there exists a unitary matrix $U \in \mathbb{C}^{n \times n}$ such that $A = UBU^*$. Then

$$\|A\|_F^2 = \operatorname{tr}(A^* A) = \operatorname{tr}((UBU^*)^*(UBU^*)) = \operatorname{tr}(UB^* BU^*) = \operatorname{tr}(B^* B) = \|B\|_F^2. \qquad \square$$

Remark 1.3. *If not specified explicitly, we always consider the consistent matrix norm.*

For $A = [a_{ij}] \in \mathbb{C}^{m \times n}$, the following equalities satisfied by the above-defined matrix norms lead to alternative definitions that are often easier to work with:

$$\|A\|_1 = \max_{1 \le j \le n} \sum_{i=1}^{m} |a_{ij}|,$$

$$\|A\|_2 = [\rho(A^*A)]^{\frac{1}{2}},$$

$$\|A\|_\infty = \max_{1 \le i \le m} \sum_{j=1}^{n} |a_{ij}|.$$

The Frobenius norm and the p-norms (especially, the norms corresponding to $p = 1, 2, \infty$) satisfy certain inequalities that are frequently used in matrix analysis and computations. For $A \in \mathbb{C}^{m \times n}$, we have

$$\|A\|_2 \le \|A\|_F \le \sqrt{\min\{m, n\}}\, \|A\|_2,$$

$$\frac{1}{\sqrt{m}} \|A\|_1 \le \|A\|_2 \le \sqrt{n}\, \|A\|_1,$$

$$\frac{1}{\sqrt{n}} \|A\|_\infty \le \|A\|_2 \le \sqrt{m}\, \|A\|_\infty,$$

$$\frac{1}{\sqrt{n}} \|A\|_\infty \le \|A\|_F \le \sqrt{m}\, \|A\|_\infty,$$

$$\|A\|_2 \le \sqrt{\|A\|_1 \|A\|_\infty}.$$

A norm $\| \cdot \|$ is **unitarily invariant** if $\|UAV\| = \|A\|$ holds for any unitary matrices U and V. The Frobenius norm and the 2-norm are unitarily invariant.

The **condition number** of a nonsingular matrix A is defined as $\|A\| \cdot \|A^{-1}\|$. We use $\kappa_p(A)$ and $\kappa_F(A)$ to denote the condition numbers of the matrix A with respect to the p-norms and the Frobenius norm, respectively, that is,

$$\kappa_p(A) = \|A\|_p \cdot \|A^{-1}\|_p, \quad \kappa_F(A) = \|A\|_F \cdot \|A^{-1}\|_F.$$

For simplicity, we always denote $\kappa_2(A)$ by $\kappa(A)$.

Let λ be an eigenvalue of the matrix $A \in \mathbb{C}^{n \times n}$ such that $\rho(A) = |\lambda|$, and let $x \in \mathbb{C}^n$ be the corresponding eigenvector. Then $Ax = \lambda x$. It follows that for any consistent matrix norm, we have

$$|\lambda| \cdot \|x\| = \|\lambda x\| = \|Ax\| \le \|A\| \cdot \|x\|.$$

This leads to the following statement.

Theorem 1.30. [199] *For $A \in \mathbb{C}^{n \times n}$, if $\| \cdot \|$ is any consistent matrix norm, then*

$$\rho(A) \le \|A\|.$$

In particular, when the matrix A is Hermitian we can easily verify that $\rho(A) = \|A\|$.

In fact, the spectral radius is the largest lower bound for the values of all consistent matrix norms.

Theorem 1.31. [199] *Let $A \in \mathbb{C}^{n \times n}$, and let $\varepsilon > 0$ be arbitrary. Then there exists a consistent matrix norm $\| \cdot \|_\varepsilon$ such that*

$$\|A\|_\varepsilon \le \rho(A) + \varepsilon.$$

Proof. Let $J = X^{-1}AX$ be the Jordan canonical form of the matrix A and

$$D = \mathrm{diag}(1, \varepsilon, \varepsilon^2, \ldots, \varepsilon^{n-1}).$$

Then

$$(XD)^{-1}A(XD) = D^{-1}JD = \begin{bmatrix} \lambda_1 & \varepsilon & & & & & & \\ & \ddots & \ddots & & & & & \\ & & \ddots & \varepsilon & & & & \\ & & & \lambda_1 & & & & \\ & & & & \lambda_2 & \varepsilon & & \\ & & & & & \ddots & \ddots & \\ & & & & & & \ddots & \varepsilon \\ & & & & & & & \lambda_2 \\ & & & & & & & & \ddots \end{bmatrix}.$$

Define $\|x\|_\varepsilon = \|(XD)^{-1}x\|_\infty$. Then $\|x\|_\varepsilon$ is a vector norm on $\mathbb{C}^n$; see Exercise 1.5. We can define the induced matrix norm

$$\|A\|_\varepsilon = \max_{x \neq 0} \frac{\|Ax\|_\varepsilon}{\|x\|_\varepsilon}.$$

Then it holds that

$$\begin{aligned}
\|A\|_\varepsilon &= \max_{x \neq 0} \frac{\|Ax\|_\varepsilon}{\|x\|_\varepsilon} = \max_{x \neq 0} \frac{\|(XD)^{-1}Ax\|_\infty}{\|(XD)^{-1}x\|_\infty} \\
&= \max_{y \neq 0} \frac{\|(XD)^{-1}A(XD)y\|_\infty}{\|y\|_\infty} \qquad \left(\text{with } y = (XD)^{-1}x\right) \\
&= \|(XD)^{-1}A(XD)\|_\infty \\
&= \max_{\lambda \in \sigma(A)} \{|\lambda|\} + \varepsilon \\
&= \rho(A) + \varepsilon. \qquad \square
\end{aligned}$$

Remark 1.4. *Another proof based on the 2-norm can be found in [91]; See Exercise 1.18.*

Definition 1.32. *A matrix $A \in \mathbb{C}^{n \times n}$ is said to be **convergent** if*

$$\lim_{k \to \infty} A^k = 0,$$

*and it is said to be **semi-convergent** if there exists a matrix $\mathring{A} \in \mathbb{C}^{n \times n}$ such that*

$$\lim_{k \to \infty} A^k = \mathring{A}.$$

Convergent and semi-convergent matrices are important in many applications, e.g., in the convergence analysis of iterative methods for solving systems of linear equations.

Theorem 1.33. [199] *For $A \in \mathbb{C}^{n \times n}$, if there exists a consistent matrix norm $\| \cdot \|$ such that $\|A\| < 1$, then*

$$\lim_{k \to \infty} A^k = 0.$$

Moreover, it holds that

$$\rho(A) = \lim_{k \to \infty} \|A^k\|^{\frac{1}{k}}.$$

The following theorem is due to Oldenburger [251], which plays a fundamental role in the convergence analysis of linear iterative methods.

Theorem 1.34. *Let $A \in \mathbb{C}^{n \times n}$. Then $\lim_{k \to \infty} A^k = 0$ if and only if $\rho(A) < 1$.*

This result can be proved by making use of the Jordan canonical form; see Exercise 1.12.

Definition 1.35. *The **index** of a matrix $A \in \mathbb{C}^{n \times n}$, denoted by $\mathrm{index}(A)$, is the smallest non-negative integer k such that $\mathrm{rank}(A^k) = \mathrm{rank}(A^{k+1})$.*

We have the following assertion for examining the semi-convergence of a matrix [72].

Theorem 1.36. *Let $A \in \mathbb{C}^{n \times n}$. Then the matrix A is semi-convergent if and only if $|\lambda| \leq 1$ for any $\lambda \in \sigma(A)$, and*

$$\mathrm{index}(I - A) \leq 1, \quad \nu(A) < 1,$$

where

$$\nu(A) \triangleq \max_{\lambda \in \sigma(A),\, \lambda \neq 1} |\lambda|.$$

At the end of this section, we briefly introduce the **Bauer–Fike theorem**, which is well known in the perturbation theory on eigenvalues of a matrix.

Theorem 1.37 (Bauer–Fike Theorem). *Let A, $\delta A \in \mathbb{C}^{n \times n}$. Assume that the matrix A is diagonalizable, that is, there exist a nonsingular matrix $Q \in \mathbb{C}^{n \times n}$ and a diagonal matrix $\Lambda \in \mathbb{C}^{n \times n}$ such that $A = Q \Lambda Q^{-1}$. Then, for each $\mu \in \sigma(A + \delta A)$, there exists a $\lambda \in \sigma(A)$ such that*

$$|\lambda - \mu| \leq \|Q\|_2 \|Q^{-1}\|_2 \|\delta A\|_2.$$

This theorem can be generalized to any square matrix as follows.

Theorem 1.38. *Let A, $\delta A \in \mathbb{C}^{n \times n}$, and let $J = Q^{-1} A Q$ be the Jordan canonical form of the matrix A. Then, for each $\mu \in \sigma(A + \delta A)$, there exists a $\lambda \in \sigma(A)$ such that*

$$\frac{|\lambda - \mu|^m}{(1 + |\lambda - \mu|)^{m-1}} \leq \|Q^{-1} \delta A Q\|_2,$$

where m is the largest order of all Jordan blocks associated with the eigenvalue λ of the matrix A.

1.4 ▪ Hermitian and Positive Definite Matrices

This section examines specific properties of Hermitian and positive definite matrices, including a few **optimality properties** related to their spectra.

1.4.1 ▪ Normal Matrix

A matrix $A \in \mathbb{C}^{n \times n}$ is said to be **normal** if it commutes with its conjugate transpose A^*, that is, if

$$A^* A = A A^*.$$

An immediate property of normal matrices is stated in the following lemma.

Lemma 1.39. *Let $A \in \mathbb{C}^{n \times n}$ be a normal matrix. If the matrix A is triangular, then it is diagonal.*

As a consequence of this lemma, we have the following important result.

Theorem 1.40. *Let $A \in \mathbb{C}^{n \times n}$. Then the matrix A is normal if and only if it is unitarily similar to a diagonal matrix, i.e., there exists a unitary matrix $U \in \mathbb{C}^{n \times n}$ such that*

$$U^* A U = \mathrm{diag}(\lambda_1, \lambda_2, \dots, \lambda_n),$$

where $\lambda_i \in \mathbb{C}$, $i = 1, 2, \dots, n$, are the eigenvalues of the matrix A.

Therefore, for any normal matrix A, each of its eigenvector is also an eigenvector of the matrix A^* (see Exercise 1.26). The converse of this statement is also true.

Proposition 1.41. [288] *Let $A \in \mathbb{C}^{n \times n}$. Then the matrix A is normal if and only if each of its eigenvectors is also an eigenvector of the matrix A^*.*

1.4.2 ▪ Hermitian Matrix

If $A \in \mathbb{C}^{n \times n}$ satisfies $A^* = A$, then the matrix A is called **Hermitian**; and if it satisfies $A^* = -A$, then it is called **skew-Hermitian**. Clearly, Hermitian and skew-Hermitian matrices are special kinds of normal matrices.

Since a normal matrix $A \in \mathbb{C}^{n \times n}$ can be written as $A = U \Lambda U^*$, with $\Lambda \in \mathbb{C}^{n \times n}$ diagonal and $U \in \mathbb{C}^{n \times n}$ unitary, the eigenvalues of the matrix A are the diagonal entries of the diagonal matrix Λ. Therefore, if all diagonal entries of Λ are real, we have $A^* = A$, or in other words, the matrix A is Hermitian; and if all diagonal entries of Λ are purely imaginary, we have $A^* = -A$, or in other words, the matrix A is skew-Hermitian. Therefore, Hermitian and skew-Hermitian matrices are special cases of the normal matrix.

The following is some basic properties about Hermitian and skew-Hermitian matrices. Let $A, B \in \mathbb{C}^{n \times n}$. Then

(1) the matrices $A + A^*$, AA^*, and A^*A are all Hermitian;

(2) the matrix A is Hermitian implies that A^k is Hermitian, $k = 2, 3, \dots$, and A^{-1} is Hermitian as well when the matrix A is nonsingular;

(3) the matrix A is skew-Hermitian implies that A^{2k+1} is skew-Hermitian, $k = 1, 2, \dots$, and A^{-1} is skew-Hermitian as well when the matrix A is nonsingular;

(4) both matrices A and B are Hermitian if and only if $\alpha A + \beta B$ is Hermitian for all real scalars α and β;

(5) the matrix $A - A^*$ is skew-Hermitian;

(6) both matrices A and B are skew-Hermitian if and only if $\alpha A + \beta B$ is skew-Hermitian for all real scalars α and β;

(7) the matrix A is Hermitian if and only if the matrix $\mathrm{i} A$ is skew-Hermitian, and the matrix A is skew-Hermitian if and only if the matrix $\mathrm{i} A$ is Hermitian;

(8) the matrix A can be written as $A = \mathscr{H}(A) + \mathscr{S}(A)$, where $\mathscr{H}(A) = \frac{1}{2}(A + A^*)$ and $\mathscr{S}(A) = \frac{1}{2}(A - A^*)$ are its **Hermitian** and **skew-Hermitian parts**, respectively.

As Property (8) is fundamental and useful, we restate it as the following theorem.

Theorem 1.42. *Each $A \in \mathbb{C}^{n \times n}$ can be uniquely written as $A = H + S$, where the matrix H is Hermitian and the matrix S is skew-Hermitian. It can also be uniquely written as $A =$*

$E + iF$, where both matrices E and F are Hermitian. Such matrices H and S are given by $H = \frac{1}{2}(A + A^*)$ and $S = \frac{1}{2}(A - A^*)$, and E and F are given by $E = \frac{1}{2}(A + A^*)$ and $F = \frac{1}{2i}(A - A^*)$.

Moreover, it holds that $\langle H, S \rangle = 0$, which implies that $A = H + S$ is an **orthogonal decomposition** in the sense of the **matrix inner product**.

More properties for Hermitian matrices are given below.

Theorem 1.43. *Let $A \in \mathbb{C}^{n \times n}$ be Hermitian. Then*

(1) $x^* A x$ *is real for all $x \in \mathbb{C}^n$,*

(2) *all eigenvalues of the matrix A are real,*

(3) $B^* A B$ *is Hermitian for all $B \in \mathbb{C}^{n \times m}$.*

Each of the properties in Theorem 1.43 can be regarded as a characterization of Hermitian matrices. Moreover, we have the following stronger results.

Theorem 1.44. *Let $A \in \mathbb{C}^{n \times n}$. Then the matrix A is Hermitian if and only if either of the following statements holds true:*

(1) $x^* A x$ *is real for all $x \in \mathbb{C}^n$,*

(2) *the matrix A is normal and all of its eigenvalues are real,*

(3) $B^* A B$ *is Hermitian for all $B \in \mathbb{C}^{n \times m}$.*

The following theorem is about the spectrum of a Hermitian matrix.

Theorem 1.45. *Let $A \in \mathbb{C}^{n \times n}$. Then the matrix A is Hermitian if and only if there is a unitary matrix $U \in \mathbb{C}^{n \times n}$ and a real diagonal matrix $\Lambda \in \mathbb{R}^{n \times n}$ such that $A = U \Lambda U^*$. Moreover, the matrix A is real symmetric if and only if there is an orthogonal matrix $Q \in \mathbb{R}^{n \times n}$ and a real diagonal matrix $\Lambda \in \mathbb{R}^{n \times n}$ such that $A = Q \Lambda Q^{\mathsf{T}}$.*

Since the eigenvalues of a Hermitian matrix $A \in \mathbb{C}^{n \times n}$ are all real, we use $\lambda_k \triangleq \lambda_k(A)$ to denote its k-th largest eigenvalue, i.e.,

$$\lambda_{\max} \triangleq \lambda_{\max}(A) = \lambda_1 \geq \lambda_2 \geq \cdots \geq \lambda_n = \lambda_{\min}(A) \triangleq \lambda_{\min}. \tag{1.9}$$

The eigenvalues of Hermitian matrices can be characterized by the following **min-max principle**, which was known to Fischer [137] but was made popular by Courant [98].

Theorem 1.46 (Courant–Fischer Theorem). *The eigenvalues of a Hermitian matrix $A \in \mathbb{C}^{n \times n}$ are characterized by the relation*

$$\lambda_k = \max_{\substack{\mathbb{S} \subseteq \mathbb{C}^n \\ \dim(\mathbb{S})=k}} \min_{\substack{x \in \mathbb{S} \\ x \neq 0}} \frac{x^* A x}{x^* x}$$

or

$$\lambda_k = \min_{\substack{\mathbb{S} \subseteq \mathbb{C}^n \\ \dim(\mathbb{S})=n-k+1}} \max_{\substack{x \in \mathbb{S} \\ x \neq 0}} \frac{x^* A x}{x^* x},$$

where $\mathbb{S}$ denotes a subspace of $\mathbb{C}^n$.

Proof. See [271], [305], or [199]. □

Corollary 1.47 (Rayleigh–Ritz Theorem). [199] *For any Hermitian matrix $A \in \mathbb{C}^{n \times n}$ and any nonzero vector $x \in \mathbb{C}^n$, it holds that*

$$\lambda_1\, x^* x \geq x^* A x \geq \lambda_n\, x^* x.$$

Moreover, we have

$$\lambda_{\max} = \lambda_1 = \max_{x \neq 0} \frac{x^* A x}{x^* x} = \max_{\|x\|_2 = 1} x^* A x$$

and

$$\lambda_{\min} = \lambda_n = \min_{x \neq 0} \frac{x^* A x}{x^* x} = \min_{\|x\|_2 = 1} x^* A x.$$

Among the applications of Courant–Fischer theorem, the comparison between the eigenvalues of the matrices $A + B$ and A is one of the simplest.

Theorem 1.48 (Weyl Theorem). [344] *Let $A, B \in \mathbb{C}^{n \times n}$ be Hermitian. If the eigenvalues of the matrices A, B, and $A + B$ are arranged in decreasing order as shown in (1.9), then for every pair of integers j, k such that $1 \leq j, k \leq n$ and $j + k \geq n + 1$, it holds that*

$$\lambda_{j+k-n}(A + B) \geq \lambda_j(A) + \lambda_k(B);$$

and for every pair of integers j, k such that $1 \leq j, k \leq n$ and $j + k \leq n + 1$, it holds that

$$\lambda_j(A) + \lambda_k(B) \geq \lambda_{j+k-1}(A + B).$$

Theorem 1.48 immediately yields the following two corollaries.

Corollary 1.49 (Weyl Inequalities). *Let $A, B \in \mathbb{C}^{n \times n}$ be Hermitian. Then*

$$\lambda_j(A) + \lambda_n(B) \leq \lambda_j(A + B) \leq \lambda_j(A) + \lambda_1(B).$$

Corollary 1.50 (Cauchy Interlacing Theorem). *Let $A \in \mathbb{C}^{n \times n}$ be a Hermitian matrix and A_1 be a principal submatrix of the matrix A obtained by deleting one row and the corresponding column from A. Then*

$$\lambda_1(A) \geq \lambda_1(A_1) \geq \lambda_2(A) \geq \lambda_2(A_1) \geq \cdots \geq \lambda_{n-1}(A) \geq \lambda_{n-1}(A_1) \geq \lambda_n(A).$$

Moreover, we have the following **inclusion principle** [199].

Corollary 1.51. *Let $A \in \mathbb{C}^{n \times n}$ be a Hermitian matrix and A_r be any r-by-r principal submatrix of the matrix A, where $1 \leq r \leq n$. Then*

$$\lambda_k(A) \geq \lambda_k(A_r) \geq \lambda_{k+n-r}(A), \quad k = 1, 2, \ldots, r.$$

For the trace and sums of eigenvalues of a Hermitian matrix, we can have a stronger result.

Theorem 1.52. *Let $A \in \mathbb{C}^{n \times n}$ be a Hermitian matrix, with its eigenvalues $\lambda_1, \lambda_2, \ldots, \lambda_n$ being ordered such that*

$$\lambda_1 \geq \lambda_2 \geq \cdots \geq \lambda_n.$$

Let $U \in \mathbb{C}^{n \times m}$, with $n \geq m$, be a unitary matrix. Then

$$\operatorname{tr}(U^* A U) \leq \sum_{i=1}^{m} \lambda_i.$$

Proof. Denote by
$$\Lambda = \mathrm{diag}(\lambda_1, \lambda_2, \ldots, \lambda_n).$$

As $A \in \mathbb{C}^{n \times n}$ is Hermitian, there exists a unitary matrix $Q \in \mathbb{C}^{n \times n}$ such that $Q^* A Q = \Lambda$. We represent the matrix U in terms of the columns of the matrix Q, which span $\mathbb{C}^n$, as $U = QX$. Hence,

$$\mathrm{tr}(U^* A U) = \mathrm{tr}(X^* Q^* A Q X) = \mathrm{tr}(X^* \Lambda X) = \sum_{i=1}^{n} \lambda_i x_i^* x_i,$$

where x_i^* is the i-th row of the matrix X.

Now
$$X^* X = X^* Q^* Q X = U^* U = I_m,$$

so either $x_i^* x_i = 0$ or $x_i^* x_i = 1$, and

$$\sum_{i=1}^{n} x_i^* x_i = m.$$

Because $\lambda_1 \geq \lambda_2 \geq \cdots \geq \lambda_n$, it holds that

$$\sum_{i=1}^{n} \lambda_i x_i^* x_i \leq \sum_{i=1}^{m} \lambda_i.$$

Therefore, it follows that

$$\mathrm{tr}(U^* A U) \leq \sum_{i=1}^{m} \lambda_i. \qquad \square$$

1.4.3 ▪ Hermitian Positive Definite Matrix

A matrix $A \in \mathbb{C}^{n \times n}$ is said to be **Hermitian positive definite** (HPD), denoted as $A \succ 0$, if it is Hermitian and positive definite; and a matrix $A \in \mathbb{C}^{n \times n}$ is said to be **Hermitian positive semidefinite** (HPS), denoted as $A \succeq 0$, if it is Hermitian and positive semidefinite.

Proposition 1.53. *For any Hermitian matrix $A \in \mathbb{C}^{n \times n}$, the following statements hold true:*

(1) *if $A \succ 0\,(A \succeq 0)$ and if $C \in \mathbb{C}^{n \times k}\,(k \leq n)$ is of full rank, then $C^* A C \succ 0\,(C^* A C \succeq 0)$;*

(2) *$\sigma(A) \subseteq [\alpha, \beta]$, with $\alpha, \beta \in \mathbb{R}$ if and only if $\alpha I \preceq A \preceq \beta I$.*

For two Hermitian matrices $A, B \in \mathbb{C}^{n \times n}$, we say that the matrix A is strictly greater than the matrix B and write $A \succ B$, if the matrix $A - B$ is Hermitian positive definite, that is, $A - B \succ 0$; and we say that the matrix A is greater than (or greater than or equal to) the matrix B and write $A \succeq B$, if the matrix $A - B$ is Hermitian positive semidefinite, that is, $A - B \succeq 0$. We can form a **partial ordering** of HPS matrices based on this **additive property**. Note that the *strictly greater than* relation implies the *greater than* relation. These relations are *partial* in the sense that they do not apply to all pairs of HPS matrices; that is, there are pairs of matrices A and B for which neither $A \succeq B$ nor $B \succeq A$.

If $A \succ B$, we also write $B \prec A$; and if $A \succeq B$, we may write $B \preceq A$.

Proposition 1.54. *For two Hermitian matrices $A, B \in \mathbb{C}^{n \times n}$, the following statements hold true:*

(1) *if $A \succ 0$ and $B \succeq 0$, then $A + B \succ 0$;*

(2) *if $A \preceq B$, then $C^* A C \preceq C^* B C$ for any matrix $C \in \mathbb{C}^{n \times k}$, and conversely, if $C^* A C \preceq C^* B C$ ($C^* A C \prec C^* B C$) for a nonsingular matrix $C \in \mathbb{C}^{n \times n}$, then $A \preceq B$ ($A \prec B$);*

(3) *if $A \succeq B$, then $\lambda_{\max}(A) \geq \lambda_{\max}(B)$ and $\lambda_{\min}(A) \geq \lambda_{\min}(B)$;*

(4) *if $A \succ 0$ and $B \succ 0$ such that $A \succ B$ ($A \succeq B$), then $B^{-1} \succ A^{-1}$ ($B^{-1} \succeq A^{-1}$).*

Let $A \in \mathbb{C}^{n \times n}$. For a given integer $k \geq 1$, if $B^k = A$, then the matrix B is called the **k-th root** of the matrix A. In particular, if $k = 2$, i.e., $B^2 = A$, then the matrix B is called the **square root** of the matrix A. Note that not all matrices have a square root; see Exercise 1.24.

When the matrix A is Hermitian positive definite, we can easily verify that

$$\|x\|_{A^{1/2}} \triangleq \sqrt{\langle x, Ax \rangle} = \sqrt{x^* A x} = \|A^{\frac{1}{2}} x\|_2$$

is a **consistent matrix norm**, and it is often referred to as the **A-norm** or the **energy norm**. If $B \in \mathbb{C}^{n \times n}$ is nonsingular, then the matrix $B^* B$ is Hermitian positive definite. Thus we can define a vector norm associated with the matrix B as follows:

$$\|x\|_B \triangleq \sqrt{\langle Bx, Bx \rangle} = \sqrt{x^* B^* B x} = \|Bx\|_2.$$

The following theorem is about the Hermitian positive semidefinite k-th root of a Hermitian positive semidefinite matrix.

Theorem 1.55. [199] *Let $A \in \mathbb{C}^{n \times n}$ be Hermitian positive semidefinite. Then there exists a unique Hermitian positive semidefinite matrix $B \in \mathbb{C}^{n \times n}$ such that $B^k = A$, and*

(1) $BA = AB$ *and there exists a polynomial $p(t)$ such that $B = p(A)$,*

(2) $\operatorname{rank}(B) = \operatorname{rank}(A)$,

(3) *the matrix B is Hermitian positive definite if and only if the matrix A is,*

(4) *the matrix B is real if and only if the matrix A is.*

The most useful case of Theorem 1.55 is $k = 2$, i.e., a Hermitian positive semidefinite (Hermitian positive definite) matrix A has a unique Hermitian positive semidefinite (Hermitian positive definite) square root, which is usually denoted as $A^{\frac{1}{2}}$.

Some basic properties of the Hermitian positive definite and the Hermitian positive semidefinite matrix, listed in the following proposition, can also be found in [134, 199].

Proposition 1.56. *Let $A = [a_{ij}] \in \mathbb{C}^{n \times n}$. Then*

(1) *the matrix A is Hermitian positive definite if and only if all of its eigenvalues are positive, and the matrix A is Hermitian positive semidefinite if and only if all of its eigenvalues are nonnegative;*

(2) *the matrix A being Hermitian positive definite (or Hermitian positive semidefinite) implies $\operatorname{tr}(A) > 0$ (or $\operatorname{tr}(A) \geq 0$) and $\det(A) > 0$ (or $\det(A) \geq 0$);*

(3) *each diagonal entry of a Hermitian positive definite (or a Hermitian positive semidefinite) matrix is positive (or nonnegative), and a zero diagonal entry of a Hermitian positive semidefinite matrix leads to the row and column containing this diagonal entry being also zero;*

(4) $|a_{ij}|^2 \leq a_{ii}a_{jj}$ $(i, j = 1, 2, \ldots, n)$ *if the matrix A is Hermitian positive semidefinite, and all of these inequalities become strict if the matrix A is Hermitian positive definite;*

(5) *the matrix A being Hermitian positive definite implies that the matrix A^{-1} is Hermitian positive definite, too;*

(6) *any principal submatrix of a Hermitian positive definite (or a Hermitian positive semidefinite) matrix is Hermitian positive definite (or Hermitian positive semidefinite);*

(7) *the matrix A is Hermitian positive semidefinite if and only if there exists a matrix B such that $A = BB^*$, and the matrix A is Hermitian positive definite if and only if there exists a nonsingular matrix C such that $A = CC^*$.*

Theorem 1.57. *Let $A \in \mathbb{C}^{n \times n}$ be Hermitian positive definite. Then, for any $x, y \in \mathbb{C}^n$, it holds that*

$$(x^* A^{-1} x)(y^* A y) \geq |y^* x|^2.$$

In particular, for any $x \in \mathbb{C}^n$, we have

$$(x^* A x)(x^* A^{-1} x) \geq (x^* x)^2.$$

Proof. The inequality follows from

$$|y^* x|^2 = \left| \left(y^* A^{\frac{1}{2}} \right) \left(A^{-\frac{1}{2}} x \right) \right|^2 = |\langle A^{\frac{1}{2}} y, A^{-\frac{1}{2}} x \rangle|^2$$
$$\leq \langle A^{\frac{1}{2}} y, A^{\frac{1}{2}} y \rangle \langle A^{-\frac{1}{2}} x, A^{-\frac{1}{2}} x \rangle = (y^* A y)(x^* A^{-1} x),$$

where the inequality is achieved by using the **Cauchy–Schwarz inequality.** $\square$

Furthermore, we have the following **Kantorovich matrix inequality.**

Theorem 1.58. *Let $A \in \mathbb{C}^{n \times n}$ be Hermitian positive definite, and $\lambda_{\min}$ and $\lambda_{\max}$ be its smallest and largest eigenvalues. Then, for any $x \in \mathbb{C}^n$, it holds that*

$$(x^* x)^2 \leq (x^* A x)(x^* A^{-1} x) \leq \frac{(\lambda_{\min} + \lambda_{\max})^2}{4 \lambda_{\min} \lambda_{\max}} (x^* x)^2.$$

Proof. The lower bound has been given in Theorem 1.57. The upper bound is straightforward from the spectral decomposition of the matrix A and the **Kantorovich inequality** for positive numbers. $\square$

Below, we present more properties about Hermitian positive definite and semidefinite matrices.

Proposition 1.59. [134, 233] *Let*

$$A = \begin{bmatrix} A_{11} & A_{12} \\ A_{21} & A_{22} \end{bmatrix},$$

*with A_{11} invertible and $A_{21}^* = A_{12}$. Then the matrix A is Hermitian positive definite if and only if both A_{11} and its **Schur complement** $S = A_{22} - A_{21} A_{11}^{-1} A_{12}$ are Hermitian positive definite. Moreover, if the matrix A is Hermitian positive definite, then any column of A_{12} belongs to $\mathrm{span}(A_{11})$.*

Proof. If the matrix A is Hermitian positive definite, then its principal submatrix A_{11} is also Hermitian positive definite, and so is its inverse A^{-1}. By employing the relations (1.15) and (1.16) (see Exercise 1.32), we know that the principal submatrix B_{22} of A^{-1} is also Hermitian positive definite, and so is its inverse S.

Conversely, let $x = [x_1^\mathsf{T}, x_2^\mathsf{T}]^\mathsf{T} \in \mathbb{C}^n$ be a nonzero vector partitioned conformally with the matrix A. If both matrices A_{11} and S are Hermitian positive definite, then

$$
\begin{aligned}
x^* A x &= [x_1^*, x_2^*] \begin{bmatrix} A_{11} & A_{12} \\ A_{21} & A_{22} \end{bmatrix} \begin{bmatrix} x_1 \\ x_2 \end{bmatrix} \\
&= x_1^* A_{11} x_1 + x_1^* A_{12} x_2 + x_2^* A_{21} x_1 + x_2^* A_{22} x_2 \\
&= (x_1^* + x_2^* A_{21} A_{11}^{-1}) A_{11} (x_1 + A_{11}^{-1} A_{12} x_2) \\
&\quad + x_2^* (A_{22} - A_{21} A_{11}^{-1} A_{12}) x_2 \\
&= \tilde{x}_1^* A_{11} \tilde{x}_1 + x_2^* S x_2 \\
&\geq 0,
\end{aligned}
$$

where

$$
\tilde{x}_1 = x_1 + A_{11}^{-1} A_{12} x_2.
$$

The equality holds if and only if $\tilde{x}_1 = 0$ and $x_2 = 0$, i.e., $x_1 = 0$ and $x_2 = 0$, which contradicts with $x \neq 0$. Hence $x^* A x > 0$ for all nonzero vector $x \in \mathbb{C}^n$, which shows that the matrix A is Hermitian positive definite.

If the matrix A is Hermitian positive definite, then it admits a Cholesky decomposition $A = R^* R$, where R is an upper-triangular matrix; see Theorem 2.16. Partition

$$
R = \begin{bmatrix} R_{11} & R_{12} \\ 0 & R_{22} \end{bmatrix}
$$

conformally with the matrix A. Then by direct computations we have

$$
A_{11} = R_{11}^* R_{11} \quad \text{and} \quad A_{12} = R_{11}^* R_{12}.
$$

Hence,

$$
A_{12} = (A_{11} R_{11}^{-1}) R_{12} = A_{11} (R_{11}^{-1} R_{12}),
$$

which implies that each column of the matrix A_{12} is a linear combination of the columns of the matrix A_{11}. □

For any Hermitian positive semidefinite matrix

$$
A = \begin{bmatrix} A_{11} & A_{12} \\ A_{21} & A_{22} \end{bmatrix}, \quad \text{with } A_{11} \in \mathbb{C}^{n \times n} \text{ and } A_{22} \in \mathbb{C}^{m \times m},
$$

we have the ***Cauchy–Bunyakowski–Schwarz*** (CBS) inequality [11, 12]

$$
|x^* A_{12} y| \leq \sqrt{(x^* A_{11} x)(y^* A_{22} y)}, \quad \forall x \in \mathbb{C}^n \text{ and } \forall y \in \mathbb{C}^m.
$$

Moreover, if the **strengthened CBS inequality** can be satisfied, we can obtain stronger results with respect to the matrix A and its Schur complement S.

Proposition 1.60. [8, 11, 12, 16] *Let*

$$A = \begin{bmatrix} A_{11} & A_{12} \\ A_{21} & A_{22} \end{bmatrix}, \quad \text{with } A_{11} \in \mathbb{C}^{n \times n} \text{ and } A_{22} \in \mathbb{C}^{m \times m},$$

be a Hermitian positive definite matrix satisfying the strengthened **CBS inequality**

$$|x^* A_{12} y| \le \gamma \sqrt{(x^* A_{11} x)(y^* A_{22} y)}, \quad \forall x \in \mathbb{C}^n \text{ and } \forall y \in \mathbb{C}^m,$$

where $\gamma \in [0, 1)$ *is the* **CBS constant.** *Denote by* $S = A_{22} - A_{21} A_{11}^{-1} A_{12}$ *the Schur complement of the matrix* A. *Then the following estimates hold true:*

(i) $y^* A_{21} A_{11}^{-1} A_{12} y \le \gamma^2 y^* A_{22} y$;

(ii) $(1 - \gamma^2) y^* A_{22} y \le y^* S y \le y^* A_{22} y$;

(iii) *for* $z = [x^\mathsf{T}, y^\mathsf{T}]^\mathsf{T}$,

$$z^* A z \ge (1 - \gamma^2) x^* A_{11} x \quad \text{and} \quad z^* A z \ge (1 - \gamma^2) y^* A_{22} y;$$

(iv) *for* $z = [x^\mathsf{T}, y^\mathsf{T}]^\mathsf{T}$,

$$(1 - \gamma)(x^* A_{11} x + y^* A_{22} y) \le z^* A z \le (1 + \gamma)(x^* A_{11} x + y^* A_{22} y).$$

Proof. Take $\tilde{x} = A_{11}^{-1} A_{12} y$. Then we have

$$\begin{aligned}
y^* A_{21} A_{11}^{-1} A_{12} y &= \tilde{x}^* A_{12} y \\
&\le \gamma \sqrt{(\tilde{x}^* A_{11} \tilde{x})(y^* A_{22} y)} \\
&= \gamma \sqrt{(y^* A_{21} A_{11}^{-1} A_{12} y)(y^* A_{22} y)}.
\end{aligned}$$

It follows immediately that

$$y^* A_{21} A_{11}^{-1} A_{12} y \le \gamma^2 y^* A_{22} y.$$

Using this estimate, we can further obtain

$$y^* S y = y^* A_{22} y - y^* A_{21} A_{11}^{-1} A_{12} y \ge (1 - \gamma^2) y^* A_{22} y.$$

Note that the upper bound on $y^* S y$ in (ii) is immediate.

To verify the validity of (iii) and (iv), with straightforward computations we have

$$z^* A z = x^* A_{11} x + x^* A_{12} y + y^* A_{21} x + y^* A_{22} y.$$

Then, for any positive real ξ, it follows from the **strengthened CBS inequality** that

$$\begin{aligned}
z^* A z &\ge x^* A_{11} x - |x^* A_{12} y| - |y^* A_{21} x| + y^* A_{22} y \\
&\ge x^* A_{11} x - 2\gamma \sqrt{(x^* A_{11} x)(y^* A_{22} y)} + y^* A_{22} y \\
&\ge x^* A_{11} x - \gamma \left(\xi x^* A_{11} x + \frac{1}{\xi} y^* A_{22} y \right) + y^* A_{22} y \\
&= (1 - \gamma \xi) x^* A_{11} x + \left(1 - \frac{\gamma}{\xi} \right) y^* A_{22} y
\end{aligned} \tag{1.10}$$

and

$$z^* A z \leq x^* A_{11} x + |x^* A_{12} y| + |y^* A_{21} x| + y^* A_{22} y$$
$$\leq x^* A_{11} x + 2\gamma \sqrt{(x^* A_{11} x)(y^* A_{22} y)} + y^* A_{22} y$$
$$\leq x^* A_{11} x + \gamma \left(\xi\, x^* A_{11} x + \frac{1}{\xi}\, y^* A_{22} y \right) + y^* A_{22} y$$
$$= (1 + \gamma\xi)\, x^* A_{11} x + \left(1 + \frac{\gamma}{\xi} \right) y^* A_{22} y. \tag{1.11}$$

Now, by taking $\xi = \gamma$ or $\xi = \frac{1}{\gamma}$ in (1.10), we get the inequalities in (iii); while by taking $\xi = 1$ in both (1.10) and (1.11), we get the inequality in (iv). □

Theorem 1.61 (Stein Theorem). [303] *Let $B \in \mathbb{C}^{n \times n}$. Then $\rho(B) < 1$ if and only if there exists a Hermitian positive definite matrix $A \in \mathbb{C}^{n \times n}$ such that $A - B^* A B$ is Hermitian positive definite.*

Proof. Suppose $\rho(B) < 1$. It follows from Exercise 1.18 that there exists a nonsingular matrix G such that

$$\|GBG^{-1}\|_2 < 1.$$

Let $A = G^* G$. Then the matrix A is Hermitian positive definite and, for any nonzero vector $x \in \mathbb{C}^n$, we have

$$x^*(A - B^* A B)x = x^* A x - x^* B^* A B x$$
$$= x^* G^* G x - (Bx)^* G^* G B x$$
$$= \|Gx\|_2^2 - \|GBx\|_2^2$$
$$= \|Gx\|_2^2 - \|GBG^{-1} Gx\|_2^2$$
$$\geq \|Gx\|_2^2 - \|GBG^{-1}\|_2^2 \cdot \|Gx\|_2^2$$
$$= \|Gx\|_2^2 \cdot (1 - \|GBG^{-1}\|_2^2) > 0.$$

Hence $A - B^* A B$ is Hermitian positive definite.

Conversely, suppose that there exists a Hermitian positive definite matrix A such that $A - B^* A B$ is Hermitian positive definite. Let $G = A^{\frac{1}{2}}$. Then the matrix G is Hermitian positive definite, so that $\|x\|_G \triangleq \|Gx\|_2$ defines a vector norm; see Exercise 1.5. As $A - B^* A B$ is Hermitian positive definite, for any nonzero vector $x \in \mathbb{C}^n$ we have

$$0 < x^*(A - B^* A B)x = x^* A x - x^* B^* A B x$$
$$= x^* G^* G x - x^* B^* G^* G B x$$
$$= \|Gx\|_2^2 - \|GBx\|_2^2,$$

or $\|GBx\|_2^2 < \|Gx\|_2^2$. Hence

$$\|Bx\|_G = \|GBx\|_2 < \|Gx\|_2 = \|x\|_G,$$

which implies

$$\|B\|_G \triangleq \max_{x \neq 0} \frac{\|Bx\|_G}{\|x\|_G} < 1.$$

As $\| \cdot \|_G$ is a matrix norm induced from the corresponding vector norm, it is consistent. Therefore, we have

$$\rho(B) \leq \|B\|_G < 1. \qquad □$$

Cao [91] generalized this theorem to the Hermitian positive semidefinite case.

Theorem 1.62. [91] *Let $B \in \mathbb{C}^{n \times n}$. Then the matrix B is semi-convergent if and only if there exists a Hermitian positive semidefinite matrix $A \in \mathbb{C}^{n \times n}$ such that $A - B^* A B$ is Hermitian positive semidefinite.*

Proof. Left as Exercise 1.37. □

1.4.4 · Positive Definite Matrix

Let $A \in \mathbb{C}^{n \times n}$. Then the matrix A is said to be **positive definite** or **positive real** if

$$\Re(x^* A x) > 0, \quad \forall\, x \in \mathbb{C}^n \text{ with } x \neq 0, \tag{1.12}$$

and the matrix A is said to be **positive semidefinite** if

$$\Re(x^* A x) \geq 0, \quad \forall\, x \in \mathbb{C}^n \text{ with } x \neq 0. \tag{1.13}$$

If neither A nor $-A$ is positive semidefinite, then the matrix A is called **indefinite**. Here, $\Re(\cdot)$ is used to represent the real part of the corresponding complex number.

Remark 1.5. *In some literature, positive definite or positive semidefinite matrices are required to be Hermitian. In this book, we do not impose this restriction.*

If $A \in \mathbb{R}^{n \times n}$ is real, then the conditions (1.12) and (1.13) can be reduced to those applied to all nonzero real vectors $x \in \mathbb{R}^n$. In this case, the matrix A is called **symmetric positive definite** (SPD) if it is real, symmetric, and positive definite; and **symmetric positive semidefinite** (SPS) if it is real, symmetric, and positive semidefinite.

If $A \in \mathbb{C}^{n \times n}$ is Hermitian, then $x^* A x$ is real for all $x \in \mathbb{C}^n$, and Condition (1.12) is equivalent to $x^* A x > 0$ for all nonzero vectors $x \in \mathbb{C}^n$. Conversely, if $x^* A x$ is real for all $x \in \mathbb{C}^n$, then $A \in \mathbb{C}^{n \times n}$ is Hermitian.

Immediately, we have the following consequence.

Proposition 1.63. *A matrix $A \in \mathbb{C}^{n \times n}$ is positive definite (or positive semidefinite) if and only if its Hermitian part $\mathscr{H}(A) = \frac{1}{2}(A + A^*)$ is Hermitian positive definite (or Hermitian positive semidefinite).*

If both A and x are real, then $x^\mathsf{T} A x$ is real and we have

$$x^\mathsf{T} A x = x^\mathsf{T} \mathscr{H}(A)\, x,$$

which results in the following theorem.

Theorem 1.64. *Let $A \in \mathbb{R}^{n \times n}$ be a real positive definite matrix. Then it is nonsingular. Moreover, there exists a real scalar $\alpha > 0$ such that*

$$x^\mathsf{T} A x \geq \alpha \|x\|_2^2$$

for any vector $x \in \mathbb{R}^n$.

The following **Bendixson theorem** is an important result that locates the eigenvalues of a matrix in terms of the spectra of its Hermitian and skew-Hermitian parts.

Theorem 1.65 (Bendixson Theorem). [309] *Let $\mathscr{H}(A)$ and $\mathscr{S}(A)$ be the Hermitian and the skew-Hermitian part of the matrix $A \in \mathbb{C}^{n \times n}$, respectively, that is,*

$$\mathscr{H}(A) = \frac{1}{2}(A + A^*) \quad and \quad \mathscr{S}(A) = \frac{1}{2}(A - A^*).$$

Then any eigenvalue λ of the matrix A satisfies

$$\lambda_{\min}(\mathscr{H}(A)) \leq \Re(\lambda) \leq \lambda_{\max}(\mathscr{H}(A)),$$

$$\lambda_{\min}(\frac{1}{i}\mathscr{S}(A)) \leq \Im(\lambda) \leq \lambda_{\max}(\frac{1}{i}\mathscr{S}(A)),$$

where i denotes the imaginary unit.

In [45], Bai and Ng derived a distribution domain for the generalized eigenvalues of a matrix pair (A, B), and obtained the so-called **generalized Bendixson theorem**.

Theorem 1.66 (Generalized Bendixson Theorem). [45] *Let $A, B \in \mathbb{C}^{n \times n}$ and $x \in \mathbb{C}^n \setminus \{0\}$ satisfy $x^* \mathscr{H}(A) x \neq 0$ and $x^* \mathscr{H}(B) x \neq 0$. Define*

$$h(x) = \frac{x^* \mathscr{H}(A) x}{x^* \mathscr{H}(B) x}, \quad f_A(x) = \frac{1}{i} \cdot \frac{x^* \mathscr{S}(A) x}{x^* \mathscr{H}(A) x}, \quad f_B(x) = \frac{1}{i} \cdot \frac{x^* \mathscr{S}(B) x}{x^* \mathscr{H}(B) x}.$$

Assume that there exist positive constants γ_1 and γ_2 such that

$$\gamma_1 \leq h(x) \leq \gamma_2, \quad \forall x \in \mathbb{C}^n \setminus \{0\},$$

and nonnegative constants α and β such that

$$-\alpha \leq f_A(x) \leq \alpha \quad and \quad -\beta \leq f_B(x) \leq \beta, \quad \forall x \in \mathbb{C}^n \setminus \{0\}.$$

Then the real parts of the eigenvalues $\lambda(B^{-1}A)$ of the matrix $B^{-1}A$ can be bounded as follows:

(i) *when $\alpha\beta < 1$, it holds that*

$$\frac{(1 - \alpha\beta)\gamma_1}{1 + \beta^2} \leq \Re(\lambda(B^{-1}A)) \leq (1 + \alpha\beta)\gamma_2;$$

(ii) *when $f_A(x)$ and $f_B(x)$ have the same sign for all $x \in \mathbb{C}^n \setminus \{0\}$, it holds that*

$$\frac{\gamma_1}{1 + \beta^2} \leq \Re(\lambda(B^{-1}A)) \leq (1 + \alpha\beta)\gamma_2;$$

(iii) *when $f_A(x)$ and $f_B(x)$ have different signs for all $x \in \mathbb{C}^n \setminus \{0\}$, it holds that*

$$\left(\sigma\gamma_1 + (1 - \sigma)\gamma_2\right)\left(\frac{1 - \alpha\beta}{1 + \sigma\beta^2}\right) \leq \Re(\lambda(B^{-1}A)) \leq \gamma_2,$$

where

$$\sigma = \frac{1}{2}\left(\operatorname{sign}(1 - \alpha\beta) + 1\right),$$

with $\operatorname{sign}(\cdot)$ being the sign function defined as $\operatorname{sign}(\gamma) = 1$ if $\gamma > 0$, $\operatorname{sign}(\gamma) = 0$ if $\gamma = 0$, and $\operatorname{sign}(\gamma) = -1$ otherwise.

Correspondingly, with respect to each of the above three cases, the imaginary parts of the eigenvalues $\lambda(B^{-1}A)$ of the matrix $B^{-1}A$ can be bounded as

$$-(\alpha + \beta)\gamma_2 \leq \Im(\lambda(B^{-1}A)) \leq (\alpha + \beta)\gamma_2.$$

The **generalized Bendixson theorem** is particularly useful in analyzing the eigenproperties of a preconditioned matrix and the convergence behavior of the corresponding preconditioned Krylov subspace iteration methods for solving large sparse and non-Hermitian systems of linear equations; see, e.g., [27, 28, 40, 41] and the references therein. A refinement of the generalized Bendixson theorem can be found in [58].

1.4.5 ▪ Matrix Congruence

We introduce a **matrix transformation** that preserves the sign of the eigenvalues.

Definition 1.67. *Two matrices $A, B \in \mathbb{C}^{n \times n}$ are said to be **congruent** if there exists a nonsingular matrix $P \in \mathbb{C}^{n \times n}$ such that $B = P^* A P$, and the transformation from A to $B = P^* A P$ is called the **congruence transformation**.*

Theorem 1.68 (Sylvester Law). *Let $A, B \in \mathbb{C}^{n \times n}$ be Hermitian matrices. Then there exists a nonsingular matrix $S \in \mathbb{C}^{n \times n}$ such that $B = S^* A S$ if and only if both matrices A and B have the same number of positive, negative, and zero eigenvalues.*

If we denote by $i_+(A)$, $i_-(A)$, and $i_0(A)$ the numbers of positive, negative, and zero eigenvalues of the matrix A, respectively, then the ordered triple

$$i(A) = \big(i_+(A), i_-(A), i_0(A)\big)$$

is called the **inertia** of the matrix A, and the quantity $i_+(A) - i_-(A)$ is called the **signature** of the matrix A. From the Sylvester law we know that the congruence is an **inertia preserving transformation**.

If $A \in \mathbb{C}^{n \times n}$ is a Hermitian matrix, then it is congruent with

$$\mathring{I}(A) = \begin{bmatrix} 1 & & & & & & & & \\ & \ddots & & & & & \mathbf{0} & & \\ & & 1 & & & & & & \\ & & & -1 & & & & & \\ & & & & \ddots & & & & \\ & & & & & -1 & & & \\ & & & & & & 0 & & \\ & \mathbf{0} & & & & & & \ddots & \\ & & & & & & & & 0 \end{bmatrix},$$

where the numbers of terms $+1$, -1, and 0 are exactly equal to $i_+(A), i_-(A)$, and $i_0(A)$, respectively. The matrix $\mathring{I}(A)$ is called the **inertia matrix** of the matrix A.

Theorem 1.69. [199] *The product of a Hermitian positive definite matrix $A \in \mathbb{C}^{n \times n}$ and a Hermitian matrix $B \in \mathbb{C}^{n \times n}$ is a diagonalizable matrix, all of whose eigenvalues are real, and the matrix AB (or the matrix BA) has the same number of positive, negative, and zero eigenvalues as the matrix B. Furthermore, any diagonalizable matrix with real eigenvalues is the product of a Hermitian positive definite matrix and a Hermitian matrix.*

Proof. For the first part, since the matrix A is Hermitian positive definite, $A^{\frac{1}{2}}$ is well-defined and also Hermitian positive definite. Therefore, we have

$$A^{-\frac{1}{2}}(AB)A^{\frac{1}{2}} = A^{\frac{1}{2}} B A^{\frac{1}{2}},$$

which indicates that AB is similar to $A^{\frac{1}{2}}BA^{\frac{1}{2}}$ and they have the same eigenvalues. On the other hand, as the matrix $A^{\frac{1}{2}}BA^{\frac{1}{2}}$ is congruent to the matrix B, it follows from the Sylvester law (see Theorem 1.68) that the eigenvalues of the matrix B have the same set of signs as those of the matrix $A^{\frac{1}{2}}BA^{\frac{1}{2}}$, as well as those of the matrix AB. Moreover, since $A^{\frac{1}{2}}BA^{\frac{1}{2}}$ is Hermitian, it is diagonalizable and its eigenvalues are all real. It then follows that the matrix AB is diagonalizable and has real eigenvalues.

For the last assertion, suppose that $C \in \mathbb{C}^{n \times n}$ is diagonalizable and has real eigenvalues, i.e., $C = SDS^{-1}$, with D being a real diagonal matrix. Then we have

$$C = SS^*(S^*)^{-1}DS^{-1} \triangleq AB,$$

where $A = SS^*$ is Hermitian positive definite, and $B = (S^*)^{-1}DS^{-1}$ is Hermitian. □

Simultaneous diagonalizability of two matrices by similarity requires the strong assumption of commutativity. But simultaneous diagonalizability of two Hermitian matrices by congruence requires less.

Theorem 1.70. [199] *Let $A, B \in \mathbb{C}^{n \times n}$ be two Hermitian matrices. Suppose that there exists a real linear combination of the matrices A and B that is positive definite. Then there exists a nonsingular matrix $P \in \mathbb{C}^{n \times n}$ such that both matrices P^*AP and P^*BP are diagonal.*

Corollary 1.71. *If $A \in \mathbb{C}^{n \times n}$ is Hermitian positive definite and $B \in \mathbb{C}^{n \times n}$ is Hermitian, then there exists a nonsingular matrix $S \in \mathbb{C}^{n \times n}$ such that S^*BS is diagonal and $S^*AS = I$.*

1.5 ▪ Canonical Forms of Matrices

Most of the eigenvalue problems involve transforming a matrix $A \in \mathbb{C}^{n \times n}$ into a simpler, or a **canonical form**, from which the eigenvalues and eigenvectors of the matrix A may be easily computed. The use of **similarity transformations** aims to reduce the complexity of computing the eigenvalues of a matrix. Indeed, if a given matrix could be transformed into a **similar matrix** in diagonal or triangular form, then the computation of the eigenvalues would be immediate. The main result in this direction is the **Jordan form** and the **Schur form**.

1.5.1 ▪ Jordan Form

From the theoretical viewpoint, one of the most important canonical forms of matrices is the well-known **Jordan canonical form**.

Let $A \in \mathbb{C}^{n \times n}$ have the distinct eigenvalues $\lambda_1, \lambda_2, \ldots, \lambda_p$, with $p \leq n$. Let μ_i be the algebraic multiplicity of an individual eigenvalue λ_i, and let l_i be its **index**, i.e., l_i is the smallest integer such that

$$\mathrm{Ker}(A - \lambda_i I)^{l_i+1} = \mathrm{Ker}(A - \lambda_i I)^{l_i}.$$

Then we easily see that $l_i \leq \mu_i$.

Theorem 1.72. [288] *Let $A \in \mathbb{C}^{n \times n}$ have p distinct eigenvalues $\lambda_1, \lambda_2, \ldots, \lambda_p$. Then the matrix A can be reduced to a block-diagonal form with p diagonal blocks, each associated with a distinct eigenvalue λ_i. Each of these diagonal blocks has itself a block-diagonal structure consisting of ν_i sub-blocks, where ν_i is the geometric multiplicity of the eigenvalue λ_i. Each of the sub-blocks, referred to as a Jordan block, is an upper-bidiagonal matrix of size not exceeding l_i, with the constant λ_i on the diagonal and the constant 1 on the super diagonal.*

For the proof of this theorem, we refer to [156, 310].

Theorem 1.72 shows that there exists a nonsingular matrix $X \in \mathbb{C}^{n \times n}$ such that

$$
X^{-1}AX = \begin{bmatrix} J_1 & & & \\ & J_2 & & \\ & & \ddots & \\ & & & J_p \end{bmatrix},
$$

where each J_i is associated with λ_i and is of size μ_i, and it has the structure

$$
J_i = \begin{bmatrix} J_{i1} & & & \\ & J_{i2} & & \\ & & \ddots & \\ & & & J_{i\nu_i} \end{bmatrix}, \quad \text{with} \quad J_{ik} = \begin{bmatrix} \lambda_i & 1 & & \\ & \ddots & \ddots & \\ & & \lambda_i & 1 \\ & & & \lambda_i \end{bmatrix}.
$$

The bidiagonal matrices J_{ik} are called **Jordan blocks**. Each J_{ik} corresponds to a different eigenvector associated with λ_i.

The **Jordan canonical form** possesses the following properties:

(1) the total number of Jordan blocks is equal to the number of independent eigenvectors of the matrix A;

(2) the matrix A is diagonalizable if and only if each of the Jordan blocks is a scalar, in this case the columns of the matrix X are the eigenvectors of the matrix A;

(3) the set of diagonalizable matrices is dense in the set of all matrices;

(4) the matrix A is normal if and only if it is diagonalizable and the matrix X is unitary.

1.5.2 ▪ Schur Form

The Jordan canonical form is very useful in theoretical research, but it is quite difficult in practical computations. That is why we should introduce the **Schur canonical form**, which shows that any matrix is unitarily similar to an upper-triangular matrix.

Theorem 1.73. *Let $A \in \mathbb{C}^{n \times n}$. Then there exists a unitary matrix $U \in \mathbb{C}^{n \times n}$ such that*

$$
U^*AU = \begin{bmatrix} \lambda_1 & b_{12} & \cdots & b_{1n} \\ 0 & \lambda_2 & \ddots & b_{2n} \\ \vdots & \ddots & \ddots & \vdots \\ 0 & \cdots & 0 & \lambda_n \end{bmatrix} \triangleq R,
$$

where $\lambda_1, \lambda_2, \ldots, \lambda_n$ are the eigenvalues of the matrix A.

Proof. We use induction on n. The statement is obviously true for $n = 1$.

Let λ be any eigenvalue of the matrix $A \in \mathbb{C}^{n \times n}$ and $x \in \mathbb{C}^n$ be the corresponding eigenvector, with $\|x\|_2 = 1$. By the MGS procedure, we can choose a matrix $\tilde{X} \in \mathbb{C}^{n \times (n-1)}$ so that $X = [x, \tilde{X}]$ is a square and unitary matrix. Then

$$
X^*AX = \begin{bmatrix} x^* \\ \tilde{X}^* \end{bmatrix} A [x, \tilde{X}] = \begin{bmatrix} x^*Ax & x^*A\tilde{X} \\ \tilde{X}^*Ax & \tilde{X}^*A\tilde{X} \end{bmatrix}.
$$

Since

$$
x^*Ax = x^* \cdot \lambda x = \lambda x^*x = \lambda
$$

and
$$\tilde{X}^* A x = \tilde{X}^* \cdot \lambda x = \lambda \tilde{X}^* x = 0,$$

we have
$$X^* A X = \begin{bmatrix} \lambda & x^* A \tilde{X} \\ 0 & \tilde{X}^* A \tilde{X} \end{bmatrix} \triangleq \begin{bmatrix} \lambda & \tilde{A}_{12} \\ 0 & \tilde{A}_{22} \end{bmatrix},$$

with
$$\tilde{A}_{12} = x^* A \tilde{X}, \quad \tilde{A}_{22} = \tilde{X}^* A \tilde{X}.$$

By induction, there exists a unitary matrix $\tilde{U} \in \mathbb{C}^{(n-1) \times (n-1)}$ such that $\tilde{U}^* \tilde{A}_{22} \tilde{U} = \tilde{R}$ is an $(n-1)$-by-$(n-1)$ upper-triangular matrix. Let

$$U = X \begin{bmatrix} 1 & 0 \\ 0 & \tilde{U} \end{bmatrix}.$$

Then

$$\begin{aligned} U^* A U &= \begin{bmatrix} 1 & 0 \\ 0 & \tilde{U}^* \end{bmatrix} X^* A X \begin{bmatrix} 1 & 0 \\ 0 & \tilde{U} \end{bmatrix} \\ &= \begin{bmatrix} 1 & 0 \\ 0 & \tilde{U}^* \end{bmatrix} \begin{bmatrix} \lambda & \tilde{A}_{12} \\ 0 & \tilde{A}_{22} \end{bmatrix} \begin{bmatrix} 1 & 0 \\ 0 & \tilde{U} \end{bmatrix} \\ &= \begin{bmatrix} \lambda & \tilde{A}_{12} \tilde{U} \\ 0 & \tilde{U}^* \tilde{A}_{22} \tilde{U} \end{bmatrix} = \begin{bmatrix} \lambda & \tilde{A}_{12} \tilde{U} \\ 0 & \tilde{R} \end{bmatrix} \\ &\triangleq R, \end{aligned}$$

which is an upper-triangular matrix.

Since the matrix R is triangular and similar to the matrix A, its diagonal elements are equal to the eigenvalues of the matrix A ordered in a certain manner. ☐

Perhaps the most fundamental and useful fact in the elementary matrix theory is that any matrix is unitarily similar to an upper-triangular matrix (or a lower-triangular matrix). This form represents the simplest form achievable under unitary equivalence. Note that the matrices U and R are not necessarily unique because the eigenvalues may appear on the diagonal of the matrix R in any order.

An important fact is that for any positive integer k satisfying $k \le n$ the subspace spanned by the first k columns of the matrix U is invariant under the action of the matrix A. Indeed, if we let $U = [u_1, u_2, \ldots, u_n]$ and $R = [r_{ij}]$, then the relation $AU = UR$ implies

$$A u_j = \sum_{i=1}^{j} r_{ij} u_i, \quad 1 \le j \le n.$$

Denote by $U_k = [u_1, u_2, \ldots, u_k]$ and R_k the leading k-dimensional principal submatrix of the matrix R. Then the above relation can be rewritten as

$$A U_k = U_k R_k,$$

which is known as the **partial Schur decomposition** of the matrix A.

As the eigenvalue λ and the eigenvector x may be complex even if the matrix A is real, in practical computations, when the matrix A is real, we prefer to a canonical form in real arithmetic due to cheaper computational cost. Therefore, we may consider the **quasi-triangular matrices**.

Here, diagonal blocks of size 2-by-2 are allowed in the upper-triangular matrix R, which avoids complex arithmetic when the original matrix is real. This slight variant of the Schur canonical form is called **quasi-Schur canonical form**, or **real Schur canonical form**.

Theorem 1.74. *Let $A \in \mathbb{R}^{n \times n}$. Then there exists an orthogonal matrix $Q \in \mathbb{R}^{n \times n}$ such that*

$$Q^\mathsf{T} A Q = T,$$

where T is a block upper-triangular matrix with 1-by-1 or 2-by-2 blocks on its diagonal. The 1-by-1 blocks correspond to real eigenvalues of the matrix A, and the 2-by-2 blocks correspond to complex conjugate pairs of eigenvalues of the matrix A.

Proof. We also use induction on n. Let λ be an eigenvalue of the matrix A. If λ is real, then it has a real eigenvector and we can proceed as in Theorem 1.73. If λ is complex, then it has a complex eigenvector u. As

$$\overline{\lambda} \overline{u} = \overline{\lambda u} = \overline{Au} = \overline{A} \overline{u} = A \overline{u},$$

$(\overline{\lambda}, \overline{u})$ is also an eigenpair of the matrix A. Let

$$\tilde{u} = \frac{1}{2}(u + \overline{u}) \quad \text{and} \quad \tilde{v} = \frac{1}{2\mathrm{i}}(u - \overline{u})$$

be the real and the imaginary part of the vector u, respectively. Then $\operatorname{span}\{\tilde{u}, \tilde{v}\} = \operatorname{span}\{u, \overline{u}\}$ is a two-dimensional invariant subspace of $\mathbb{C}^n$ with respect to the matrix A. Let $\tilde{U} = \tilde{Q}\tilde{R}$ be the QR decomposition of the matrix $\tilde{U} = [\tilde{u}, \tilde{v}]$, where the matrix $\tilde{Q} \in \mathbb{R}^{n \times 2}$ has orthonormal columns. Then $\operatorname{span}(\tilde{Q}) = \operatorname{span}(\tilde{U})$ is also invariant with respect to the matrix A. It follows from Theorem 1.15 that there exists a matrix $B \in \mathbb{R}^{2 \times 2}$ such that $A\tilde{Q} = \tilde{Q}B$. Let $\hat{Q} \in \mathbb{R}^{n \times (n-2)}$ be a matrix such that the matrix $[\tilde{Q}, \hat{Q}]$ is orthogonal. Then we have

$$[\tilde{Q}, \hat{Q}]^\mathsf{T} A [\tilde{Q}, \hat{Q}] = \begin{bmatrix} \tilde{Q}^\mathsf{T} A \tilde{Q} & \tilde{Q}^\mathsf{T} A \hat{Q} \\ \hat{Q}^\mathsf{T} A \tilde{Q} & \hat{Q}^\mathsf{T} A \hat{Q} \end{bmatrix} = \begin{bmatrix} B & \tilde{Q}^\mathsf{T} A \hat{Q} \\ 0 & \hat{Q}^\mathsf{T} A \hat{Q} \end{bmatrix}.$$

By applying induction to the matrix $\hat{Q}^\mathsf{T} A \hat{Q}$, we have then proved the result. □

If all eigenvalues of a real matrix A are real, then the following statement is immediate.

Corollary 1.75. *Let $A \in \mathbb{R}^{n \times n}$. If all eigenvalues of the matrix A are real, then there exists an orthogonal matrix $Q \in \mathbb{R}^{n \times n}$ and a real upper-triangular matrix $R \in \mathbb{R}^{n \times n}$ such that*

$$Q^\mathsf{T} A Q = R.$$

The diagonal entries of the matrix R are the eigenvalues of the matrix A.

1.6 ▪ Kronecker Product

The **Kronecker product**, known also as the **direct product** or the **tensor product**, has numerous applications in statistics, economics, particle physics, control, matrix theory, etc. In this section, we will introduce definition and properties for the Kronecker product, as well as its applications in solving **linear matrix equations**.

1.6.1 ▪ Definition and Properties

Definition 1.76. *For $A \in \mathbb{C}^{m \times n}$ and $B \in \mathbb{C}^{p \times q}$, the **Kronecker product** of the matrices A and B, denoted by $A \otimes B$, is defined as the block matrix*

$$A \otimes B = \begin{bmatrix} a_{11}B & a_{12}B & \cdots & a_{1n}B \\ a_{21}B & a_{22}B & \cdots & a_{2n}B \\ \vdots & \vdots & \ddots & \vdots \\ a_{m1}B & a_{m2}B & \cdots & a_{mn}B \end{bmatrix} \in \mathbb{C}^{mp \times nq}.$$

Note that the Kronecker product is well defined for any two matrices of arbitrary sizes. In general, it holds that $A \otimes B \neq B \otimes A$.

The following are several basic facts about the Kronecker product.

Proposition 1.77. *Let $A \in \mathbb{C}^{m \times n}$ and $B \in \mathbb{C}^{p \times q}$. Then*

(1) $(\alpha A) \otimes B = A \otimes (\alpha B) = \alpha (A \otimes B)$, *for $\alpha \in \mathbb{C}$;*

(2) $(A \otimes B)^{\mathsf{T}} = A^{\mathsf{T}} \otimes B^{\mathsf{T}}$ *and* $(A \otimes B)^* = A^* \otimes B^*$;

(3) $(A \otimes B) \otimes C = A \otimes (B \otimes C)$, *for $C \in \mathbb{C}^{r \times s}$; (associative law)*

(4) $A \otimes (B + C) = A \otimes B + A \otimes C$, *for $C \in \mathbb{C}^{p \times q}$; (right distributive law)*

(5) $(A + C) \otimes B = A \otimes B + C \otimes B$, *for $C \in \mathbb{C}^{m \times n}$. (left distributive law)*

Proposition 1.78 (The Mixed Product Property). *Let $A \in \mathbb{C}^{m \times n}, B \in \mathbb{C}^{p \times q}, C \in \mathbb{C}^{n \times k}$, and $D \in \mathbb{C}^{q \times r}$. Then*

$$(A \otimes B)(C \otimes D) = (AC) \otimes (BD).$$

Proof. The (i, j)-th block of the matrix $(A \otimes B)(C \otimes D)$ is given by

$$\left[(A \otimes B)(C \otimes D) \right]_{ij} = [a_{i1}B, a_{i2}B, \ldots, a_{in}B] \begin{bmatrix} c_{1j}D \\ c_{2j}D \\ \vdots \\ c_{nj}D \end{bmatrix}$$

$$= \left(\sum_{k=1}^{n} a_{ik}c_{kj} \right) BD = (AC)_{ij}BD = [(AC) \otimes (BD)]_{ij}.$$

This is exactly the equality that we were proving. □

This mixed product property can be further generalized as follows:

(1) $(A_1 \otimes A_2 \otimes \cdots \otimes A_k)(B_1 \otimes B_2 \otimes \cdots \otimes B_k) = (A_1 B_1) \otimes (A_2 B_2) \otimes \cdots \otimes (A_k B_k)$,

(2) $(A_1 \otimes B_1)(A_2 \otimes B_2) \cdots (A_k \otimes B_k) = (A_1 A_2 \cdots A_k) \otimes (B_1 B_2 \cdots B_k)$.

Corollary 1.79. *If $A \in \mathbb{C}^{n \times n}$ and $B \in \mathbb{C}^{m \times m}$ are nonsingular, then the matrix $A \otimes B$ is nonsingular and $(A \otimes B)^{-1} = A^{-1} \otimes B^{-1}$.*

For the eigenvalues of the Kronecker product of two matrices, we have the following result.

Theorem 1.80. *Let $A \in \mathbb{C}^{n \times n}$ and $B \in \mathbb{C}^{m \times m}$. Let (λ, x) and (μ, y) be eigenpairs of the matrices A and B, respectively. Then $(\lambda\mu, x \otimes y)$ is an eigenpair of the matrix $A \otimes B$.*

Furthermore, if $\sigma(A) = \{\lambda_1, \lambda_2, \ldots, \lambda_n\}$ and $\sigma(B) = \{\mu_1, \mu_2, \ldots, \mu_m\}$, then $\sigma(A \otimes B) = \{\lambda_i \mu_j : i = 1, 2, \ldots, n, j = 1, 2, \ldots, m\}$. In particular, $\sigma(A \otimes B) = \sigma(B \otimes A)$.

It follows immediately that for $A \in \mathbb{C}^{n \times n}$ and $B \in \mathbb{C}^{m \times m}$ the trace and the determinant of the Kronecker product $A \otimes B$ are given by

$$\operatorname{tr}(A \otimes B) = \operatorname{tr}(B \otimes A) = \operatorname{tr}(A) \operatorname{tr}(B)$$

and

$$\det(A \otimes B) = \det(B \otimes A) = [\det(A)]^n \ [\det(B)]^m ,$$

respectively. Hence, the matrix $A \otimes B$ is nonsingular if and only if both matrices A and B are nonsingular.

The following theorem is about the singular values (see Section 2.6 for the definition) of the Kronecker product.

Theorem 1.81. *Let $A \in \mathbb{C}^{n \times n}$ and $B \in \mathbb{C}^{m \times m}$ satisfy $\operatorname{rank}(A) = r_1$ and $\operatorname{rank}(B) = r_2$. Assume that the matrices A and B have the singular value decompositions $A = U_1 \Sigma_1 V_1$ and $B = U_2 \Sigma_2 V_2$. Then*

$$A \otimes B = (U_1 \otimes U_2)(\Sigma_1 \otimes \Sigma_2)(V_1 \otimes V_2).$$

From Theorem 1.81, we see that the matrix $A \otimes B$ has $r_1 r_2$ nonzero singular values and

$$\operatorname{rank}(A \otimes B) = \operatorname{rank}(B \otimes A) = r_1 r_2.$$

Therefore, the matrices $A \otimes B$ and $B \otimes A$ can be nonsingular only if both matrices A and B are square.

1.6.2 ▪ Matrix Equations and Kronecker Products

We briefly introduce a few relationships between the matrix equations and the Kronecker products. For details, we refer to [1, 200].

For $A = [a_{ij}] \in \mathbb{C}^{m \times n}$, we define the associated vector $\operatorname{vec}(A)$ by

$$\operatorname{vec}(A) = [a_{11}, \ldots, a_{m1}, a_{12}, \ldots, a_{m2}, \ldots, a_{1n}, \ldots, a_{mn}]^\mathsf{T},$$

i.e., $\operatorname{vec}(A)$ is the column vector obtained by successively stacking the columns of the matrix A from the first to the last column.

Proposition 1.82. *Let $A \in \mathbb{C}^{m \times n}$ and $B \in \mathbb{C}^{n \times m}$. Then*

$$\operatorname{tr}(AB) = \left(\operatorname{vec}(A^\mathsf{T}) \right)^\mathsf{T} \operatorname{vec}(B) = \left(\operatorname{vec}(B^\mathsf{T}) \right)^\mathsf{T} \operatorname{vec}(A).$$

Proposition 1.83. *Let $A \in \mathbb{C}^{m \times n}, B \in \mathbb{C}^{n \times k}$, and $C \in \mathbb{C}^{k \times l}$. Then*

$$\operatorname{vec}(ABC) = (C^\mathsf{T} \otimes A) \operatorname{vec}(B).$$

Lemma 1.84. [200] *Let $A \in \mathbb{C}^{m \times n}$, $B \in \mathbb{C}^{p \times q}$, and $C \in \mathbb{C}^{m \times q}$ be given matrices, and $X \in \mathbb{C}^{n \times p}$ be an unknown matrix. Then the linear matrix equation*

$$AXB = C$$

is equivalent to the system of linear equations

$$(B^\mathsf{T} \otimes A) \operatorname{vec}(X) = \operatorname{vec}(C),$$

i.e.,

$$\operatorname{vec}(AXB) = (B^\mathsf{T} \otimes A) \operatorname{vec}(X).$$

Proof. For a given matrix W, we denote its k-th column by w_k or $[W]_k$. By direct computations we have

$$[AXB]_k = A[XB]_k = AX \cdot b_k$$

$$= A\left[\sum_{i=1}^{p} b_{ik}x_i \right] = \left[b_{1k}A, \, b_{2k}A, \, \ldots, \, b_{pk}A \right] \text{vec}(X)$$

$$= (b_k^\mathsf{T} \otimes A) \, \text{vec}(X).$$

Therefore,

$$\text{vec}(AXB) = \left[b_1^\mathsf{T} \otimes A, \, b_2^\mathsf{T} \otimes A, \, \ldots, \, b_q^\mathsf{T} \otimes A \right]^\mathsf{T} \text{vec}(X)$$

$$= (B^\mathsf{T} \otimes A) \, \text{vec}(X). \qquad \square$$

Analogously, we have the following statements [200]:

(i) $AX = B \iff (I \otimes A) \, \text{vec}(X) = \text{vec}(B)$,

(ii) $AX + XB = C \iff (I \otimes A + B^\mathsf{T} \otimes I) \, \text{vec}(X) = \text{vec}(C)$,

(iii) $A_1 X B_1 + \cdots + A_k X B_k = C \iff (B_1^\mathsf{T} \otimes A_1 + \cdots + B_k^\mathsf{T} \otimes A_k) \, \text{vec}(X) = \text{vec}(C)$,

(iv) $AX + YB = C \iff (I \otimes A) \, \text{vec}(X) + (B^\mathsf{T} \otimes I) \, \text{vec}(Y) = \text{vec}(C)$.

In particular, the continuous **Lyapunov equation**

$$XA + A^*X = H$$

can be rewritten as

$$\left[(A^\mathsf{T} \otimes I) + (I \otimes A^*) \right] \text{vec}(X) = \text{vec}(H),$$

and the **commutativity equation**

$$XA = AX$$

is equivalent to

$$\left[(I \otimes A) - (A^\mathsf{T} \otimes I) \right] \text{vec}(X) = 0.$$

Theorem 1.85. [200] *For all $X \in \mathbb{C}^{m \times n}$, there exists a unique matrix $P_{mn} \in \mathbb{C}^{mn \times mn}$ such that*

$$\text{vec}(X^\mathsf{T}) = P_{mn} \, \text{vec}(X),$$

with P_{mn} being given by

$$P_{mn} = \sum_{i=1}^{m} \sum_{j=1}^{n} E_{ij} \otimes E_{ij}^\mathsf{T} = \begin{bmatrix} E_{11}^\mathsf{T} & E_{12}^\mathsf{T} & \cdots & E_{1n}^\mathsf{T} \\ E_{21}^\mathsf{T} & E_{22}^\mathsf{T} & \cdots & E_{2n}^\mathsf{T} \\ \vdots & \vdots & \ddots & \vdots \\ E_{m1}^\mathsf{T} & E_{m2}^\mathsf{T} & \cdots & E_{mn}^\mathsf{T} \end{bmatrix}, \qquad (1.14)$$

where $E_{ij} \in \mathbb{C}^{m \times n}$ has entry 1 at position (i, j) and zeros elsewhere. Moreover, P_{mn} is a **permutation matrix** *satisfying $P_{mn}^\mathsf{T} = P_{mn}^{-1} = P_{mn}$.*

Note that P_{mn} defined in (1.14) only depends on the dimensions m and n.

In general, the Kronecker product is not commutative. That is to say, $A \otimes B$ and $B \otimes A$ may be different matrices, or $A \otimes B \neq B \otimes A$. However, the matrices $A \otimes B$ and $B \otimes A$ are permutationally equivalent.

Corollary 1.86. *Let $P_{pm} \in \mathbb{C}^{pm \times pm}$ and $P_{nq} \in \mathbb{C}^{nq \times nq}$ be the permutation matrices defined in (1.14). Then*

$$B \otimes A = P_{pm}^{\mathsf{T}}(A \otimes B)P_{nq}$$

holds for all $A \in \mathbb{C}^{m \times n}$ and $B \in \mathbb{C}^{p \times q}$. Thus, if both matrices A and B are square, the matrix $B \otimes A$ is permutationally similar to the matrix $A \otimes B$.

1.7 ▪ Stable Matrices

In the stability analysis of the equilibrium in a dynamical system governed by a linear ordinary differential equation, it is important to know whether the real part of every eigenvalue of a certain matrix is negative. The matrix with all eigenvalues being of negative real parts is called a (negative) **stable matrix**. Similarly, we call a matrix **positive stable** if all of its eigenvalues have positive real parts. Clearly, the matrix A is positive stable if and only if the matrix $-A$ is **stable**.

Proposition 1.87. *If $A \in \mathbb{C}^{n \times n}$ is stable (or positive stable), then the matrix A is nonsingular and the matrix A^{-1} is also stable (or positive stable).*

The following theorem gives some fundamental properties about stable or positive stable matrices.

Theorem 1.88. [134] *Let $A \in \mathbb{C}^{n \times n}$ and $B = (A+I)^{-1}(A-I)$. Then the following statements are equivalent:*

(1) *the matrix A is positive stable;*

(2) *the matrix B is well-defined and $\rho(B) < 1$;* [303]

(3) *the matrix B is well-defined, and for any Hermitian positive definite matrix C, there exists a Hermitian positive definite matrix P such that $P - BPB^* = C$;* [303]

(4) *the matrix B is well-defined, and there exists a Hermitian positive definite matrix P such that $P - BPB^* = I$;*

(5) *the matrix B is well-defined, and there exists a Hermitian positive definite matrix P such that $P - BPB^*$ is Hermitian positive definite;*

(6) *there exists a Hermitian positive definite matrix P such that $AP + PA^*$ is Hermitian positive definite;* [312]

(7) *for any Hermitian positive definite matrix C, there exists a Hermitian positive definite matrix P such that $AP + PA^* = C$;*

(8) *there exists a Hermitian positive definite matrix P such that $AP + PA^* = I$;* [312]

(9) *there exists a Hermitian positive definite matrix P such that $PAP^{-1} + P^{-1}A^*P$ is Hermitian positive definite;*

(10) *there exists a nonsingular matrix G such that the Hermitian part of the matrix GAG^{-1} is Hermitian positive definite.*

1.8 ▪ Exercises

1.1. Prove the inequalities (1.1), (1.2), and (1.3).

1.2. Let $x \in \mathbb{C}^n$. Show that

$$\lim_{p \to +\infty} \|x\|_p = \|x\|_\infty.$$

1.3. Prove Proposition 1.6.

1.4. Let $u \in \mathbb{C}^m$ and $v \in \mathbb{C}^n$. Show that

$$\|uv^*\|_2 = \|u\|_2 \cdot \|v\|_2.$$

Does this equality holds for the F-norm?

1.5. Let $G \in \mathbb{C}^{n \times n}$ be a nonsingular matrix. Show that

(1) if $\| \cdot \|$ is a vector norm, then

$$\|x\|_G \triangleq \|Gx\|, \quad x \in \mathbb{C}^n,$$

is also a vector norm;

(2) if $\| \cdot \|$ is a consistent matrix norm, then

$$\|A\|_G \triangleq \|GAG^{-1}\|, \quad A \in \mathbb{C}^{n \times n},$$

is also a consistent matrix norm.

1.6. Let $x, y \in \mathbb{C}^n$. Show that

$$\Re(\langle x, y \rangle) = \frac{1}{4} \left(\|x + y\|_2^2 - \|x - y\|_2^2 \right).$$

This is known as the **polarization identity**. Show also that

$$\Re(\langle x, y \rangle) = \frac{1}{2} \left(\|x + y\|_2^2 - \|x\|_2^2 - \|y\|_2^2 \right).$$

1.7. Let A and B be matrices such that both matrices AB and BA are well-defined. Show that $\text{tr}(AB) = \text{tr}(BA)$.

1.8. Prove the following **Cauchy–Schwarz inequalities** for matrices:

(1) $|\text{tr}(A^*B)|^2 \le \text{tr}(A^*A)\,\text{tr}(B^*B)$,

(2) $|\det(A^*B)|^2 \le \det(A^*A)\,\det(B^*B)$. Under what conditions is equality achieved?

1.9. Let $U \in \mathbb{C}^{n \times n}$ be a unitary matrix. Show that $\det(U) = \pm 1$.

1.10. Let $A \in \mathbb{C}^{n \times n}$, $B \in \mathbb{C}^{n \times m}$, $C \in \mathbb{C}^{m \times n}$ and $D \in \mathbb{C}^{m \times m}$. Show the validity of the following statements:

- if $I - CB$ is nonsingular, then $I - BC$ is nonsingular and

$$(I - BC)^{-1} = I + B(I - CB)^{-1}C;$$

- if A and $I - CA^{-1}B$ are nonsingular, then $A - BC$ is nonsingular and

$$(A - BC)^{-1} = A^{-1} + A^{-1}B(I - CA^{-1}B)^{-1}CA^{-1};$$

- if D and $D - CB$ are nonsingular, then $I - BD^{-1}C$ is nonsingular and

$$(I - BD^{-1}C)^{-1} = I + B(D - CB)^{-1}C;$$

- if A, D and $D - CA^{-1}B$ are nonsingular, then $A - BD^{-1}C$ is nonsingular and

$$(A - BD^{-1}C)^{-1} = A^{-1} + A^{-1}B(D - CA^{-1}B)^{-1}CA^{-1}.$$

These matrix identities are variations and generalizations of the **Sherman–Morrison formula** as well as the **Sherman–Morrison–Woodbury formula** [167].

1.11. Let $A, B \in \mathbb{C}^{n \times n}$, and assume both matrices A and $I - A^{-1}B$ are nonsingular. Show that the matrix $A - B$ is nonsingular and

$$(A - B)^{-1} = A^{-1} + A^{-1}B(I - A^{-1}B)^{-1}A^{-1}.$$

If, in addition, the matrix B is nonsingular, then

$$(A - B)^{-1} = A^{-1} + A^{-1}(B^{-1} - A^{-1})^{-1}A^{-1}.$$

1.12. Prove Theorems 1.34 and 1.36.
(Hint: make use of the Jordan canonical form.)

1.13. Let $A \in \mathbb{C}^{n \times n}$. Show that

(1) $\sum_{k=0}^{\infty} A^k$ is convergent if and only if $\rho(A) < 1$;

(2) if $\sum_{k=0}^{\infty} A^k$ converges, then $\sum_{k=0}^{\infty} A^k = (I - A)^{-1}$, and there exists a matrix norm, say, e.g., $\| \cdot \|$, on $\mathbb{C}^{n \times n}$ such that

$$\left\| (I - A)^{-1} - \sum_{k=0}^{m} A^k \right\| \le \frac{\|A\|^{m+1}}{1 - \|A\|},$$

where m is an arbitrary natural number.

1.14. Prove Theorem 1.37, i.e., the Bauer–Fike theorem.

1.15. Let $H_1, H_2 \in \mathbb{C}^{n \times n}$ be Hermitian matrices and assume the matrix H_1 to be positive definite. Show that the matrix $H_1 + H_2$ is positive definite if and only if all eigenvalues of the matrix $H_1^{-1}H_2$ are larger than -1.

1.16. Let $A = [a_{ij}] \in \mathbb{C}^{n \times n}$ be a Hermitian positive semidefinite matrix. Show that

- the diagonal entries are real and nonnegative, i.e., $a_{ii} \ge 0$, $i = 1, 2, \ldots, n$;
- $|a_{ij}|^2 \le a_{ii}a_{jj}$ for $i \ne j$ and $i, j = 1, 2, \ldots, n$;
- $\max\limits_{\substack{1 \le i, j \le n \\ i \ne j}} |a_{ij}| \le \max\limits_{1 \le i \le n} a_{ii}$.

If, in addition, the matrix A is Hermitian positive definite, then all of the above inequalities hold strictly, i.e.,

$$a_{ii} > 0, \quad |a_{ij}|^2 < a_{ii}a_{jj} \quad (i \ne j, \; i, j = 1, 2, \ldots, n)$$

and

$$\max\limits_{\substack{1 \le i, j \le n \\ i \ne j}} |a_{ij}| < \max\limits_{1 \le i \le n} a_{ii}.$$

1.17. Let $\langle \cdot, \cdot \rangle$ be a given inner product defined on $\mathbb{R}^n$ (or $\mathbb{C}^n$). Show that there exists a symmetric (or Hermitian) positive definite matrix $A \in \mathbb{R}^{n \times n}$ (or $A \in \mathbb{C}^{n \times n}$) such that

$$\langle x, y \rangle = y^{\mathsf{T}} A x, \quad \forall x, y \in \mathbb{R}^n \quad (\text{or } \langle x, y \rangle = y^* A x, \quad \forall x, y \in \mathbb{C}^n).$$

Conversely, if $A \in \mathbb{R}^{n \times n}$ (or $A \in \mathbb{C}^{n \times n}$) is a symmetric (or Hermitian) positive definite matrix, then

$$f(x, y) \triangleq y^{\mathsf{T}} A x \quad (\text{or} \quad f(x, y) \triangleq y^* A x)$$

defines an inner product on $\mathbb{R}^n$ (or $\mathbb{C}^n$).
(Hint: $A = [a_{ij}]$ with $a_{ij} = \langle e_i, e_j \rangle$.)

1.18. [91] Let $A \in \mathbb{C}^{n \times n}$ be a given matrix and $\varepsilon > 0$ be any given positive number. Then there exits a nonsingular matrix G such that

$$\|GAG^{-1}\|_2 \leq \rho(A) + \varepsilon.$$

(Hint: $G = (XD)^{-1}$.)

1.19. Let λ be an eigenvalue of the matrix $A \in \mathbb{C}^{n \times n}$. Show that, even if the matrix A is not Hermitian, the following inequality holds true:

$$\min_{x \in \mathbb{C}^n \setminus \{0\}} \frac{|x^* A x|}{x^* x} \leq |\lambda| \leq \max_{x \in \mathbb{C}^n \setminus \{0\}} \frac{|x^* A x|}{x^* x}.$$

Let $A = \begin{bmatrix} 1 & 1 \\ 0 & 1 \end{bmatrix}$. Show that neither of the bounds needs to be sharp.

1.20. Let $A \in \mathbb{C}^{n \times n}$ be a skew-Hermitian matrix. Show that the matrix $Q(\alpha) = (\alpha I + A)^{-1}(\alpha I - A)$, with $\alpha \neq 0$ being a real number, satisfies $Q(\alpha)^{-1} = Q(\alpha)^*$, i.e., $Q(\alpha)$ is a unitary matrix. $Q(\alpha)$ is called the **Cayley transform** of the matrix A.

1.21. Given the nonsymmetric real matrix

$$A = \begin{bmatrix} 0 & 1 & 1 \\ 1 & 0 & -1 \\ -1 & -1 & 0 \end{bmatrix},$$

check that it is similar to the diagonal matrix $D = \mathrm{diag}(1, 0, -1)$ and find its eigenvectors. Is the matrix A normal?

1.22. Let $A \in \mathbb{C}^{n \times n}$. Show that $\rho(A)$ is not a matrix norm.

1.23. Let $A \in \mathbb{C}^{n \times n}$ be nonsingular. Show that for any eigenvalue λ of the matrix A, it holds that [84]

$$\frac{1}{\|A^{-1}\|_2} \leq |\lambda| \leq \|A\|_2.$$

1.24. Show by direct calculations that there is no matrix $B \in \mathbb{C}^{2 \times 2}$ such that

$$B^2 = \begin{bmatrix} 0 & 1 \\ 0 & 0 \end{bmatrix}.$$

1.25. Let $A \in \mathbb{R}^{n \times n}$ be a tridiagonal matrix of the form

$$A = \begin{bmatrix} b_1 & c_1 & & & \\ a_1 & \ddots & \ddots & & \\ & \ddots & \ddots & c_{n-1} \\ & & a_{n-1} & b_n \end{bmatrix},$$

and assume $a_i c_i > 0$ for $i = 1, 2, \ldots, n-1$. Show that all eigenvalues of the matrix A are real.

(Hint: DAD^{-1} is symmetric, where $D = \mathrm{diag}(d_1, d_2, \ldots, d_n)$ with $d_1 = 1$ and $d_{i+1} = d_i \left(\frac{c_i}{a_i} \right)^{\frac{1}{2}}$.)

1.26. Let $A \in \mathbb{C}^{n \times n}$ be normal. Show that if $Ax = \lambda x$ with $x \neq 0$, then $A^* x = \overline{\lambda} x$.

1.27. $A \in \mathbb{C}^{n \times n}$ is called **idempotent** if $A^2 = A$. Show that each eigenvalue of an idempotent matrix is either 0 or 1.

1.28. $A \in \mathbb{C}^{n \times n}$ is called **nilpotent** if $A^m = 0$ for some positive integer m. The minimum of such an m is called the **index** of nilpotence. Show that all eigenvalues of a nilpotent matrix are 0.

1.29. Let $A \in \mathbb{C}^{m \times n}$. Show that $\operatorname{rank}(A) = 1$ if and only if there exist vectors $u \in \mathbb{C}^m$ and $v \in \mathbb{C}^n$ such that $A = uv^*$.

1.30. Let $A \in \mathbb{C}^{m \times k}$ and $B \in \mathbb{C}^{k \times n}$. Show that

$$\operatorname{rank}(A) + \operatorname{rank}(B) - k \leq \operatorname{rank}(AB) \leq \min\{\operatorname{rank}(A), \operatorname{rank}(B)\}.$$

1.31. Let $A = [a_{ij}] \in \mathbb{C}^{n \times n}$. Show that

$$|\det(A)|^2 \leq \min\left\{\prod_{j=1}^{n}\left(\sum_{i=1}^{n}|a_{ij}|^2\right), \ \prod_{i=1}^{n}\left(\sum_{j=1}^{n}|a_{ij}|^2\right)\right\}.$$

1.32. Let $A \in \mathbb{C}^{n \times n}$ be partitioned into the block two-by-two form

$$A = \begin{bmatrix} A_{11} & A_{12} \\ A_{21} & A_{22} \end{bmatrix},$$

and assume both diagonal blocks A_{11} and A_{22} to be square with A_{11} being nonsingular. Show that

$$\det(A) = \det(A_{11}) \det(S)$$

and, therefore, the matrix A is nonsingular if and only if both matrices A_{11} and S are nonsingular, where $S = A_{22} - A_{21}A_{11}^{-1}A_{12}$ is the Schur complement of the matrix A with respect to its $(2,2)$-block A_{22}. Furthermore, if A^{-1} exists and is partitioned as

$$A^{-1} = \begin{bmatrix} B_{11} & B_{12} \\ B_{21} & B_{22} \end{bmatrix}, \tag{1.15}$$

then

$$B_{22}^{-1} = S. \tag{1.16}$$

1.33. Consider the block upper-triangular matrix

$$A = \begin{bmatrix} A_{11} & A_{12} & \cdots & A_{1k} \\ & A_{22} & \cdots & A_{2k} \\ & & \ddots & \vdots \\ & & & A_{kk} \end{bmatrix},$$

with each A_{ii} being a square matrix. Show that the eigenvalues of the matrix A are the union of the eigenvalues of the matrices $A_{11}, A_{22}, \ldots, A_{kk}$.

1.34. Consider the Cayley–Hamilton theorem, i.e., Theorem 1.21. What is wrong with the following argument for the statement $P_A(A) = 0$?

(a) Since $P_A(\lambda) = 0$ for every eigenvalue λ of the matrix A, and since the eigenvalues of a polynomial matrix $p(A)$, with p being a polynomial, are $p(\lambda)$, it follows that all eigenvalues of the matrix $P_A(A)$ are 0. Therefore, $P_A(A)$ is 0. Give an explicit example to illustrate where the error occurs.

(b) Since $P_A(\lambda) = \det(\lambda I - A)$, we have

$$P_A(A) = \det(AI - A) = \det(0) = 0.$$

Therefore, $P_A(A) = 0$.

1.35. (a) Assume that $A \in \mathbb{C}^{n \times n}$ can be reduced to a diagonal matrix. Show that

$$\det(\exp(A)) = e^{\operatorname{tr}(A)}.$$

(b) Show that $\exp(A + B) = \exp(A) \exp(B)$ if and only if $AB = BA$.

1.36. Prove Theorem 1.40.

(Hint: use the Schur canonical form.)

1.37. Prove Theorem 1.62.

1.38. Let $A \in \mathbb{C}^{m \times n}$ and $B \in \mathbb{C}^{p \times q}$. Show that $A \otimes B = 0$ if and only if either $A = 0$ or $B = 0$.

1.39. Let $A \in \mathbb{C}^{n \times n}$ and $B \in \mathbb{C}^{m \times m}$. Show that if both matrices A and B are normal, then the matrix $A \otimes B$ is normal. Conversely, if neither the matrix A nor the matrix B is zero, then the matrix $A \otimes B$ is normal if and only if both matrices A and B are normal.

1.40. Let $A, B \in \mathbb{C}^{m \times n}$. Show that $A \otimes B = B \otimes A$ if and only if $A = \alpha B$ or $B = \alpha A$ for some $\alpha \in \mathbb{C}$.

1.41. Let $A \in \mathbb{C}^{n \times n}, B \in \mathbb{C}^{m \times m}$, and $x \in \mathbb{C}^n, y \in \mathbb{C}^m$. Show that

$$\|x \otimes y\|_2 = \|x\|_2 \|y\|_2$$

and

$$\|(A \otimes B)(x \otimes y)\|_2 = \|Ax\|_2 \|By\|_2.$$

1.42. Let $A \in \mathbb{C}^{n \times n}, B \in \mathbb{C}^{m \times m}$, and $C \in \mathbb{C}^{p \times p}$. Show that

$$(A \oplus B) \otimes C = (A \otimes C) \oplus (B \otimes C).$$

Note that

$$A \otimes (B \oplus C) = (A \otimes B) \oplus (A \otimes C)$$

may be not correct.

Chapter 2

Matrix Decompositions

This chapter will focus on computations of matrix decompositions, that is, the factorizations of matrices into products of simpler ones such as triangular, diagonal, and unitary matrices, and so on.

2.1 ▪ Basic Transform Matrices

2.1.1 ▪ Elementary Matrices

If a matrix in $\mathbb{C}^{n \times n}$ has the form

$$E(u, v, \tau) = I - \tau u v^*,$$

where $u, v \in \mathbb{C}^n$ are nonzero vectors and $\tau \neq 0$ is a complex number, then we call $E(u, v, \tau)$ an **elementary matrix**. It is clear that the matrix uv^* is of rank 1. Hence, $E(u, v, \tau)$ is a rank-1 modification of the identity matrix I.

Proposition 2.1. *Let $E(u, v, \tau)$ be an elementary matrix. Then*

(1) $\det(E(u, v, \tau)) = 1 - \tau v^* u;$

(2) *when $1 - \tau v^* u \neq 0$, $E(u, v, \tau)$ is nonsingular and*

$$(E(u, v, \tau))^{-1} = E(u, v, \gamma), \quad with \ \gamma = \frac{\tau}{\tau v^* u - 1}.$$

Proof. It is easy to see that

$$\begin{bmatrix} I & 0 \\ v^* & 1 \end{bmatrix} \begin{bmatrix} I - \tau u v^* & -\tau u \\ 0 & 1 \end{bmatrix} \begin{bmatrix} I & 0 \\ -v^* & 1 \end{bmatrix} = \begin{bmatrix} I & -\tau u \\ 0 & 1 - \tau v^* u \end{bmatrix}.$$

Applying the product rule of determinant, we obtain

$$\det\left(\begin{bmatrix} I & 0 \\ v^* & 1 \end{bmatrix}\right) \cdot \det\left(\begin{bmatrix} I - \tau u v^* & -\tau u \\ 0 & 1 \end{bmatrix}\right) \cdot \det\left(\begin{bmatrix} I & 0 \\ -v^* & 1 \end{bmatrix}\right) = \det\left(\begin{bmatrix} I & -\tau u \\ 0 & 1 - \tau v^* u \end{bmatrix}\right)$$

and, hence,

$$\det\left(E(u, v, \tau)\right) = \det(I - \tau u v^*) = 1 - \tau v^* u.$$

For the second statement, if $1 - \tau v^* u \neq 0$, then $\det\big(E(u, v, \tau)\big) \neq 0$, which implies that $E(u, v, \tau)$ is nonsingular. By direct computations, we have

$$
\begin{aligned}
E(u, v, \tau)\, E(u, v, \gamma) &= I - \tau u v^* - \gamma(1 - \tau v^* u) u v^* \\
&= I - \tau u v^* - \frac{\tau}{\tau v^* u - 1}(1 - \tau v^* u) u v^* \\
&= I.
\end{aligned}
$$

Therefore, it holds that $\big(E(u, v, \tau)\big)^{-1} = E(u, v, \gamma)$. $\qquad\square$

Example 2.2. Denote by e_i the i-th column vector of the identity matrix I. By choosing different vectors u and v, we can obtain some kinds of useful elementary transform matrices. For example,

(1) when $u = e_j$, $v = e_i$, and $\tau = -\alpha$, we get $E_{\alpha i+j} = I + \alpha e_j e_i^\mathsf{T}$ (multiplying a matrix by $E_{\alpha i+j}$ from the left is equivalent to adding α times of the i-th row of the matrix to the j-th row of the matrix);

(2) when $u = v = e_i - e_j$, and $\tau = 1$, we get $E_{i,j} = I - (e_i - e_j)(e_i - e_j)^\mathsf{T}$ (multiplying a matrix by $E_{i,j}$ from the left is equivalent to switching the i-th and the j-th row of the matrix);

(3) when $u = v = e_i$ and $\tau = 1 - \alpha$ with $\alpha \neq 0$, we get $E_{\alpha i} = I - (1 - \alpha)e_i e_i^\mathsf{T}$ (multiplying a matrix by $E_{\alpha i}$ from the left is equivalent to multiplying the i-th row of the matrix by a scalar α).

Alternatively, these elementary transform matrices can be acted on a matrix from its right. Correspondingly, multiplying a matrix by $E_{\alpha i+j}$ from the right is equivalent to adding α times of the i-th column of the matrix to the j-th column of the matrix, multiplying a matrix by $E_{i,j}$ from the right is equivalent to switching the i-th and the j-th column of the matrix, and multiplying a matrix by $E_{\alpha i}$ from the right is equivalent to multiplying the i-th column of the matrix by a scalar α.

The above three elementary matrices are called the elementary matrices of Type 1, Type 2, and Type 3, respectively (see, e.g., [339]), which are very useful in the theoretical linear algebra.

The following result characterizes the invertibility of a matrix associated with the elementary matrices.

Theorem 2.3. *Let $A \in \mathbb{C}^{n \times n}$. Then the matrix A is invertible if and only if there exist a finite number of nonsingular elementary matrices $E_1, E_2, \ldots, E_k$ such that*

$$
A = E_1 E_2 \cdots E_k.
$$

Another kind of useful elementary matrix is the so-called Gauss transform [167]. Let

$$
l_j = [0, \ldots, 0, l_{j+1,j}, \ldots, l_{n,j}]^\mathsf{T}, \quad j = 1, 2, \ldots, n-1.
$$

Then the **Gauss transform** is defined as

$$
L(l_j) \triangleq E(l_j, e_j, -1) = I + l_j e_j^\mathsf{T} =
\begin{bmatrix}
1 & & & & & \\
& \ddots & & & & \\
& & 1 & & & \\
& & l_{j+1,j} & 1 & & \\
& & \vdots & & \ddots & \\
& & l_{n,j} & & & 1
\end{bmatrix}. \tag{2.1}
$$

The vectors $l_j, j = 1, 2, \ldots, n - 1$, are called the **Gauss vectors** [167]. By Proposition 2.1, we have

$$\det(L(l_j)) = 1,$$
$$(L(l_j))^{-1} = E(l_j, e_j, 1) = E(-l_j, e_j, -1) = L(-l_j).$$

The Gauss transform is useful to transform a matrix to an upper-triangular one.

2.1.2 ▪ Householder Transform

Definition 2.4. [167] *A matrix* $H \in \mathbb{C}^{n \times n}$ *of the form*

$$H = I - \frac{2}{v^* v} vv^* = I - \frac{2}{\|v\|_2^2} vv^*, \quad 0 \neq v \in \mathbb{C}^n,$$

*is called a **Householder matrix** (also known as a **Householder transform** or a **Householder reflector**). The vector v is called the **Householder vector**.*

Geometrically, a Householder transform corresponds to a reflection across the hyperplane $\text{span}\{v\}^\perp$. To see this, for any vector $x \in \mathbb{C}^n$, we write

$$x = \frac{v^* x}{v^* v} v + y \triangleq \alpha v + y, \quad \text{with} \quad y \perp v \text{ and } \alpha = \frac{v^* x}{v^* v}.$$

Then $\alpha v \in \text{span}\{v\}$ and $y \in \text{span}\{v\}^\perp$. By direct computations we have

$$Hx = \left(I - \frac{2}{\|v\|_2^2} vv^* \right) x = x - \frac{2}{v^* v} vv^* x = x - 2\alpha v = -\alpha v + y,$$

which indicates that Hx has the opposite component $-\alpha v$ in the v-direction and the same component y orthogonal to v. Because of this, the Householder matrix is also called the **reflection matrix**. This is illustrated geometrically by the following figure.

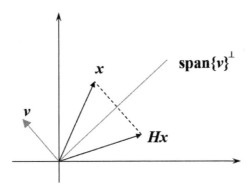

It is easy to see that a Householder matrix has the following properties.

Proposition 2.5. *Let* $H \in \mathbb{C}^{n \times n}$ *be a Householder matrix. Then*

(1) $H^* = H$, *i.e., the matrix H is Hermitian;*

(2) $H^* H = I$, *i.e., the matrix H is unitary;*

(3) $H^2 = I$;

(4) $\det(H) = -1$;

(5) *the matrix H has two distinct eigenvalues: $\lambda = 1$ with multiplicity $n - 1$, and $\lambda = -1$ with multiplicity* 1.

A very useful property of the Householder matrix is given below.

Theorem 2.6. *For any two distinct vectors $x, y \in \mathbb{C}^n$, there exists a Householder matrix H such that $y = Hx$ if and only if $\|x\|_2 = \|y\|_2$ and $x^*y \in \mathbb{R}$.*

Proof. If $\|x\|_2 = \|y\|_2$ and $x^*y \in \mathbb{R}$, then we have $y^*y = x^*x$ and $x^*y = y^*x$. It follows that

$$\|x - y\|_2^2 = (x - y)^*(x - y) = x^*x - y^*x - x^*y + y^*y = 2(x^*x - y^*x).$$

Let

$$H = I - \frac{2}{\|v\|_2^2} vv^*$$

be the Householder matrix with the Householder vector $v \in \mathbb{C}^n$ being given by $v = x - y$. Then it holds that

$$Hx = x - \frac{2(x - y)(x - y)^*x}{\|x - y\|_2^2} = x - \frac{2(x - y)(x^*x - y^*x)}{2(x^*x - y^*x)} = y.$$

On the other hand, if there exists a Householder matrix H such that $y = Hx$, then we have $x^*y = x^*Hx \in \mathbb{R}$ as the matrix H is Hermitian. Since the matrix H is unitary and the 2-norm is unitarily invariant, we have $\|y\|_2 = \|Hx\|_2 = \|x\|_2$. □

The following is an immediate consequence of this theorem.

Theorem 2.7. *For any nonzero vector $x = [x_1, x_2, \ldots, x_n]^\mathsf{T} \in \mathbb{R}^n$, there exists a Householder matrix H such that $Hx = \alpha e_1$, where $\alpha = \|x\|_2$ (or $\alpha = -\|x\|_2$) and $e_1 = [1, 0, \ldots, 0]^\mathsf{T} \in \mathbb{R}^n$.*

Here, the Householder vector $v = [v_1, v_2, \ldots, v_n]^\mathsf{T}$ is given by

$$v = x - \alpha e_1 = [x_1 - \alpha, x_2, \ldots, x_n]^\mathsf{T}.$$

In practical computations, if $x_1 \neq 0$, in order to reduce the **cancellation error** induced by the sum of two numbers close in module but opposite in sign, we usually set $\alpha = -\operatorname{sign}(x_1) \cdot \|x\|_2$. In fact, the other sign is perfectly satisfactory when at least one of x_i, $i = 2, 3, \ldots, n$, is nonzero, provided that the formula for computing v_1 is given by

$$\alpha = \operatorname{sign}(x_1) \|x\|_2,$$

$$v_1 = x_1 - \alpha = \frac{x_1^2 - \|x\|_2^2}{x_1 + \alpha} = \frac{-(x_2^2 + x_3^2 + \cdots + x_n^2)}{x_1 + \alpha},$$

which is suggested in [104, 270, 271]. This choice does not suffer from the defect of cancellation. For both choices of sign it is easy to show that $H = I - \beta vv^\mathsf{T}$ with

$$\beta = \frac{2}{v^\mathsf{T}v} = -\frac{1}{\alpha v_1}.$$

An algorithm for computing the Householder vector $v \in \mathbb{R}^n$ is as follows; see [167].

Algorithm 2.1: Algorithm for Computing a Householder Vector

% Given $x \in \mathbb{R}^n$, compute $v \in \mathbb{R}^n$ with $v_1 = 1$ and $\beta \in \mathbb{R}$ such that $Hx = \|x\|_2 e_1$, where $H = I - \beta vv^\mathsf{T}$

1: **function** $[\beta, v] = \textbf{House}(x)$
2: $n = \text{length}(x)$ (Here $\text{length}(x)$ denotes the dimension of x)
3: $\sigma = x_2^2 + x_3^2 + \cdots + x_n^2$
4: $v = \begin{bmatrix} 1 \\ x(2:n) \end{bmatrix}$
5: **if** $\sigma = 0$ **then**
6:     **if** $x_1 < 0$ **then**
7:         $\beta = 2$
8:     **else**
9:         $\beta = 0$
10:     **end if**
11: **else**
12:     $\alpha = \sqrt{x_1^2 + \sigma}$ % $\alpha = \|x\|_2$
13:     **if** $x_1 < 0$ **then**
14:         $v_1 = x_1 - \alpha$
15:     **else**
16:         $v_1 = -\sigma/(x_1 + \alpha)$
17:     **end if**
18:     $\beta = 2v_1^2/(v_1^2 + \sigma)$
19:     $v := v/v_1$
20: **end if**

The computational cost of this algorithm is about $3n$. We emphasize again that Algorithm 2.1 is only applicable to computing a real Householder vector.

Remark 2.1. *In Algorithm 2.1, we normalize the Householder vector v so that $v_1 = 1$. This permits the storage of $v(2:n)$ where the zeros have been introduced in the vector x, i.e., $x(2:n)$. In practice, we may also scale the vector x ($x := \frac{x}{\|x\|_2}$) preliminarily to avoid possible overflow.*

Note that we do not need to form the Householder matrix explicitly when applying a House-holder transform to a matrix. Let $A \in \mathbb{C}^{m \times n}$ and $H = I - \beta vv^* \in \mathbb{C}^{m \times m}$. Then

$$HA = (I - \beta vv^*)A = A - \beta vv^*A = A - \beta v(A^*v)^*.$$

Hence, applying a Householder transform on an m-by-n matrix from its left involves a matrix-vector multiplication and an **outer product**. The computational cost is about $4mn$. However, in this situation the conjugate transpose of that matrix is demanded.

2.1.3 ▪ Givens Transform

For $\theta, \varphi \in [0, 2\pi)$, let $G(i, j, \theta, \varphi) \in \mathbb{C}^{n \times n}$ be modified from an $n \times n$ identity matrix so that the (i, i)- and the (j, j)-entries are replaced by $c = \cos(\theta)$, and the (i, j)- and the (j, i)-entries are replaced by s and $-\bar{s}$, respectively, where $s = e^{i\varphi}\sin(\theta)$. That is to say,

$$
G(i, j, \theta, \varphi) =
\begin{bmatrix}
1 & & & & & & & \\
 & \ddots & & & & & & \\
 & & c & & s & & & i \\
 & & & \ddots & & & & \\
 & & -\bar{s} & & c & & & j \\
 & & & & & \ddots & & \\
 & & & & & & 1 & \\
\end{bmatrix}
\begin{array}{c} \\ \\ \\ \\ \\ \\ \\ \end{array} .
$$
$$
\quad\quad\quad i\quad\quad\ j
$$

Then $G(i, j, \theta, \varphi)$ is called a **Givens transform** or a **Givens rotation**. Note that c is real while s may be complex.

The following property of Givens transform is obvious.

Proposition 2.8. [167] *Any Givens transform is unitary and has determinant* 1.

It is important to understand the effect of a Givens transform on a matrix. Let $A \in \mathbb{C}^{n\times n}$, and let $G(i, j, \theta, \varphi)$ be a Givens transform. Then the transformation $A \to GA$ only changes the i-th and the j-th rows of the matrix A. More precisely, the i-th and the j-th rows of the matrix GA are linear combinations of the i-th and the j-th rows of the matrix A. Analogously, the transformation $A \to AG$ only changes the i-th and the j-th columns of the matrix A.

Example 2.9. For any vector $x = \begin{bmatrix} x_1 \\ x_2 \end{bmatrix} \in \mathbb{C}^2$, there exists a Givens transform

$$
G = \begin{bmatrix} c & s \\ -\bar{s} & c \end{bmatrix} \in \mathbb{C}^{2\times 2}
$$

such that $Gx = \begin{bmatrix} r \\ 0 \end{bmatrix}$, where c, s, and r are determined by the following rule:

- if $x_1 = x_2 = 0$, then $c = 1$, $s = 0$, and $r = 0$;
- if $x_1 = 0$ and $x_2 \neq 0$, then $c = 0$, $s = \dfrac{\bar{x}_2}{|x_2|}$, and $r = |x_2|$;
- if $x_1 \neq 0$ and $x_2 = 0$, then $c = 1$, $s = 0$, and $r = x_1$;
- if $x_1 \neq 0$ and $x_2 \neq 0$, then $c = \left|\dfrac{x_1}{r}\right|$, $s = \dfrac{\bar{x}_2}{\bar{r}}$, and $r = \sqrt{|x_1|^2 + |x_2|^2} \cdot \dfrac{x_1}{|x_1|}$.

This example shows that we can transform any vector $x \in \mathbb{C}^2$ to the one whose second entry is zero by applying a Givens transform. In fact, with the Givens transform, we can transform any vector $x \in \mathbb{C}^n$ to the one whose j-th entry is zero and, moreover, to the one whose entries are all zero except for the first one; see Exercise 2.4.

If $\varphi = 0$, then $G(i, j, \theta, \varphi)$ is real and orthogonal, and is simply denoted by $G(i, j, \theta)$. The geometric interpretation of $G(i, j, \theta)$ is clear. All vectors lying in the (x_i, x_j)-plane are rotated through an angle θ, and vectors orthogonal to the (x_i, x_j)-plane are unchanged; if the vector x is neither in the (x_i, x_j)-plane nor orthogonal to it, but can be expressed uniquely as a sum $x = y + y^\perp$, where the vector y is in the (x_i, x_j)-plane and the vector $y^\perp$ is orthogonal to it, then the Givens transform rotates the vector y through an angle θ and leaves the vector $y^\perp$ unchanged.

2.2 ▪ Triangular Decompositions

In this section, we introduce some useful triangular decompositions.

2.2.1 ▪ LU Decomposition

It is known that the famous **Gaussian elimination method** without pivoting can be viewed as a process of the LU decomposition.

Definition 2.10. *Let $A \in \mathbb{C}^{n \times n}$. Then the **LU decomposition** of the matrix A is of the form*

$$A = LU,$$

where $L \in \mathbb{C}^{n \times n}$ and $U \in \mathbb{C}^{n \times n}$ are lower-triangular and upper-triangular matrices, respectively.

The LU decomposition is one of the most useful matrix factorizations. Suppose that we need to solve a system of linear equations $Ax = b$. If we know the LU decomposition of the coefficient matrix A, then this linear system can be equivalently reformulated into the following two coupled triangular linear systems:

$$\begin{cases} Ly = b, \\ Ux = y, \end{cases}$$

which can be easily solved by a forward elimination (for the lower-triangular linear system $Ly = b$) followed by a backward substitution (for the upper-triangular linear system $Ux = y$).

Unfortunately, not every matrix admits an LU decomposition.

Example 2.11. Consider the matrix

$$A = \begin{bmatrix} 0 & 1 \\ 1 & 0 \end{bmatrix}.$$

If the matrix A could be decomposed as

$$A = LU = \begin{bmatrix} l_{11} & 0 \\ l_{21} & l_{22} \end{bmatrix} \begin{bmatrix} u_{11} & u_{12} \\ 0 & u_{22} \end{bmatrix},$$

then we have $l_{11}u_{11} = 0$, which implies that either the matrix L or the matrix U is singular. But the matrix A is nonsingular, which leads to a contradiction.

The following theorem gives a sufficient condition for a matrix A to admit an LU decomposition.

Theorem 2.12. [199] *Let $A \in \mathbb{C}^{n \times n}$ and suppose $\mathrm{rank}(A) = r$. For $j = 1, 2, \ldots, r$, if the j-th leading principal submatrix of the matrix A is nonsingular, then the matrix A can be factorized as*

$$A = LU,$$

with $L \in \mathbb{C}^{n \times n}$ being a lower-triangular matrix and $U \in \mathbb{C}^{n \times n}$ an upper-triangular matrix. Furthermore, the factorization can be chosen so that either the matrix L or the matrix U is nonsingular, and both matrices L and U are nonsingular if and only if the matrix A is nonsingular.

For the proof, we refer to [199].

It is clear that the LU decomposition may be not unique. But when the matrix A is nonsingular, we can impose a normalization to make the LU decomposition be unique.

Theorem 2.13. [199] *Let $A \in \mathbb{C}^{n \times n}$ be a nonsingular matrix. Then it can be factorized as*

$$A = LU,$$

with $L \in \mathbb{C}^{n \times n}$ being a lower-triangular matrix and $U \in \mathbb{C}^{n \times n}$ an upper-triangular matrix, if and only if all the leading principal submatrices of the matrix A are nonsingular. Furthermore, this decomposition is unique if the matrix L is unit lower-triangular, i.e., all diagonal entries of the matrix L are equal to 1.

The LU decomposition with L being a unit lower-triangular matrix is also known as the **Doolittle decomposition**. Similarly, we can obtain an LU decomposition with U being a unit upper-triangular matrix, which is known as the **Crout decomposition**.

An important variant of the LU decomposition is the **LDU decomposition**.

Theorem 2.14. *Let $A \in \mathbb{C}^{n \times n}$ be a nonsingular matrix. Then the matrix A can be uniquely factorized as*

$$A = LDU,$$

with $L, D, U \in \mathbb{C}^{n \times n}$ being unit lower-triangular, diagonal, and unit upper-triangular matrices, respectively, if and only if all leading principal submatrices of the matrix A are nonsingular.

Not all matrices have an LU decomposition, but for any matrix $A \in \mathbb{C}^{n \times n}$, we can write it as $A = PLUQ$, where P and Q are permutation matrices.

Theorem 2.15. [199] *Let $A \in \mathbb{C}^{n \times n}$. Then there exist permutation matrices $P, Q \in \mathbb{C}^{n \times n}$, a lower-triangular matrix $L \in \mathbb{C}^{n \times n}$, and an upper-triangular matrix $U \in \mathbb{C}^{n \times n}$ such that*

$$A = PLUQ.$$

If the matrix A is nonsingular, then it can be written as

$$A = PLU.$$

The PLU decomposition corresponds to the Gaussian elimination with pivoting.

2.2.2 ▪ Cholesky Decomposition

We know that a matrix $A \in \mathbb{C}^{n \times n}$ is Hermitian positive definite if and only if there exists a nonsingular matrix $C \in \mathbb{C}^{n \times n}$ such that $A = C^*C$; see Proposition 1.56 (7). Moreover, the matrix C can be chosen to have a special form.

Theorem 2.16 (Cholesky Decomposition). *Let $A \in \mathbb{C}^{n \times n}$ be a Hermitian positive definite matrix. Then it can be uniquely factorized as*

$$A = R^*R,$$

*where $R \in \mathbb{C}^{n \times n}$ is an upper-triangular matrix with positive diagonal entries. The matrix R is called the **Cholesky factor** of the matrix A.*

Proof. We first show the existence by making use of induction on n. When $n = 1$, $A = [a_{11}]$. Since the matrix A is Hermitian positive definite, we have $a_{11} > 0$ and $R = [\sqrt{a_{11}}]$. Suppose that any $(n-1) \times (n-1)$ Hermitian positive definite matrix has the Cholesky decomposition. Let $A \in \mathbb{C}^{n \times n}$ be Hermitian positive definite and partitioned as

$$A = \begin{bmatrix} a_{11} & \alpha^* \\ \alpha & A_{22} \end{bmatrix},$$

where $\alpha = [a_{21}, a_{31}, \ldots, a_{n1}]^\mathsf{T}$. Then we know that $a_{11} > 0$. It follows from Proposition 1.59 that the matrix $A_{22} - \alpha a_{11}^{-1} \alpha^*$ is Hermitian positive definite too. Let

$$r_{11} = \sqrt{a_{11}}, \quad \tilde{A} = A_{22} - \alpha a_{11}^{-1} \alpha^*.$$

Then

$$A = \begin{bmatrix} r_{11} & 0 \\ r_{11}^{-1}\alpha & I \end{bmatrix} \begin{bmatrix} 1 & 0 \\ 0 & \tilde{A} \end{bmatrix} \begin{bmatrix} r_{11} & 0 \\ r_{11}^{-1}\alpha & I \end{bmatrix}^*.$$

By induction we have had $\tilde{A} = \tilde{R}^* \tilde{R}$, where $\tilde{R} \in \mathbb{C}^{(n-1)\times(n-1)}$ is an upper-triangular matrix with positive diagonal entries. It follows that

$$\begin{aligned} A &= \begin{bmatrix} r_{11} & 0 \\ r_{11}^{-1}\alpha & I \end{bmatrix} \begin{bmatrix} 1 & 0 \\ 0 & \tilde{R}^*\tilde{R} \end{bmatrix} \begin{bmatrix} r_{11} & 0 \\ r_{11}^{-1}\alpha & I \end{bmatrix}^* \\ &= \begin{bmatrix} r_{11} & 0 \\ r_{11}^{-1}\alpha & I \end{bmatrix} \begin{bmatrix} 1 & 0 \\ 0 & \tilde{R}^* \end{bmatrix} \begin{bmatrix} 1 & 0 \\ 0 & \tilde{R} \end{bmatrix} \begin{bmatrix} r_{11} & 0 \\ r_{11}^{-1}\alpha & I \end{bmatrix}^* \\ &= \begin{bmatrix} r_{11} & 0 \\ r_{11}^{-1}\alpha & \tilde{R}^* \end{bmatrix} \begin{bmatrix} r_{11} & r_{11}^{-1}\alpha^* \\ 0 & \tilde{R} \end{bmatrix} \\ &\triangleq R^* R, \end{aligned}$$

with

$$R = \begin{bmatrix} r_{11} & r_{11}^{-1}\alpha^* \\ 0 & \tilde{R} \end{bmatrix} \in \mathbb{C}^{n \times n}$$

being an upper-triangular matrix of positive diagonal entries. This completes the proof of the existence.

We now turn to show the uniqueness.

Suppose that the matrix A has two Cholesky decompositions $A = P^*P = R^*R$, where $P = [p_{ij}] \in \mathbb{C}^{n \times n}$ and $R = [r_{ij}] \in \mathbb{C}^{n \times n}$ are upper-triangular matrices of positive diagonal entries. Then we have

$$RP^{-1} = (R^*)^{-1}P^*.$$

As both R and P are upper-triangular matrices, the matrix P^{-1} is upper triangular, and so is the matrix RP^{-1}. Moreover, the main diagonal entries of the matrix RP^{-1} are

$$r_{11}p_{11}^{-1}, \ r_{22}p_{22}^{-1}, \ \ldots, \ r_{nn}p_{nn}^{-1};$$

see Exercise 2.5.

Analogously, we can show that $(R^*)^{-1}P^*$ is a lower-triangular matrix with the main diagonal entries

$$r_{11}^{-1}p_{11}, \ r_{22}^{-1}p_{22}, \ \ldots, \ r_{nn}^{-1}p_{nn}.$$

Therefore, both RP^{-1} and $(R^*)^{-1}P^*$ are diagonal matrices satisfying

$$r_{ii}^{-1}p_{ii} = r_{ii}p_{ii}^{-1}, \quad i = 1, 2, \ldots, n.$$

Because r_{ii} and p_{ii} are positive numbers, we have

$$r_{ii} = p_{ii}, \quad i = 1, 2, \ldots, n,$$

which implies

$$RP^{-1} = I,$$

or equivalently, $P = R$. This readily shows the uniqueness of the Cholesky decomposition. □

Algorithm 2.2: Cholesky Decomposition

1: Set $R = 0$, the $n \times n$ zero matrix; and $v = 0$, the $1 \times n$ zero row vector
2: $R(1, 1 : n) = A(1, 1 : n)/\sqrt{A(1,1)}$
3: **for** $j = 2 : n$ **do**
4:     $v(j : n) = A(j, j : n)$
5:     **for** $k = 1 : j - 1$ **do**
6:         $v(j : n) := v(j : n) - R(k, j)^* R(k, j : n)$
7:     **end for**
8:     $R(j, j : n) = v(j : n)/\sqrt{v(j)}$
9: **end for**

The algorithm to compute the Cholesky decomposition requires about $\frac{1}{3}n^3$ operations while that to compute the LU decomposition needs about $\frac{2}{3}n^3$ operations.

2.2.3 ▪ WZ Decomposition

The **WZ decomposition** is a variant of the LU decomposition, which provides an alternative of the Gaussian elimination method for solving systems of linear equations. The idea is to decompose the matrix A into the form WZ, which naturally appeals to parallelism.

The WZ decomposition was proposed by Evans and Hatzopoulos [127] as a manner of matrix factorization intended for SIMD (Single Instruction stream, Multiple Data stream) parallel machines, and was modified and implemented further in [93, 126, 356]. The WZ decomposition has the same numerical stability as the Gaussian elimination for Hermitian positive definite or diagonally dominant matrices [243].

Let $A = [a_{i,j}] \in \mathbb{C}^{n \times n}$. Then its **WZ decomposition** is defined as

$$A = WZ,$$

where $W = [w_{i,j}] \in \mathbb{C}^{n \times n}$ and $Z = [z_{i,j}] \in \mathbb{C}^{n \times n}$ have the following forms:

$$W = \begin{bmatrix} 1 & 0 & \cdots & \cdots & \cdots & 0 & 0 \\ w_{2,1} & 1 & \ddots & & & 0 & w_{2,n} \\ \vdots & & \ddots & \ddots & 0 & & \vdots \\ \vdots & & \vdots & 1 & & \vdots & \vdots \\ \vdots & & & 0 & \ddots & \ddots & \vdots \\ w_{n-1,1} & 0 & & & \ddots & 1 & w_{n-1,n} \\ 0 & 0 & \cdots & \cdots & \cdots & 0 & 1 \end{bmatrix},$$

$$
Z = \begin{bmatrix}
z_{1,1} & \cdots & \cdots & \cdots & \cdots & \cdots & z_{1,n} \\
0 & z_{2,2} & \ddots & & \cdot^{\cdot} & z_{2,n-1} & 0 \\
\vdots & \ddots & \ddots & \cdots & \cdot^{\cdot} & & \vdots \\
\vdots & & 0 & z_{i,i} & 0 & & \vdots \\
\vdots & \cdot^{\cdot} & \cdot^{\cdot} & \cdots & \ddots & \ddots & \vdots \\
0 & z_{n-1,2} & \cdot^{\cdot} & & \ddots & z_{n-1,n-1} & 0 \\
z_{n,1} & \cdots & \cdots & \cdots & \cdots & \cdots & z_{n,n}
\end{bmatrix},
$$

with

$$
w_{i,j} = \begin{cases}
1 & \text{if } i = j, \\
0 & \text{if } i+1 \le j \le n-i+1 \quad \text{or} \quad n-i+1 \le j \le i-1,
\end{cases}
$$
$$
z_{i,j} = 0 \quad \text{if} \quad j+1 \le i \le n-j \quad \text{or} \quad n-j+2 \le i \le j-1.
$$

The other elements of the matrices W and Z can be computed as follows:

- Initially:

  (1) the first and the last rows of the matrix Z are computed by

  $$
  z_{1,j} = a_{1,j} \quad \text{and} \quad z_{n,j} = a_{n,j}, \quad j = 1, 2, \ldots, n;
  $$

  (2) for the first and the last columns of the matrix W, we solve the following 2-by-2 systems of linear equations:

  $$
  \begin{cases}
  z_{1,1}\, w_{i,1} + z_{n,1}\, w_{i,n} = a_{i,1}, \\
  z_{1,n}\, w_{i,1} + z_{n,n}\, w_{i,n} = a_{i,n},
  \end{cases}
  \quad i = 2, 3, \ldots, n-1.
  $$

- Generally: by recursion on $k = 2, 3, \ldots, \lfloor \frac{1}{2}(n+1) \rfloor$, where $\lfloor \cdot \rfloor$ denotes the nearest integer less than or equal to that real number,

  (3) the k-th and the $(n-k+1)$-th rows of the matrix Z can be computed by

  $$
  z_{l,j} = a_{l,j} - \sum_{p=1}^{k-1} w_{l,p}\, z_{p,j} - \sum_{p=n-k+2}^{n} w_{l,p}\, z_{p,j}, \quad l = k, n-k+1;
  $$
  $$
  j = k, k+1, \ldots, n-k+1;
  $$

  (4) the k-th and the $(n-k+1)$-th columns of the matrix W can be computed by solving the following pairs of linear equations for $i = k+1, k+2, \ldots, n-k$:

  $$
  z_{k,l}\, w_{i,k} + z_{n-k+1,l}\, w_{i,n-k+1} = a_{i,l} - \sum_{p=1}^{k-1} w_{i,p}\, z_{p,l} - \sum_{p=n-k+2}^{n} w_{i,p}\, z_{p,l},
  $$
  $$
  l = k, n-k+1.
  $$

It is obvious that the WZ decomposition is very suitable for parallel computations.

The WZ decomposition can be intuitively illustrated by the following pictures:

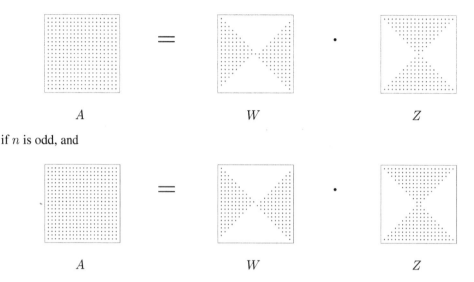

$$A \qquad\qquad W \qquad\qquad Z$$

if n is odd, and

$$A \qquad\qquad W \qquad\qquad Z$$

if n is even.

2.3 ▪ QR Decomposition and Its Computations

2.3.1 ▪ QR Decomposition

The **QR decomposition** factorizes a matrix into a product of an orthogonal and a triangular matrix. The QR decomposition is often used to solve **linear least-squares problems** [76, 324, 341], and is also the basis of the QR algorithm widely used in eigenvalue computations [101, 178, 179, 217, 271, 285].

Theorem 2.17 (QR Decomposition). [199] *Let $A \in \mathbb{C}^{m \times n}$, with $m \geq n$. Then there exist a matrix $Q \in \mathbb{C}^{m \times n}$ with orthonormal columns (that is, $Q^*Q = I_n$) and an upper-triangular matrix $R \in \mathbb{C}^{n \times n}$ such that*

$$A = QR.$$

If $m = n$, then the matrix Q is unitary, and if, in addition, the matrix A is nonsingular, then the matrix R can be chosen so that all of its diagonal entries are positive; in this situation, the factors Q and R are unique.

Proof. If $A \in \mathbb{C}^{m \times n}$ with rank$(A) = n$, then the QR decomposition of the matrix A is just a description; in matrix notation, it is the result of applying the Gram–Schmidt process to the columns of the matrix A, which form an independent set in $\mathbb{C}^m$.

A natural extension of the Gram–Schmidt process can be applied to the general case in which the columns of the matrix A may be not independent. Let $A = [a_1, a_2, \ldots, a_n]$, where $a_i \in \mathbb{C}^m$. If $a_1 = 0$, set $q_1 = 0$. Otherwise, set $q_1 = \frac{a_1}{\|a_1\|_2}$. As in the Gram–Schmidt process, for $k = 2, 3, \ldots, n$, compute

$$\tilde{q}_k = a_k - \sum_{i=1}^{k-1} (a_k^* q_i) q_i.$$

If $\tilde{q}_k = 0$, which happens if and only if a_k is a linear combination of $a_1, a_2, \ldots, a_{k-1}$, set $q_k = 0$. Otherwise, set $q_k = \frac{\tilde{q}_k}{\|\tilde{q}_k\|_2}$. Then $q_1, q_2, \ldots, q_n$ form an orthogonal set and each element is either a unit vector or the zero vector. Therefore, we have

$$A = QR,$$

where $R = [r_{ij}]$ is defined by

$$r_{ij} = \begin{cases} q_i^* a_j, & \text{for } i \leq j, \\ 0, & \text{for } i > j. \end{cases}$$

Note that the matrix Q may not have orthonormal columns since it may contain zero columns.

If $\text{rank}(A) = k < n$, i.e., the columns of the matrix A are not linearly independent, then the matrix Q has zero columns. Suppose all the nonzero columns of the matrix Q are $q_{i_1}, q_{i_2}, \ldots, q_{i_k}$, which form an orthonormal set. Then by Theorem 1.4 we can extend it to an orthonormal basis of $\mathbb{C}^m$, say,

$$q_{i_1}, \; q_{i_2}, \; \ldots, \; q_{i_k}, \; \hat{q}_1, \; \ldots, \; \hat{q}_{m-k}.$$

Now we replace the first zero column of the matrix Q by $\hat{q}_1$, the second zero column of the matrix Q by $\hat{q}_2$, and so on, until all zero columns of the matrix Q have been replaced in this way. Denote the resulting matrix by $\hat{Q}$. Then the matrix $\hat{Q}$ has orthonormal columns and satisfies $\hat{Q}R = QR$, since the new columns of the matrix $\hat{Q}$ are matched by zero rows of the matrix R. As a result, $A = \hat{Q}R$ is the QR decomposition of the desired form.

If $\text{rank}(A) = n$, then the matrix Q obviously has orthonormal columns. In addition, if $m = n$, i.e., the matrix A is nonsingular, then the matrix Q is unitary and the matrix $R = Q^{-1}A$ has nonzero diagonal entries. Note that R is an upper-triangular matrix, and so is its inverse R^{-1}. It follows from $Q = AR^{-1}$ that q_1 is a scalar multiple of a_1, and q_i is a linear combination of $a_1, a_2, \ldots, a_i$. So

$$q_i \in \text{span}\{a_1, a_2, \ldots, a_i\}.$$

At the same time, q_i is orthogonal to the linear subspace

$$\text{span}\{q_1, q_2, \ldots, q_{i-1}\} = \text{span}\{a_1, a_2, \ldots, a_{i-1}\}.$$

Hence, q_i lies in the one-dimensional subspace that is the orthogonal complement of $\text{span}\{a_1, a_2, \ldots, a_{i-1}\}$ with respect to $\text{span}\{a_1, a_2, \ldots, a_i\}$. Therefore, q_i is uniquely determined up to a scalar factor of absolute value 1. Let

$$D = \text{diag}(\text{sign}(r_{11}), \text{sign}(r_{22}), \ldots, \text{sign}(r_{nn}))$$

and

$$\hat{R} = D^{-1}R, \quad \hat{Q} = QD.$$

Then all diagonal entries of the matrix $\hat{R}$ are positive and the decomposition $A = \hat{Q}\hat{R}$ is unique. □

Remark 2.2. *If $A \in \mathbb{R}^{n \times n}$ is a real matrix, then all operations in the above proof can be carried out in real arithmetic. So, the factors Q and R can be taken to be real.*

Like the LU decomposition, the QR decomposition can also be used to solve the system of linear equations $Ax = b$. If we have the QR decomposition $A = QR$, this linear system can be rewritten as a unitary linear system coupled with an upper-triangular linear system as follows:

$$\begin{cases} Qy = b, \\ Rx = y. \end{cases}$$

The solution of the first equation is $y = Q^*b$, which can be computed easily, and the second equation can be solved by a backward substitution.

2.3.2 ▪ Computations of QR Decomposition

There are several methods for computing the QR decomposition, such as the Gram–Schmidt process, the Householder transforms, or the Givens rotations. For simplicity, we suppose $m = n$ in this subsection.

2.3.2.1 ▪ QR Decomposition with the Modified Gram–Schmidt Process

In fact, the proof of Theorem 2.17 also gives a method for computing the QR decomposition. For the sake of stability, we use the ***modified Gram–Schmidt*** (MGS) process instead.

Algorithm 2.3: QR Decomposition with MGS

1: Set $R = 0$, the $n \times n$ zero matrix
2: **if** $a_1 = 0$ **then**
3:      $q_1 = 0$
4: **else**
5:      $q_1 = a_1/\|a_1\|_2$
6: **end if**
7: $r_{11} = q_1^* a_1$
8: **for** $k = 2 : n$ **do**
9:      $q_k = a_k$
10:     **for** $i = 1 : k - 1$ **do**
11:         $q_k := q_k - (q_k^* q_i) q_i$
12:     **end for**
13:     **if** $q_k \neq 0$ **then**
14:         $q_k := q_k/\|q_k\|_2$
15:     **end if**
16:     **for** $i = 1 : k$ **do**
17:         $r_{ik} = q_i^* a_k$
18:     **end for**
19: **end for**

Note that in the above algorithm, we do not deal with the zero columns of the matrix Q.

2.3.2.2 ▪ QR Decomposition with Householder Transform

From Theorem 2.7, we know that any vector $x \in \mathbb{R}^n$ can be transformed to

$$[r, 0, \dots, 0]^\mathsf{T} \in \mathbb{R}^n$$

by a Householder transform, where $r = \|x\|_2$ or $-\|x\|_2$. Actually, any vector $x \in \mathbb{C}^n$ can be transformed to

$$[r, 0, \dots, 0]^\mathsf{T} \in \mathbb{C}^n$$

by a **Householder transform**, where $r \in \mathbb{C}$. Here we present a second algorithm for computing the QR decomposition based on the Householder transform.

For a given matrix $A = [a_{ij}] \in \mathbb{C}^{n \times n}$, let $H_1 \in \mathbb{C}^{n \times n}$ be the Householder transform such that

$$H_1 \begin{bmatrix} a_{11} \\ a_{21} \\ \vdots \\ a_{n1} \end{bmatrix} = \begin{bmatrix} r_1 \\ 0 \\ \vdots \\ 0 \end{bmatrix}.$$

Then we have

$$H_1 A = \left[\begin{array}{c|ccc} r_1 & \tilde{a}_{12} & \cdots & \tilde{a}_{1n} \\ \hline 0 & & & \\ \vdots & & \tilde{A}_2 & \\ 0 & & & \end{array} \right],$$

where $\tilde{A}_2 \in \mathbb{C}^{(n-1)\times(n-1)}$. Similarly, we can choose a Householder transform $\tilde{H}_2 \in \mathbb{C}^{(n-1)\times(n-1)}$ that transforms all entries of the first column of the submatrix $\tilde{A}_2$ to zeros except for the $(1,1)$-entry, i.e.,

$$\tilde{H}_2 \tilde{A}_2 = \left[\begin{array}{c|ccc} r_2 & \tilde{a}_{23} & \cdots & \tilde{a}_{2n} \\ \hline 0 & & & \\ \vdots & & \tilde{A}_3 & \\ 0 & & & \end{array} \right].$$

Let

$$H_2 = \begin{bmatrix} 1 & 0 \\ 0 & \tilde{H}_2 \end{bmatrix}.$$

Then $H_2 \in \mathbb{C}^{n\times n}$ and

$$H_2 H_1 A = \left[\begin{array}{cc|ccc} r_1 & \tilde{a}_{12} & \tilde{a}_{13} & \cdots & \tilde{a}_{1n} \\ 0 & r_2 & \tilde{a}_{23} & \cdots & \tilde{a}_{2n} \\ \hline 0 & 0 & & & \\ \vdots & \vdots & & \tilde{A}_3 & \\ 0 & 0 & & & \end{array} \right].$$

This procedure can be repeated for $\tilde{A}_3, \tilde{A}_4, \ldots, \tilde{A}_{n-1}$ and, in general, we obtain

$$H_k = \begin{bmatrix} I_{k-1} & 0 \\ 0 & \tilde{H}_k \end{bmatrix}, \quad k = 3, 4, \ldots, n-1,$$

where I_{k-1} denotes the identity matrix of dimension $k-1$ and $\tilde{H}_k \in \mathbb{C}^{(n-k+1)\times(n-k+1)}$, such that

$$H_{n-1} \cdots H_2 H_1 A = \begin{bmatrix} r_1 & \tilde{a}_{12} & \tilde{a}_{13} & \cdots & & \tilde{a}_{1n} \\ 0 & r_2 & \tilde{a}_{23} & \cdots & & \tilde{a}_{2n} \\ \vdots & \ddots & \ddots & & \vdots & \vdots \\ 0 & \cdots & 0 & r_{n-1} & \tilde{a}_{(n-1)n} \\ 0 & \cdots & 0 & 0 & r_n \end{bmatrix} \triangleq R,$$

which is an upper-triangular matrix.

Note that the Householder transform is unitary. Thus, the matrices $H_1, H_2, \ldots, H_{n-1}$ are all unitary, and so is the matrix $H_{n-1} \cdots H_2 H_1$. Let

$$Q = (H_{n-1} \cdots H_2 H_1)^{-1}.$$

Then the matrix Q is unitary and

$$A = QR.$$

Remark 2.3. *If the $(1,1)$-entry of the submatrix $\tilde{A}_k$ is zero in the k-th step, $k \geq 2$, or if $a_{11} = 0$, then we need to use pivoting.*

Given $A \in \mathbb{R}^{n \times n}$, the following algorithm finds Householder matrices $H_1, H_2, \ldots, H_{n-1}$ such that if

$$Q = H_1 H_2 \cdots H_{n-1},$$

then $Q^\mathsf{T} A = R$ is upper triangular. The upper-triangular part of the matrix A is overwritten by the upper-triangular part of the matrix R, and the components $2 : n - j + 1$ of the j-th Householder vectors are stored in $A(j+1 : n, j)$, $j < n$. For more details, we refer to [167, pages 224–225].

Algorithm 2.4: QR Decomposition with Householder Transform

1: **for** $j = 1 : n - 1$ **do**
2:     $[\beta, v] = \textbf{House}(A(j : n, j))$
3:     $A(j : n, j : n) := (I_{n-j+1} - \beta v v^\mathsf{T}) A(j : n, j : n)$
4:     $A(j+1 : n, j) = v(2 : n - j + 1)$
5: **end for**

The number of operations in the k-th step of this QR decomposition is about

$$3(n - k + 1)^2 + (n - k + 1)(n - k + 4).$$

Therefore, the total complexity of this QR algorithm is about

$$\frac{4}{3}n^3 + \frac{7}{2}n^2 + \frac{13}{6}n - 7 = \mathcal{O}(n^3).$$

2.3.2.3 ▪ QR Decomposition with Givens Rotation

Givens rotation can be used to compute the QR decomposition, too.

Recall that a **Givens rotation** only changes two specified rows (or columns) of a matrix. For $A = [a_{ij}] \in \mathbb{C}^{n \times n}$, let G_{21} be the **Givens transform** acting on the first and the second rows of the matrix A such that

$$G_{21} \begin{bmatrix} a_{11} \\ a_{21} \\ a_{31} \\ \vdots \\ a_{n1} \end{bmatrix} = \begin{bmatrix} \tilde{a}_{11} \\ 0 \\ a_{31} \\ \vdots \\ a_{n1} \end{bmatrix},$$

i.e., G_{21} transforms the $(2, 1)$-entry of the matrix A to zero. Similarly, we can find a Givens transform G_{31} such that the $(3, 1)$-entry of the matrix $G_{21} A$ is transformed to zero. Note that G_{31} only changes the values of the first and the third rows of the matrix $G_{21} A$. Hence the $(2, 1)$-entry of the matrix $G_{21} A$ remains zero. In this way, we can find a series of Givens transforms $G_{41}, G_{51}, \ldots, G_{n1}$ such that the first column of the matrix

$$\tilde{A} \triangleq G_{n1} \cdots G_{21} A$$

is annihilated except for the first entry.

Now we work on the second column. Let G_{32} be the Givens transform acting on the second and the third rows of the matrix $\tilde{A}$, which transforms the $(3, 2)$-entry of the matrix $\tilde{A}$ to zero. Note that G_{32} does not change the first column of the matrix $\tilde{A}$. Similarly to what we have done on the first column, there exists a series of Givens transforms $G_{42}, G_{52}, \ldots, G_{n2}$ such that the entries under the $(2, 2)$-position in the second column of the matrix

$$G_{n2} \cdots G_{32} \tilde{A}$$

are all annihilated.

Analogously, we can deal with the other columns in the same fashion. Finally, we can use $\frac{1}{2}n(n-1)$ Givens transforms

$$G_{21}, \ldots, G_{n1}, G_{32}, \ldots, G_{n2}, \ldots, G_{n(n-1)}$$

to transform the matrix A into an upper-triangular one, i.e.,

$$R = G_{n(n-1)} G_{n(n-2)} \cdots G_{21} A.$$

Let

$$Q = (G_{n(n-1)} G_{n(n-2)} \cdots G_{21})^*.$$

Because the Givens transform is unitary, we know that the matrix Q is unitary, too. Therefore, we have found a unitary matrix Q and an upper-triangular matrix R such that

$$A = QR$$

by making use of the Givens rotation.

Like the QR decomposition with the Householder transform, we may need to adopt pivoting to guarantee the stability of the above decomposition procedure and the sparsity of the induced matrix factors.

In practice, Givens rotation is not actually performed by explicitly building a whole matrix and then straightforwardly doing a matrix multiplication. The Givens transform procedure is useful in situations where only a relatively few off-diagonal elements need to be zeroed, and it is more easily parallelized than the Householder transform procedure.

Given $A \in \mathbb{R}^{n \times n}$, the following algorithm overwrites the matrix A with the matrix $Q^{\mathsf{T}} A = R$, where $R \in \mathbb{R}^{n \times n}$ is upper triangular and $Q \in \mathbb{R}^{n \times n}$ is orthogonal. For more details, we refer to [167, pages 226–227].

Algorithm 2.5: QR Decomposition with Givens Rotation

1: **for** $j = 1 : n - 1$ **do**
2:     **for** $i = j + 1 : n$ **do**
3:         **if** $A(i, j) = 0$ **then**
4:             $c = 1, s = 0$
5:         **else**
6:             **if** $|A(i, j)| > |A(j, j)|$ **then**
7:                 $\tau = -A(j, j)/A(i, j)$, $s = 1/\sqrt{1 + \tau^2}$, $c = s\tau$
8:             **else**
9:                 $\tau = -A(i, j)/A(j, j)$, $c = 1/\sqrt{1 + \tau^2}$, $s = c\tau$
10:            **end if**
11:        **end if**
12:        $A([j, i], j : n) := \begin{bmatrix} c & s \\ -s & c \end{bmatrix}^{\mathsf{T}} A([j, i], j : n)$
13:     **end for**
14: **end for**

2.3.2.4 ▪ Stability of QR Decompositions

The numerical stabilities of the QR decompositions by Householder and Givens transforms are excellent. For detailed analyses, see [348] and [196].

2.4 ▪ Full-Rank Decomposition

If a matrix has some linearly dependent columns, it is natural to seek a more economical representation. For example, for

$$A = [b_1 a, b_2 a, \ldots, b_n a], \quad a \in \mathbb{C}^m, \ b_i \in \mathbb{C}, \quad i = 1, 2, \ldots, n,$$

we can rewrite it as

$$A = ab^{\mathsf{T}},$$

where

$$b = [b_1, b_2, \ldots, b_n]^{\mathsf{T}}.$$

This shows that we only need to use $m + n$ scalars, instead of mn scalars, to represent the matrix A. The following result shows that any matrix can admit a **full-rank decomposition**.

Theorem 2.18. *Let* $A \in \mathbb{C}^{m \times n}$ *and* $\operatorname{rank}(A) = k \leq \min\{m, n\}$. *Then the matrix* A *has a full-rank decomposition of the form*

$$A = XY,$$

where both matrices $X \in \mathbb{C}^{m \times k}$ *and* $Y \in \mathbb{C}^{k \times n}$ *have full ranks.*

Proof. Let $A = [a_1, a_2, \ldots, a_n]$. As $\operatorname{rank}(A) = k$, there exist k linearly independent vectors $x_1, x_2, \ldots, x_k$ such that a_i can be represented in terms of these k vectors. Let

$$X \triangleq [x_1, x_2, \ldots, x_k].$$

Then there exists a matrix $Y \in \mathbb{C}^{k \times n}$ such that $A = XY$. It is easy to see that

$$\operatorname{rank}(X) = \operatorname{rank}(Y) = \operatorname{rank}(A) = k. \qquad \square$$

2.5 ▪ Schur and QZ Decompositions

2.5.1 ▪ Schur Decomposition

One of the purposes of similarity transformations is to reduce the complexity in computing eigenvalues of a matrix. Indeed, if a given matrix could be similarly transformed into a diagonal or triangular one, then its eigenvalues would be obtained immediately. The main result in this direction is the **Schur decomposition** described as follows; see [291].

Theorem 2.19. *For any matrix* $A \in \mathbb{C}^{n \times n}$, *there exist a unitary matrix* $U \in \mathbb{C}^{n \times n}$ *and an upper-triangular matrix* $R \in \mathbb{C}^{n \times n}$ *such that*

$$A = URU^*,$$

with the diagonal entries of the matrix R *being the eigenvalues of the matrix* A.

Theorem 2.19 states that any matrix $A \in \mathbb{C}^{n \times n}$ is unitarily similar to an upper-triangular matrix, which is called the **Schur canonical form** of the matrix A; see Section 1.5.2.

Corollary 2.20. *Let* $A \in \mathbb{C}^{n \times n}$ *be Hermitian. Then the matrix* A *has the **spectral decomposition***

$$A = UDU^*,$$

where $U \in \mathbb{C}^{n \times n}$ *is unitary and* $D \in \mathbb{R}^{n \times n}$ *is diagonal. In addition, the diagonal entries of the diagonal matrix* D *are the eigenvalues of the matrix* A.

If $A \in \mathbb{R}^{n \times n}$ is a real matrix, we may consider similar factorizations in the real space $\mathbb{R}^{n \times n}$.

Theorem 2.21. *Let $A \in \mathbb{R}^{n \times n}$ be a real matrix. Then*

$$A = QRQ^\mathsf{T},$$

where $Q \in \mathbb{R}^{n \times n}$ is orthogonal and

$$R = \begin{bmatrix} R_{11} & R_{12} & R_{13} & \cdots & R_{1k} \\ 0 & R_{22} & R_{23} & \cdots & R_{2k} \\ 0 & 0 & R_{33} & \cdots & R_{3k} \\ \vdots & \vdots & \vdots & \ddots & \vdots \\ 0 & 0 & 0 & \cdots & R_{kk} \end{bmatrix},$$

with diagonal blocks R_{ii} $(i = 1, 2, \ldots, k)$ being either a real scalar or a real 2×2 matrix having a pair of complex conjugate eigenvalues.

Theorem 2.21 is called the **real Schur decomposition** or the **quasi-Schur decomposition**. If R_{ii} is a real scalar, then it is an eigenvalue of the matrix A. If R_{ii} is a real 2×2 matrix, then it has two distinct eigenvalues μ and ν satisfying $\mu = \overline{\nu}$, and both μ and ν are eigenvalues of the matrix A.

A block upper-triangular matrix with either 1-by-1 or 2-by-2 diagonal blocks is called an **upper quasi-triangular matrix**, and a block lower-triangular matrix with either 1-by-1 or 2-by-2 diagonal blocks is called a **lower quasi-triangular matrix**. Note that the above-described real Schur decomposition amounts to a real reduction to upper quasi-triangular form; see [167].

In general, we cannot hope to reduce a real matrix to a real upper-triangular form only by a real similarity transformation. If all eigenvalues of the matrix $A \in \mathbb{R}^{n \times n}$ are real, however, we can reduce it to a real upper-triangular matrix.

Corollary 2.22. *Let $A \in \mathbb{R}^{n \times n}$ be a real matrix. Assume that all eigenvalues of the matrix A are real. Then there exist an orthogonal matrix $Q \in \mathbb{R}^{n \times n}$ and a real upper-triangular matrix $R \in \mathbb{R}^{n \times n}$ such that*

$$A = QRQ^\mathsf{T}.$$

*In particular, if the matrix A is symmetric, then it has the **spectral decomposition***

$$A = QDQ^\mathsf{T},$$

where $D \in \mathbb{R}^{n \times n}$ is a real diagonal matrix and $Q \in \mathbb{R}^{n \times n}$ is an orthogonal matrix.

If $A \in \mathbb{C}^{n \times n}$ is normal, i.e., $AA^* = A^*A$, it follows from the Schur decomposition that

$$AA^* = (URU^*)(URU^*)^* = URR^*U^*$$

and

$$A^*A = (URU^*)^*(URU^*) = UR^*RU^*.$$

Hence, it holds that $RR^* = R^*R$, where $R = [r_{ij}] \in \mathbb{C}^{n \times n}$ is an upper-triangular matrix. By comparing the diagonals of the matrices RR^* and R^*R, we obtain $r_{ij} = 0$ for $i \neq j$, $i, j = 1, 2, \ldots, n$. Therefore, R is a diagonal matrix. Conversely, if $A = UDU^*$, where $U \in \mathbb{C}^{n \times n}$ is a unitary matrix and $D \in \mathbb{C}^{n \times n}$ is a diagonal matrix, then

$$AA^* = (UDU^*)(UDU^*)^* = UDD^*U^* = UD^*DU^* = (UDU^*)^*(UDU^*) = A^*A,$$

which implies that $A \in \mathbb{C}^{n \times n}$ is a **normal matrix**.

Corollary 2.23. *Let $A \in \mathbb{C}^{n \times n}$. Then the matrix A is normal if and only if there exist a unitary matrix $U \in \mathbb{C}^{n \times n}$ and a diagonal matrix $D \in \mathbb{C}^{n \times n}$ such that*

$$A = UDU^*.$$

2.5.2 ▪ QZ Decomposition

The **QZ decomposition** is a generalization of the Schur decomposition to a matrix pair (A, B). It can be used to compute the **generalized eigenvalues** of a **matrix pencil**.

Theorem 2.24 (QZ Decomposition). [244] *Let $A, B \in \mathbb{C}^{n \times n}$. Then there exist unitary matrices $Q, Z \in \mathbb{C}^{n \times n}$ such that*
$$Q^* A Z = R \quad and \quad Q^* B Z = S,$$
where $R, S \in \mathbb{C}^{n \times n}$ are upper-triangular matrices.

For the proof, we refer to [167, page 377].

This decomposition is also called the **generalized Schur decomposition** [244].

When the matrices A and B are real, the following decomposition, which corresponds to the **real Schur decomposition**, is of particular interest.

Theorem 2.25 (Generalized Real Schur Decomposition). [304] *Let $A, B \in \mathbb{R}^{n \times n}$. Then there exist orthogonal matrices $Q, Z \in \mathbb{R}^{n \times n}$ such that*

$$Q^\mathsf{T} A Z = R \quad and \quad Q^\mathsf{T} B Z = S,$$

where $R \in \mathbb{R}^{n \times n}$ is an upper quasi-triangular matrix and $S \in \mathbb{R}^{n \times n}$ is an upper-triangular matrix.

2.6 ▪ Singular Value Decomposition and Its Generalizations

The *singular value decomposition* (SVD) is of great theoretical and practical importance in many areas related to matrix computations.

2.6.1 ▪ SVD

Let $A \in \mathbb{C}^{m \times n}$. Then both matrices $A^* A \in \mathbb{C}^{n \times n}$ and $A A^* \in \mathbb{C}^{m \times m}$ are Hermitian positive semidefinite. Hence, their eigenvalues are all nonnegative. It follows from Theorem 1.19 that the matrices $A^* A$ and $A A^*$ have the same nonzero eigenvalues with the same multiplicities. Without loss of generality, we assume $m \geq n$ in this section.

Theorem 2.26 (SVD). [167] *Let $A \in \mathbb{C}^{m \times n}$ with $m \geq n$. Then there exist unitary matrices $U \in \mathbb{C}^{m \times m}$ and $V \in \mathbb{C}^{n \times n}$ such that*

$$U^* A V = \begin{bmatrix} \Sigma \\ 0 \end{bmatrix} \quad or \quad A = U \begin{bmatrix} \Sigma \\ 0 \end{bmatrix} V^*, \tag{2.2}$$

*where $\Sigma = \mathrm{diag}(\sigma_1, \sigma_2, \ldots, \sigma_n) \in \mathbb{R}^{n \times n}$, and, $\sigma_1, \sigma_2, \ldots, \sigma_n$, called the **singular values** of the matrix A, are the nonnegative square roots of the eigenvalues of the matrix $A^* A$ satisfying $\sigma_1 \geq \sigma_2 \geq \cdots \geq \sigma_n \geq 0$. The decomposition (2.2) is the singular value decomposition of the matrix A.*

Proof. We prove this theorem by induction on m and n. First, assume that $A \neq 0$, as otherwise we can take $\Sigma = 0$ and let U and V be arbitrary unitary matrices.

For $n = 1$ and $m \geq n$, we can obtain the SVD of the matrix A as

$$A = U \begin{bmatrix} \Sigma \\ 0 \end{bmatrix} V^*,$$

where $\Sigma = [\|A\|_2]$, $V = [1]$, and $U \in \mathbb{C}^{m \times m}$ is a unitary matrix with its first column being $u_1 = \frac{1}{\|A\|_2} A$.

Suppose that all matrices in $\mathbb{C}^{(m-1) \times (n-1)}$ have the SVD. Let $A \in \mathbb{C}^{m \times n}$. Then, by the definition of $\|A\|_2 = \max\limits_{\|x\|_2=1} \|Ax\|_2$, there exists a vector $v \in \mathbb{C}^n$ such that $\|v\|_2 = 1$ and

$$\|A\|_2 = \|Av\|_2 \triangleq \sigma.$$

Let $u = \frac{1}{\sigma} Av \in \mathbb{C}^m$. Then $\|u\|_2 = 1$. By Theorem 1.4, there exist matrices $\tilde{U} \in \mathbb{C}^{m \times (m-1)}$ and $\tilde{V} \in \mathbb{C}^{n \times (n-1)}$ such that $[u, \tilde{U}] \in \mathbb{C}^{m \times m}$ and $[v, \tilde{V}] \in \mathbb{C}^{n \times n}$ are unitary matrices. As

$$\tilde{U}^* Av = \tilde{U}^* (\sigma u) = 0$$

and

$$u^* Av = u^* (\sigma u) = \sigma,$$

we have

$$\tilde{A} = [u, \tilde{U}]^* A[v, \tilde{V}] = \begin{bmatrix} u^* \\ \tilde{U}^* \end{bmatrix} A \begin{bmatrix} v, \tilde{V} \end{bmatrix} = \begin{bmatrix} u^* Av & u^* A\tilde{V} \\ \tilde{U}^* Av & \tilde{U}^* A\tilde{V} \end{bmatrix} = \begin{bmatrix} \sigma & u^* A\tilde{V} \\ 0 & \tilde{U}^* A\tilde{V} \end{bmatrix}.$$

Since

$$\sigma = \|A\|_2 = \|\tilde{A}\|_2 = \|\tilde{A}^*\|_2 \geq \|\tilde{A}^* e_1\|_2 = \|[\sigma, (u^* A\tilde{V})^*]^{\mathsf{T}}\|_2 = \sqrt{\sigma^2 + \|u^* A\tilde{V}\|_2^2},$$

we must have $\|u^* A\tilde{V}\|_2 = 0$. Hence, $u^* A\tilde{V} = 0$, so that

$$[u, \tilde{U}]^* A[v, \tilde{V}] = \begin{bmatrix} \sigma & 0 \\ 0 & A_1 \end{bmatrix},$$

where $A_1 = \tilde{U}^* A\tilde{V} \in \mathbb{C}^{(m-1) \times (n-1)}$. By the induction assumption, the submatrix A_1 has the SVD $A_1 = U_1 [\Sigma_1, 0]^{\mathsf{T}} V_1^*$, where $U_1 \in \mathbb{C}^{(m-1) \times (m-1)}$ and $V_1 \in \mathbb{C}^{(n-1) \times (n-1)}$ are unitary matrices. Let

$$U = [u, \tilde{U}] \begin{bmatrix} 1 & 0 \\ 0 & U_1 \end{bmatrix} \quad \text{and} \quad V = [v, \tilde{V}] \begin{bmatrix} 1 & 0 \\ 0 & V_1 \end{bmatrix}.$$

Then $U \in \mathbb{C}^{m \times m}$ and $V \in \mathbb{C}^{n \times n}$ are unitary matrices and

$$\begin{aligned} U^* AV &= \begin{bmatrix} 1 & 0 \\ 0 & U_1 \end{bmatrix}^* [u, \tilde{U}]^* A[v, \tilde{V}] \begin{bmatrix} 1 & 0 \\ 0 & V_1 \end{bmatrix} \\ &= \begin{bmatrix} 1 & 0 \\ 0 & U_1 \end{bmatrix}^* \begin{bmatrix} \sigma & 0 \\ 0 & A_1 \end{bmatrix} \begin{bmatrix} 1 & 0 \\ 0 & V_1 \end{bmatrix} \\ &= \begin{bmatrix} \sigma & 0 \\ 0 & U_1^* A_1 V_1 \end{bmatrix} \\ &= \begin{bmatrix} \sigma & 0 \\ 0 & \Sigma_1 \\ 0 & 0 \end{bmatrix}, \end{aligned}$$

which is the SVD of the matrix A. $\square$

Remark 2.4. *If $A \in \mathbb{R}^{m \times n}$ is a real matrix, then U, V, and Σ can be taken to be real matrices, too; see* [199].

Note that singular values are always real and nonnegative. If $\text{rank}(A) = k \leq n$, then $\text{rank}(A^*A) = k$ and the singular values $\sigma_1, \sigma_2, \ldots, \sigma_n$ of the matrix A satisfy

$$\sigma_1 \geq \sigma_2 \geq \cdots \geq \sigma_k > 0 \quad \text{and} \quad \sigma_{k+1} = \sigma_{k+2} = \cdots = \sigma_n = 0.$$

In particular, if $\text{rank}(A) = n$, then all σ_i, $i = 1, 2, \ldots, n$, are positive and the diagonal matrix Σ is nonsingular.

The columns of the matrices

$$U = [u_1, u_2, \ldots, u_m] \quad \text{and} \quad V = [v_1, v_2, \ldots, v_n]$$

are called the **left-** and the **right-singular vectors** of the matrix A, respectively. That is to say, it holds that

$$Av_i = \sigma_i u_i, \quad A^*u_i = \sigma_i v_i, \quad i = 1, 2, \ldots, n,$$
$$A^*u_i = 0, \quad i = n+1, n+2, \ldots, m,$$

and

$$A = U \begin{bmatrix} \Sigma \\ 0 \end{bmatrix} V^* = \sigma_1 u_1 v_1^* + \sigma_2 u_2 v_2^* + \cdots + \sigma_n u_n v_n^* = \sum_{i=1}^{n} \sigma_i u_i v_i^*.$$

Denote by $\hat{U} = [u_1, u_2, \ldots, u_n] \in \mathbb{C}^{m \times n}$. Then $\hat{U}^* \hat{U} = I_{n \times n}$ and

$$A = \hat{U} \Sigma V^*, \tag{2.3}$$

which is called the ***thin SVD*** (TSVD) [167] or the ***reduced SVD*** (RSVD) [317]. This immediately leads to a **low-rank approximation** to the matrix A.

Theorem 2.27. *Suppose $A = \sum_{i=1}^{n} \sigma_i u_i v_i^* \in \mathbb{C}^{m \times n}$ and $A_l = \sum_{i=1}^{l} \sigma_i u_i v_i^*$. Then*

$$\|A - A_l\|_2 = \sigma_{l+1} \quad \text{and} \quad \|A - A_l\|_F = \sqrt{\sigma_{l+1}^2 + \sigma_{l+2}^2 + \cdots + \sigma_n^2}.$$

If $\text{rank}(A) = k \leq n$, then $\sigma_i = 0$, $i = k+1, k+2, \ldots, n$. Hence,

$$A = \sum_{i=1}^{k} \sigma_i u_i v_i^* = A_k.$$

Theorem 2.28. *Suppose $A = \sum_{i=1}^{n} \sigma_i u_i v_i^* \in \mathbb{C}^{m \times n}$. If $\text{rank}(A) = k$, then*

$$\text{Ran}(A) = \text{span}\{u_1, u_2, \ldots, u_k\} \quad \text{and} \quad \text{Ker}(A) = \text{span}\{v_{k+1}, v_{k+2}, \ldots, v_n\}.$$

Proof. The proof is left as Exercise 2.6. □

Here and in the sequel, we use $\sigma_{\max}(A)$ and $\sigma_{\min}(A)$ to denote the largest and the smallest singular value of the matrix A, respectively.

Both the 2-norm and the Frobenius norm of a matrix A can be characterized by its singular values, i.e.,

$$\|A\|_2 = \sigma_{\max}(A) \quad \text{and} \quad \|A\|_F = \sqrt{\sum_{i=1}^{n} \sigma_i^2(A)}.$$

Theorem 2.29 (Weyl Theorem). [308] *Let $A, B \in \mathbb{C}^{m \times n}$ with $m \geq n$. Assume $\mathrm{rank}(B) = k$. Then, if $k < n$,*

$$\max_{x \in \mathrm{Ker}(B), \|x\|_2 = 1} \|Ax\|_2 \geq \sigma_{k+1}(A)$$

and

$$\min_{x \in \mathrm{Ker}(B), \|x\|_2 = 1} \|Ax\|_2 \leq \sigma_{n-k}(A).$$

Therefore,

$$\sigma_1(A - B) \geq \sigma_{k+1}(A)$$

and

$$\sigma_n(A + B) \leq \sigma_{n-k}(A).$$

Moreover, for $C \in \mathbb{C}^{m \times n}$, if $A = B + C$, then

$$\sigma_{i+j-1}(A) \leq \sigma_i(B) + \sigma_j(C), \quad i = 1, 2, \ldots, n, \ j = 1, 2, \ldots, n - i + 1.$$

The **min-max characterization** of singular values follows immediately from Theorem 2.29.

Theorem 2.30. *The singular values of a matrix $A \in \mathbb{C}^{m \times n}$ have the following characterizations:*

$$\sigma_k(A) = \min_{\dim(\mathcal{L}) = n-k+1} \max_{x \in \mathcal{L}, \|x\|_2 = 1} \|Ax\|_2, \quad k = 1, 2, \ldots, n,$$

and

$$\sigma_k(A) = \max_{\dim(\mathcal{L}) = k} \min_{x \in \mathcal{L}, \|x\|_2 = 1} \|Ax\|_2, \quad k = 1, 2, \ldots, n,$$

where $\mathcal{L}$ is a linear subspace of $\mathbb{C}^n$.

The following result is about the perturbation of singular values.

Theorem 2.31. [308] *Let $A, E \in \mathbb{C}^{m \times n}$. Then*

$$|\sigma_i(A + E) - \sigma_i(A)| \leq \|E\|_2, \quad i = 1, 2, \ldots, n.$$

Proof. Left as Exercise 2.7. □

One useful application of the SVD is to show that every matrix is the limit of matrices with distinct eigenvalues.

Corollary 2.32. *Let $A \in \mathbb{C}^{n \times n}$ and $\|\cdot\|$ be any **consistent matrix norm**. Then, for any $\varepsilon > 0$, there exists a matrix A_ε with distinct eigenvalues such that $\|A - A_\varepsilon\| \leq \varepsilon$.*

Theorem 2.33 (Schmidt–Mirsky Theorem). [308] *For any matrices A, $B \in \mathbb{C}^{m \times n}$, if* $\mathrm{rank}(B)$ *$= k$, then*

$$\|A - B\|_2 \geq \sigma_{k+1}(A)$$

and

$$\|A - B\|_F \geq \sqrt{\sigma_{k+1}^2(A) + \sigma_{k+2}^2(A) + \cdots + \sigma_n^2(A)}.$$

The inequalities become equalities when $B = A_k = \sum\limits_{i=1}^{k} \sigma_i u_i v_i^*$ and $\mathrm{rank}(A) \geq k$.

2.6.2 ▪ CS Decomposition

We first introduce the **thin Cosine–Sine** (CS) decomposition.

Theorem 2.34 (Thin CS Decomposition). [167] *Let*

$$Q = \begin{bmatrix} Q_1 \\ Q_2 \end{bmatrix}, \quad with \quad Q_1 \in \mathbb{C}^{m_1 \times n}, \ Q_2 \in \mathbb{C}^{m_2 \times n}, \quad m_1 \geq n, \ m_2 \geq n,$$

be a column-orthonormal matrix. Then there exist unitary matrices $U_1 \in \mathbb{C}^{m_1 \times m_1}$, $U_2 \in \mathbb{C}^{m_2 \times m_2}$ and $V_1 \in \mathbb{C}^{n \times n}$ such that

$$\begin{bmatrix} U_1 & \\ & U_2 \end{bmatrix}^* Q V_1 = \begin{bmatrix} C \\ S \end{bmatrix},$$

where

$$C = \begin{bmatrix} C_1 \\ 0 \end{bmatrix} \in \mathbb{R}^{m_1 \times n}, \quad C_1 = \mathrm{diag}(c_1, c_2, \ldots, c_n) \in \mathbb{R}^{n \times n},$$

$$S = \begin{bmatrix} 0 \\ S_1 \end{bmatrix} \in \mathbb{R}^{m_2 \times n}, \quad S_1 = \mathrm{diag}(s_1, s_2, \ldots, s_n) \in \mathbb{R}^{n \times n},$$

with

$$1 \geq c_1 \geq c_2 \geq \cdots \geq c_n \geq 0, \quad 0 \leq s_1 \leq s_2 \leq \cdots \leq s_n \leq 1,$$

and

$$c_i^2 + s_i^2 = 1, \quad i = 1, 2, \ldots, n.$$

Proof. As the matrix Q has orthonormal columns, we have

$$Q^* Q = Q_1^* Q_1 + Q_2^* Q_2 = I.$$

Hence, the singular values of the matrix Q_1 are not greater than 1. Let $c_1, c_2, \ldots, c_n$ be the singular values of the matrix Q_1, where

$$1 \geq c_1 \geq c_2 \geq \cdots \geq c_n \geq 0.$$

Then the SVD of the matrix Q_1 is given by $Q_1 = U_1 C V_1^*$, where $U_1 \in \mathbb{C}^{m_1 \times m_1}$ and $V_1 \in \mathbb{C}^{n \times n}$ are unitary matrices, and $C = \begin{bmatrix} C_1 \\ 0 \end{bmatrix} \in \mathbb{R}^{m_1 \times n}$ with

$$C_1 = \mathrm{diag}(c_1, c_2, \ldots, c_n) \in \mathbb{R}^{n \times n}.$$

As
$$(QV_1)^*(QV_1) = V_1^* Q^* Q V_1 = I,$$

we have
$$
\begin{aligned}
I = (QV_1)^*(QV_1) &= (Q_1 V_1)^*(Q_1 V_1) + (Q_2 V_1)^*(Q_2 V_1)\\
&= (U_1 C)^* U_1 C + (Q_2 V_1)^*(Q_2 V_1)\\
&= C^* C + (Q_2 V_1)^*(Q_2 V_1).
\end{aligned}
$$

It then follows that
$$(Q_2 V_1)^*(Q_2 V_1) = I - C^* C = \operatorname{diag}(1 - c_1^2, 1 - c_2^2, \ldots, 1 - c_n^2).$$

Therefore, there exists a unitary matrix $U_2 \in \mathbb{C}^{m_2 \times m_2}$ such that $Q_2 V_1 = U_2 S$, where $S = \begin{bmatrix} 0 \\ S_1 \end{bmatrix} \in \mathbb{R}^{m_2 \times n}$ with
$$S_1 = \operatorname{diag}(s_1, s_2, \ldots, s_n) \in \mathbb{R}^{n \times n}$$

and
$$s_i = \sqrt{1 - c_i^2};$$

see Exercise 2.11. As a result, it holds that
$$0 \le s_1 \le s_2 \le \cdots \le s_n \le 1$$

and
$$\begin{bmatrix} U_1 & \\ & U_2 \end{bmatrix}^* Q V_1 = \begin{bmatrix} U_1^* Q_1 V_1 \\ U_2^* Q_2 V_1 \end{bmatrix} = \begin{bmatrix} C \\ S \end{bmatrix}. \qquad \square$$

Remark 2.5. *For $m_1 \le n$ or $m_2 \le n$, we can prove the similar statement.*

Suppose $\operatorname{rank}(Q_1) = r$. As
$$1 \ge c_1 \ge c_2 \ge \cdots \ge c_n \ge 0,$$

there exist integers k and $l \triangleq r - k$ such that
$$1 = c_1 = \cdots = c_k > c_{k+1} \ge \cdots \ge c_{k+l} > c_{k+l+1} = \cdots = c_n = 0.$$

Therefore, we can write the diagonal matrices C and S as

$$
C = \begin{bmatrix} I & & \\ & \tilde{C}_1 & \\ & & 0 \end{bmatrix} \begin{matrix} k \\ l \\ m_1 - r \end{matrix} \quad \text{and} \quad S = \begin{bmatrix} 0 & & \\ & \tilde{S}_1 & \\ & & I \end{bmatrix} \begin{matrix} k + m_2 - n \\ l \\ n - r \end{matrix},
$$
$$\begin{matrix} k & l & n-r \end{matrix} \qquad\qquad\qquad\qquad \begin{matrix} k & l & n-r \end{matrix}$$

where
$$
\begin{aligned}
\tilde{C}_1 &= \operatorname{diag}(c_{k+1}, c_{k+2}, \ldots, c_{k+l}), & 1 &> c_{k+1} \ge c_{k+2} \ge \cdots \ge c_{k+l} > 0,\\
\tilde{S}_1 &= \operatorname{diag}(s_{k+1}, s_{k+2}, \ldots, s_{k+l}), & 0 &< s_{k+1} \le s_{k+2} \le \cdots \le s_{k+l} < 1,\\
c_i^2 + s_i^2 &= 1, \quad i = k+1, k+2, \ldots, k+l.
\end{aligned}
$$

Now, we present the **CS decomposition** of a unitary matrix.

Theorem 2.35 (CS Decomposition). [264] *Let* $Q \in \mathbb{C}^{n \times n}$ *be a unitary matrix partitioned as*

$$Q = \begin{bmatrix} Q_{11} & Q_{12} \\ Q_{21} & Q_{22} \end{bmatrix},$$

where $Q_{11} \in \mathbb{C}^{m_1 \times n_1}$ *and* $Q_{22} \in \mathbb{C}^{(n-m_1) \times (n-n_1)}$. *Then there exist unitary matrices* $U_1 \in \mathbb{C}^{m_1 \times m_1}$, $U_2 \in \mathbb{C}^{(n-m_1) \times (n-m_1)}$ *and* $V_1 \in \mathbb{C}^{n_1 \times n_1}$, $V_2 \in \mathbb{C}^{(n-n_1) \times (n-n_1)}$ *such that*

$$\begin{bmatrix} U_1 & \\ & U_2 \end{bmatrix}^* Q \begin{bmatrix} V_1 & \\ & V_2 \end{bmatrix} = \begin{bmatrix} U_1 & \\ & U_2 \end{bmatrix}^* \begin{bmatrix} Q_{11} & Q_{12} \\ Q_{21} & Q_{22} \end{bmatrix} \begin{bmatrix} V_1 & \\ & V_2 \end{bmatrix} = \begin{bmatrix} D_{11} & D_{12} \\ D_{21} & D_{22} \end{bmatrix},$$

where $D_{11} \in \mathbb{R}^{m_1 \times n_1}$, $D_{22} \in \mathbb{R}^{(n-m_1) \times (n-n_1)}$, *and*

$$
\left[\begin{array}{c|c} D_{11} & D_{12} \\ \hline D_{21} & D_{22} \end{array} \right]
$$

$$
= \left[\begin{array}{ccc|ccc} I & & & 0_s^\mathsf{T} & & \\ & C & & & S & \\ & & 0_c & & & I \\ \hline 0_s & & & I & & \\ & S & & & -C & \\ & & I & & & 0_c^\mathsf{T} \\ k & l & n_1-k-l & n-n_1-m_1+k & l & m_1-k-l \end{array} \right]
\begin{array}{l} k \\ l \\ m_1-k-l \\ n-m_1-n_1+k \\ l \\ n_1-k-l \end{array},
$$

with

$$C = \mathrm{diag}(c_1, c_2, \ldots, c_l) \in \mathbb{R}^{l \times l}, \quad 1 > c_1 \geq c_2 \geq \cdots \geq c_l > 0,$$

$$S = \mathrm{diag}(s_1, s_2, \ldots, s_l) \in \mathbb{R}^{l \times l}, \quad 0 < s_1 \leq s_2 \leq \cdots \leq s_l < 1,$$

satisfying

$$C^2 + S^2 = I \in \mathbb{R}^{l \times l}.$$

Here, k *is the number of singular values of the submatrix* Q_{11} *equal to* 1, l *is the number of singular values of the submatrix* Q_{11} *within the interval* $(0, 1)$, *and* 0_c *and* 0_s *are zero matrices of consistent dimensions.*

Proof. See [264] *or* [341]. □

Remark 2.6. *Stewart* [306] *gave the following decomposition, which is a spacial case of the CS decomposition. Let* $Q \in \mathbb{C}^{n \times n}$ *be a unitary matrix partitioned into the* 2×2 *block form*

$$Q = \begin{bmatrix} Q_{11} & Q_{12} \\ Q_{21} & Q_{22} \end{bmatrix} \in \mathbb{C}^{n \times n},$$

with $Q_{11} \in \mathbb{C}^{m \times m}$ *satisfying* $m \leq \dfrac{n}{2}$. *Then there exist unitary matrices* $U_1, V_1 \in \mathbb{C}^{m \times m}$ *and* $U_2, V_2 \in \mathbb{C}^{(n-m) \times (n-m)}$ *such that*

$$\begin{bmatrix} U_1^* & \\ & U_2^* \end{bmatrix} \begin{bmatrix} Q_{11} & Q_{12} \\ Q_{21} & Q_{22} \end{bmatrix} \begin{bmatrix} V_1 & \\ & V_2 \end{bmatrix} = \begin{bmatrix} \Gamma & \Sigma & 0 \\ -\Sigma & \Gamma & 0 \\ 0 & 0 & I_{n-2m} \end{bmatrix},$$

where Γ *and* Σ *are diagonal matrices of order* m *satisfying*

$$\Gamma^2 + \Sigma^2 = I \in \mathbb{R}^{m \times m}.$$

For the history and generalization of the CS decomposition, we refer to [266].

2.6.3 ▪ Generalized SVD

The **generalized singular value decomposition** (GSVD), or the **quotient singular value decomposition** (QSVD) [106], is a generalization of the SVD to the matrix pair (A, B), where the matrices A and B have the same number of columns. In [325], Van Loan first introduced the generalized singular value decomposition and called it the **B-singular value decomposition** of the matrix A.

Theorem 2.36 (B-Singular Value Decomposition (BSVD)). *Let $A \in \mathbb{C}^{m \times n}$ with $m \geq n$ and $B \in \mathbb{C}^{p \times n}$. Then there exist two unitary matrices $U \in \mathbb{C}^{m \times m}$ and $V \in \mathbb{C}^{p \times p}$, and a nonsingular matrix $X \in \mathbb{C}^{n \times n}$, such that*

$$U^* A X = \Sigma_A = \operatorname{diag}(\alpha_1, \alpha_2, \ldots, \alpha_n) \in \mathbb{R}^{m \times n}, \quad \alpha_i \geq 0 \ (i = 1, 2, \ldots, n),$$
$$V^* B X = \Sigma_B = \operatorname{diag}(\beta_1, \beta_2, \ldots, \beta_l) \in \mathbb{R}^{p \times n}, \quad \beta_i \geq 0 \ (i = 1, 2, \ldots, l), \tag{2.4}$$

where $l = \min\{p, n\}$.

Proof. See [325]. ☐

However, the transform matrix X in (2.4) can be ill-conditioned and, in general, we cannot expect to compute the transformations of (A, B) in (2.4) in a numerically stable way.

If we choose a unitary matrix $Q \in \mathbb{C}^{n \times n}$ such that $QX^{-1} = R$ is upper triangular and combine this with (2.4), we obtain

$$U^* A Q = \Sigma_A R \quad \text{and} \quad V^* B Q = \Sigma_B R. \tag{2.5}$$

As U, V, and Q are unitary matrices, we could hope to compute the transformations in (2.5) in a more numerically stable manner. Based on this idea, Paige and Saunders [264] proposed an alternative of the GSVD, which shows better numerical properties in computing the generalized singular values.

Theorem 2.37. [264] *Let $A \in \mathbb{C}^{m \times n}$, $B \in \mathbb{C}^{p \times n}$, and $C = \begin{bmatrix} A \\ B \end{bmatrix} \in \mathbb{C}^{(m+p) \times n}$. Then we have*

$$U^* A Q = \Sigma_1 [W^* R, 0] \quad \text{and} \quad V^* B Q = \Sigma_2 [W^* R, 0], \tag{2.6}$$

where

- $U \in \mathbb{C}^{m \times m}$, $V \in \mathbb{C}^{p \times p}$, $Q \in \mathbb{C}^{n \times n}$, *and* $W \in \mathbb{C}^{r \times r}$ *are unitary matrices, with* $r = \operatorname{rank}(C) \leq n$;
- $R \in \mathbb{C}^{r \times r}$ *is a nonsingular upper-triangular matrix, with its singular values equal to the nonzero singular values of the matrix C;*
- $\Sigma_1 \in \mathbb{R}^{m \times r}$ *and* $\Sigma_2 \in \mathbb{R}^{p \times r}$ *are nonnegative diagonal matrices satisfying* $\Sigma_1^{\mathsf{T}} \Sigma_1 + \Sigma_2^{\mathsf{T}} \Sigma_2 = I$.

Remark 2.7. *Note that*

(1) *there is no restriction on m, n, and p in Theorem 2.37;*

(2) *the matrix R in (2.6) can be taken as a diagonal matrix.*

More precisely, the matrices Σ_1 and Σ_2 have the following structures:

$$\Sigma_1 = \begin{bmatrix} I_A & & \\ & S_1 & \\ & & 0_A \end{bmatrix} \quad \text{and} \quad \Sigma_2 = \begin{bmatrix} 0_B & & \\ & S_2 & \\ & & I_B \end{bmatrix},$$

where $I_A \in \mathbb{R}^{k \times k}$ and $I_B \in \mathbb{R}^{(r-k-s) \times (r-k-s)}$ are identity matrices, $0_A \in \mathbb{R}^{(m-k-s) \times (r-k-s)}$ and $0_B \in \mathbb{R}^{(p-r+k) \times k}$ are zero matrices, and $S_1, S_2 \in \mathbb{R}^{s \times s}$ are diagonal matrices. If we write

$$\Sigma_1^\mathsf{T} \Sigma_1 = \mathrm{diag}(\alpha_1^2, \alpha_2^2, \dots, \alpha_r^2)$$

and

$$\Sigma_2^\mathsf{T} \Sigma_2 = \mathrm{diag}(\beta_1^2, \beta_2^2, \dots, \beta_r^2),$$

then $0 \le \alpha_i, \beta_i \le 1$ and it holds that $\alpha_i^2 + \beta_i^2 = 1$, $i = 1, 2, \dots, r$.

The **generalized singular value**, σ_i, of the matrix pair (A, B) is given as follows:

$$\sigma_i = \begin{cases} \dfrac{\alpha_i}{\beta_i}, & \text{for} \quad \beta_i \ne 0, \\ \infty, & \text{for} \quad \beta_i = 0, \end{cases} \qquad i = 1, 2, \dots, r.$$

The GSVD of two matrices A and B is a tool used in many applications, such as the Kronecker canonical form of a general matrix pencil [213], least-squares problems [76, 341], and so on.

As a further generalization of the SVD, Ewerbring and Luk [128] and Zha [359] proposed a generalized SVD for matrix triplets, and De Moor, Golub, and Zha [106, 107] generalized the SVD to a factorization of any number of matrices.

For numerical algorithms for computing the GSVD, we refer to [13, 15, 191, 260, 307, 326].

2.6.4 ▪ Polar Decomposition

Theorem 2.38. *Let* $A \in \mathbb{C}^{m \times n}$ *with* $m \ge n$. *Then the matrix* A *has the* ***polar decomposition***

$$A = UH,$$

where the matrix $H \in \mathbb{C}^{n \times n}$ *is Hermitian positive semidefinite and the matrix* $U \in \mathbb{C}^{m \times n}$ *has orthonormal columns (i.e.,* $U^*U = I_n$*). The matrices* H *and* U *are always uniquely determined by* $H = (A^*A)^{\frac{1}{2}}$ *and* $U = A(A^*A)^{-\frac{1}{2}}$ *whenever* $\mathrm{rank}(A) = n$.

Proof. It follows from (2.3) that

$$A = X\Sigma Y = XYY^*\Sigma Y = (XY)(Y^*\Sigma Y),$$

where $\Sigma \in \mathbb{C}^{n \times n}$ is a diagonal matrix, $Y \in \mathbb{C}^{n \times n}$ is a unitary matrix, and $X \in \mathbb{C}^{m \times n}$ is a matrix satisfying $X^*X = I_n$. Set $U = XY \in \mathbb{C}^{m \times n}$ and $H = Y^*\Sigma Y \in \mathbb{C}^{n \times n}$. Then we have $A = UH$, where the matrix U satisfies

$$U^*U = (XY)^*(XY) = Y^*(X^*X)Y = Y^*Y = I,$$

and the matrix H is Hermitian positive semidefinite.

If $A = UH$, then

$$A^*A = (UH)^*UH = H^*H = H^2.$$

Hence, the matrix H is the unique Hermitian positive semidefinite **square root** of the matrix A^*A, that is, $H = (A^*A)^{\frac{1}{2}}$. If $\mathrm{rank}(A) = n$, then

$$\mathrm{rank}(A^*A) = \mathrm{rank}(A) = n,$$

which implies that the matrix A^*A is nonsingular and is, hence, Hermitian positive definite. Therefore, the matrix H is Hermitian positive definite, too. As a result,

$$U = AH^{-1} = A(A^*A)^{-\frac{1}{2}}$$

is uniquely determined. □

Remark 2.8. *Analogously, it can be shown that $A = WU$, where the matrix $W = (AA^*)^{\frac{1}{2}} \in \mathbb{C}^{m \times m}$ is Hermitian positive semidefinite and the matrix $U \in \mathbb{C}^{m \times n}$ has orthonormal columns (i.e., $U^*U = I_n$).*

If A is a square matrix, then we immediately have the following result.

Theorem 2.39. *Let $A \in \mathbb{C}^{n \times n}$. Then there exist Hermitian positive semidefinite matrices $H, W \in \mathbb{C}^{n \times n}$ and unitary matrices $U, V \in \mathbb{C}^{n \times n}$ such that*

$$A = UH = WV.$$

The matrices H and W are always uniquely determined as $H = (A^*A)^{\frac{1}{2}}$ and $W = (AA^*)^{\frac{1}{2}}$, respectively, and the matrices U and V are uniquely determined whenever the matrix A is nonsingular.

Remark 2.9. *If the matrix $A \in \mathbb{R}^{n \times n}$ is real, then H, W, and U, V in Theorems 2.38 and 2.39 can be taken to be real matrices, too.*

Proposition 2.40. *Let $A = UH$ be the polar decomposition of the matrix $A \in \mathbb{C}^{n \times n}$. Then the matrix A is **normal** if and only if $HU = UH$.*

Proof. If $HU = UH$, then

$$AA^* = UH(UH)^* = HU(HU)^* = H^2$$

and

$$A^*A = (UH)^*UH = H^*U^*UH = H^2.$$

Therefore, $AA^* = A^*A$, which implies that the matrix A is normal.

On the other hand, if the matrix A is normal, we can obtain

$$H^2 = UH^2U^*.$$

Let

$$B = H^2 = UH^2U^*.$$

Then the matrix B is Hermitian positive semidefinite and, obviously, both matrices H and UHU^* are its Hermitian positive semidefinite square roots. Since the Hermitian positive semidefinite square root of a Hermitian positive semidefinite matrix is unique (see Theorem 1.55), it holds that $H = UHU^*$ or, equivalently, $HU = UH$. □

Theorem 2.41. *Let $A \in \mathbb{C}^{n \times n}$. Assume that A is a nonsingular matrix. Then the matrix A can be decomposed into $A = HQ$, where the matrices $H, Q \in \mathbb{C}^{n \times n}$ satisfy that H is Hermitian positive definite and $QQ^* = I$. Moreover, if the matrix $A \in \mathbb{R}^{n \times n}$ is real, then both matrices H and Q are real.*

For the stability about the polar decomposition, we refer to [94].

2.7 ▪ Other Decompositions

Theorem 2.42. *Let $A \in \mathbb{C}^{n \times n}$. Then there exist unique matrices $S, N \in \mathbb{C}^{n \times n}$ such that*

(i) *S is diagonalizable, i.e., the matrix S is similar to a diagonal matrix;*

(ii) *N is nilpotent, i.e., there exists an integer k such that $N^k = 0$;*

(iii) *$A = S + N$;*

(iv) *$SN = NS$.*

This result is called the **SN decomposition** or the **Jordan–Chevalley decomposition** [73].

Theorem 2.43. [73] *The following statements hold true:*

- *Let $A \in \mathbb{C}^{n \times n}$. Then the matrix A is normal if and only if there exists a unitary matrix $U \in \mathbb{C}^{n \times n}$ such that $A^* = AU$.*

- *Let $A \in \mathbb{C}^{n \times n}$. Assume that the matrix A is nonsingular. Then the matrices A^{-1} and A^* are similar if and only if there exists a nonsingular matrix $B \in \mathbb{C}^{n \times n}$ such that $A = B^{-1}B^*$. Furthermore, the matrix A is unitary if and only if there exists a normal and nonsingular matrix $C \in \mathbb{C}^{n \times n}$ such that $A = C^{-1}C^*$.*

- *Let $A, B \in \mathbb{C}^{n \times n}$. Assume that both matrices A and B are nonsingular. Then the matrices A and B are similar if and only if there exist nonsingular matrices $C, D \in \mathbb{C}^{n \times n}$ such that $A = CD$ and $B = DC$.*

- *Let $A \in \mathbb{C}^{m \times n}$. Assume that $\mathrm{rank}(A) = n$. Then there exists a unique matrix $B \in \mathbb{C}^{m \times n}$ and an upper-triangular matrix $C \in \mathbb{C}^{n \times n}$ of positive diagonal entries such that $B^*B = I$ and $A = BC$.*

2.8 ▪ Exercises

2.1. Let $u, v \in \mathbb{C}^n$ with $v^*u \neq 0$. Show that the eigenvalues of the matrix $E(u, v, \tau)$ are 1 (with multiplicity $n - 1$) and $1 - \tau v^*u$. Hence,

$$\det\left(E(u, v, \tau)\right) = 1^{n-1} \cdot (1 - \tau v^*u) = 1 - \tau v^*u. \tag{2.7}$$

Does (2.7) hold when $v^*u = 0$?

2.2. Let $A \in \mathbb{C}^{n \times n}$. Show that the matrix A can be written as

$$A = LP_0U,$$

where $L \in \mathbb{C}^{n \times n}$ is a nonsingular lower-triangular matrix, $U \in \mathbb{C}^{n \times n}$ is a nonsingular upper-triangular matrix, and $P_0 \in \mathbb{C}^{n \times n}$ is a **sub-permutation matrix** (a permutation matrix with as many $n - \mathrm{rank}(A)$ of 1s are replaced by 0s).
(Hint: use elementary row and column operations.)

2.3. Prove Proposition 2.5.

2.4. Let $x \in \mathbb{C}^n$. Show that there exists a Givens transform G such that the j-th entry of the vector Gx is zero. Moreover, there exist Givens transforms $G_1, G_2, \ldots, G_{n-1}$ such that all entries of the vector $G_{n-1} \cdots G_2 G_1 x$ are zero except for the first one.

2.5. Let $R = [r_{ij}] \in \mathbb{C}^{n \times n}$ and $S = [s_{ij}] \in \mathbb{C}^{n \times n}$ be upper-triangular matrices. Show that

- the matrix RS is upper triangular;
- the main diagonal entries of the matrix RS are $r_{11}s_{11}, r_{22}s_{22}, \ldots, r_{nn}s_{nn}$;

- if the matrix R is nonsingular, i.e., its main diagonal entries $r_{11}, r_{22}, \ldots, r_{nn}$ are nonzero, then the matrix R^{-1} is upper triangular and its main diagonal entries are $r_{11}^{-1}, r_{22}^{-1}, \ldots, r_{nn}^{-1}$.

(Remark: the above statements are also true for lower-triangular matrices.)

2.6. Prove Theorem 2.28.

2.7. Prove Theorem 2.31.

2.8. Let $\sigma_1, \sigma_2, \ldots, \sigma_n$ be the singular values of the matrix $A \in \mathbb{C}^{n \times n}$. Show that

$$|\det(A)| = \prod_{i=1}^{n} \sigma_i.$$

2.9. Let $A \in \mathbb{C}^{n \times n}$ be a nonsingular matrix and its singular values be $\sigma_1, \sigma_2, \ldots, \sigma_n$ satisfying $\sigma_1 \geq \sigma_2 \geq \cdots \geq \sigma_n > 0$. Show that

$$\kappa_2(A) = \|A^{-1}\|_2 \cdot \|A\|_2 = \frac{\sigma_1}{\sigma_n}.$$

2.10. Let $A \in \mathbb{C}^{n \times n}$ and $B = \begin{bmatrix} 0 & A^* \\ A & 0 \end{bmatrix} \in \mathbb{C}^{2n \times 2n}$. If $A = U\Sigma V^*$ is the SVD of the matrix A, where $\Sigma = \mathrm{diag}(\sigma_1, \sigma_2, \ldots, \sigma_n)$, $U = [u_1, u_2, \ldots, u_n]$, and $V = [v_1, v_2, \ldots, v_n]$, prove that the eigenvalues of the matrix B are $\pm\sigma_i$ and the corresponding unit eigenvectors are $\frac{1}{\sqrt{2}} \begin{bmatrix} v_i \\ \pm u_i \end{bmatrix}$, $i = 1, 2, \ldots, n$.

2.11. Let $A \in \mathbb{C}^{m \times n}$ satisfy

$$(A^*A)^{\frac{1}{2}} = S_1 \triangleq \mathrm{diag}(s_1, s_2, \ldots, s_n) \in \mathbb{R}^{n \times n}.$$

Show that there exists a unitary matrix $U \in \mathbb{C}^{m \times m}$ such that

$$A = US, \quad \text{with} \quad S = \begin{bmatrix} S_1 \\ 0 \end{bmatrix} \begin{matrix} n \\ m-n \end{matrix}, \quad \text{or} \quad S = \begin{bmatrix} 0 \\ S_1 \end{bmatrix} \begin{matrix} m-n \\ n \end{matrix}.$$

2.12. Let $A \in \mathbb{C}^{m \times n}$ and $m \leq n$. Show that the matrix A can be written as

$$A = PU,$$

where $P \in \mathbb{C}^{m \times m}$ is Hermitian positive semidefinite and $U \in \mathbb{C}^{m \times n}$ has orthonormal rows.

2.13. Let $x \in \mathbb{C}^n$ be a nonzero vector and set $A = [x] \in \mathbb{C}^{n \times 1}$. Show that the polar decomposition of the matrix A is

$$A = u \|x\|_2,$$

where $u = \dfrac{x}{\|x\|_2}$. Thus, the polar decomposition may be regarded as a generalization to matrices of the convenient factorization $x = \dfrac{x}{\|x\|_2} \cdot \|x\|_2$ of nonzero vectors.

2.14. Let $A \in \mathbb{C}^{n \times n}$. Use the polar decomposition to show that the matrices AA^* and A^*A are unitarily similar.

Chapter 3

Numerical Range

The numerical range is also called **field of values** [200]. Like the spectrum, the numerical range can be used to explore useful properties of a matrix, such as location of eigenvalues, bounds of norm, and estimate of spectral radius. It can also give important information that the spectrum cannot. In applications, the numerical range provides a powerful tool for constructing high-quality preconditioners and analyzing convergence properties of the corresponding preconditioned Krylov subspace iteration methods used to solve large sparse systems of linear equations.

3.1 ▪ Definition and Basic Properties

3.1.1 ▪ Definition

Definition 3.1. [8] *Let $A \in \mathbb{C}^{n \times n}$. Then the **Rayleigh quotient** of the matrix A for a nonzero vector $x \in \mathbb{C}^n$ is defined as*

$$q(x) \triangleq \frac{x^* A x}{x^* x}.$$

It is easy to see that $q(\cdot)$ is a homogeneous function of degree zero on $\mathbb{C}^n$, i.e., $q(\alpha x) = q(x)$ holds true for all $\alpha \in \mathbb{C}$ with $\alpha \neq 0$.

Definition 3.2. [200] *The **numerical range** of the matrix $A \in \mathbb{C}^{n \times n}$ is*

$$\mathcal{F}(A) \triangleq \{x^* A x : x \in \mathbb{C}^n, \ x^* x = 1\},$$

*and the **numerical radius** of the matrix $A \in \mathbb{C}^{n \times n}$ is*

$$r(A) \triangleq \max\{|x^* A x| : x \in \mathbb{C}^n, \ x^* x = 1\}.$$

Note that, unlike the spectrum that is a set of discrete points, the numerical range can be a continuum, and it is always a compact **convex set**. We will prove the convexity of $\mathcal{F}(A)$ in the next section.

A straightforward fact from the definitions of the numerical range and the numerical radius is that for $A \in \mathbb{C}^{n \times n}$ both $\mathcal{F}(A)$ and $r(A)$ are unitarily invariant, that is, they possess the invariant property under unitary **similarity transformations** in the sense that

$$\mathcal{F}(U^* A U) = \mathcal{F}(A) \quad \text{and} \quad r(U^* A U) = r(A)$$

are valid for any unitary matrix $U \in \mathbb{C}^{n \times n}$. Moreover, in general there holds

$$\mathcal{F}(A) \subseteq \{z \,:\, z \in \mathbb{C}, \ |z| \leq r(A)\}.$$

Example 3.3. [181] Let

$$A = \begin{bmatrix} 0 & a \\ 0 & 0 \end{bmatrix}, \quad \text{with} \quad a \in \mathbb{C} \quad \text{and} \quad a \neq 0.$$

Let $x = [x_1, x_2]^{\mathsf{T}} \in \mathbb{C}^2$ with $|x_1|^2 + |x_2|^2 = 1$. Then

$$|x^* A x| = |a \bar{x}_1 x_2| \leq \frac{1}{2} |a|(|x_1|^2 + |x_2|^2) = \frac{|a|}{2}.$$

Therefore,

$$\mathcal{F}(A) \subseteq \Omega \triangleq \left\{ z \,:\, |z| \leq \frac{|a|}{2} \right\}.$$

On the other hand, for any $z \in \Omega$, we can write $z = s e^{\mathrm{i}\theta}$, with

$$0 \leq s \leq \frac{|a|}{2} \quad \text{and} \quad 0 \leq \theta < 2\pi.$$

By denoting $a = |a| e^{\mathrm{i}\beta}$ and letting

$$x = [\cos(\alpha), e^{\mathrm{i}(\theta - \beta)} \sin(\alpha)],$$

with

$$0 \leq \alpha \leq \frac{\pi}{4} \quad \text{and} \quad \sin(2\alpha) = \frac{2s}{|a|},$$

we have

$$x^* x = \cos^2(\alpha) + \sin^2(\alpha) = 1$$

and

$$x^* A x = a e^{\mathrm{i}(\theta - \beta)} \cos(\alpha) \sin(\alpha) = \frac{1}{2} a e^{\mathrm{i}(\theta - \beta)} \sin(2\alpha)$$
$$= s e^{\mathrm{i}(\theta - \beta)} \frac{a}{|a|} = s e^{\mathrm{i}\theta} = z.$$

Therefore,

$$\mathcal{F}(A) = \left\{ z \,:\, |z| \leq \frac{|a|}{2} \right\}.$$

Example 3.4. [181] Let

$$A = \begin{bmatrix} c & 2f \\ 0 & -c \end{bmatrix}, \quad \text{with} \quad c \in \mathbb{R}, \ f \in \mathbb{C} \quad \text{and} \quad f \neq 0.$$

As any complex unit vector $x = [x_1, x_2]^{\mathsf{T}} \in \mathbb{C}^2$ can be written as

$$x_1 = e^{\mathrm{i}\alpha} \cos(\theta), \quad x_2 = e^{\mathrm{i}\beta} \sin(\theta),$$

with

$$\theta \in \left[0, \frac{\pi}{2}\right] \quad \text{and} \quad \alpha, \beta \in [0, 2\pi),$$

by denoting $f = |f|e^{i\gamma}$ we have

$$x^*Ax = c(\cos^2(\theta) - \sin^2(\theta)) + 2fe^{i(\beta-\alpha)}\sin(\theta)\cos(\theta)$$
$$\triangleq z_1 + iz_2,$$

where

$$\begin{cases} z_1 = c\cos(2\theta) + |f|\sin(2\theta)\cos(\beta - \alpha + \gamma), \\ z_2 = |f|\sin(2\theta)\sin(\beta - \alpha + \gamma). \end{cases}$$

Hence,

$$(z_1 - c\cos(2\theta))^2 + z_2^2 = |f|^2\sin^2(2\theta), \tag{3.1}$$

which is a family of circles whose union can be easily obtained.

Now we consider the boundary of the union of this family of circles, for which $\theta \in (0, \frac{\pi}{2})$. Let $\varphi = 2\theta$. Then $\varphi \in (0, \pi)$ and (3.1) can be rewritten as

$$\Phi(z_1, z_2, \varphi) = 0, \tag{3.2}$$

where

$$\Phi(z_1, z_2, \varphi) = (z_1 - c\cos(\varphi))^2 + z_2^2 - |f|^2\sin^2(\varphi). \tag{3.3}$$

Differentiating $\Phi(z_1, z_2, \varphi)$ with respect to φ, we obtain

$$c(z_1 - c\cos(\varphi)) = |f|^2\cos(\varphi). \tag{3.4}$$

After eliminating φ from the last two equations (3.3) and (3.4), we get the envelope of the domain defined in (3.2) with respect to z_1 and z_2 as follows:

$$\frac{z_1^2}{c^2 + |f|^2} + \frac{z_2^2}{|f|^2} = 1, \tag{3.5}$$

which is an ellipse with center at 0, minor axis being $2|f|$, and major axis being $2\sqrt{c^2 + |f|^2}$.

It is easy to verify that $r(A)$ is a **matrix norm** but not a **consistent matrix norm**, i.e.,

- $r(A) \geq 0$, and $r(A) = 0$ if and only if $A = 0$,
- $r(\alpha A) = |\alpha|\, r(A)$, for any $\alpha \in \mathbb{C}$,
- $r(A + B) \leq r(A) + r(B)$.

In general,

$$r(AB) \leq r(A)\, r(B)$$

does not hold. However, $4\, r(\cdot)$ is a consistent matrix norm; see Exercise 3.3.

Example 3.5. Let

$$A = \begin{bmatrix} 0 & 1 \\ 0 & 0 \end{bmatrix} \quad \text{and} \quad B = \begin{bmatrix} 0 & 0 \\ 1 & 0 \end{bmatrix}.$$

Then

$$|x^*Ax| = |\bar{x}_1 x_2| \leq \frac{1}{2}(|x_1|^2 + |x_2|^2),$$

which implies $r(A) \leq \frac{1}{2}$. On the other hand, let

$$x = \left[\frac{\sqrt{2}}{2}, \frac{\sqrt{2}}{2}\right]^{\mathsf{T}}.$$

Then we have $|x^*Ax| = \frac{1}{2}$, so that $r(A) = \frac{1}{2}$. Analogously, we can show that $r(B) = \frac{1}{2}$ and $r(AB) = 1$. Obviously, the relationship $r(AB) \leq r(A)\, r(B)$ does not hold.

3.1.2 ▪ Basic Properties

Some basic facts about the **numerical range** are listed below, which can be found in the references, e.g., [8, 181, 190, 200].

Proposition 3.6. *Let $A, B \in \mathbb{C}^{n \times n}$. Then the following statements hold true:*

(1) $\sigma(A) \subseteq \mathcal{F}(A)$.

(2) $\rho(A) \leq r(A) \leq \|A\|_2 \leq 2\,r(A)$.

(3) $\mathcal{F}(A + \alpha I) = \mathcal{F}(A) + \alpha$, *for any* $\alpha \in \mathbb{C}$.

(4) $\mathcal{F}(\alpha A) = \alpha\,\mathcal{F}(A)$, *for any* $\alpha \in \mathbb{C}$.

(5) $\mathcal{F}(A + B) \subseteq \mathcal{F}(A) + \mathcal{F}(B)$.

(6) $\mathcal{F}(A^{\mathsf{T}}) = \mathcal{F}(A)$ *and* $\mathcal{F}(A^*) = \overline{\mathcal{F}(A)}$.

(7) $\mathcal{F}(U^* A U) = \mathcal{F}(A)$ *for any unitary matrix* $U \in \mathbb{C}^{n \times n}$, *i.e., the numerical range is invariant under unitary similarity transformations.*

(8) *For* $X \in \mathbb{C}^{n \times k}$ *with* $k \leq n$ *satisfying* $X^* X = I$, $\mathcal{F}(X^* A X) \subseteq \mathcal{F}(A)$ *and, in particular, for any principal submatrix* A_k *of the matrix* A, $\mathcal{F}(A_k) \subseteq \mathcal{F}(A)$.

(9) *For any normal matrix* A, $\mathcal{F}(A) = \mathcal{F}(\mathrm{diag}(\lambda_1, \lambda_2, \ldots, \lambda_n))$, *where* λ_i $(1 \leq i \leq n)$ *are the eigenvalues of the matrix* A, *and it follows that* $\rho(A) = r(A) = \|A\|_2$.

(10) $\mathcal{F}(A)$ *is a subset of a straight line if and only if there exist* $\alpha, \beta \in \mathbb{C}$, *with* $\alpha \neq 0$, *such that the matrix* $\alpha A + \beta I$ *is Hermitian; in particular,*

- $A = \alpha I$ *if and only if* $\mathcal{F}(A) = \{\alpha\}$,
- $A = A^*$ *if and only if* $\mathcal{F}(A) \subseteq \mathbb{R}$,
- $A = A^*$ *is positive definite if and only if* $\mathcal{F}(A) \subseteq (0, \infty)$,
- $A = A^*$ *is positive semidefinite if and only if* $\mathcal{F}(A) \subseteq [0, \infty)$.

Let $\mathcal{S}$ be a subset of the real or the complex vector space. We denote by $\mathrm{Co}(\mathcal{S})$ the **convex hull** of the subset $\mathcal{S}$, i.e., $\mathrm{Co}(\mathcal{S})$ is the set of all **convex combinations** of finitely many points in the subset $\mathcal{S}$. Note that $\mathrm{Co}(\mathcal{S})$ is the smallest convex set that contains $\mathcal{S}$. If $S = \mathrm{Co}(\mathcal{S})$, then $\mathcal{S}$ is called a **convex subset**.

A stronger statement than Property (1) in Proposition 3.6 is the inclusion relationship

$$\mathrm{Co}(\sigma(A)) \subseteq \mathcal{F}(A).$$

Moreover, if the matrix $A \in \mathbb{C}^{n \times n}$ is normal, then

$$\mathrm{Co}(\sigma(A)) = \mathcal{F}(A).$$

The converse is true for $n \leq 4$. If $n > 4$, there are examples showing that $\mathrm{Co}(\sigma(A)) = \mathcal{F}(A)$, but the matrix A is not normal [209].

Proposition 3.7. [8] *Let* $A \in \mathbb{C}^{n \times n}$. *Then*

(1) $r(A) \leq 1$ *implies* $r(A^m) \leq 1$, *for* $m = 1, 2, \ldots$;

(2) $r(A^m) \leq \left(r(A)\right)^m$, *for* $m = 1, 2, \ldots$.

Proof. We first prove the validity of (1).

Since $\omega_j = e^{\mathrm{i} \frac{2\pi j}{m}}$ $(j = 1, 2, \ldots, m)$ are the m-th roots of the unity, we have the polynomial equalities

$$1 - z^m = \prod_{j=1}^{m} (1 - \omega_j z) \tag{3.6}$$

and

$$1 = \frac{1}{m} \sum_{j=1}^{m} \prod_{\substack{k=1 \\ k \neq j}}^{m} (1 - \omega_k z). \tag{3.7}$$

We remark that these two equalities hold true even when the complex variable z is replaced by any square matrix B, that is,

$$I - B^m = \prod_{j=1}^{m} (I - \omega_j B)$$

and

$$I = \frac{1}{m} \sum_{j=1}^{m} \prod_{\substack{k=1 \\ k \neq j}}^{m} (I - \omega_k B).$$

Let

$$v_j = \prod_{\substack{k=1 \\ k \neq j}}^{m} (I - \omega_k B)x, \quad j = 1, 2, \ldots, m,$$

with $x \in \mathbb{C}^n$ satisfying $x^* x = 1$. Then it holds that

$$x = \frac{1}{m} \sum_{j=1}^{m} \prod_{\substack{k=1 \\ k \neq j}}^{m} (I - \omega_k B)x = \frac{1}{m} \sum_{j=1}^{m} v_j$$

and

$$\prod_{k=1}^{m} (I - \omega_k B)x = (I - \omega_j B) \prod_{\substack{k=1 \\ k \neq j}}^{m} (I - \omega_k B)x = (I - \omega_j B)v_j.$$

Hence, we have

$$x^*(I - B^m)x = \left(\frac{1}{m} \sum_{j=1}^{m} v_j \right)^* (I - B^m)x$$

$$= \frac{1}{m} \sum_{j=1}^{m} v_j^* (I - B^m)x$$

$$= \frac{1}{m} \sum_{j=1}^{m} v_j^* \left(\prod_{k=1}^{m} (I - \omega_k B) \right) x$$

$$= \frac{1}{m} \sum_{j=1}^{m} v_j^* (I - \omega_j B)v_j. \tag{3.8}$$

Denote by $B_\theta = e^{i\theta} A$ with $\theta \in \mathbb{R}$. Then $r(B_\theta) \leq 1$ due to $r(A) \leq 1$. As a result, we know that for any normalized complex vector $x \in \mathbb{C}^n$ there holds

$$\Re(x^*(I - \omega_j B_\theta)x) = 1 - \Re(\omega_j x^* B_\theta x) \geq 0, \quad j = 1, 2, \ldots, m.$$

By replacing the matrix B in (3.8) with the matrix B_θ we can further get

$$\Re(x^*(I - B_\theta^m)x) = \frac{1}{m}\sum_{j=1}^m \Re(v_j^*(I - \omega_j B_\theta)v_j)$$

$$= \frac{1}{m}\sum_{j=1}^m \|v_j\|_2^2 \left[1 - \Re\left(\omega_j \left(\frac{v_j}{\|v_j\|_2}\right)^* B_\theta \frac{v_j}{\|v_j\|_2}\right)\right]$$

$$\geq 0.$$

Therefore, it holds that

$$\Re(x^*(e^{\mathrm{i}m\theta}A^m)x) = \Re(x^* B_\theta^m x) \leq 1.$$

For each unit vector $x \in \mathbb{C}^n$, by first taking a proper $\theta := \theta(x)$ such that $\Im(e^{\mathrm{i}m\theta}x^*A^m x) = 0$, and then letting $\tilde{\theta} = \theta + \frac{\pi}{m}$, we see that $\Im(e^{\mathrm{i}m\tilde{\theta}}x^*A^m x) = 0$ and

$$-1 \leq -\Re(x^*(e^{\mathrm{i}m\tilde{\theta}}A^m)x) = \Re(x^*(e^{\mathrm{i}m\theta}A^m)x) \leq 1.$$

Consequently, it follows that

$$|x^* A^m x| = |x^*(e^{\mathrm{i}m\theta}A^m)x| = |\Re(x^*(e^{\mathrm{i}m\theta}A^m)x)| \leq 1,$$

which implies $r(A^m) \leq 1$.

Next, we demonstrate the validity of (2). Assume that $A \neq 0$, as, otherwise, the inequality holds trivially. Then we know that $r(A) > 0$. Moreover, by letting $C = \frac{A}{r(A)}$ we see that $r(C) = 1$. In accordance with (1) we have

$$r(C^m) = r\left(\frac{A^m}{r(A)^m}\right) \leq 1,$$

which implies straightforwardly that $r(A^m) \leq (r(A))^m$. □

Recalling that $\mathscr{H}(A) = \frac{1}{2}(A + A^*)$ is the Hermitian part of the matrix $A \in \mathbb{C}^{n\times n}$, we have the following projection property about the **numerical range**.

Theorem 3.8. *Let* $A \in \mathbb{C}^{n\times n}$. *Then*

$$\Re(\mathcal{F}(A)) = \mathcal{F}(\mathscr{H}(A)).$$

Proof. By direct computations, we have

$$x^* \mathscr{H}(A)\, x = \frac{1}{2}x^*(A + A^*)x = \frac{1}{2}(x^* Ax + x^* A^* x) = \frac{1}{2}(x^* Ax + \overline{x^* Ax}) = \Re(x^* Ax).$$

Therefore, each point in $\mathcal{F}(\mathscr{H}(A))$ is of the form $\Re(z)$ for some $z \in \mathcal{F}(A)$, and vice versa. □

A more general result can be found in Exercise 3.6.

Theorem 3.9. [163] *Let* $A \in \mathbb{R}^{n\times n}$ *be a **nonnegative matrix** and* $\mathscr{H}(A) = \frac{1}{2}(A + A^\mathsf{T})$ *be its symmetric part. Then*

$$r(A) = \rho(\mathscr{H}(A)).$$

Proof. By the definition of $r(A)$, we know that there exists a unit vector

$$\tilde{x} = [\tilde{x}_1, \tilde{x}_2, \ldots, \tilde{x}_n]^\mathsf{T} \in \mathbb{C}^n$$

such that $r(A) = |\tilde{x}^* A \tilde{x}|$. Let

$$\tilde{y} = |\tilde{x}| = [|\tilde{x}_1|, |\tilde{x}_2|, \ldots, |\tilde{x}_n|]^\mathsf{T}.$$

Then $\tilde{y} \in \mathbb{R}^n$ is a nonnegative unit vector. Since the matrix $A \in \mathbb{R}^{n \times n}$ is nonnegative, it holds that

$$r(A) = |\tilde{x}^* A \tilde{x}| \leq |\tilde{x}|^\mathsf{T} A |\tilde{x}| = \tilde{y}^\mathsf{T} A \tilde{y} \leq r(A),$$

which shows that $r(A) = \tilde{y}^\mathsf{T} A \tilde{y}$. So, $r(A)$ can be described as

$$r(A) = \max\{x^\mathsf{T} A x \, : \, x \in \mathbb{R}^n, \, x^\mathsf{T} x = 1\}.$$

Similarly, as the matrix $\mathcal{H}(A)$ is also nonnegative, we can describe $r(\mathcal{H}(A))$ as

$$r(\mathcal{H}(A)) = \max\{x^\mathsf{T} \mathcal{H}(A) x \, : \, x \in \mathbb{R}^n, \, x^\mathsf{T} x = 1\}.$$

Note that $\mathcal{H}(A)$ is symmetric and $x^\mathsf{T} \mathcal{H}(A) x = x^\mathsf{T} A x$ when $x \in \mathbb{R}^n$. Then we find that

$$r(A) = r(\mathcal{H}(A)) = \rho(\mathcal{H}(A)). \qquad \square$$

From the proof of Theorem 3.9, we see that the numerical radius of a nonnegative matrix $A \in \mathbb{R}^{n \times n}$ can be described as

$$r(A) = \max\{x^\mathsf{T} A x \, : \, x \in \mathbb{R}^n, \, x \geq 0, \, x^\mathsf{T} x = 1\}.$$

3.1.3 ▪ Numerical Range of Matrix Product

First of all, we need to point out that the **sub-multiplicativity** of the **numerical range** is not true. This fact can be illustrated by the following example.

Example 3.10. Let

$$A = \begin{bmatrix} 1 & 0 \\ 0 & -1 \end{bmatrix} \quad \text{and} \quad B = \begin{bmatrix} 0 & 1 \\ 1 & 0 \end{bmatrix}.$$

Then $\lambda(AB) = \pm\mathrm{i}$ and $\mathcal{F}(AB)$ is a line segment joining the points $-\mathrm{i}$ and i, while

$$\mathcal{F}(A) = \mathcal{F}(B) = \mathcal{F}(A)\,\mathcal{F}(B) = [-1, 1]$$

is a line segment located on the real axis. Here, the product of the two sets $\mathcal{F}(A)$ and $\mathcal{F}(B)$ is defined as

$$\mathcal{F}(A)\,\mathcal{F}(B) \triangleq \{yz \, : \, y \in \mathcal{F}(A), \, z \in \mathcal{F}(B)\}.$$

Thus, neither $\sigma(AB)$ nor $\mathcal{F}(AB)$ is a subset of $\mathcal{F}(A)\,\mathcal{F}(B)$. Note that, in this example, neither $\sigma(AB)$ nor $\mathcal{F}(AB)$ is contained in $\mathrm{Co}(\mathcal{F}(A)\,\mathcal{F}(B))$.

Although the inclusion relationship $\sigma(AB) \subseteq \mathcal{F}(A)\,\mathcal{F}(B)$ does not hold in general, the following theorem indicates that this relationship can be true under certain condition.

Theorem 3.11. *Let* $A, B \in \mathbb{C}^{n \times n}$. *If* $0 \notin \mathcal{F}(A)$, *then*

$$\sigma(A^{-1}B) \subseteq \left\{ \frac{\nu}{\mu} \, : \, \mu \in \mathcal{F}(A), \, \nu \in \mathcal{F}(B) \right\}.$$

Proof. Note that the matrix A is nonsingular under the condition $0 \notin \mathcal{F}(A)$; see Exercise 3.5.

Assume $\lambda \in \sigma(A^{-1}B)$. Then there exists a unit vector $x \in \mathbb{C}^n$ such that $A^{-1}Bx = \lambda x$ or, equivalently, $Bx = \lambda Ax$. Multiplying both sides of this equality from left by x^*, we have $x^*Bx = \lambda x^*Ax$. Since $x^*Ax \neq 0$ for any $x \in \mathbb{C}^n \setminus \{0\}$, we have

$$\lambda = \frac{x^*Bx}{x^*Ax} = \frac{\nu}{\mu},$$

where $\nu \in \mathcal{F}(B)$ and $\mu \in \mathcal{F}(A)$. Therefore, it holds that

$$\sigma(A^{-1}B) \subseteq \left\{ \frac{\nu}{\mu} : \mu \in \mathcal{F}(A), \, \nu \in \mathcal{F}(B) \right\}. \qquad \square$$

If $A \in \mathbb{C}^{n \times n}$ is **Hermitian positive definite**, then

$$\mathcal{F}(A^{-1}) = \{ z^{-1} : z \in \mathcal{F}(A) \}.$$

This directly leads to the following inclusion relationship.

Theorem 3.12. *Let $A, B \in \mathbb{C}^{n \times n}$. If the matrix A is Hermitian positive definite, then*

$$\sigma(AB) \subseteq \mathcal{F}(A)\,\mathcal{F}(B).$$

Proof.

$$\sigma(AB) = \sigma\left((A^{-1})^{-1}B\right) \subseteq \left\{ \frac{\nu}{\mu} : \mu \in \mathcal{F}(A^{-1}), \, \nu \in \mathcal{F}(B) \right\}$$

$$= \left\{ \frac{\nu}{\mu} : \mu^{-1} \in \mathcal{F}(A), \, \nu \in \mathcal{F}(B) \right\} = \{ \mu\nu : \mu \in \mathcal{F}(A), \, \nu \in \mathcal{F}(B) \}$$

$$\subseteq \mathcal{F}(A)\,\mathcal{F}(B). \qquad \square$$

In general, we have the following result.

Corollary 3.13. *Let $A, B \in \mathbb{C}^{n \times n}$. If either the matrix A or the matrix B is Hermitian positive semidefinite, then $\sigma(AB) \subseteq \mathcal{F}(A)\,\mathcal{F}(B)$.*

Proof. Without loss of generality, we assume that the matrix A is **Hermitian positive semidefinite**.

If the matrix A is nonsingular, then it is Hermitian positive definite. So it holds that $\mathcal{F}(A^{-1}) = \{z^{-1} : z \in \mathcal{F}(A)\}$. From Theorem 3.11 we know that for any $\lambda \in \sigma(AB)$, there exist $\mu \in \mathcal{F}(A^{-1})$ and $\nu \in \mathcal{F}(B)$ such that $\lambda = \frac{\nu}{\mu}$. As $\mu^{-1} \in \mathcal{F}(A)$, it holds that $\lambda = \nu\mu^{-1} \in \mathcal{F}(A)\,\mathcal{F}(B)$, which shows that $\sigma(AB) \subseteq \mathcal{F}(A)\,\mathcal{F}(B)$. We remark that this argument is exactly a literal restatement of the proof of Theorem 3.12.

If the matrix A is singular, then it is Hermitian positive semidefinite. For this case, we let $A_\varepsilon = A + \varepsilon I$, with $\varepsilon > 0$ being an arbitrary small number. Then the matrix A_ε is nonsingular and is, hence, Hermitian positive definite. From the previous argument, by making use of the fact $\mathcal{F}(A_\varepsilon) = \mathcal{F}(A) + \varepsilon$ we know that

$$\sigma(A_\varepsilon B) \subseteq \mathcal{F}(A_\varepsilon)\,\mathcal{F}(B).$$

In the light of the continuity of the eigenvalues of a matrix with respect to its entries, by letting $\varepsilon \to 0$ we then obtain $\sigma(AB) \subseteq \mathcal{F}(A)\,\mathcal{F}(B)$. $\qquad \square$

It is hard to obtain general result for $\mathcal{F}(AB)$. For some special cases, however, we can obtain something about $\mathcal{F}(AB)$.

Theorem 3.14. *Let* $A, B \in \mathbb{C}^{n \times n}$ *with* $AB = BA$*, and let the matrix* A *be Hermitian positive semidefinite. Then* $\mathcal{F}(AB) \subseteq \mathcal{F}(A)\,\mathcal{F}(B)$.

Proof. We claim that $A^{\frac{1}{2}}B = BA^{\frac{1}{2}}$ is valid under the assumptions; see Exercise 3.1. In fact, from the Hermitian positive semidefiniteness of the matrix A we know that there exist a unitary matrix U and a nonnegative diagonal matrix $\Lambda = \mathrm{diag}(\lambda_1, \lambda_2, \ldots, \lambda_n)$ such that $A = U\Lambda U^*$. Hence, it holds that $A^{\frac{1}{2}} = U\Lambda^{\frac{1}{2}}U^*$. Since $AB = BA$, we have $U\Lambda U^* B = BU\Lambda U^*$, which implies that $\Lambda \tilde{B} = \tilde{B}\Lambda$ with $\tilde{B} = [\tilde{b}_{ij}] \triangleq U^*BU$. Then it follows that $\lambda_i \tilde{b}_{ij} = \tilde{b}_{ij}\lambda_j$, or equivalently, either $\lambda_i = \lambda_j$ or $\tilde{b}_{ij} = 0$ holds for any i, j such that $1 \le i, j \le n$. These relationships are obviously equivalent to $\lambda_i^{\frac{1}{2}}\tilde{b}_{ij} = \tilde{b}_{ij}\lambda_j^{\frac{1}{2}}$, $1 \le i, j \le n$, or in the matrix form, $\Lambda^{\frac{1}{2}}U^*BU = U^*BU\Lambda^{\frac{1}{2}}$, which straightforwardly leads to the matrix equality $U\Lambda^{\frac{1}{2}}U^*B = BU\Lambda^{\frac{1}{2}}U^*$ or $A^{\frac{1}{2}}B = BA^{\frac{1}{2}}$.

Note that the above equality readily results in $AB = A^{\frac{1}{2}}BA^{\frac{1}{2}}$. Then, for any $x \in \mathbb{C}^n$ with $\|x\|_2 = 1$, it holds that

$$x^*ABx = x^*A^{\frac{1}{2}}BA^{\frac{1}{2}}x = (A^{\frac{1}{2}}x)^*B(A^{\frac{1}{2}}x) = (y^*By)(x^*Ax), \tag{3.9}$$

where

$$y = \frac{1}{\|A^{1/2}x\|_2} A^{\frac{1}{2}}x$$

satisfies

$$\|y\|_2^2 = y^*y = \frac{x^*Ax}{\|A^{1/2}x\|_2^2} = 1,$$

so that $\|y\|_2 = 1$. Therefore, the equality (3.9) straightforwardly shows that

$$\mathcal{F}(AB) \subseteq \mathcal{F}(A)\,\mathcal{F}(B). \qquad \square$$

Theorem 3.15. [181, page 37]. *Let* $A, B \in \mathbb{C}^{n \times n}$*. Then*

(1) $r(AB) \le 4\,r(A)\,r(B)$;
(2) $r(AB) \le 2\,r(A)\,r(B)$ *if* $AB = BA$; *in addition,* $r(AB) \le r(A)\,r(B)$ *if either the matrix* A *or the matrix* B *is normal;*
(3) $r(AB) \le \min\{r(A)\|B\|_2, \|A\|_2\,r(B)\}$ *if* $AB = BA$ *and* $AB^* = B^*A$;
(4) $r(AB) \le \|A\|_2\,r(B)$ *if* $AB = BA$ *and* $A^2 = \alpha I$.

Proof. (1) In accordance with Property (2) in Proposition 3.6, we have

$$r(AB) \le \|AB\|_2 \le \|A\|_2\|B\|_2 \le 2\,r(A) \cdot 2\,r(B) = 4\,r(A)\,r(B).$$

(2) We assume that both matrices A and B are nonzero, as, otherwise, the inequalities are obvious. Without loss of generality, we further assume that $r(A) = r(B) = 1$, as, otherwise, we can replace the matrices A and B by the scaled matrices $\frac{1}{r(A)}A$ and $\frac{1}{r(B)}B$, respectively. Then, the first part of this statement is equivalent to $r(AB) \le 2$ whenever $r(A) = r(B) = 1$.

In the commuting case, it holds that

$$AB = \frac{1}{4}\left[(A+B)^2 - (A-B)^2\right].$$

By the triangle inequality, the sub-additivity, and the power inequality of $r(\cdot)$ (see Proposition 3.7), we have

$$\begin{aligned}
r(AB) &= \frac{1}{4}\left[r((A+B)^2 - (A-B)^2)\right] \\
&\leq \frac{1}{4}\left[r((A+B)^2) + r((A-B)^2)\right] \\
&\leq \frac{1}{4}\left[(r(A+B))^2 + (r(A-B))^2\right] \\
&\leq \frac{1}{4}\left[(r(A)+r(B))^2 + (r(A)+r(B))^2\right] \\
&= 2.
\end{aligned}$$

We now turn to demonstrate the second part of this statement. If, in addition, the matrix A is normal, then there exist a unitary matrix $U \in \mathbb{C}^{n \times n}$ and a diagonal matrix $\Lambda \in \mathbb{C}^{n \times n}$ such that $A = U\Lambda U^*$. Hence, it holds that

$$r(AB) = r(U\Lambda U^* B) = r(\Lambda U^* BU).$$

Let

$$\tilde{B} = [\tilde{b}_{ij}] \triangleq U^* BU.$$

Then

$$r(\tilde{B}) = r(B) \quad \text{and} \quad \Lambda\tilde{B} = \tilde{B}\Lambda$$

due to the **unitary invariance** of the numerical radius and the commutative assumption of the matrices A and B (that is, $AB = BA$). Without loss of generality, we assume that

$$\Lambda = \begin{bmatrix} \lambda_1 I & & & \\ & \lambda_2 I & & \\ & & \ddots & \\ & & & \lambda_k I \end{bmatrix},$$

where $\lambda_1, \lambda_2, \ldots, \lambda_k$ are the distinct eigenvalues of the matrix A, and each scalar matrix $\lambda_i I$ ($i = 1, 2, \ldots, k$) has the same size as the multiplicity of the eigenvalue λ_i ($i = 1, 2, \ldots, k$). By partitioning the matrix $\tilde{B}$ conformally with the block-diagonal matrix Λ, and by making use of the equality $\Lambda\tilde{B} = \tilde{B}\Lambda$, we have

$$\tilde{B} = \begin{bmatrix} \tilde{B}_1 & & & \\ & \tilde{B}_2 & & \\ & & \ddots & \\ & & & \tilde{B}_k \end{bmatrix}.$$

For any $x \in \mathbb{C}^n$ with $x^*x = 1$, by partitioning $x = [x_1^\mathsf{T}, x_2^\mathsf{T}, \ldots, x_k^\mathsf{T}]^\mathsf{T}$ also conformally with Λ, we see that

$$
\begin{aligned}
|x^* \Lambda \tilde{B} x| &= \left| \sum_{i=1}^{k} \lambda_i x_i^* \tilde{B}_i x_i \right| \\
&\leq \sum_{i=1}^{k} |\lambda_i| (x_i^* x_i) \, r(\tilde{B}_i) \\
&\leq \rho(A) \, r(\tilde{B}) \sum_{i=1}^{k} x_i^* x_i \\
&= r(A) \, r(B).
\end{aligned}
$$

Hence, the inequality $r(AB) \leq r(A) \, r(B)$ is valid in this case, too.

(3) Firstly we prove that if the matrix A is **isometry** and if it is commutative with the matrix B, then it holds that

$$
r(AB) \leq \|A\|_2 \, r(B) = r(B).
$$

In fact, if the matrix A is isometry, then $A^*A = I$, and the equalities

$$
x^* ABx = x^* (A^*A) ABx = x^* (A^*A) BAx = (Ax)^* AB(Ax)
$$

hold true for any $x \in \mathbb{C}^n$ with $x^*x = 1$. Hence, in this case, we only need to consider $r(AB)$ restricted on $\mathrm{Ran}(A)$. Note that $AA^*Ax = Ax$, which means that the matrix AA^* is the identity on $\mathrm{Ran}(A)$. Then the matrix A is unitary on $\mathrm{Ran}(A)$ and is, hence, normal on $\mathrm{Ran}(A)$ too. In accordance with Statement (2), we have

$$
r(AB) \leq r(A) \, r(B) \leq \|A\|_2 \, r(B) = r(B).
$$

To demonstrate the general case, for $\mathcal{H} \triangleq \mathbb{C}^n$ we define the **Hilbert space**

$$
\mathcal{V} \triangleq \mathcal{H} \oplus \mathcal{H} \oplus \cdots,
$$

which is equipped with the **inner product**

$$
\langle v, w \rangle_\mathcal{V} = \langle v_1, w_1 \rangle_\mathcal{H} + \langle v_2, w_2 \rangle_\mathcal{H} + \cdots
$$

and the correspondingly **induced norm**

$$
\|v\|_\mathcal{V} = \sqrt{\langle v, v \rangle_\mathcal{V}} = \left(\|v_1\|_\mathcal{H}^2 + \|v_2\|_\mathcal{H}^2 + \cdots \right)^{\frac{1}{2}},
$$

where

$$
v = (v_1, v_2, \ldots) \in \mathcal{V}, \quad w = (w_1, w_2, \ldots) \in \mathcal{V},
$$

with $v_i, w_i \in \mathcal{H}$ for $i = 1, 2, \ldots$. Here

$$
\langle \cdot, \cdot \rangle_\mathcal{H} = \langle \cdot, \cdot \rangle \quad \text{and} \quad \| \cdot \|_\mathcal{H} = \| \cdot \|_2
$$

are the inner product and the **Euclidean norm** in $\mathcal{H} = \mathbb{C}^n$, respectively.

Now we introduce the matrix

$$\tilde{A} = \frac{A}{\|A\|_2 + \varepsilon}, \quad \text{with} \quad \varepsilon > 0.$$

Then $\|\tilde{A}\|_2 < 1$, and the matrix $\tilde{A}$ commutes with both matrices B and B^*. It follows that the matrix

$$\tilde{D} = (I - \tilde{A}^* \tilde{A})^{\frac{1}{2}}$$

is well defined, and is Hermitian positive definite. In addition, we define two operators $\tilde{S}$ and $\tilde{T}$ as follows:

$$\tilde{S}v := \tilde{S}(v_1, v_2, v_3, \ldots) \triangleq (\tilde{A}v_1, \tilde{D}v_1, v_2, v_3, \ldots),$$
$$\tilde{T}v := \tilde{T}(v_1, v_2, v_3, \ldots) \triangleq (Bv_1, \tilde{D}B\tilde{D}^{-1}v_2, \tilde{D}B\tilde{D}^{-1}v_3, \ldots).$$

Then, we see that $\tilde{S}$ and $\tilde{T}$ are commutative, with $\tilde{S}$ being also **isometry**, as

$$\begin{aligned}
\tilde{S}\tilde{T}v &= \tilde{S}(Bv_1, \tilde{D}B\tilde{D}^{-1}v_2, \tilde{D}B\tilde{D}^{-1}v_3, \ldots) \\
&= (\tilde{A}Bv_1, \tilde{D}Bv_1, \tilde{D}B\tilde{D}^{-1}v_2, \tilde{D}B\tilde{D}^{-1}v_3, \ldots) \\
&= (B\tilde{A}v_1, \tilde{D}Bv_1, \tilde{D}B\tilde{D}^{-1}v_2, \tilde{D}B\tilde{D}^{-1}v_3, \ldots)
\end{aligned}$$

and

$$\begin{aligned}
\tilde{T}\tilde{S}v &= \tilde{T}(\tilde{A}v_1, \tilde{D}v_1, v_2, v_3, \ldots) \\
&= (B\tilde{A}v_1, \tilde{D}B\tilde{D}^{-1}(\tilde{D}v_1), \tilde{D}B\tilde{D}^{-1}v_2, \tilde{D}B\tilde{D}^{-1}v_3, \ldots) \\
&= \tilde{S}\tilde{T}v,
\end{aligned}$$

as well as

$$\begin{aligned}
\|\tilde{S}v\|_{\mathcal{V}}^2 &= \|\tilde{A}v_1\|_2^2 + \|\tilde{D}v_1\|_2^2 + \|v_2\|_2^2 + \|v_3\|_2^2 + \cdots \\
&= \|\tilde{A}v_1\|_2^2 + \|\tilde{D}v_1\|_2^2 + \|v\|_{\mathcal{V}}^2 - \|v_1\|_2^2 \\
&= \|v\|_{\mathcal{V}}^2.
\end{aligned}$$

Hence, it follows that

$$r_{\mathcal{V}}(\tilde{S}\tilde{T}) \leq r_{\mathcal{V}}(\tilde{T}),$$

where

$$r_{\mathcal{V}}(\tilde{T}) \triangleq \max\left\{ \left| \langle \tilde{T}v, v \rangle_{\mathcal{V}} \right| : v \in \mathcal{V} \quad \text{and} \quad \|v\|_{\mathcal{V}} = 1 \right\},$$

with $r_{\mathcal{V}}(\tilde{S}\tilde{T})$ being of a similar definition.

Also, as the matrix $\tilde{A}$ commutes with both matrices B and B^*, the Hermitian positive definite matrix

$$\tilde{D}^2 = I - \tilde{A}^* \tilde{A}$$

commutes with them, too. Hence, according to Exercise 3.1 we know that the matrix $\tilde{D}$ commutes with the matrices B and B^*. By direct operations we have

$$\begin{aligned}
\langle \tilde{T}v, v \rangle_{\mathcal{V}} &= \langle Bv_1, v_1 \rangle + \langle \tilde{D}B\tilde{D}^{-1}v_2, v_2 \rangle + \langle \tilde{D}B\tilde{D}^{-1}v_3, v_3 \rangle + \cdots \\
&= \langle Bv_1, v_1 \rangle + \langle Bv_2, v_2 \rangle + \langle Bv_3, v_3 \rangle + \cdots
\end{aligned}$$

and

$$\langle \tilde{S}\tilde{T}v, v \rangle_{\mathcal{V}} = \langle \tilde{A}Bv_1, v_1 \rangle + \langle \tilde{D}Bv_1, v_2 \rangle + \langle \tilde{D}B\tilde{D}^{-1}v_2, v_3 \rangle + \cdots$$
$$= \langle \tilde{A}Bv_1, v_1 \rangle + \langle \tilde{D}Bv_1, v_2 \rangle + \langle Bv_2, v_3 \rangle + \cdots .$$

As a result, for $v \in \mathcal{V}$ with $\|v\|_{\mathcal{V}} = 1$, it holds that

$$\left| \langle \tilde{T}v, v \rangle_{\mathcal{V}} \right| \leq |\langle Bv_1, v_1 \rangle| + |\langle Bv_2, v_2 \rangle| + |\langle Bv_3, v_3 \rangle| + \cdots$$
$$\leq r(B) \left(|\langle v_1, v_1 \rangle| + |\langle v_2, v_2 \rangle| + |\langle v_3, v_3 \rangle| + \cdots \right)$$
$$= r(B) \|v\|_{\mathcal{V}}^2$$
$$= r(B),$$

or equivalently, $r_{\mathcal{V}}(\tilde{T}) \leq r(B)$; and for the special choice $v = (v_1, 0, 0, \ldots)$ with $\|v_1\|_2 = 1$, it holds that

$$|\langle \tilde{A}Bv_1, v_1 \rangle| = |\langle \tilde{S}\tilde{T}v, v \rangle_{\mathcal{V}}| \leq r_{\mathcal{V}}(\tilde{S}\tilde{T}).$$

It then follows that

$$r(\tilde{A}B) \leq r_{\mathcal{V}}(\tilde{S}\tilde{T}) \leq r_{\mathcal{V}}(\tilde{T}) \leq r(B),$$

or in other words,

$$r(AB) \leq (\|A\|_2 + \varepsilon) \, r(B).$$

Letting $\varepsilon \to 0$, we immediately see that

$$r(AB) \leq \|A\|_2 \, r(B).$$

In an analogous fashion, we can demonstrate the validity of the inequality

$$r(AB) \leq r(A) \, \|B\|_2.$$

Hence, Statement (3) holds true.

(4) In fact, this statement is trivial for $\alpha = 0$, and it is true whenever

$$r\left(\frac{A}{\|A\|_2 + \varepsilon} B \right) \leq r(B)$$

is valid for any arbitrarily small positive constant ε. Therefore, without loss of generality, we assume that $\alpha \neq 0$ and $\|A\|_2 < 1$, so that it is only necessary to prove $r(AB) \leq r(B)$ under the assumptions that $AB = BA$ and $A^2 = \alpha I$, as well as under the assumption that the matrix A is nonsingular with $\|A\|_2 < 1$. Note that $\|A\|_2 < 1$ implies $\|A^*\|_2 < 1$, as well as the inequalities

$$|\alpha| = \|A^2\|_2 \leq \|A\|_2^2 < 1.$$

We let

$$D = (I + A^*A + (A^*)^2 A^2 + (A^*)^3 A^3 + \cdots)^{\frac{1}{2}}.$$

As $A^2 = \alpha I$, we see that $(A^*)^2 = \bar{\alpha} I$ with $\bar{\alpha}$ being the conjugate complex of α. Hence, it holds that

$$D = [(1 + |\alpha|^2 + |\alpha|^4 + \cdots)(I + A^*A)]^{\frac{1}{2}}.$$

Since $|\alpha| < 1$, the matrix D is well defined, invertible, and equal to the matrix $\nu(I + A^*A)^{\frac{1}{2}}$, with $\nu = \frac{1}{(1-|\alpha|^2)^{1/2}}$ being a positive constant. In particular, the matrix

$$D = \nu(I + A^*A)^{\frac{1}{2}} \in \mathbb{C}^{n \times n}$$

is Hermitian positive definite.

In $\mathcal{H} \triangleq \mathbb{C}^n$, we define the **weighted inner product**

$$\langle x, y \rangle_D = \langle Dx, Dy \rangle, \quad \forall\, x, y \in \mathcal{H},$$

and the correspondingly induced **weighted norm**

$$\|x\|_D = \sqrt{\langle Dx, Dx \rangle} = \|Dx\|_2, \quad \forall\, x, y \in \mathcal{H}.$$

Analogous to the proof of Property (3), we further define the **Hilbert space**

$$\mathcal{V} \triangleq \mathcal{H} \oplus \mathcal{H} \oplus \cdots,$$

which is equipped with the weighted inner product

$$\langle v, w \rangle_{\mathcal{V}} = \langle v_1, w_1 \rangle_D + \langle v_2, w_2 \rangle_D + \cdots$$

and the correspondingly induced weighted norm

$$\|v\|_{\mathcal{V}} \triangleq \sqrt{\langle v, v \rangle_{\mathcal{V}}} = \left(\|v_1\|_D^2 + \|v_2\|_D^2 + \cdots \right)^{\frac{1}{2}},$$

where

$$v = (v_1, v_2, \ldots) \in \mathcal{V}, \quad w = (w_1, w_2, \ldots) \in \mathcal{V},$$

with $v_i, w_i \in \mathcal{H}$ for $i = 1, 2, \ldots$. In addition, we define two operators S and T as follows:

$$Sv := S(v_1, v_2, v_3, \ldots) \triangleq (Av_1, D^{-1}v_1, v_2, v_3, \ldots),$$
$$Tv := T(v_1, v_2, v_3, \ldots) \triangleq (Bv_1, D^{-1}BDv_2, D^{-1}BDv_3, \ldots).$$

By direct operations, we can get

$$D^2 = I + A^*D^2A, \quad ST = TS, \tag{3.10}$$

and

$$\begin{aligned}
\|Sv\|_{\mathcal{V}}^2 &= \|Av_1\|_D^2 + \|D^{-1}v_1\|_D^2 + \|v_2\|_D^2 + \|v_3\|_D^2 + \cdots \\
&= \|DAv_1\|_2^2 + \|v_1\|_2^2 + \|Dv_2\|_2^2 + \|Dv_3\|_2^2 + \cdots \\
&= \langle A^*D^2Av_1, v_1 \rangle + \langle v_1, v_1 \rangle + \|v\|_{\mathcal{V}}^2 - \langle D^2v_1, v_1 \rangle \\
&= \|v\|_{\mathcal{V}}^2,
\end{aligned}$$

which show that the operators S and T are commutative and the operator S is **isometry**. Then, in accordance with the proof process of Property (3), we know that

$$r_{\mathcal{V}}(ST) \leq r_{\mathcal{V}}(T), \tag{3.11}$$

where

$$r_{\mathcal{V}}(T) = \max\{|\langle Tv, v \rangle_{\mathcal{V}}| : v \in \mathcal{V} \quad \text{and} \quad \|v\|_{\mathcal{V}} = 1\},$$

with $r_{\mathcal{V}}(ST)$ being of an analogous definition.

Besides, for any $v \in \mathcal{V}$ with $\|v\|_{\mathcal{V}} = 1$, it holds that

$$\langle Tv, v \rangle_{\mathcal{V}} = \langle Bv_1, v_1 \rangle_D + \langle D^{-1}BDv_2, v_2 \rangle_D + \langle D^{-1}BDv_3, v_3 \rangle_D + \cdots$$
$$= \langle D^2 Bv_1, v_1 \rangle + \langle BDv_2, Dv_2 \rangle + \langle BDv_3, Dv_3 \rangle + \cdots. \tag{3.12}$$

Recalling from (3.10) that $D^2 = I + A^* D^2 A$, we have

$$D^2 B = B + A^* D^2 AB.$$

Hence, we know that

$$\langle D^2 Bv_1, v_1 \rangle = \langle Bv_1, v_1 \rangle + \langle A^* D^2 ABv_1, v_1 \rangle$$
$$= \langle Bv_1, v_1 \rangle + \langle D^2 ABv_1, Av_1 \rangle.$$

As

$$D^2 A = \nu^2 (I + A^* A) A = \nu^2 (A + \alpha A^*),$$

we can further obtain the equalities

$$\langle D^2 Bv_1, v_1 \rangle = \langle Bv_1, v_1 \rangle + \nu^2 \langle (A + \alpha A^*) Bv_1, Av_1 \rangle$$
$$= \langle Bv_1, v_1 \rangle + \nu^2 \left(\langle ABv_1, Av_1 \rangle + \alpha \langle A^* Bv_1, Av_1 \rangle \right)$$
$$= \langle Bv_1, v_1 \rangle + \nu^2 \left(\langle ABv_1, Av_1 \rangle + \alpha \langle Bv_1, A^2 v_1 \rangle \right)$$
$$= \langle Bv_1, v_1 \rangle + \nu^2 \left(\langle ABv_1, Av_1 \rangle + |\alpha|^2 \langle Bv_1, v_1 \rangle \right).$$

It then follows from

$$AB = BA \quad \text{and} \quad 1 + \nu^2 |\alpha|^2 = \nu^2$$

that

$$\langle D^2 Bv_1, v_1 \rangle = \nu^2 \left(\langle Bv_1, v_1 \rangle + \langle BAv_1, Av_1 \rangle \right),$$

which straightforwardly results in the inequalities

$$\left| \langle D^2 Bv_1, v_1 \rangle \right| \leq \nu^2 \left(|\langle Bv_1, v_1 \rangle| + |\langle BAv_1, Av_1 \rangle| \right)$$
$$\leq \nu^2 r(B) \left(\langle v_1, v_1 \rangle + \langle Av_1, Av_1 \rangle \right). \tag{3.13}$$

Therefore, based on (3.12) and (3.13) we have

$$|\langle Tv, v \rangle_{\mathcal{V}}| \leq \left| \langle D^2 Bv_1, v_1 \rangle \right| + |\langle BDv_2, Dv_2 \rangle| + |\langle BDv_3, Dv_3 \rangle| + \cdots$$
$$\leq \nu^2 r(B) \left(\langle v_1, v_1 \rangle + \langle Av_1, Av_1 \rangle \right) + r(B) \left(\langle Dv_2, Dv_2 \rangle + \langle Dv_3, Dv_3 \rangle + \cdots \right)$$
$$= \nu^2 r(B) \langle (I + A^* A) v_1, v_1 \rangle + r(B) \left(\langle Dv_2, Dv_2 \rangle + \langle Dv_3, Dv_3 \rangle + \cdots \right)$$
$$= r(B) \left(\langle Dv_1, Dv_1 \rangle + \langle Dv_2, Dv_2 \rangle + \cdots \right)$$
$$= r(B) \|v\|_{\mathcal{V}}$$
$$= r(B),$$

which implies that

$$r_{\mathcal{V}}(T) \leq r(B). \tag{3.14}$$

Moreover, in accordance with (3.11) and (3.14) we see that

$$r_{\mathcal{V}}(ST) \leq r(B). \tag{3.15}$$

We further claim that

$$r(AB) \leq r_{\mathcal{V}}(ST), \tag{3.16}$$

which, together with (3.15), then shows the validity of Statement (4).

As a matter of fact, if for any $v_1 \in \mathcal{H}$ we define the vector $v_2 \in \mathcal{H}$ such that

$$Dv_2 = \nu^2 A^*(I - A^*A)v_1 \triangleq A^*\tilde{D}^2 v_1, \tag{3.17}$$

where

$$\tilde{D} = \nu(I - A^*A)^{\frac{1}{2}}$$

is a Hermitian positive definite matrix, and if for $i = 3, 4, \ldots$ we take $v_i = 0$, then it follows from

$$STv = (ABv_1, D^{-1}Bv_1, D^{-1}BDv_2, D^{-1}BDv_3, \ldots)$$

that

$$\begin{aligned}
\langle STv, v \rangle_{\mathcal{V}} &= \langle ABv_1, v_1 \rangle_D + \langle D^{-1}Bv_1, v_2 \rangle_D \\
&= \langle D^2 ABv_1, v_1 \rangle + \langle Bv_1, Dv_2 \rangle \\
&= \langle D^2 ABv_1, v_1 \rangle + \langle Bv_1, A^*\tilde{D}^2 v_1 \rangle \\
&= \langle D^2 ABv_1, v_1 \rangle + \langle \tilde{D}^2 ABv_1, v_1 \rangle \\
&= \langle (D^2 + \tilde{D}^2)ABv_1, v_1 \rangle \\
&= 2\nu^2 \langle ABv_1, v_1 \rangle. \tag{3.18}
\end{aligned}$$

Furthermore, straightforward computations give the estimates

$$\begin{aligned}
\|v\|_{\mathcal{V}}^2 &= \|v_1\|_D^2 + \|v_2\|_D^2 \\
&= \|Dv_1\|_2^2 + \|Dv_2\|_2^2 \\
&= \|Dv_1\|_2^2 + \|A^*\tilde{D}^2 v_1\|_2^2 \\
&\leq \|Dv_1\|_2^2 + \|A^*\|_2^2 \|\tilde{D}\|_2^2 \|\tilde{D}v_1\|_2^2.
\end{aligned}$$

Recalling that the matrix A is nonsingular and satisfies

$$\|A\|_2 = \|A^*\|_2 < 1,$$

for any $x, y \in \mathcal{H}$ satisfying $x = Ay$ we can obtain

$$\begin{aligned}
\|\tilde{D}\|_2^2 &= \max_{x \neq 0} \frac{\|\tilde{D}x\|_2^2}{\|x\|_2^2} = \max_{x \neq 0} \frac{\langle \tilde{D}x, \tilde{D}x \rangle}{\langle x, x \rangle} \\
&= \max_{x \neq 0} \frac{\langle \tilde{D}^2 x, x \rangle}{\langle x, x \rangle} = \max_{y \neq 0} \frac{\langle \tilde{D}^2 Ay, Ay \rangle}{\langle Ay, Ay \rangle} \\
&= \nu^2 \max_{y \neq 0} \frac{\langle (I - A^*A)Ay, Ay \rangle}{\langle Ay, Ay \rangle} = \nu^2 \max_{y \neq 0} \frac{\langle Ay, Ay \rangle - |\alpha|^2 \langle y, y \rangle}{\langle Ay, Ay \rangle} \\
&= \nu^2 \left(1 - |\alpha|^2 \min_{y \neq 0} \frac{\langle y, y \rangle}{\langle Ay, Ay \rangle} \right) = \nu^2 \left(1 - |\alpha|^2 \frac{1}{\max_{y \neq 0} \frac{\langle Ay, Ay \rangle}{\langle y, y \rangle}} \right) \\
&= \nu^2 \left(1 - \frac{|\alpha|^2}{\|A\|_2^2} \right) < \nu^2 \left(1 - |\alpha|^2 \right) \\
&= 1.
\end{aligned}$$

Consequently, the above argument shows that

$$
\begin{aligned}
\|v\|_{\mathcal{V}}^2 &\leq \|Dv_1\|_2^2 + \|\tilde{D}v_1\|_2^2 \\
&= \langle D^2 v_1, v_1 \rangle + \langle \tilde{D}^2 v_1, v_1 \rangle \\
&= \langle (D^2 + \tilde{D}^2) v_1, v_1 \rangle \\
&= 2\nu^2 \langle v_1, v_1 \rangle.
\end{aligned}
\tag{3.19}
$$

Now, for $v_1 \in \mathcal{H}$ such that $v_1 \neq 0$, let $\tilde{v}_1 = \frac{v_1}{\|v_1\|_2}$. Then, in accordance with (3.18) and (3.19), for the vector

$$
v = (v_1, v_2, 0, 0, \ldots) \in \mathcal{V}
$$

with $v_2 \in \mathcal{H}$ being defined as in (3.17), it holds that

$$
\begin{aligned}
r(AB) &= \max |\langle AB\tilde{v}_1, \tilde{v}_1 \rangle| = \max \frac{|\langle AB v_1, v_1 \rangle|}{\langle v_1, v_1 \rangle} \\
&= \frac{1}{2\nu^2} \max \frac{|\langle STv, v \rangle_{\mathcal{V}}|}{\langle v_1, v_1 \rangle} \leq \max \frac{|\langle STv, v \rangle_{\mathcal{V}}|}{\langle v, v \rangle_{\mathcal{V}}}.
\end{aligned}
$$

Therefore, for any $w \in \mathcal{V}$, by denoting $\tilde{w} = \frac{w}{\|w\|_{\mathcal{V}}}$ we have

$$
r(AB) \leq \max_{w \neq 0} \frac{|\langle STw, w \rangle_{\mathcal{V}}|}{\langle w, w \rangle_{\mathcal{V}}} = \max_{\|\tilde{w}\|_{\mathcal{V}}=1} |\langle ST\tilde{w}, \tilde{w} \rangle_{\mathcal{V}}| = r_{\mathcal{V}}(ST),
$$

which is exactly the inequality in (3.16). □

The **numerical range** of a **Kronecker product** preserves the following property.

Proposition 3.16. *Let $A \in \mathbb{C}^{n \times n}$ and $B \in \mathbb{C}^{m \times m}$. Then*

$$
\mathcal{F}(A)\,\mathcal{F}(B) \subseteq \mathrm{Co}(\mathcal{F}(A)\,\mathcal{F}(B)) \subseteq \mathcal{F}(A \otimes B) = \mathcal{F}(B \otimes A).
$$

In particular, if either the matrix A or the matrix B is normal, then

$$
\mathrm{Co}(\mathcal{F}(A)\,\mathcal{F}(B)) = \mathcal{F}(A \otimes B);
$$

and if either the matrix A or the matrix B is Hermitian positive semidefinite, then

$$
\mathcal{F}(A)\,\mathcal{F}(B) = \mathcal{F}(A \otimes B).
$$

Proof. For $x, y \in \mathbb{C}^n$ with $x^* x = y^* y = 1$, we have

$$
(x^* A x)(y^* B y) = (x^* A x) \otimes (y^* B y) = (x \otimes y)^* (A \otimes B)(x \otimes y).
$$

Since

$$
(x \otimes y)^* (x \otimes y) = (x^* x) \otimes (y^* y) = 1,
$$

it holds that

$$
(x^* A x)(y^* B y) \in \mathcal{F}(A \otimes B),
$$

which implies that

$$
\mathcal{F}(A)\,\mathcal{F}(B) \subseteq \mathcal{F}(A \otimes B).
$$

We know from Corollary 1.86 that the matrix $A \otimes B$ is permutationally similar to the matrix $B \otimes A$. Then $\mathcal{F}(A \otimes B) = \mathcal{F}(B \otimes A)$ is true according to the fact that the numerical range is invariant under unitary similarity transformation.

By the convexity of $\mathcal{F}(A \otimes B)$, we finally have

$$\mathcal{F}(A)\,\mathcal{F}(B) \subseteq \mathrm{Co}(\mathcal{F}(A)\,\mathcal{F}(B)) \subseteq \mathcal{F}(A \otimes B) = \mathcal{F}(B \otimes A).$$

If we assume that the matrix $A \in \mathbb{C}^{n \times n}$ is normal, then there exist a unitary matrix $U \in \mathbb{C}^{n \times n}$ and a diagonal matrix $\Lambda = \mathrm{diag}(\lambda_1, \lambda_2, \ldots, \lambda_n) \in \mathbb{C}^{n \times n}$ such that $U^*AU = \Lambda$. So

$$\mathcal{F}(A \otimes B) = \mathcal{F}((U \otimes I)^*(\Lambda \otimes B)(U \otimes I)) = \mathcal{F}(\Lambda \otimes B).$$

For $x = [x_1^\mathsf{T}, x_2^\mathsf{T}, \ldots, x_n^\mathsf{T}]^\mathsf{T} \in \mathbb{C}^{nm}$ with $x_1, x_2, \ldots, x_n \in \mathbb{C}^m$ and $x^*x = 1$, i.e., $\sum\limits_{i=1}^{n} x_i^*x_i = 1$, we have

$$x^*(\Lambda \otimes B)x = \sum_{i=1}^{n} \lambda_i\, x_i^* B x_i = \sum_{i=1}^{n} x_i^* x_i \left[\lambda_i \frac{x_i^* B x_i}{x_i^* x_i} \right] \in \mathrm{Co}(\mathcal{F}(\Lambda)\,\mathcal{F}(B)),$$

or equivalently,

$$\mathcal{F}(\Lambda \otimes B) \subseteq \mathrm{Co}(\mathcal{F}(\Lambda)\,\mathcal{F}(B)).$$

It follows from $\mathcal{F}(A) = \mathcal{F}(\Lambda)$ that

$$\mathcal{F}(A \otimes B) = \mathcal{F}(\Lambda \otimes B) \subseteq \mathrm{Co}(\mathcal{F}(A)\,\mathcal{F}(B)).$$

The above argument readily leads to

$$\mathrm{Co}(\mathcal{F}(A)\,\mathcal{F}(B)) = \mathcal{F}(A \otimes B).$$

If we assume that the matrix A is Hermitian positive semidefinite, then $\mathcal{F}(A) \subseteq [0, \infty)$. For this situation, we only need to prove that $\mathcal{F}(A)\,\mathcal{F}(B)$ is convex. To this end, let $\theta_1, \theta_2 \in (0, 1)$ with $\theta_1 + \theta_2 = 1$, and let $z_1 = \mu_1 \nu_1$ and $z_2 = \mu_2 \nu_2$ be two distinct elements in $\mathcal{F}(A)\,\mathcal{F}(B)$, with $\mu_1, \mu_2 \in \mathcal{F}(A)$ and $\nu_1, \nu_2 \in \mathcal{F}(B)$. Then it holds that $\theta_1 \mu_1 + \theta_2 \mu_2 \in (0, \infty)$, so that $\theta_1 \mu_1 + \theta_2 \mu_2 \neq 0$. As

$$\theta_1 z_1 + \theta_2 z_2 = \theta_1 \mu_1 \nu_1 + \theta_2 \mu_2 \nu_2$$
$$= (\theta_1 \mu_1 + \theta_2 \mu_2) \left(\frac{\theta_1 \mu_1}{\theta_1 \mu_1 + \theta_2 \mu_2} \nu_1 + \frac{\theta_2 \mu_2}{\theta_1 \mu_1 + \theta_2 \mu_2} \nu_2 \right),$$

the convexity of $\mathcal{F}(A)$ and $\mathcal{F}(B)$ straightforwardly results in

$$\theta_1 z_1 + \theta_2 z_2 \in \mathcal{F}(A)\,\mathcal{F}(B),$$

which shows that $\mathcal{F}(A)\,\mathcal{F}(B)$ is convex. Hence, we have

$$\mathcal{F}(A)\,\mathcal{F}(B) = \mathrm{Co}(\mathcal{F}(A)\,\mathcal{F}(B)) = \mathcal{F}(A \otimes B). \qquad \square$$

Recall that the **Hadamard product** $A \circ B$ is the entrywise product of two matrices $A = [a_{ij}]$ and $B = [b_{ij}]$ of the same size, i.e., $C = [c_{ij}] = A \circ B$ with $c_{ij} = a_{ij}b_{ij}$. Evidently, for matrices A, B, and C of the same size we have the following facts (see [199, 200]):

(a) $A \circ B = B \circ A$;

(b) $A \circ (B \circ C) = (A \circ B) \circ C$ and $A \circ (B + C) = A \circ B + A \circ C$;

(c) $(\alpha A) \circ B = A \circ (\alpha B) = \alpha(A \circ B), \quad \forall \alpha \in \mathbb{C}$;

(d) $(A \circ B)^* = A^* \circ B^*$;

(e) if the matrices A and B are Hermitian, then so is the matrix $A \circ B$;

(f) if the matrices A and B are Hermitian positive definite (Hermitian positive semidefinite), then so is the matrix $A \circ B$;

(g) $\mathrm{rank}(A \circ B) \le \mathrm{rank}(A)\,\mathrm{rank}(B)$.

Proposition 3.17. *Let $A, B \in \mathbb{C}^{n \times n}$. Then*

(1) $\mathcal{F}(A \circ B) \subseteq \mathrm{Co}(\mathcal{F}(A)\,\mathcal{F}(B))$ *if either the matrix A or the matrix B is normal;*

(2) $\mathcal{F}(A \circ B) \subseteq \mathcal{F}(A)\,\mathcal{F}(B)$ *if either the matrix A or the matrix B is Hermitian positive semidefinite;*

(3) $r(A \circ B) \le r(A)\,r(B)$ *if either the matrix A or the matrix B is normal;*

(4) $r(A \circ B) \le 2\,r(A)\,r(B)$.

Proof. (1) Since $A \circ B$ is the **principal submatrix** of the matrix $A \otimes B$, by Property (8) in Proposition 3.6 and by Proposition 3.16 we have

$$\mathcal{F}(A \circ B) \subseteq \mathcal{F}(A \otimes B) = \mathrm{Co}(\mathcal{F}(A)\,\mathcal{F}(B))$$

if either the matrix A or the matrix B is normal.

(2) Similar to the proof of Statement (1), if either the matrix A or the matrix B is Hermitian positive semidefinite, we have

$$\mathcal{F}(A \circ B) \subseteq \mathcal{F}(A \otimes B) = \mathcal{F}(A)\,\mathcal{F}(B).$$

(3) We know from Property (1) that for any element $z \in \mathcal{F}(A \circ B)$, there exist nonnegative reals $k_1, k_2, \ldots, k_m \in [0, 1]$ with $k_1 + k_2 + \cdots + k_m = 1$, and there exist elements $\omega_1, \omega_2, \ldots, \omega_m \in \mathcal{F}(A)\,\mathcal{F}(B)$ such that $z = \sum\limits_{i=1}^{m} k_i \omega_i$, where m is a positive integer. Then it holds that

$$|z| = \left| \sum_{i=1}^{m} k_i \omega_i \right| \le \sum_{i=1}^{m} k_i |\omega_i| \le \sum_{i=1}^{m} k_i\, r(A)\, r(B) = r(A)\, r(B),$$

which implies that $r(A \circ B) \le r(A)\, r(B)$.

(4) Let $\mathscr{H}(A)$ and $\mathscr{S}(A)$ be the Hermitian and skew-Hermitian parts of the matrix A, respectively. Then the matrices $\mathscr{H}(A)$ and $\mathrm{i}\mathscr{S}(A)$ are Hermitian. By Property (3) we have

$$\begin{aligned}
r(A \circ B) &= r((\mathscr{H}(A) + \mathscr{S}(A)) \circ B) \\
&= r(\mathscr{H}(A) \circ B + \mathscr{S}(A) \circ B) \\
&\le r(\mathscr{H}(A) \circ B) + r(\mathrm{i}\mathscr{S}(A) \circ B) \\
&\le r(\mathscr{H}(A))\, r(B) + r(\mathrm{i}\mathscr{S}(A))\, r(B) \\
&\le 2\, r(A)\, r(B). \qquad \Box
\end{aligned}$$

Again, note that the matrix $A \circ B$ is a principal submatrix of the matrix $A \otimes B$. Hence, we always have $\mathcal{F}(A \circ B) \subseteq \mathcal{F}(A \otimes B)$.

Proposition 3.18. *Let $A, B \in \mathbb{C}^{n \times n}$. Then*

$$r(A \circ B) \le r(A \otimes B) \le \min\big\{ r(A)\, \|B\|_2,\; \|A\|_2\, r(B) \big\} \le 2\, r(A)\, r(B).$$

If, in addition, either the matrix A or the matrix B is normal, then

$$\mathcal{F}(A \circ B) \subseteq \mathcal{F}(A \otimes B) = \mathrm{Co}(\mathcal{F}(A)\,\mathcal{F}(B))$$

and, consequently,

$$r(A \circ B) \leq r(A \otimes B) = r(A)\,r(B).$$

Proof. First, we know that $r(A \circ B) \leq r(A \otimes B)$ since $\mathcal{F}(A \circ B) \subseteq \mathcal{F}(A \otimes B)$.
Let $\tilde{A} = A \otimes I$ and $\tilde{B} = I \otimes B$. Then

$$\tilde{A}\tilde{B} = \tilde{B}\tilde{A} = A \otimes B$$

and

$$\tilde{A}\tilde{B}^* = A \otimes B^* = \tilde{B}^* \tilde{A}.$$

It follows from Property (3) in Theorem 3.15 that

$$r(A \otimes B) = r(\tilde{A}\tilde{B}) \leq \|\tilde{A}\|_2\, r(\tilde{B}).$$

For $x = [x_1^\mathsf{T}, x_2^\mathsf{T}, \ldots, x_n^\mathsf{T}]^\mathsf{T} \in \mathbb{C}^{n^2}$ with $x_1, x_2, \ldots, x_n \in \mathbb{C}^n$ and $x^*x = 1$, we have

$$|x^*\tilde{B}x| = \left| \sum_{k=1}^{n} x_k^* B x_k \right| \leq \sum_{k=1}^{n} x_k^* x_k\, r(B) = r(B),$$

which implies that $r(\tilde{B}) \leq r(B)$.

Assume that the matrix A has the singular value decomposition $A = U\Sigma V$, where $U, V \in \mathbb{C}^{n \times n}$ are unitary and $\Sigma = \mathrm{diag}(\sigma_1, \sigma_2, \ldots, \sigma_n)$. Then we have

$$\tilde{A} = (U \otimes I)(\Sigma \otimes I)(V \otimes I),$$

where $U \otimes I, V \otimes I$ are also unitary, and

$$\Sigma \otimes I = \mathrm{Diag}(\sigma_1 I, \sigma_2 I, \ldots, \sigma_n I).$$

Therefore,

$$\|\tilde{A}\|_2 = \max_{1 \leq i \leq n}\{\sigma_i\} = \|A\|_2.$$

As a conclusion, it holds that

$$r(A \otimes B) \leq \|A\|_2\, r(B).$$

Similarly, replacing the matrices $\tilde{A}$, $\tilde{B}$ by the matrices $I \otimes A$ and $B \otimes I$, respectively, we can obtain

$$r(A \otimes B) \leq r(A)\, \|B\|_2.$$

Finally, with Property (2) in Proposition 3.6 and the above conclusions, we have

$$r(A \circ B) \leq r(A \otimes B) \leq \min\{\|A\|_2\, r(B),\ r(A)\, \|B\|_2\}$$
$$\leq 2\,r(A)\, r(B).$$

In addition, if the matrix A or the matrix B is normal, it follows from Propositions 3.16 and 3.17 that

$$\mathcal{F}(A \circ B) \subseteq \mathcal{F}(A \otimes B) = \mathrm{Co}(\mathcal{F}(A)\,\mathcal{F}(B)),$$

which implies that

$$r(A \circ B) \leq r(A \otimes B) \leq r(A)\,r(B). \qquad \square$$

Proposition 3.19. *Let $A \in \mathbb{C}^{n \times n}$. Then $r(A \circ B) \leq r(B)$ holds for all $B \in \mathbb{C}^{n \times n}$ if and only if $A = X^*WX$ such that the matrix $W \in \mathbb{C}^{m \times m}$ satisfies $\|W\|_2 \leq 1$ and the matrix $X \in \mathbb{C}^{m \times n}$ satisfies that all diagonal entries of the matrix X^*X are bounded by 1.*

3.2 ▪ Convexity and Location

We first consider the convex property about the **numerical range**.

Theorem 3.20 (Toeplitz–Hausdorff Theorem). *For any $A \in \mathbb{C}^{n \times n}$, the numerical range $\mathcal{F}(A)$ is a **convex set**.*

It is well known that a set $\mathcal{S} \subseteq \mathbb{C}$ is convex if and only if $\alpha s + (1 - \alpha)t \in \mathcal{S}$ holds true for any $s, t \in \mathcal{S}$ and any $\alpha \in [0, 1]$. Therefore, in order to show that $\mathcal{F}(A)$ is convex for $A \in \mathbb{C}^{n \times n}$, we only need to show that $\alpha\, x^* A x + (1 - \alpha)\, y^* A y \in \mathcal{F}(A)$ holds true for any $x, y \in \mathbb{C}^n$ with $x^* x = y^* y = 1$ and for any $\alpha \in [0, 1]$. In fact, it suffices to prove this argument only for the 2×2 case, i.e., for $A \in \mathbb{C}^{2 \times 2}$, due to the following fact.

Lemma 3.21. *Let $x, y \in \mathbb{C}^n$ be two given vectors. Then there exists a unitary matrix $U \in \mathbb{C}^{n \times n}$ such that all entries of the vectors $v = Ux$ and $w = Uy$ after the first two are equal to zero.*

Proof. We just give an approach to construct the unitary matrix U based on the **Householder transform**. Assume that $x_1 = se^{i\theta}$ is the first element of the vector x, where $s \in \mathbb{R}$ and $\theta \in [0, 2\pi)$. For $z = x \pm e^{i\theta}\|x\|_2 e_1$ with $e_1 \in \mathbb{R}^n$ being the first unit basis vector in $\mathbb{R}^n$, i.e., $e_1 = [1, 0, \ldots, 0]^{\mathsf{T}} \in \mathbb{R}^n$, by taking the **Householder matrix**

$$H_1 = I_n - \frac{2}{z^* z} z z^* \in \mathbb{C}^{n \times n}$$

we have

$$H_1 x = \mp e^{i\theta}\|x\|_2 e_1 \triangleq \alpha e_1,$$

in which the signs can be determined by maximizing $\|z\|_2$ for the sake of numerical stability. Let $H_1 y = [\beta, \tilde{y}^{\mathsf{T}}]^{\mathsf{T}}$ with $\tilde{y} \in \mathbb{C}^{n-1}$. Analogously, by taking the Householder matrix $\tilde{H}_2 \in \mathbb{C}^{(n-1) \times (n-1)}$ we know that all entries of the vector $\tilde{H}_2\tilde{y}$ after the first element are equal to zero. Define

$$H_2 = \mathrm{Diag}(1, \tilde{H}_2) \quad \text{and} \quad U = H_2 H_1.$$

Then it holds that

$$v = Ux = \alpha e_1 \quad \text{and} \quad w = Uy = \begin{bmatrix} \beta \\ \tilde{H}_2\tilde{y} \end{bmatrix}.$$

Clearly, we see that only the first two elements of the vectors v and w are nonzero. ☐

With the above lemma, we have

$$\alpha\, x^* A x + (1 - \alpha)\, y^* A y = \alpha\, v^* U A U^* v + (1 - \alpha)\, w^* U A U^* w$$
$$= \alpha\, \xi^* B \xi + (1 - \alpha)\, \eta^* B \eta,$$

where the matrix B is the upper-left 2×2 **principal submatrix** of the matrix UAU^*, and the vectors ξ, η consist of the first two entries of the vectors v and w, respectively. Thus, it is sufficient to show that the numerical range of any 2×2 matrix is convex. This reduction is possible because of the unitary similarity invariance property of the numerical range.

Lemma 3.22. *Let $A \in \mathbb{C}^{2 \times 2}$. Then there exists a unitary matrix $U \in \mathbb{C}^{2 \times 2}$ such that the main diagonal entries of the matrix $U^* A U$ are equal.*

Proof. Let

$$B = A - \frac{1}{2}\operatorname{tr}(A)\, I.$$

Then $\operatorname{tr}(B) = 0$. Hence, the eigenvalues λ_1 and λ_2 of the matrix B satisfy $\lambda_1 + \lambda_2 = 0$. Let x and y be the **normalized eigenvectors** of the matrix B associated with the eigenvalues λ_1 and λ_2, respectively. We claim that there exists a unit vector $v \in \mathbb{C}^2$ such that $v^* B v = 0$. In fact, if $\lambda_1 = \lambda_2 = 0$, we can take either $v = x$ or $v = y$. And if $\lambda_1 = -\lambda_2 \neq 0$, then the eigenvectors x and y are linearly independent, which implies that $\tilde{v} = e^{\mathrm{i}\theta}x + y$ is nonzero for any $\theta \in \mathbb{R}$. Straightforward calculations show that

$$\tilde{v}^* B \tilde{v} = 2\mathrm{i}\lambda_1 \Im(e^{\mathrm{i}\theta}y^*x).$$

Then we can just take a proper angle θ such that $\Im(e^{\mathrm{i}\theta}y^*x) = 0$, resulting in $\tilde{v}^* B \tilde{v} = 0$. So, in this case, we can take $v = \frac{\tilde{v}}{\|\tilde{v}\|_2}$. Let $U = [v, u]$ be a unitary matrix. Then

$$U^* B U = \begin{bmatrix} v^* B v & v^* B u \\ u^* B v & u^* B u \end{bmatrix} = \begin{bmatrix} 0 & v^* B u \\ u^* B v & u^* B u \end{bmatrix}.$$

As

$$\operatorname{tr}(U^* B U) = \operatorname{tr}(B) = 0,$$

we know that the $(2,2)$-entry $u^* B u$ of the matrix $U^* B U$ is also zero, which shows that the matrix $U^* A U$ has two equal entries on its main diagonal. $\quad\square$

This property can be extended to the general case [181] as follows.

Corollary 3.23. *Let $A \in \mathbb{C}^{n \times n}$. Then there exists a unitary matrix $U \in \mathbb{C}^{n \times n}$ such that the main diagonal entries of the matrix $U^* A U$ are equal.*

Proof. We have proved the statement when $n = 2$. Assume that the statement is true for a matrix of order being less than n.

Let

$$B = A - \frac{1}{n}\operatorname{tr}(A)\, I,$$

and $\lambda_1, \lambda_2, \ldots, \lambda_n$ be the eigenvalues of the matrix B. Then

$$\lambda_1 + \lambda_2 + \cdots + \lambda_n = \operatorname{tr}(B) = 0.$$

Since $\mathcal{F}(B)$ is convex and $\sigma(B) \subseteq \mathcal{F}(B)$, we have $\operatorname{Co}(\sigma(B)) \subseteq \mathcal{F}(B)$, which leads to

$$0 = \frac{1}{n}(\lambda_1 + \lambda_2 + \cdots + \lambda_n) \in \mathcal{F}(B).$$

Hence, there exists a vector $x \in \mathbb{C}^n$ with $x^* x = 1$ such that $x^* B x = 0$. Let $W = [x, W_1] \in \mathbb{C}^{n \times n}$ be a unitary matrix. Then

$$W^* B W = \begin{bmatrix} 0 & x^* B W_1 \\ W_1^* B x & W_1^* B W_1 \end{bmatrix}.$$

Denote by

$$\hat{B} = W_1^* B W_1 \in \mathbb{C}^{(n-1)\times(n-1)}.$$

Then it holds that $\operatorname{tr}(\hat{B}) = 0$. By the induction hypothesis, there exists a unitary matrix $V \in \mathbb{C}^{(n-1)\times(n-1)}$ such that the main diagonal entries of the matrix $V^*\hat{B}V$ are equal to zero. For the matrix

$$U = W \begin{bmatrix} 1 & 0 \\ 0 & V \end{bmatrix} \in \mathbb{C}^{n \times n},$$

we see that the matrix U is unitary and

$$U^* B U = \begin{bmatrix} 0 & x^* B W_1 V \\ V^* W_1^* B x & V^* \hat{B} V \end{bmatrix},$$

which has a zero main diagonal. Consequently, there exists a unitary matrix $U \in \mathbb{C}^{n \times n}$ such that the main diagonal entries of the matrix $U^* A U$ are equal to $\frac{1}{n}\operatorname{tr}(A)$. $\square$

By Property (3) in Proposition 3.6, we see that $\mathcal{F}(A)$ is convex if and only if $\mathcal{F}(A + \alpha I)$ is convex for any $\alpha \in \mathbb{C}$ and, for letting $\alpha = -\frac{1}{2}\operatorname{tr}(A)$, we only need to focus on the matrix of zero trace. With Lemma 3.22 and the unitary similarity invariance property of the numerical range, without loss of generality, we can assume that both main diagonal entries of the 2×2 matrix are zero, i.e., the considered matrix is of the form

$$\begin{bmatrix} 0 & c \\ d & 0 \end{bmatrix}.$$

Write $c = |c|e^{i\theta_1}$ and $d = |d|e^{i\theta_2}$, and let $\theta = \frac{1}{2}(\theta_2 - \theta_1)$. Then we have

$$\begin{bmatrix} 1 & 0 \\ 0 & e^{-i\theta} \end{bmatrix} \begin{bmatrix} 0 & c \\ d & 0 \end{bmatrix} \begin{bmatrix} 1 & 0 \\ 0 & e^{-i\theta} \end{bmatrix}^* = \begin{bmatrix} 0 & ce^{i\theta} \\ de^{-i\theta} & 0 \end{bmatrix} = e^{i\varphi}\begin{bmatrix} 0 & |c| \\ |d| & 0 \end{bmatrix},$$

where $\varphi = \frac{1}{2}(\theta_1 + \theta_2)$. By Property (4) in Proposition 3.6, i.e., the scalar multiplication property, it turns out that we only need to consider matrices of the special form

$$\begin{bmatrix} 0 & a_{12} \\ a_{21} & 0 \end{bmatrix}, \quad \text{with} \quad a_{12}, a_{21} \geq 0. \tag{3.20}$$

Theorem 3.24. *For any matrix $A \in \mathbb{R}^{2\times 2}$ of the form (3.20), $\mathcal{F}(A)$ is an ellipse with the interior centered at the origin, the minor axis along the imaginary axis having length $|a_{12} - a_{21}|$, the major axis along the real axis having length $a_{12} + a_{21}$, and the foci being $\pm\sqrt{a_{12}a_{21}}$ that are the eigenvalues of the matrix A.*

Proof. Without loss of generality, we assume that $a_{12} \neq a_{21}$. We write $x = [x_1, x_2]^\mathsf{T} \in \mathbb{C}^2$ as

$$x_1 = e^{i\alpha}\cos(\theta), \quad x_2 = e^{i\beta}\sin(\theta),$$

with

$$\theta \in [0, \frac{\pi}{2}] \text{ and } \alpha, \beta \in [0, 2\pi).$$

Then

$$x^* A x = a_{12} \bar{x}_1 x_2 + a_{21} \bar{x}_2 x_1$$
$$= a_{12} \, e^{\mathrm{i}(\beta - \alpha)} \sin(\theta) \cos(\theta) + a_{21} \, e^{\mathrm{i}(\alpha - \beta)} \sin(\theta) \cos(\theta)$$
$$= \frac{1}{2}(a_{12} + a_{21}) \sin(2\theta) \cos(\alpha - \beta)$$
$$+ \, \mathrm{i} \, \frac{1}{2}(a_{21} - a_{12}) \sin(2\theta) \sin(\alpha - \beta)$$
$$\triangleq \gamma_1 + \mathrm{i}\gamma_2,$$

where

$$\gamma_1 = \frac{1}{2}(a_{12} + a_{21}) \sin(2\theta) \cos(\alpha - \beta) \quad \text{and} \quad \gamma_2 = \frac{1}{2}(a_{21} - a_{12}) \sin(2\theta) \sin(\alpha - \beta).$$

Hence,

$$\frac{\gamma_1^2}{(\frac{1}{2}(a_{12} + a_{21}))^2} + \frac{\gamma_2^2}{(\frac{1}{2}(a_{21} - a_{12}))^2} = (\sin(2\theta))^2.$$

As the angle θ varies from 0 to $\frac{\pi}{2}$, the value of the function $(\sin(2\theta))^2$ varies from 0 to 1. It follows from the above representation that $\mathcal{F}(A)$ is a closed elliptical disc with the interior centered at the origin. Moreover, since $a_{12}, a_{21} \geq 0$ and $a_{12} \neq a_{21}$, its minor axis is along the imaginary axis and of length $|a_{21} - a_{12}|$, and its major axis is along the real axis and of length $a_{12} + a_{21}$. Straightforward calculations show that its foci are $\pm\sqrt{a_{12} a_{21}}$ at the real axis, which are just the two eigenvalues of the matrix A. □

Up to now, we have proved Theorem 3.20.

From the proof of Theorem 3.24, we see that when $a_{12} = a_{21}$, the matrix $A \in \mathbb{R}^{2 \times 2}$ of the form (3.20) is symmetric and indefinite, and it holds that $\gamma_2 = 0$ and $x^* A x = \gamma_1$. Hence, for this situation the numerical range of the matrix A degenerates to an interval on the real axis or, more precisely, $\mathcal{F}(A) = [-\nu, \nu]$, with $\nu = \frac{1}{2}(a_{12} + a_{21})$.

Remark 3.1. *For a general matrix $A \in \mathbb{C}^{2 \times 2}$, $\mathcal{F}(A)$ is a closed elliptical disc (possibly degenerate) centered at the point $\left(\frac{1}{2} \operatorname{tr}(A)\right)$ with the foci being the two eigenvalues of the matrix A. Let*

$$B = A - \frac{1}{2} \operatorname{tr}(A) \, I.$$

Then the minor axis of $\mathcal{F}(A)$ is of the length

$$(\operatorname{tr}(B^* B) - 2|\det(B)|)^{\frac{1}{2}},$$

and the major axis is of the length

$$(\operatorname{tr}(B^* B) + 2|\det(B)|)^{\frac{1}{2}}.$$

Moreover, $\mathcal{F}(A)$ is a closed line segment (the degenerate case) if and only if the matrix A is normal.

Below we give a **Geršgorin-type inclusion region** for $\mathcal{F}(A)$ and some observations. To this end, we let $A = [a_{ij}] \in \mathbb{C}^{n \times n}$ and

$$g_k(A) = \frac{1}{2} \left(\sum_{\substack{j=1 \\ j \neq k}}^{n} |a_{kj}| + \sum_{\substack{i=1 \\ i \neq k}}^{n} |a_{ik}| \right), \quad k = 1, 2, \ldots, n.$$

In addition, we define the complex **set-valued function**

$$G_F(A) = \mathrm{Co} \left(\bigcup_{k=1}^{n} \{z \ : \ |z - a_{kk}| \leq g_k(A)\} \right).$$

Theorem 3.25. [200] *Let $A \in \mathbb{C}^{n \times n}$. Then $\mathcal{F}(A) \subseteq G_F(A)$.*

Proof. Let $A = [a_{ij}] \in \mathbb{C}^{n \times n}$, and

$$\mathscr{H}(A) = [h_{ij}] = \frac{1}{2}(A + A^*)$$

be the Hermitian part of the matrix A.

We first prove that if

$$G_F(A) \subseteq \{z \ : \ z \in \mathbb{C}^n, \ \Re(z) > 0\},$$

then

$$\mathcal{F}(A) \subseteq \{z \ : \ z \in \mathbb{C}^n, \ \Re(z) > 0\}.$$

In fact, under the assumption we have $\Re(a_{kk}) > g_k(A)$ for $k = 1, 2, \ldots, n$. Let

$$R_k(A) = \sum_{\substack{j=1 \\ j \neq k}}^{n} |a_{kj}|.$$

Then we have

$$R_k(\mathscr{H}(A)) = \frac{1}{2} \left(\left| \sum_{\substack{j=1 \\ j \neq k}}^{n} a_{kj} + \sum_{\substack{j=1 \\ j \neq k}}^{n} \bar{a}_{jk} \right| \right)$$

$$\leq \frac{1}{2} \left(\sum_{\substack{j=1 \\ j \neq k}}^{n} |a_{kj}| + \sum_{\substack{i=1 \\ i \neq k}}^{n} |a_{ik}| \right) = g_k(A).$$

It follows that

$$h_{kk} = \Re(a_{kk}) > g_k(A) \geq R_k(\mathscr{H}(A)), \quad k = 1, 2, \ldots, n.$$

Moreover, we can obtain

$$\sigma(\mathscr{H}(A)) \subseteq \bigcup_{k=1}^{n} \{z \ : \ |z - h_{kk}| \leq R_k(\mathscr{H}(A))\}$$
$$\subseteq \{z \ : \ z \in \mathbb{C}^n, \ \Re(z) > 0\}.$$

Since the matrix $\mathscr{H}(A)$ is Hermitian, it holds that

$$\Re(\mathcal{F}(A)) = \mathcal{F}(\mathscr{H}(A)) = \mathrm{Co}(\sigma(\mathscr{H}(A)))$$
$$\subseteq \{z \,:\, z \in \mathbb{C}^n, \, \Re(z) > 0\}.$$

Therefore,

$$\mathcal{F}(A) \subseteq \{z \,:\, z \in \mathbb{C}^n, \, \Re(z) > 0\}.$$

Next, we assume that $0 \notin G_F(A)$. Then there exists a $\theta \in [0, 2\pi)$ such that

$$e^{i\theta} G_F(A) \subseteq \{z \,:\, z \in \mathbb{C}^n, \, \Re(z) > 0\}.$$

Based upon the above argument, we have

$$\mathcal{F}(e^{i\theta}A) \subseteq \{z \,:\, z \in \mathbb{C}^n, \, \Re(z) > 0\},$$

which implies $0 \notin \mathcal{F}(A)$.

Now we further assume that $\alpha \notin G_F(A)$. Then $0 \notin G_F(A - \alpha I)$. According to the above discussion we have $0 \notin \mathcal{F}(A - \alpha I)$, which implies $\alpha \notin \mathcal{F}(A)$ too. In conclusion, it holds that $\mathcal{F}(A) \subseteq G_F(A)$. □

A simple bound for the **numerical radius** follows directly from Theorem 3.25.

Corollary 3.26. *Let $A \in \mathbb{C}^{n \times n}$. Then*

$$r(A) \le \frac{1}{2} \max_{1 \le i \le n} \sum_{j=1}^{n} (|a_{ij}| + |a_{ji}|).$$

Hence, it holds that

$$\rho(A) \le r(A) \le \frac{1}{2} (\|A\|_1 + \|A\|_\infty).$$

Proof. If $z \in G_F(A)$, then there exist nonnegative real numbers $l_1, l_2, \ldots, l_m \in [0, 1]$ with

$$l_1 + l_2 + \cdots + l_m = 1,$$

and complex numbers

$$\omega_1, \omega_2, \ldots, \omega_m \in \bigcup_{i=1}^{n} \{z \,:\, |z - a_{ii}| \le g_i(A)\}$$

such that $z = \sum_{k=1}^{m} l_k \omega_k$, where m is a positive integer.

Since

$$|\omega_k| \le g_i(A) + |a_{ii}| = \frac{1}{2} \sum_{j=1}^{n} (|a_{ij}| + |a_{ji}|)$$

holds true for some $i \in \{1, 2, \ldots, n\}$, we have

$$|\omega_k| \le \frac{1}{2} \max_{1 \le i \le n} \sum_{j=1}^{n} (|a_{ij}| + |a_{ji}|), \quad k = 1, 2, \ldots, m.$$

Hence, for $z \in \mathcal{F}(A) \subseteq G_F(A)$, it follows that

$$|z| = \left| \sum_{k=1}^{m} l_k \omega_k \right| \leq \sum_{k=1}^{m} l_k |\omega_k| \leq \max_{1 \leq k \leq m} |\omega_k|$$

$$\leq \frac{1}{2} \max_{1 \leq i \leq n} \sum_{j=1}^{n} (|a_{ij}| + |a_{ji}|),$$

which implies that

$$r(A) \leq \frac{1}{2} \max_{1 \leq i \leq n} \sum_{j=1}^{n} (|a_{ij}| + |a_{ji}|).$$

Therefore, we can straightforwardly obtain

$$\rho(A) \leq r(A) \leq \frac{1}{2}(\|A\|_1 + \|A\|_\infty). \qquad \square$$

3.3 ▪ Applications

Recall that a matrix is called **positive stable** if all of its eigenvalues have positive real parts. An important sufficient condition for a matrix to be positive stable is given below.

Theorem 3.27. Let $A \in \mathbb{C}^{n \times n}$. If the matrix $A + A^*$ is positive definite, then the matrix A is positive stable.

Proof. By the spectral containment Property (1) in Proposition 3.6 and by Theorem 3.8, we have

$$\Re(\sigma(A)) \subseteq \Re(\mathcal{F}(A)) = \mathcal{F}\left(\frac{1}{2}(A + A^*)\right).$$

Since the matrix $A + A^*$ is positive definite, so is the matrix $\frac{1}{2}(A + A^*)$. Hence, $\mathcal{F}\left(\frac{1}{2}(A + A^*)\right)$ is contained in the positive real axis. It follows that all eigenvalues of the matrix A have positive real parts. That is to say, the matrix A is positive stable. $\square$

A more general result is given in the following.

Corollary 3.28. Let $A, P \in \mathbb{C}^{n \times n}$. If the matrix $A + A^*$ is positive definite and the matrix P is Hermitian positive definite, then the matrix PA is positive stable.

Proof. In fact, we have

$$P^{\frac{1}{2}} A P^{\frac{1}{2}} + (P^{\frac{1}{2}} A P^{\frac{1}{2}})^* = P^{\frac{1}{2}}(A + A^*)P^{\frac{1}{2}} = (P^{\frac{1}{2}})^*(A + A^*)P^{\frac{1}{2}},$$

where $P^{\frac{1}{2}}$ is the unique **square root** of the matrix P, which is Hermitian positive definite. Since the matrix $A + A^*$ is positive definite, it follows from Theorems 1.68 and 3.27 that the matrix $P^{\frac{1}{2}} A P^{\frac{1}{2}}$ is positive stable. It is clear that

$$(P^{\frac{1}{2}})^{-1}(PA)P^{\frac{1}{2}} = P^{\frac{1}{2}} A P^{\frac{1}{2}},$$

i.e., the matrices PA and $P^{\frac{1}{2}} A P^{\frac{1}{2}}$ are similar. Therefore, the matrix PA is also positive stable. $\square$

At the end of this section, we introduce a theorem to illustrate the necessity of some properties of $\mathcal{F}(A)$.

Theorem 3.29. *The following properties characterize the numerical range. That is to say, $\mathcal{F}(\cdot)$ is the unique complex set-valued function on $\mathbb{C}^{n \times n}$ such that*

(1) *$\mathcal{F}(A)$ is compact and convex for any $A \in \mathbb{C}^{n \times n}$,*

(2) *$\mathcal{F}(A + \alpha I) = \mathcal{F}(A) + \alpha$ and $\mathcal{F}(\alpha A) = \alpha \mathcal{F}(A)$ for any $\alpha \in \mathbb{C}$ and $A \in \mathbb{C}^{n \times n}$,*

(3) *$\mathcal{F}(A) \subseteq \{z : \Re(z) \geq 0\}$ for any $A \in \mathbb{C}^{n \times n}$ if and only if the matrix $A + A^*$ is positive semidefinite.*

Proof. Assume that $\mathcal{F}_1(\cdot)$ and $\mathcal{F}_2(\cdot)$ are two complex set-valued functions on $\mathbb{C}^{n \times n}$ satisfying the specified three conditions.

Let $\mu \in \mathcal{F}_1(A)$ and $\mu \notin \mathcal{F}_2(A)$. Then from the **separating hyperplane theorem** for convex sets, there exists a straight line $\mathcal{L}$ in the complex plane such that the point μ and the set $\mathcal{F}_2(A)$ are located on different sides of $\mathcal{L}$. By rotating and translating the plane such that $\mathcal{L}$ coincides with the imaginary axis and μ lies on the left of the imaginary axis, we see that there exist complex numbers α and β, with $\alpha \neq 0$, such that

$$\Re(\alpha \mu + \beta) < 0$$

and

$$\mathcal{F}_2(\alpha A + \beta I) = \alpha \mathcal{F}_2(A) + \beta \subseteq \{z : \Re(z) > 0\}.$$

In addition, under Condition (3) we know that

$$(\alpha A + \beta I) + (\alpha A + \beta I)^*$$

is positive semidefinite. It then follows that

$$\mathcal{F}_1(\alpha A + \beta I) \subseteq \{z : \Re(z) \geq 0\},$$

so

$$\alpha \mu + \beta \in \mathcal{F}_1(\alpha A + \beta I),$$

or equivalently,

$$\Re(\alpha \mu + \beta) \geq 0.$$

However, this contradicts with the fact

$$\Re(\alpha \mu + \beta) < 0.$$

Therefore, for any $\mu \in \mathcal{F}_1(A)$, it must hold $\mu \in \mathcal{F}_2(A)$, which implies that $\mathcal{F}_1(A) \subseteq \mathcal{F}_2(A)$.

Similarly, we can also demonstrate the validity of the inclusion relationship $\mathcal{F}_2(A) \subseteq \mathcal{F}_1(A)$. Consequently, we obtain $\mathcal{F}_1(A) = \mathcal{F}_2(A)$.

Hence, there exist a unique complex set-valued function on $\mathbb{C}^{n \times n}$ satisfying the three conditions (1)-(3). □

3.4 ▪ Generalizations

Numerical range has many generalizations motivated by different applications; see, e.g., [181, 190, 200]. Here we only present a few that have been extensively studied.

3.4.1 ▪ k-Numerical Range

The *k-numerical range*, first introduced in [190], is a generalization based on replacing the normalized vector with a set of orthonormal vectors. The modified definition given in [235] is stated as follows.

Definition 3.30. *Let $A \in \mathbb{C}^{n \times n}$ and k ($k \leq n$) be a given positive integer. Then the **k-numerical range** of the matrix A is defined as*

$$\mathcal{F}_k(A) = \left\{ \sum_{i=1}^{k} x_i^* A x_i : x_i \in \mathbb{C}^n \quad and \quad x_i^* x_j = \delta_{ij} \right\},$$

where δ_{ij} is the Kronecker symbol, i.e., $\delta_{ij} = 1$ when $i = j$, and $\delta_{ij} = 0$ otherwise.

Let $X = [x_1, x_2, \ldots, x_k]$. Then

$$\operatorname{tr}(X^* A X) = x_1^* A x_1 + x_2^* A x_2 + \cdots + x_k^* A x_k.$$

Lemma 3.31. *Let $A \in \mathbb{C}^{n \times n}$ and k ($k \leq n$) be a given positive integer. Then $\mu \in \mathcal{F}_k(A)$ if and only if there exists a matrix $X \in \mathbb{C}^{n \times k}$, satisfying $X^* X = I$, such that $\mu = \operatorname{tr}(X^* A X)$.*

Proof. Assume $\mu \in \mathcal{F}_k(A)$. Then $\mu = \sum_{i=1}^{k} x_i^* A x_i$, with $x_i \in \mathbb{C}^n$ and $x_i^* x_j = \delta_{ij}$, $i, j = 1, 2, \ldots, k$. Let $X = [x_1, x_2, \ldots, x_k] \in \mathbb{C}^{n \times k}$. Then by direct calculations we have

$$X^* X = I \quad and \quad [X^* A X]_{ij} = x_i^* A x_j, \quad i, j = 1, 2, \ldots, k.$$

It follows that

$$\mu = \sum_{i=1}^{k} x_i^* A x_i = \sum_{i=1}^{k} [X^* A X]_{ii} = \operatorname{tr}(X^* A X).$$

Conversely, assume that $X = [x_1, x_2, \ldots, x_k] \in \mathbb{C}^{n \times k}$ satisfies $X^* X = I$, and let $\mu = \operatorname{tr}(X^* A X)$. Then we have

$$\mu = \operatorname{tr}(X^* A X) = \sum_{i=1}^{k} [X^* A X]_{ii} = \sum_{i=1}^{k} x_i^* A x_i,$$

where $x_i^* x_j = \delta_{ij}$, $i, j = 1, 2, \ldots, k$. This shows that $\mu \in \mathcal{F}_k(A)$. □

Using this lemma, we can straightforwardly demonstrate the following properties [223].

Proposition 3.32. *Let $A \in \mathbb{C}^{n \times n}$ and k ($k \leq n$) be a given positive integer. Then*

(1) $\mathcal{F}_1(A) = \mathcal{F}(A)$,
(2) $\mathcal{F}_n(A) = \{\operatorname{tr}(A)\}$,
(3) $\mathcal{F}_k(A) = \operatorname{tr}(A) - \mathcal{F}_{n-k}(A)$,
(4) $\mathcal{F}_k(A)$ *is convex.*

Proof. (1) The equality holds trivially according to the definitions of $\mathcal{F}_1(A)$ and $\mathcal{F}(A)$.

(2) In the light of Lemma 3.31, we know that $\mu \in \mathcal{F}_n(A)$ if and only if there exists a **unitary matrix** $X \in \mathbb{C}^{n \times n}$ such that $\mu = \text{tr}(X^*AX)$. As

$$\text{tr}(X^*AX) = \text{tr}(AXX^*) = \text{tr}(A),$$

it holds that $\mu = \text{tr}(A)$. Hence, $\mathcal{F}_n(A) = \{\text{tr}(A)\}$.

(3) Let k be a positive integer satisfying $1 \le k \le n$, and $X_1 \in \mathbb{C}^{n \times k}$ and $X_2 \in \mathbb{C}^{n \times (n-k)}$ be two matrices of **orthonormal columns**, i.e., they satisfy $X_1^*X_1 = I_k$ and $X_2^*X_2 = I_{n-k}$. Denote by $X = [X_1, \, X_2]$.

For $\mu \in \mathcal{F}_k(A)$, from Lemma 3.31 we know that $\mu = \text{tr}(X_1^*AX_1)$. By further restricting the column-orthonormal matrix $X_2 \in \mathbb{C}^{n \times (n-k)}$ such that X is a unitary matrix, we have

$$I = XX^* = [X_1, \, X_2] \begin{bmatrix} X_1^* \\ X_2^* \end{bmatrix} = X_1X_1^* + X_2X_2^*,$$

or equivalently,

$$X_1X_1^* = I - X_2X_2^*.$$

It then follows that

$$\mu = \text{tr}(X_1^*AX_1) = \text{tr}(AX_1X_1^*) = \text{tr}(A(I - X_2X_2^*))$$
$$= \text{tr}(A - AX_2X_2^*) = \text{tr}(A) - \text{tr}(AX_2X_2^*) = \text{tr}(A) - \text{tr}(X_2^*AX_2).$$

Again, in accordance with Lemma 3.31 we see that $\text{tr}(X_2^*AX_2) \in \mathcal{F}_{n-k}(A)$. Therefore, it holds that

$$\mu \in \text{tr}(A) - \mathcal{F}_{n-k}(A),$$

which implies that

$$\mathcal{F}_k(A) \subseteq \text{tr}(A) - \mathcal{F}_{n-k}(A).$$

On the other hand, let $B \triangleq \text{tr}(A)\, I - A$. Then we have

$$\text{tr}(B) = (n-1)\,\text{tr}(A), \quad \mathcal{F}_k(B) = k\,\text{tr}(A) - \mathcal{F}_k(A)$$

and

$$\mathcal{F}_{n-k}(B) = (n-k)\,\text{tr}(A) - \mathcal{F}_{n-k}(A).$$

Moreover, in an analogous fashion we can demonstrate the inclusion relationship

$$\mathcal{F}_{n-k}(B) \subseteq \text{tr}(B) - \mathcal{F}_k(B),$$

or in other words,

$$(n-k)\,\text{tr}(A) - \mathcal{F}_{n-k}(A) \subseteq (n-1)\,\text{tr}(A) - [k\,\text{tr}(A) - \mathcal{F}_k(A)],$$

which can be reformulated into the inclusion relationship

$$\text{tr}(A) - \mathcal{F}_{n-k}(A) \subseteq \mathcal{F}_k(A).$$

As a consequence, we have demonstrated the validity of the statement in (3).

(4) For $\mu, \nu \in \mathcal{F}_k(A)$, by the definition of $\mathcal{F}_k(A)$ we know that there exist two sets of orthonormal vectors $\{x_1, x_2, \ldots, x_k\} \subseteq \mathbb{C}^n$ and $\{y_1, y_2, \ldots, y_k\} \subseteq \mathbb{C}^n$ such that

$$\mu = \sum_{i=1}^{k} x_i^* A x_i \quad \text{and} \quad \nu = \sum_{i=1}^{k} y_i^* A y_i.$$

Denote by

$$X = [x_1, x_2, \ldots, x_k] \quad \text{and} \quad Y = [y_1, y_2, \ldots, y_k],$$

and let the matrix $X^* Y \in \mathbb{C}^{k \times k}$ have the **singular value decomposition** $X^* Y = U \Sigma V^*$, where $U, V \in \mathbb{C}^{k \times k}$ are unitary matrices and $\Sigma \in \mathbb{R}^{k \times k}$ is a positive diagonal matrix. Furthermore, denote by

$$\tilde{X} := [\tilde{x}_1, \tilde{x}_2, \ldots, \tilde{x}_k] = XU \quad \text{and} \quad \tilde{Y} := [\tilde{y}_1, \tilde{y}_2, \ldots, \tilde{y}_k] = YV.$$

Then, it holds that

$$\tilde{X}^* \tilde{Y} = (XU)^* YV = U^* X^* YV = \Sigma,$$

which indicates that

$$\tilde{x}_i^* \tilde{y}_j = 0, \quad \text{for all} \quad i \neq j, \, i, j = 1, 2, \ldots, k.$$

Let V_i be the subspace spanned by the two vectors $\tilde{x}_i$ and $\tilde{y}_i$, that is, $V_i = \text{span}\{\tilde{x}_i, \tilde{y}_i\}$, and let A_i be the **restricted operator** of the linear operator A onto the subspace V_i. Then, for any $z \in V_i$, it holds that

$$\langle A_i z, z \rangle = \langle Az, z \rangle = z^* Az,$$

where $\langle \cdot, \cdot \rangle$ represents the Euclidean inner product in the Hilbert space. In addition, the subspaces

$$V_1, V_2, \ldots, V_k$$

are mutually orthogonal, since $\{\tilde{x}_i\}_{i=1}^{k}$ and $\{\tilde{y}_i\}_{i=1}^{k}$ are sets of orthonormal vectors and $\tilde{x}_i$ and $\tilde{y}_j$ are orthogonal for all $i, j = 1, 2, \ldots, k$ whenever $i \neq j$.

Now, for any $\theta \in [0, 1]$, by making use of the **unitary invariance property** of the **trace** we have

$$\begin{aligned}
\theta \mu + (1 - \theta) \nu &= \theta \, \text{tr}(X^* AX) + (1 - \theta) \, \text{tr}(Y^* AY) \\
&= \theta \, \text{tr}(\tilde{X}^* A\tilde{X}) + (1 - \theta) \, \text{tr}(\tilde{Y}^* A\tilde{Y}) \\
&= \sum_{i=1}^{k} [\theta \langle A\tilde{x}_i, \tilde{x}_i \rangle + (1 - \theta) \langle A\tilde{y}_i, \tilde{y}_i \rangle] \\
&= \sum_{i=1}^{k} [\theta \langle A_i \tilde{x}_i, \tilde{x}_i \rangle + (1 - \theta) \langle A_i \tilde{y}_i, \tilde{y}_i \rangle].
\end{aligned}$$

Using repeatedly the **Toeplitz–Hausdorff theorem** k times, we can then obtain

$$\theta \mu + (1 - \theta) \nu = \sum_{i=1}^{k} \langle A_i \tilde{z}_i, \tilde{z}_i \rangle = \sum_{i=1}^{k} \langle A\tilde{z}_i, \tilde{z}_i \rangle = \sum_{i=1}^{k} \tilde{z}_i^* A\tilde{z}_i \in \mathcal{F}_k(A),$$

where $\tilde{z}_i \in V_i$, $i = 1, 2, \ldots, k$, are orthonormal vectors. As a result, $\mathcal{F}_k(A)$ is convex. $\qquad \square$

The k-numerical range is unitarily invariant, i.e., $\mathcal{F}_k(A) = \mathcal{F}_k(U^*AU)$, where $U \in \mathbb{C}^{n \times n}$ is unitary. The following result is about the converse of the unitarily invariant property.

Proposition 3.33. [223] *Let $A, B \in \mathbb{C}^{n \times n}$ with either the matrix A or the matrix B being normal, and let k ($k \leq n$) be a given positive integer. Then $\mathcal{F}_k(A) = \mathcal{F}_k(B)$ holds for all $k \leq \frac{n}{2}$ if and only if the matrices A and B are unitarily similar.*

Proof. The sufficiency is straightforward due to the unitarily invariant property of $\mathcal{F}_k(\cdot)$, $\forall k \in \{1, 2, \ldots, n\}$.

The proof of the necessity is left as Exercise 3.18. □

3.4.2 ▪ c-Numerical Range

A further generalization of the k-numerical range is the *c-numerical range*; see [343].

Definition 3.34. *Let $c = [c_1, c_2, \ldots, c_n]^\mathsf{T} \in \mathbb{C}^n$ be a given vector and $A \in \mathbb{C}^{n \times n}$. Then the c-numerical range of the matrix A is defined as*

$$\mathcal{F}_c(A) = \left\{ \sum_{i=1}^n c_i \, x_i^* A x_i \ : \ x_i \in \mathbb{C}^n \quad and \quad x_i^* x_j = \delta_{ij} \right\},$$

where δ_{ij} is the Kronecker symbol, i.e., $\delta_{ij} = 1$ when $i = j$, and $\delta_{ij} = 0$ otherwise.

Example 3.35. Let $c = [\underbrace{1, \ldots, 1}_{k}, 0, \ldots, 0]^\mathsf{T}$. Then it holds that $\mathcal{F}_k(A) = \mathcal{F}_c(A)$ for the matrix $A \in \mathbb{C}^{n \times n}$.

Note that the c-numerical range is not always convex, but is convex for any real vector c.

Proposition 3.36. *If $A \in \mathbb{C}^{2 \times 2}$ and $c = [c_1, c_2]^\mathsf{T} \in \mathbb{C}^2$, then $\mathcal{F}_c(A)$ is convex.*

Proof. For any $\mu \in \mathcal{F}_c(A)$, we have

$$\begin{aligned}
\mu &= c_1 x_1^* A x_1 + c_2 x_2^* A x_2 \\
&= (c_1 - c_2) x_1^* A x_1 + c_2 (x_1^* A x_1 + x_2^* A x_2).
\end{aligned}$$

Since

$$x_1^* A x_1 + x_2^* A x_2 \in \mathcal{F}_2(A),$$

from Property (2) in Proposition 3.32 we see that

$$x_1^* A x_1 + x_2^* A x_2 \in \{\mathrm{tr}(A)\}.$$

Hence, it holds that

$$\begin{aligned}
\mu &\in (c_1 - c_2) \, x_1^* A x_1 + c_2 \, \{\mathrm{tr}(A)\} \\
&\in x_1^* \big((c_1 - c_2) A + c_2 \, \{\mathrm{tr}(A)\} \, I\big) x_1 \\
&\in \mathcal{F}\big((c_1 - c_2) A + c_2 \, \mathrm{tr}(A) \, I\big).
\end{aligned}$$

Analogously, we can show that

$$\mu \in \mathcal{F}\big((c_1 - c_2)A + c_2 \operatorname{tr}(A)\, I\big)$$

also implies $\mu \in \mathcal{F}_c(A)$. Therefore, it follows that

$$\mathcal{F}_c(A) = \mathcal{F}\big((c_1 - c_2)A + c_2 \operatorname{tr}(A)\, I\big),$$

which shows that $\mathcal{F}_c(A)$ is convex. $\quad\square$

We see that

$$\mathcal{F}_c(A) = \{\operatorname{tr}(CU^*AU) \ : \ U \in \mathbb{C}^{n \times n} \text{ is unitary}\},$$

where $C = \operatorname{diag}(c_1, c_2, \ldots, c_n)$. This motivates immediately the definition of the C-numerical range.

3.4.3 ▪ C-Numerical Range

The C-numerical range is one of the generalized numerical ranges that has attracted much attention.

Definition 3.37. [162] *Let $C \in \mathbb{C}^{n \times n}$ be given and $A \in \mathbb{C}^{n \times n}$. Then the **$C$-numerical range** of the matrix A is defined as*

$$\mathcal{F}_C(A) = \big\{\operatorname{tr}(CU^*AU) \ : \ U \in \mathbb{C}^{n \times n} \text{ is unitary}\big\}.$$

Proposition 3.38. *Let $A, C \in \mathbb{C}^{n \times n}$. Then*

(1) *$\mathcal{F}_C(A) = \mathcal{F}_A(C)$ for all $A, C \in \mathbb{C}^{n \times n}$,*
(2) *$\mathcal{F}_C(V^*AV) = \mathcal{F}_C(A)$ and $\mathcal{F}_{V^*CV}(A) = \mathcal{F}_C(A)$ if $V \in \mathbb{C}^{n \times n}$ is unitary,*
(3) *$\mathcal{F}_C(A) = \mathcal{F}_c(A)$ if $C \in \mathbb{C}^{n \times n}$ is normal, where c is the vector of the eigenvalues of the matrix C,*
(4) *$\mathcal{F}_C(A)$ is convex if either the matrix A or the matrix C is Hermitian.*

Proof. (1) Since

$$\operatorname{tr}(CU^*AU) = \operatorname{tr}(AUCU^*)$$

and the matrix U is unitary, by the definition we immediately have $\mathcal{F}_C(A) = \mathcal{F}_A(C)$.

(2) For $\mu \in \mathcal{F}_C(V^*AV)$, we have

$$\mu = \operatorname{tr}(CU^*(V^*AV)U) = \operatorname{tr}(C(VU)^*A(VU)) \in F_C(A),$$

as the matrix VU is unitary. Therefore, it holds that

$$\mathcal{F}_C(V^*AV) \subseteq \mathcal{F}_C(A).$$

Conversely, for $\mu \in \mathcal{F}_C(A)$, we have

$$\begin{aligned}
\mu &= \operatorname{tr}(CU^*AU) = \operatorname{tr}(C(VV^*U)^*A(VV^*U)) \\
&= \operatorname{tr}(C(V^*U)^*(V^*AV)(V^*U)) \in \mathcal{F}_C(V^*AV),
\end{aligned}$$

as the matrix V^*U is unitary. Therefore, it holds that $\mathcal{F}_C(A) \subseteq \mathcal{F}_C(V^*AV)$.

It then follows that $\mathcal{F}_C(A) = \mathcal{F}_C(V^*AV)$.

Moreover, in the light of Property (1) and with the exchange of the matrices A and C, we can further obtain

$$\mathcal{F}_C(A) = \mathcal{F}_A(C) = \mathcal{F}_A(V^*CV) = \mathcal{F}_{V^*CV}(A).$$

(3) Assume that the matrix C is normal, with $\lambda_1, \lambda_2, \ldots, \lambda_n$ being its eigenvalues. Denote by

$$\Lambda = \text{diag}(\lambda_1, \lambda_2, \ldots, \lambda_n).$$

Then there exists a unitary matrix $V \in \mathbb{C}^{n \times n}$ such that $V^*CV = \Lambda$. Based on Property (2) we have

$$\mathcal{F}_C(A) = \mathcal{F}_{V^*CV}(A) = \mathcal{F}_\Lambda(A).$$

Denote by

$$c = [\lambda_1, \lambda_2, \ldots, \lambda_n]^\mathsf{T}.$$

Then from the definition of $\mathcal{F}_c(A)$ in Section 3.4.2 we know that

$$\mathcal{F}_c(A) = \mathcal{F}_\Lambda(A) = \mathcal{F}_C(A).$$

(4) Since $\mathcal{F}_C(A) = \mathcal{F}_A(C)$, without loss of generality, we assume that the matrix C is Hermitian with its eigenvalues being $\lambda_1, \lambda_2, \ldots, \lambda_n$. Then $\lambda_1, \lambda_2, \ldots, \lambda_n$ are all reals, so that

$$c = [\lambda_1, \lambda_2, \ldots, \lambda_n]^\mathsf{T}$$

is a real vector. In accordance with Property (3) we see that $\mathcal{F}_C(A) = \mathcal{F}_c(A)$, and in the light of the statement in Section 3.4.2 we know that $\mathcal{F}_c(A)$ is convex. It then follows that $\mathcal{F}_C(A)$ is convex too. □

A slight extension of Property (4) in Proposition 3.38 is given below; see [223].

Proposition 3.39. *Let $C \in \mathbb{C}^{n \times n}$ be a given matrix. Then $\mathcal{F}_C(A)$ is convex for all $A \in \mathbb{C}^{n \times n}$ if there exist $\alpha, \beta \in \mathbb{C}$, with $\alpha \neq 0$, such that the matrix $\alpha C + \beta I$ is Hermitian, i.e., the matrix C is normal and its eigenvalues are collinear on the complex plane.*

Proof. As the matrix $\alpha C + \beta I$ is Hermitian, according to Properties (1) and (4) in Proposition 3.38 we know that $\mathcal{F}_A(\alpha C + \beta I) = \mathcal{F}_{\alpha C + \beta I}(A)$ is convex. In addition, in the light of the definition of the C-numerical range, it holds that

$$\begin{aligned}
\mathcal{F}_A(\alpha C + \beta I) &= \left\{ \text{tr}(AU^*(\alpha C + \beta I)U) : U \in \mathbb{C}^{n \times n} \text{ is unitary} \right\} \\
&= \left\{ \text{tr}(\alpha AU^*CU + \beta A) : U \in \mathbb{C}^{n \times n} \text{ is unitary} \right\} \\
&= \alpha \mathcal{F}_A(C) + \beta \, \text{tr}(A) \\
&= \alpha \mathcal{F}_C(A) + \beta \, \text{tr}(A).
\end{aligned}$$

As $\alpha \neq 0$, the above relationship then implies

$$\mathcal{F}_C(A) = \alpha^{-1} \left[\mathcal{F}_A(\alpha C + \beta I) - \beta \, \text{tr}(A) \right],$$

that is, $\mathcal{F}_C(A)$ is resulted from $\mathcal{F}_A(\alpha C + \beta I)$ with only translation, rotation, and scaling operations. Recalling that $\mathcal{F}_A(\alpha C + \beta I)$ is convex, we then know that $\mathcal{F}_C(A)$ is convex too. □

Associated with the C-numerical range are the **C-numerical radius**, the **C-spectrum**, the **C-spectral radius**, and the **C-spectral norm**, which are defined sequentially in the following:

$$r_C(A) = \max\{|\mu| : \mu \in \mathcal{F}_C(A)\},$$

$$\sigma_C(A) = \left\{ \sum_{k=1}^{n} \lambda_k(C)\lambda_{i_k}(A) : (i_1, i_2, \ldots, i_n) \text{ is a permutation of } (1, 2, \ldots, n) \right\},$$

$$\rho_C(A) = \max\{|z| : z \in \sigma_C(A)\}, \quad \text{and}$$

$$\|A\|_C = \max\{|\operatorname{tr}(CUAV)| : U, V \in \mathbb{C}^{n \times n} \text{ are unitary}\},$$

where $\lambda_i(A)$ and $\lambda_i(C)$ are eigenvalues of the matrices A and C, respectively.

Evidently, for any $A, C \in \mathbb{C}^{n \times n}$ we have $\sigma_C(A) \subseteq \mathcal{F}_C(A)$.

Proposition 3.40. [223] *Let $C = \operatorname{diag}(c_1, c_2, \ldots, c_n) \in \mathbb{C}^{n \times n}$. If $A \in \mathbb{C}^{n \times n}$ is normal, then $\mathcal{F}_C(A) \subseteq \operatorname{Co}(\sigma_C(A))$.*

Proof. Assume that $\lambda_1, \lambda_2, \ldots, \lambda_n$ are eigenvalues of the matrix A, and $u_1, u_2, \ldots, u_n$ are the associated orthonormal eigenvectors. Let $\{x_1, x_2, \ldots, x_n\}$ be a set of orthonormal vectors, and

$$z = [x_1^* A x_1, x_2^* A x_2, \ldots, x_n^* A x_n]^\mathsf{T}.$$

As $\{u_1, u_2, \ldots, u_n\}$ form an orthonormal basis of $\mathbb{C}^{n \times n}$, it holds that

$$x_i = \sum_{k=1}^{n} \langle x_i, u_k \rangle u_k, \quad i = 1, 2, \ldots, n.$$

Straightforward calculations show that $z = Sv$, where

$$v = [\lambda_1, \lambda_2, \ldots, \lambda_n]^\mathsf{T},$$

and

$$S = \left[|\langle x_i, u_j \rangle|^2 \right]$$

is a doubly stochastic matrix. By making use of the Birkhoff's theorem [237] we know that the matrix S is a convex combination of permutation matrices, i.e., for

$$\mathbb{S}_n = \{\boldsymbol{\pi} : \{1, 2, \ldots, n\} \to \{1, 2, \ldots, n\}\},$$

there holds

$$S = \sum_{\boldsymbol{\pi} \in \mathbb{S}_n} \alpha_{\boldsymbol{\pi}} P_{\boldsymbol{\pi}},$$

where for $\boldsymbol{\pi} \in \mathbb{S}_n$ the combination coefficients $\alpha_{\boldsymbol{\pi}}$ are real and nonnegative such that $\sum_{\boldsymbol{\pi} \in \mathbb{S}_n} \alpha_{\boldsymbol{\pi}} = 1$, and the permutation matrices $P_{\boldsymbol{\pi}} = [\delta_{i, \pi(j)}]$. For $c = [c_1, c_2, \ldots, c_n]^\mathsf{T}$, we have

$$\sum_{i=1}^{n} c_i x_i^* A x_i = \langle c, z \rangle = \langle c, Sv \rangle$$

$$= \sum_{\boldsymbol{\pi} \in \mathbb{S}_n} \alpha_{\boldsymbol{\pi}} \langle c, P_{\boldsymbol{\pi}} v \rangle = \sum_{\boldsymbol{\pi} \in \mathbb{S}_n} \alpha_{\boldsymbol{\pi}} \sum_{i=1}^{n} c_i v_{\pi^{-1}(i)}$$

$$= \sum_{\boldsymbol{\pi} \in \mathbb{S}_n} \alpha_{\pi^{-1}} \sum_{i=1}^{n} c_i v_{\pi(i)} \in \operatorname{Co}(\sigma_C(A)),$$

where π^{-1} is the inverse function of the permutation π. Hence, it holds that

$$\mathcal{F}(A) \subseteq \text{Co}(\sigma_C(A)). \qquad \square$$

Proposition 3.41. [223] *Let $A, C \in \mathbb{C}^{n \times n}$. Then $\rho_C(A) \leq r_C(A) \leq \|A\|_C$.*

Proof. The inequality is straightforward from $\sigma_C(A) \subseteq \mathcal{F}_C(A)$ and

$$\mathcal{F}_C(A) \subseteq \{\text{tr}(CUAV) : U, V \in \mathbb{C}^{n \times n} \text{ are unitary}\}. \qquad \square$$

Proposition 3.42. [223] *Let $C \in \mathbb{C}^{n \times n}$ be a normal matrix with distinct nonzero eigenvalues in terms of module. Then $A \in \mathbb{C}^{n \times n}$ satisfies $\rho_C(A) = \|A\|_C$ if and only if $r_C(A) = \|A\|_C$.*

Proof. By Proposition 3.41, we see that $\rho_C(A) = \|A\|_C$ implies $r_C(A) = \|A\|_C$.

Conversely, let us assume that $r_C(A) = \|A\|_C$. Denote by $\sigma_i(A)$ $(i = 1, 2, \ldots, n)$ and $\lambda_i(C)$ $(i = 1, 2, \ldots, n)$ the singular values of the matrix A and the eigenvalues of the matrix C, which are ordered as

$$\sigma_1(A) \geq \sigma_2(A) \geq \cdots \geq \sigma_n(A)$$

and

$$|\lambda_1(C)| > |\lambda_2(C)| > \cdots > |\lambda_m(C)| > 0 = |\lambda_{m+1}(C)| = \cdots = |\lambda_n(C)|,$$

with m being a positive integer satisfying $1 < m \leq n$. Besides, we write

$$\Lambda_C = \text{diag}(\lambda_1(C), \lambda_2(C), \ldots, \lambda_n(C)).$$

As the matrix C is normal, from the definition of $r_C(A)$ we know that there exists a unitary matrix $U \in \mathbb{C}^{n \times n}$ such that

$$r_C(A) = |\text{tr}(\Lambda_C U^* A U)|.$$

Represent briefly $\tilde{A} = [\tilde{a}_{ij}] \triangleq U^* A U$. Then the matrix $\tilde{A}$ has the same eigenvalues and the same singular values as the matrix A, and from Exercise 3.19 we know that

$$\sum_{k=1}^{r} |\tilde{a}_{kk}| \leq \sum_{k=1}^{r} \sigma_k(A), \quad r = 1, 2, \ldots, m.$$

It then follows that

$$(|\lambda_k(C)| - |\lambda_{k+1}(C)|) \sum_{j=1}^{k} \sigma_j(A) \geq (|\lambda_k(C)| - |\lambda_{k+1}(C)|) \sum_{j=1}^{k} |\tilde{a}_{jj}| \qquad (3.21)$$

holds for $k = 1, 2, \ldots, m - 1$, and

$$|\lambda_m(C)| \sum_{j=1}^{m} \sigma_j(A) \geq |\lambda_m(C)| \sum_{j=1}^{m} |\tilde{a}_{jj}| \qquad (3.22)$$

holds for $k = m$. By summing up all the m inequalities in (3.21) and (3.22), we have

$$\sum_{k=1}^{m} |\lambda_k(C)| \sigma_k(A) \geq \sum_{k=1}^{m} |\lambda_k(C)| |\tilde{a}_{kk}|.$$

As

$$\sum_{k=1}^{m} |\lambda_k(C)| \, \sigma_k(A) = \|A\|_C$$

and

$$\sum_{k=1}^{m} |\lambda_k(C)| \, |\tilde{a}_{kk}| \geq \left| \sum_{k=1}^{m} \lambda_k(C) \, \tilde{a}_{kk} \right| = r_C(A),$$

and as we have assumed that $r_C(A) = \|A\|_C$, the inequalities in (3.21) and (3.22) must become equalities, which implies that

$$|\tilde{a}_{kk}| = \sigma_k(A), \quad k = 1, 2, \ldots, m.$$

Notice that for

$$\tilde{I}_n = \mathrm{Diag}(I_m, 0) \in \mathbb{R}^{n \times n}$$

we have

$$\sum_{k=1}^{m} |\tilde{a}_{kk}|^2 = \sum_{k=1}^{m} [\sigma_k(A)]^2 \geq \mathrm{tr}(\tilde{I}_n \tilde{A} \tilde{A}^*) = \sum_{i=1}^{m} \sum_{k=1}^{n} |\tilde{a}_{ik}|^2$$

and

$$\sum_{k=1}^{m} |\tilde{a}_{kk}|^2 = \sum_{k=1}^{m} [\sigma_k(A)]^2 \geq \mathrm{tr}(\tilde{I}_n \tilde{A}^* \tilde{A}) = \sum_{i=1}^{n} \sum_{k=1}^{m} |\tilde{a}_{ik}|^2.$$

Then it follows that

$$\tilde{a}_{ij} = 0$$

either when

$$i \neq j, \ i = 1, 2, \ldots, m, \ j = 1, 2, \ldots, n,$$

or when

$$i \neq j, \ i = 1, 2, \ldots, n, \ j = 1, 2, \ldots, m.$$

That is to say, it must hold

$$\tilde{A} = \mathrm{diag}(\tilde{a}_{11}, \tilde{a}_{22}, \ldots, \tilde{a}_{mm}) \oplus \hat{A},$$

with $\hat{A}$ being some matrix of order $n - m$. Hence, it follows that $\tilde{a}_{11}, \tilde{a}_{22}, \ldots, \tilde{a}_{mm}$ are m eigenvalues of the matrix $\tilde{A}$ as well as the matrix A.

By direct computations, we can obtain

$$\|A\|_C = \sum_{k=1}^{m} |\lambda_k(C)| \, \sigma_k(A) = \left| \sum_{k=1}^{m} \lambda_k(C) \, \tilde{a}_{kk} \right|$$
$$= \left| \sum_{k=1}^{n} \lambda_k(C) \, \lambda_{\pi(k)}(A) \right| \leq \rho_C(A),$$

where

$$\lambda_{\pi(k)}(A) = \tilde{a}_{kk}, \quad \text{for} \quad k = 1, 2, \ldots, m.$$

Since Proposition 3.41 shows that $\rho_C(A) \leq \|A\|_C$, we finally know that $\rho_C(A) = \|A\|_C$. See also [224]. $\qquad \square$

The C-numerical range can be used to characterize normal matrices.

Proposition 3.43. [222, 223] *Assume that $C \in \mathbb{C}^{n \times n}$ has n distinct eigenvalues. Then the matrix A is normal if $\mathcal{F}_C(A) = \mathrm{Co}(\sigma_C(A))$.*

Proof. Assume that the matrix A is not normal.

Since $\mathcal{F}_C(A)$ is invariant under unitary similarity transformations, we can assume that $A = [a_{ij}]$ and $C = [c_{ij}]$ are lower-triangular matrices with their eigenvalues on the main diagonals. Without loss of generality, we may further assume that $a_{21} \neq 0$ as the matrix A is not normal.

Let

$$\mathbb{S}_n = \{\pi : \{1, 2, \ldots, n\} \to \{1, 2, \ldots, n\}\}.$$

Because $\mathcal{F}_C(A) = \mathrm{Co}(\sigma_C(A))$ is a convex polygonal disc, there exists a permutation $\pi \in \mathbb{S}_n$ such that $\sum_{k=1}^{n} a_{kk} c_{\pi(k), \pi(k)}$ is a vertex of $\mathcal{F}_C(A)$. For simplicity, we assume that

$$\sigma_{12} = a_{11} c_{22} + a_{22} c_{11} + \sum_{k=3}^{n} a_{kk} c_{kk}$$

is a vertex of $\mathcal{F}_C(A)$. Besides, we introduce the matrix

$$U = \begin{bmatrix} 0 & \theta \\ 1 & 0 \end{bmatrix} \oplus I_{n-2},$$

with $\theta \in \mathbb{C}$ satisfying $|\theta| = 1$. Then it holds that

$$\mathrm{tr}(CU^* AU) = c_{11} a_{22} + c_{22} a_{11} + \sum_{k=3}^{n} c_{kk} a_{kk} + \theta c_{21} a_{21}$$

$$\triangleq \sigma_{12} + \theta c_{21} a_{21} \in \mathcal{F}_C(A),$$

where

$$\sigma_{12} = c_{11} a_{22} + c_{22} a_{11} + \sum_{k=3}^{n} c_{kk} a_{kk}.$$

If $c_{21} \neq 0$, then

$$\{z : |z - \sigma_{12}| \leq |c_{21} a_{21}|\} \subseteq \mathcal{F}_C(A),$$

which contradicts with the fact that σ_{12} is one of the vertex of $\mathcal{F}_C(A)$.

In the case that $c_{21} = 0$, we let

$$A_2 = \begin{bmatrix} a_{11} & 0 \\ a_{21} & a_{22} \end{bmatrix} \quad \text{and} \quad C_2 = \mathrm{diag}(c_{11}, c_{22})$$

be the 2×2 sequential principal submatrices of the matrices A and C, respectively. Then, for any unitary matrix $V \in \mathbb{C}^{2 \times 2}$ and $U = V \oplus I_{n-2}$, we have

$$\mathrm{tr}(CU^* AU) = \mathrm{tr}(C_2 V^* A_2 V) + \sum_{k=3}^{n} c_{kk} a_{kk} \in \mathcal{F}_C(A).$$

Therefore, it holds that $\mathcal{F}_{C_2}(A_2) + \sum_{k=3}^{n} c_{kk} a_{kk} \subseteq \mathcal{F}_C(A)$.

With Proposition 3.36, we have

$$\mathcal{F}_{C_2}(A_2) = \mathcal{F}((c_{11} - c_{22})A_2 + c_{22}(a_{11} + a_{22})I),$$

which is a nondegenerate elliptical disc as the matrix

$$(c_{11} - c_{22})A_2 + c_{22}(a_{11} + a_{22})I$$

is not normal. Moreover,

$$c_{11}a_{22} + c_{22}a_{11} \quad \text{and} \quad c_{11}a_{11} + c_{22}a_{22}$$

are the (interior) foci of $\mathcal{F}_{C_2}(A_2)$. Therefore, σ_{12} is in the interior of $\mathcal{F}_C(A)$, which also leads to a contradiction.

Consequently, the matrix A must be normal. □

Proposition 3.44. [223] *Let $[c_1, c_2, \ldots, c_n]^\mathsf{T} \in \mathbb{R}^n$ have at least $n - 1$ distinct entries and $C = \mathrm{diag}(c_1, c_2, \ldots, c_n) \in \mathbb{R}^{n \times n}$. Then $A \in \mathbb{C}^{n \times n}$ is normal if and only if $\mathcal{F}_C(A) = \mathrm{Co}(\sigma_C(A))$.*

Proof. We first prove the necessity. To this end, we assume that $A \in \mathbb{C}^{n \times n}$ is normal. Then, in accordance with Proposition 3.40 we know that $\mathcal{F}_C(A) \subseteq \mathrm{Co}(\sigma_C(A))$. In addition, as $C \in \mathbb{R}^{n \times n}$ is Hermitian, in the light of Proposition 3.39 we see that $\mathcal{F}_C(A)$ is convex. Hence, $\sigma_C(A) \subseteq \mathcal{F}_C(A)$ implies $\mathrm{Co}(\sigma_C(A)) \subseteq \mathcal{F}_C(A)$. It then follows that $\mathcal{F}_C(A) = \mathrm{Co}(\sigma_C(A))$.

The proof of the sufficiency is left as Exercise 3.20. □

3.5 ▪ Exercises

3.1. Let $A, B \in \mathbb{C}^{n \times n}$, with $AB = BA$, and let the matrix A be Hermitian and positive semidefinite. Then for any nonnegative number p it holds that $A^p B = B A^p$.

3.2. Derive the elliptic equation (3.5) from the equations (3.3) and (3.4).

3.3. Show that $4\, r(\cdot)$ is a consistent matrix norm on $\mathbb{C}^{n \times n}$. Moreover, the equality

$$4\, r(AB) = 4\, r(A) \cdot 4\, r(B)$$

holds true if

$$A = B^\mathsf{T} = \begin{bmatrix} 0 & 2 \\ 0 & 0 \end{bmatrix}.$$

3.4. Prove the polynomial equalities (3.6) and (3.7).

3.5. Let $A \in \mathbb{C}^{n \times n}$. Show that if $0 \notin \mathcal{F}(A)$, then the matrix A is invertible.

3.6. Let $A = H_1 + \mathrm{i}\, H_2$, where $H_1, H_2 \in \mathbb{C}^{n \times n}$ are Hermitian. Show that

$$\mathcal{F}(A) \subseteq \mathcal{F}(H_1) + \mathrm{i}\, \mathcal{F}(H_2) \triangleq \{\alpha + \mathrm{i}\beta \, : \, \alpha \in \mathcal{F}(H_1), \, \beta \in \mathcal{F}(H_2)\}.$$

3.7. Assume that $A \in \mathbb{C}^{n \times n}$ is positive definite but not necessarily Hermitian. Show that

(1) $\mathcal{F}(A^{-1}) = \{\mu^{-1} \, : \, \mu \in \mathcal{F}(A)\}$,

(2) $\sigma(AB) \subseteq \mathcal{F}(A)\,\mathcal{F}(B)$, for all $B \in \mathbb{C}^{n \times n}$.

3.8. Let $A \in \mathbb{C}^{n \times n}$ with $0 \in \mathcal{F}(A)$. Show that the definition of $\mathcal{F}(A)$ can be replaced by

$$\mathcal{F}(A) = \{x^* A x \,:\, x \in \mathbb{C}^n, \, x^* x \leq 1\}.$$

3.9. Let $A \in \mathbb{C}^{2 \times 2}$, $A_0 = A - \frac{1}{2} \operatorname{tr}(A) \, I$. Show that the matrix A is normal if and only if the matrix A_0 is a scalar multiple of a unitary matrix, i.e., $A_0^* A_0 = cI$ for some $c \geq 0$.

3.10. Prove Property (10) in Proposition 3.6.

3.11. Let $A, B \in \mathbb{C}^{n \times n}$ be normal, and denote by $\sigma(A) = \{\lambda_1, \lambda_2, \ldots, \lambda_n\}$ and $\sigma(B) = \{\mu_1, \mu_2, \ldots, \mu_n\}$. Show that $\sigma(A + B) \subseteq \operatorname{Co}(\{\lambda_i + \mu_j, \, i, j = 1, 2, \ldots, n\})$.

3.12. Let $x \in \mathbb{C}^n$ with $x^* x = 1$, and let $\mathscr{H}(A) = \frac{1}{2}(A + A^*)$ be the Hermitian part of the matrix $A \in \mathbb{C}^{n \times n}$. Show that the following statements are equivalent:

(1) $\Re(x^* A x) = \max\{\Re(\alpha) \,:\, \alpha \in \mathcal{F}(A)\}$,

(2) $\mathscr{H}(A) \, x = \lambda_{\max}(\mathscr{H}(A)) \, x$ with $\lambda_{\max}(\mathscr{H}(A))$ indicating the largest eigenvalue of the matrix $\mathscr{H}(A)$.

3.13. Let $A \in \mathbb{C}^{n \times n}$. Show that the following statements are equivalent:

(1) $r(A) \leq 1$,

(2) $\rho(\mathscr{H}(e^{i\theta} A)) \leq 1$ for all $\theta \in [0, 2\pi)$,

(3) $\lambda_{\max}(\mathscr{H}(e^{i\theta} A)) \leq 1$ for all $\theta \in [0, 2\pi)$.

3.14. Give an example to show that even if $A \in \mathbb{C}^{n \times n}$ is such that $A^2 = cI$, with $c \in \mathbb{C}$ being a nonzero complex constant, it is not necessary for the matrix A itself to be a scalar matrix.

3.15. Let $A \in \mathbb{C}^{n \times n}$ be such that $A^2 = cI$, where $c \in \mathbb{C}$ is a nonzero complex constant satisfying $|c| < 1$. Denote by $\nu = \frac{1}{1 - |c|^2}$ and $D = \nu(I + A^* A)^{\frac{1}{2}}$. Prove the following identities:

(1) $1 + \nu^2 |c|^2 = \nu^2$,

(2) $D^2 = I + A^* D^2 A$.

3.16. Let $A \in \mathbb{C}^{n \times n}$,

$$R_k(A) = \sum_{\substack{j=1 \\ j \neq k}}^{n} |a_{kj}| \quad \text{and} \quad C_k(A) = \sum_{\substack{i=1 \\ i \neq k}}^{n} |a_{ik}|.$$

Let $s(x, y)$ be a given function on $[0, \infty) \times [0, \infty)$, and define

$$G_s(A) = \operatorname{Co}\left(\bigcup_{k=1}^{n} \{z \,:\, |z - a_{kk}| \leq s(R_k(A), C_k(A))\} \right).$$

Show that if $\mathcal{F}(A) \subseteq G_s(A)$ for all $A \in \mathbb{C}^{n \times n}$, then

$$s(R_k(A), C_k(A)) \geq \frac{1}{2}(R_k(A) + C_k(A)) = g_k(A), \quad k = 1, 2, \ldots, n.$$

This indicates that $G_F(A)$ is the best possible region including $\mathcal{F}(A)$, which depends solely on a_{kk}, $R_k(A)$ and $C_k(A)$, $k = 1, 2, \ldots, n$.

3.17. Let $A \in \mathbb{C}^{n \times n}$ and $B = \text{tr}(A) I - A$. For any positive integer k satisfying $1 \leq k \leq n$, prove the equality

$$\mathcal{F}_k(B) = k \, \text{tr}(A) - \mathcal{F}_k(A).$$

3.18. Give the necessity proof of Proposition 3.33.

3.19. Let $A = [a_{ij}] \in \mathbb{C}^{n \times n}$, and its singular values be $\sigma_k(A)$, $k = 1, 2, \ldots, n$, which are ordered as $\sigma_1(A) \geq \sigma_2(A) \geq \cdots \geq \sigma_n(A)$. Prove the inequalities

$$\sum_{k=1}^{r} |a_{kk}| \leq \sum_{k=1}^{r} \sigma_{\pi(k)}(A), \quad r = 1, 2, \ldots, n,$$

where for each r, $\pi : \{1, 2, \ldots, r\} \to \{1, 2, \ldots, r\}$ is a permutation.

3.20. Give the sufficiency proof of Proposition 3.44.

Chapter 4

Nonnegative Matrices and M-Matrices

Nonnegative matrices arise in many applications, including economics, queuing theory, chemical engineering, and image processing. They play a crucial role in the theory of matrices, and they are important on the convergence study of iterative methods. If not specified explicitly, all the matrices considered in this chapter are real.

4.1 ▪ Nonnegative Matrices

4.1.1 ▪ Definitions and Basic Properties

For matrices $A = [a_{ij}] \in \mathbb{R}^{m \times n}$ and $B = [b_{ij}] \in \mathbb{R}^{m \times n}$, we say

$$A \geq B \quad \text{if } a_{ij} \geq b_{ij} \text{ for all } 1 \leq i \leq m, 1 \leq j \leq n, \tag{4.1}$$
$$A > B \quad \text{if } a_{ij} > b_{ij} \text{ for all } 1 \leq i \leq m, 1 \leq j \leq n, \quad \text{and}$$
$$A \gneq B \quad \text{if } \quad A \geq B \quad \text{and} \quad A \neq B.$$

The reverse relations "$\leq$", "$<$", and "$\lneq$" can be defined analogously.

The "$\geq$" (or "$\leq$") relation defines a natural (or componentwise) **partial ordering** on $\mathbb{R}^{m \times n}$. Two matrices $A, B \in \mathbb{R}^{m \times n}$ are said to be comparable under this ordering if either $A \geq B$ or $B \geq A$. The following properties are immediately verified.

Proposition 4.1. *Let $A, B, C \in \mathbb{R}^{m \times n}$. Then the ordering relation "$\geq$" defined on $\mathbb{R}^{m \times n}$ by* (4.1) *satisfies the following:*

(1) *$A \geq A$ for all $A \in \mathbb{R}^{m \times n}$;*
(2) *if $A \geq B$ and $B \geq A$, then $A = B$;*
(3) *if $A \geq B$ and $B \geq C$, then $A \geq C$;*
(4) *if $A \geq B$, then $\alpha A \geq \alpha B$ for all $\alpha \geq 0$;*
(5) *if $A \geq B$, then $A + C \geq B + C$ for all $C \in \mathbb{R}^{m \times n}$.*

Definition 4.2. *Let $A \in \mathbb{R}^{m \times n}$. We call the matrix A a **nonnegative matrix** if $A \geq 0$, a **positive matrix** if $A > 0$, and a **negative matrix** if $A < 0$.*

Note that $A > 0$ (≥ 0) if and only if $-A < 0$ (≤ 0). An immediate fact is that for $A, B \in \mathbb{R}^{m \times n}$, $P \in \mathbb{R}^{p \times m}$, and $R \in \mathbb{R}^{n \times r}$, if $A \geq B$, $P \geq 0$, and $R \geq 0$, then it holds that

$$PA \geq PB, \quad AR \geq BR.$$

For $A = [a_{ij}] \in \mathbb{C}^{m \times n}$, we denote by $|A| = [|a_{ij}|]$ the **absolute value** of the matrix A. It is clear that $|A| \geq 0$.

In the following lemmas, we list some basic properties about the nonnegative matrices.

Lemma 4.3. Let $A, B \in \mathbb{C}^{n \times n}$ and $x \in \mathbb{C}^n$. Then

(1) $|Ax| \leq |A|\,|x|$;

(2) $|AB| \leq |A|\,|B|$;

(3) $|A^k| \leq |A|^k$, $k = 0, 1, 2, \ldots$;

(4) $\|A\|_F = \||A|\|_F$;

(5) $\|A\|_F \leq \|B\|_F$ if $|A| \leq |B|$.

Lemma 4.4. Let $A, B, C, D \in \mathbb{R}^{n \times n}$ and $x \in \mathbb{R}^n$.

(1) If $0 \leq A \leq B$ and $0 \leq C \leq D$, then $0 \leq AC \leq BD$.

(2) If $0 \leq A \leq B$, then $0 \leq A^k \leq B^k$, $k = 0, 1, 2, \ldots$.

(3) If $A > 0$ and $x \gneq 0$, then $Ax > 0$.

(4) If $A \geq 0$, $x > 0$ and $Ax = 0$, then $A = 0$.

The conclusions in Lemmas 4.3 and 4.4 can be verified by straightforward computations. One application of the relationships in these two lemmas is given below.

Theorem 4.5. Let $A \in \mathbb{C}^{n \times n}$ and $B \in \mathbb{R}^{n \times n}$. If $|A| \leq B$, then

$$\rho(A) \leq \rho(|A|) \leq \rho(B).$$

Proof. The proof is based on the equality

$$\rho(X) = \lim_{k \to \infty} \|X^k\|_F^{\frac{1}{k}}, \quad X \in \mathbb{C}^{n \times n},$$

which is stated in Theorem 1.33. As $|A| \leq B$, it follows that

$$|A^k| \leq |A|^k \leq B^k, \quad k = 1, 2, \ldots.$$

Thus, from the last two properties in Lemma 4.3 we have

$$\|A^k\|_F \leq \||A|^k\|_F \leq \|B^k\|_F,$$

which implies

$$\|A^k\|_F^{\frac{1}{k}} \leq \||A|^k\|_F^{\frac{1}{k}} \leq \|B^k\|_F^{\frac{1}{k}}, \quad k = 1, 2, \ldots.$$

Therefore,

$$\lim_{k \to \infty} \|A^k\|_F^{\frac{1}{k}} \leq \lim_{k \to \infty} \||A|^k\|_F^{\frac{1}{k}} \leq \lim_{k \to \infty} \|B^k\|_F^{\frac{1}{k}}.$$

That is to say,

$$\rho(A) \leq \rho(|A|) \leq \rho(B). \qquad \square$$

The following two corollaries hold immediately.

Corollary 4.6. Let $A, B \in \mathbb{R}^{n \times n}$. If $0 \leq A \leq B$, then $\rho(A) \leq \rho(B)$.

Corollary 4.7. *Let $A = [a_{ij}] \in \mathbb{R}^{n \times n}$ be nonnegative. If $A_k \in \mathbb{R}^{k \times k}$ ($1 \le k \le n$) is a **principal submatrix** of the matrix A, then $\rho(A_k) \le \rho(A)$. In particular, it holds that*

$$\max_{1 \le i \le n} a_{ii} \le \rho(A).$$

Lemma 4.8. *Let $A \in \mathbb{R}^{n \times n}$ be nonnegative.*

(1) *If the row sums of the matrix A are constant, then $\rho(A) = \|A\|_\infty$.*
(2) *If the column sums of the matrix A are constant, then $\rho(A) = \|A\|_1$.*

Proof. It is clear that $\rho(A) \le \|A\|_\infty$. If the row sums of the matrix A are constant, it can be easily verified that $x = [1, 1, \ldots, 1]^\mathsf{T}$ is an eigenvector of the matrix A corresponding to the eigenvalue $\lambda = \|A\|_\infty$. This implies that $\|A\|_\infty \le \rho(A)$. Therefore, $\rho(A) = \|A\|_\infty$.

Statement (2) can be proved in a similar fashion by applying the same argument on the matrix A^T. □

The following theorem gives lower and upper bounds about the spectral radius of a **nonnegative matrix**.

Theorem 4.9. *Let $A = [a_{ij}] \in \mathbb{R}^{n \times n}$ be nonnegative. Then*

$$\min_{1 \le i \le n} \sum_{j=1}^n a_{ij} \le \rho(A) \le \max_{1 \le i \le n} \sum_{j=1}^n a_{ij} \tag{4.2}$$

and

$$\min_{1 \le j \le n} \sum_{i=1}^n a_{ij} \le \rho(A) \le \max_{1 \le j \le n} \sum_{i=1}^n a_{ij}. \tag{4.3}$$

Proof. Let

$$\alpha = \min_{1 \le i \le n} \sum_{j=1}^n a_{ij}$$

and construct a new matrix B such that $A \ge B \ge 0$ and

$$\sum_{j=1}^n b_{ij} = \alpha, \quad i = 1, 2, \ldots, n.$$

For example, if $\alpha = 0$, we set $B = 0$ and, if $\alpha > 0$, we could set

$$b_{ij} = \alpha a_{ij} \left(\sum_{j=1}^n a_{ij} \right)^{-1}.$$

By Lemma 4.8, we have $\rho(B) = \alpha$. Therefore, it follows from Corollary 4.6 that

$$\min_{1 \le i \le n} \sum_{j=1}^n a_{ij} = \alpha = \rho(B) \le \rho(A).$$

The upper bound for $\rho(A)$ in (4.2) can be established easily in a similar fashion.

The bounds in (4.3) can be proved analogously by applying the same argument to the matrix A^{T}.   □

Corollary 4.10. *Let $A \in \mathbb{R}^{n \times n}$ be nonnegative. If the matrix A has at least one positive row or column, then $\rho(A) > 0$. In particular, if the matrix A is positive, then $\rho(A) > 0$.*

Let $X \in \mathbb{R}^{n \times n}$ be any nonsingular matrix. Then we have $\rho(X^{-1}AX) = \rho(A)$. Hence, we can extend the results in Theorem 4.9 by choosing

$$X = \operatorname{diag}(x_1, x_2, \ldots, x_n),$$

with $x_i > 0$ for $i = 1, 2, \ldots, n$.

Corollary 4.11. *Let $A = [a_{ij}] \in \mathbb{R}^{n \times n}$ be nonnegative. Then for any **positive vector** $x = [x_1, x_2, \ldots, x_n]^{\mathsf{T}} \in \mathbb{R}^n$ we have*

$$\min_{1 \le i \le n} \frac{1}{x_i} \sum_{j=1}^{n} a_{ij} x_j \le \rho(A) \le \max_{1 \le i \le n} \frac{1}{x_i} \sum_{j=1}^{n} a_{ij} x_j \tag{4.4}$$

and

$$\min_{1 \le j \le n} x_j \sum_{i=1}^{n} \frac{a_{ij}}{x_i} \le \rho(A) \le \max_{1 \le j \le n} x_j \sum_{i=1}^{n} \frac{a_{ij}}{x_i}. \tag{4.5}$$

Theorem 4.12. *Let $A = [a_{ij}] \in \mathbb{R}^{n \times n}$ be nonnegative and $x \in \mathbb{R}^n$ be positive.*

(1) *If $\alpha x \le Ax \le \beta x$, then $\alpha \le \rho(A) \le \beta$.*
(2) *If $\alpha x < Ax < \beta x$, then $\alpha < \rho(A) < \beta$.*

Proof. If $\alpha x \le Ax$, then

$$\alpha \le \min_{1 \le i \le n} \frac{1}{x_i} \sum_{j=1}^{n} a_{ij} x_j.$$

It follows from Corollary 4.11 that $\alpha \le \rho(A)$.

If $\alpha x < Ax$, then there exists some $\tilde{\alpha} > \alpha$ such that $\tilde{\alpha} x \le Ax$, and we have $\tilde{\alpha} \le \rho(A)$. Hence $\alpha < \rho(A)$.

The upper bounds can be verified analogously.   □

Corollary 4.13. *Let $A \in \mathbb{R}^{n \times n}$ be nonnegative. If the matrix A has a positive eigenvector, then the corresponding eigenvalue must be $\rho(A)$. That is to say, if $A \ge 0, x > 0$ and $Ax = \lambda x$, then $\lambda = \rho(A)$.*

Proof. Since

$$\lambda x \le Ax \le \lambda x,$$

it follows from Theorem 4.12 that

$$\lambda \le \rho(A) \le \lambda,$$

which implies $\lambda = \rho(A)$.   □

4.1.2 ▪ Positive Matrices

Positive matrices form a special subset of the set of nonnegative matrices. Many properties of nonnegative matrices have their simplest and most elegant form for the positive matrices.

Lemma 4.14. *Let $A \in \mathbb{R}^{n \times n}$ be positive. If there exists a nonzero vector $x \in \mathbb{C}^n$ such that $Ax = \lambda x$ with $|\lambda| = \rho(A)$, then $A|x| = \rho(A)|x|$ and $|x| > 0$.*

Proof. By straightforward computations, we have

$$\rho(A)|x| = |\lambda| \cdot |x| = |\lambda x| = |Ax| \leq |A||x| = A|x|,$$

which implies that the vector

$$y \triangleq A|x| - \rho(A)|x|$$

is nonnegative. It follows from $A > 0$ and $|x| \gneqq 0$ that $\rho(A) > 0$ and $A|x| > 0$.
If $y \neq 0$, we set $z = A|x| > 0$. Then

$$Az - \rho(A)z = Ay > 0 \quad \text{or} \quad Az > \rho(A)z.$$

It follows from Theorem 4.12 that $\rho(A) > \rho(A)$, which is a contradiction. Therefore, $y = 0$, i.e., $A|x| = \rho(A)|x|$. In addition, it holds that

$$|x| = \frac{1}{\rho(A)} \cdot A|x| > 0. \qquad \square$$

Corollary 4.15. *Let $A \in \mathbb{R}^{n \times n}$ be positive. Then $\rho(A)$ is an eigenvalue of the matrix A, and there exists a vector $x \in \mathbb{R}^n$ such that $x > 0$ and $Ax = \rho(A)x$.*

Proof. Let λ be the eigenvalue of the matrix A such that $|\lambda| = \rho(A)$, and let $\tilde{x} \neq 0$ be the associated eigenvector. Define $x = |\tilde{x}|$. It follows from Lemma 4.14 that $x > 0$ and $Ax = \rho(A)x$. $\square$

By applying the same argument on the matrix A^T, we have the following result.

Corollary 4.16. *Let $A \in \mathbb{R}^{n \times n}$ be positive. Then there exists a vector $y \in \mathbb{R}^n$ such that $y > 0$ and $A^\mathsf{T} y = \rho(A)y$, or, $y^\mathsf{T} A = \rho(A)y^\mathsf{T}$.*

Lemma 4.17. *Let $A = [a_{ij}] \in \mathbb{R}^{n \times n}$ be positive. If $x \in \mathbb{C}^n$ is a nonzero vector such that $Ax = \lambda x$ with $|\lambda| = \rho(A)$, then there exists a real number $\theta \in \mathbb{R}$ such that $e^{-i\theta}x = |x| > 0$.*

Proof. Let $x = [x_1, x_2, \ldots, x_n]^\mathsf{T} \in \mathbb{C}^n$. By Lemma 4.14 we know that

$$\rho(A)|x| = |\lambda x| = A|x|$$

and $|x| > 0$. Then, for each $k = 1, 2, \ldots, n$, we have

$$\rho(A)|x_k| = |\lambda x_k| = \left|[Ax]_k\right| = \left|\sum_{j=1}^{n} a_{kj}x_j\right| \leq \sum_{j=1}^{n} |a_{kj}x_j| = \sum_{j=1}^{n} a_{kj}|x_j|.$$

On the other hand, we have

$$\rho(A)\,|x_k| = \left[A|x|\right]_k = \sum_{j=1}^{n} a_{kj}|x_j|.$$

Therefore,

$$\left| \sum_{j=1}^{n} a_{kj}x_j \right| = \sum_{j=1}^{n} |a_{kj}x_j|.$$

This equality holds if and only if the complex numbers $a_{kj}x_j$, $j = 1, 2, \ldots, n$, must lie on the same ray in $\mathbb{C}$. If we denote the angle of this ray by θ, then

$$e^{-i\theta} a_{kj}x_j = |a_{kj}x_j| = a_{kj}|x_j|, \quad k, j = 1, 2, \ldots, n,$$

implying that

$$e^{-i\theta} x_j = |x_j| > 0, \quad j = 1, 2, \ldots, n.$$

Hence, we have

$$e^{-i\theta} x = |x| > 0. \qquad \square$$

Corollary 4.18. *Let $A \in \mathbb{R}^{n \times n}$ be positive. Then $|\lambda| < \rho(A)$ for any eigenvalue $\lambda \neq \rho(A)$. That is to say, if λ is an eigenvalue of the matrix A with $|\lambda| = \rho(A)$, then $\lambda = \rho(A)$.*

Proof. Suppose that λ is an eigenvalue of the matrix A with $|\lambda| = \rho(A)$. Let $x \neq 0$ be the associated eigenvector, that is, $Ax = \lambda x$. By Lemma 4.17, there exists $\theta \in \mathbb{R}$ such that $y = e^{-i\theta}x > 0$. It is easily seen that $Ay = \lambda y$. By Corollary 4.13, we know that $\lambda = \rho(A)$. $\square$

Corollary 4.19. *Let $A \in \mathbb{R}^{n \times n}$ be positive. Then $\rho(A)$ is an eigenvalue of the matrix A with geometric multiplicity 1.*

Proof. Let $x \in \mathbb{R}^n$ be the positive eigenvector of the matrix A associated with the eigenvalue $\rho(A)$. Suppose that $y \in \mathbb{C}^n$ is a nonzero vector such that

$$Ay = \rho(A)\,y.$$

By Lemma 4.17, there exists a real number $\theta \in \mathbb{R}$ such that

$$\tilde{y} \triangleq e^{-i\theta}y = |y| > 0$$

and

$$A\tilde{y} = \rho(A)\,\tilde{y}.$$

Define

$$\alpha = \max_{1 \leq i \leq n} \left\{ \frac{\tilde{y}_i}{x_i} \right\}$$

and let

$$z = \alpha x - \tilde{y}.$$

Then $z \in \mathbb{R}^n$ is nonnegative and has at least one zero component. Suppose $z \neq 0$. It follows from

$$Az = \alpha Ax - A\tilde{y} = \alpha\,\rho(A)\,x - \rho(A)\,\tilde{y} = \rho(A)\,z$$

that the vector z is also an eigenvector of the matrix A corresponding to the eigenvalue $\rho(A)$. By Lemma 4.14, we have $|z| > 0$, which leads to a contradiction. Hence, we have $z = 0$, which implies that $\tilde{y} = \alpha x$. This means that $\rho(A)$ is of geometric multiplicity 1. □

From Corollary 4.19, we see that if z is an eigenvector of the matrix A corresponding to the eigenvalue $\rho(A)$, then $|z| > 0$, i.e., the eigenvectors of the matrix A associated with the eigenvalue $\rho(A)$ have no zero component.

Corollary 4.20. *Let $A \in \mathbb{R}^{n \times n}$ be positive. Then there exists a unique vector $x \in \mathbb{R}^n$ such that $Ax = \rho(A)\,x$, with $x > 0$ and $\sum_{i=1}^{n} x_i = 1$.*

The unique **normalized eigenvector** given in Corollary 4.20 is called the **Perron vector** of the matrix A, and the eigenvalue $\rho(A)$ is called the **Perron root** of the matrix A [199].

Lemma 4.21. *Let $A \in \mathbb{R}^{n \times n}$ be positive, and let $x, y \in \mathbb{R}^n$ be two positive vectors such that*

$$Ax = \rho(A)\,x, \quad A^\mathsf{T}y = \rho(A)\,y, \quad and \quad x^\mathsf{T}y = 1. \tag{4.6}$$

Define $L \triangleq xy^\mathsf{T} > 0$. Then

(1) $(A - \rho(A)\,L)^k = A^k - (\rho(A))^k\,L,\ k = 1, 2, \ldots;$
(2) *every nonzero eigenvalue of the matrix $A - \rho(A)L$ is also an eigenvalue of the matrix A;*
(3) $\rho\,(A - \rho(A)\,L) < \rho(A);$
(4) $\displaystyle\lim_{k \to \infty} \left(\frac{1}{\rho(A)}\,A\right)^k = xy^\mathsf{T}$, *which is a matrix of rank 1.*

Proof. (1) We prove this statement by induction. It is clear that the statement holds true for $k = 1$. Suppose

$$(A - \rho(A)\,L)^{k-1} = A^{k-1} - (\rho(A))^{k-1}\,L.$$

As $L = xy^\mathsf{T}$ and $y^\mathsf{T}x = x^\mathsf{T}y = 1$, we have

$$\begin{aligned}
L^2 &= (xy^\mathsf{T})(xy^\mathsf{T}) = x(y^\mathsf{T}x)y^\mathsf{T} = xy^\mathsf{T} = L, \\
AL &= Axy^\mathsf{T} = \rho(A)\,xy^\mathsf{T} = \rho(A)\,L, \\
LA &= xy^\mathsf{T}A = x(A^\mathsf{T}y)^\mathsf{T} = \rho(A)\,xy^\mathsf{T} = \rho(A)\,L,
\end{aligned}$$

and

$$LA^{k-1} = (LA)A^{k-2} = \rho(A)\,LA^{k-2} = \cdots = (\rho(A))^{k-1}\,L.$$

Therefore,

$$\begin{aligned}
(A - \rho(A)\,L)^k &= (A - \rho(A)\,L)(A - \rho(A)\,L)^{k-1} \\
&= (A - \rho(A)\,L)(A^{k-1} - (\rho(A))^{k-1}L) \\
&= A^k - (\rho(A))^{k-1}\,AL - \rho(A)\,LA^{k-1} + (\rho(A))^k L^2 \\
&= A^k - (\rho(A))^k L - (\rho(A))^k L + (\rho(A))^k L \\
&= A^k - (\rho(A))^k L.
\end{aligned}$$

By induction, the statement follows.

(2) Let λ be a nonzero eigenvalue of the matrix $A - \rho(A)\,L$, and $z \neq 0$ be the associated eigenvector, that is,

$$(A - \rho(A)\,L)z = \lambda z.$$

As

$$L(A - \rho(A)\,L) = LA - \rho(A)\,L^2 = \rho(A)\,L - \rho(A)\,L = 0,$$

we have

$$L(A - \rho(A)\,L)z = 0.$$

On the other hand,

$$L(A - \rho(A)\,L)z = L(\lambda z).$$

Thus, we have $\lambda L z = 0$, which, together with $\lambda \neq 0$, implies $Lz = 0$. Therefore,

$$\lambda z = (A - \rho(A)\,L)z = Az,$$

that is, λ is an eigenvalue of the matrix A, with the associated eigenvector z.

(3) If

$$\rho(A - \rho(A)\,L) = 0,$$

then the statement holds immediately from the fact $\rho(A) > 0$. Suppose

$$\rho(A - \rho(A)\,L) > 0.$$

Let λ be an eigenvalue of the matrix $A - \rho(A)\,L$ such that

$$|\lambda| = \rho(A - \rho(A)\,L),$$

and $z \neq 0$ be the associated eigenvector. It follows from Statement (2) that

$$Az = \lambda z.$$

We now show that $|\lambda| < \rho(A)$. Assume $|\lambda| = \rho(A)$. By Corollary 4.18, we have $\lambda = \rho(A)$. As $x > 0$ is the eigenvector of the matrix A associated with $\rho(A)$, it follows from Corollary 4.19 that $z = \alpha x$. Thus

$$\begin{aligned}
\lambda z &= (A - \rho(A)\,L)z \\
&= Az - \rho(A)\,Lz \\
&= \alpha\,Ax - \alpha\,\rho(A)\,xy^{\mathsf{T}}x \\
&= \alpha\,\rho(A)\,x - \alpha\,\rho(A)\,x \\
&= 0.
\end{aligned}$$

Since $z \neq 0$, we have $\lambda = 0$, which leads to a contradiction. Hence $|\lambda| < \rho(A)$, that is,

$$\rho(A - \rho(A)\,L) < \rho(A).$$

(4) It follows from

$$\rho(A - \rho(A)\,L) < \rho(A)$$

that

$$\rho\left(\frac{1}{\rho(A)}A - L\right) < 1.$$

Hence,

$$\lim_{k \to \infty}\left(\frac{1}{\rho(A)}A - L\right)^k = 0.$$

By Statement (1), we have

$$\left(\frac{1}{\rho(A)}A - L\right)^k = \frac{1}{(\rho(A))^k}A^k - L.$$

Therefore, this statement follows.   □

Theorem 4.22. *Let $A \in \mathbb{R}^{n \times n}$ be positive. Then $\rho(A)$ is an eigenvalue of the matrix A with algebraic multiplicity 1, that is, the eigenvalue $\rho(A)$ is simple.*

Proof. Suppose that the eigenvalue $\rho(A)$ is of **algebraic multiplicity** m with $m \geq 1$. We denote the other eigenvalues of the matrix A by $\lambda_{m+1}, \lambda_{m+2}, \ldots, \lambda_n$. It holds that

$$|\lambda_i| < \rho(A), \quad i = m+1, m+2, \ldots, n.$$

Let $A = URU^*$ be the **Schur decomposition** of the matrix A, where

$$R = \begin{bmatrix} \rho(A) & & & & & \\ & \ddots & & & & \\ & & \rho(A) & & \text{\Large *} & \\ & & & \lambda_{m+1} & & \\ & & & & \ddots & \\ & & & & & \lambda_n \end{bmatrix}$$

is an upper-triangular matrix. Then

$$\left(\frac{1}{\rho(A)}A\right)^k = U \begin{bmatrix} 1 & & & & & \\ & \ddots & & & & \\ & & 1 & & \text{\Large *} & \\ & & & \frac{\lambda_{m+1}}{\rho(A)} & & \\ & & & & \ddots & \\ & & & & & \frac{\lambda_n}{\rho(A)} \end{bmatrix}^k U^*$$

and

$$\lim_{k\to\infty}\left(\frac{1}{\rho(A)}A\right)^k = \lim_{k\to\infty} U \begin{bmatrix} 1 & & & & & \\ & \ddots & & & \Large* & \\ & & 1 & & & \\ & & & \frac{\lambda_{m+1}}{\rho(A)} & & \\ & & & & \ddots & \\ & & & & & \frac{\lambda_n}{\rho(A)} \end{bmatrix}^k U^*$$

$$= U \begin{bmatrix} 1 & & & & \\ & \ddots & & \Large* & \\ & & 1 & & \\ & & & 0 & \\ & & & & \ddots & \\ & & & & & 0 \end{bmatrix} U^*,$$

which is a matrix of rank at least m. It follows from Lemma 4.21 that the matrix $\lim_{k\to\infty}\left(\frac{1}{\rho(A)}A\right)^k$ is of rank 1. Hence, $m = 1$, that is, $\rho(A)$ is a simple eigenvalue of the matrix A. □

In summary, we have demonstrated the Perron theorem for positive matrices.

Theorem 4.23 (Perron Theorem). [274] *Let $A \in \mathbb{R}^{n\times n}$ be positive. Then*

(1) *$\rho(A) > 0$;*

(2) *$\rho(A)$ is a simple eigenvalue of the matrix A;*

(3) *there exists a positive vector $x \in \mathbb{R}^n$ such that $Ax = \rho(A)\,x$, and, if $y \in \mathbb{R}^n$ is an eigenvector of the matrix A associated with the eigenvalue $\rho(A)$, then $|y| > 0$;*

(4) *$|\lambda| < \rho(A)$ for any eigenvalue λ of the matrix A with $\lambda \neq \rho(A)$;*

(5) *$\lim_{k\to\infty}\left(\frac{1}{\rho(A)}A\right)^k = xy^{\mathsf{T}} > 0$, where x, y are two positive vectors satisfying (4.6).*

The following result is a direct application of the Perron theorem.

Theorem 4.24 (Ky Fan Theorem). [199] *Let $A = [a_{ij}] \in \mathbb{C}^{n\times n}$ and $B = [b_{ij}] \in \mathbb{R}^{n\times n}$. Suppose $|A| \leq B$. Then the eigenvalues of the matrix A lie in the region*

$$\bigcup_{i=1}^{n} \left\{ z \in \mathbb{C} \,:\, |z - a_{ii}| \leq \rho(B) - b_{ii} \right\}.$$

4.1.3 ▪ More Properties of Nonnegative Matrices

Now we further consider the properties of the general **nonnegative matrices**. Some of the properties about positive matrices can be extended to the nonnegative case.

Lemma 4.25. *Let $A \in \mathbb{R}^{n\times n}$ be nonnegative. Then*

(1) *$\rho(A)$ is an eigenvalue of the matrix A;*

(2) *there exist vectors $x \gneq 0$ and $y \gneq 0$ such that $Ax = \rho(A)\,x$ and $A^{\mathsf{T}}y = \rho(A)\,y$.*

Proof. (1) For any positive scalar $\varepsilon > 0$, define the matrix

$$A(\varepsilon) \triangleq A + \varepsilon e e^{\mathsf{T}},$$

with $e = [1, 1, \ldots, 1]^{\mathsf{T}} \in \mathbb{R}^n$. Then $A(\varepsilon) > 0$. Let $x(\varepsilon)$ be the **Perron vector** of the matrix $A(\varepsilon)$ satisfying

$$\sum_{i=1}^{n} x_i(\varepsilon) = 1.$$

As the set of vectors $\{x(\varepsilon) : \varepsilon > 0\}$ is contained in the compact set $\{x \in \mathbb{C}^n : \|x\|_1 \leq 1\}$, there exists a strictly monotonically decreasing sequence of positive real numbers, say, e.g., $\{\varepsilon_k\}_{k=1}^{\infty}$, with

$$\varepsilon_1 > \varepsilon_2 > \cdots > \varepsilon_k > \cdots$$

and

$$\lim_{k \to \infty} \varepsilon_k = 0,$$

such that $\lim_{k \to \infty} x(\varepsilon_k)$ exists and

$$x \triangleq \lim_{k \to \infty} x(\varepsilon_k) \geq 0.$$

As

$$\sum_{i=1}^{n} x_i = \lim_{k \to \infty} \sum_{i=1}^{n} x_i(\varepsilon_k) = 1,$$

it follows that $x \gneq 0$. Also, as

$$A(\varepsilon_1) > A(\varepsilon_2) > \cdots > A(\varepsilon_k) > \cdots,$$

by Corollary 4.6 we know that

$$\rho(A(\varepsilon_1)) \geq \rho(A(\varepsilon_2)) \geq \cdots \geq \rho(A),$$

which implies that the number sequence $\{\rho(A(\varepsilon_k))\}_{k=1}^{\infty}$ is monotonically decreasing and bounded from the below by $\rho(A)$. Hence,

$$\rho_* \triangleq \lim_{k \to \infty} \rho(A(\varepsilon_k))$$

exists and satisfies $\rho_* \geq \rho(A)$. On the other hand, we have

$$Ax = \lim_{k \to \infty} A(\varepsilon_k) x(\varepsilon_k) = \lim_{k \to \infty} \rho(A(\varepsilon_k)) x(\varepsilon_k) = \lim_{k \to \infty} \rho(A(\varepsilon_k)) \lim_{k \to \infty} x(\varepsilon_k) = \rho_* x,$$

which implies that ρ_* is an eigenvalue of the matrix A, and thus $\rho_* \leq \rho(A)$. Therefore, it must hold $\rho_* = \rho(A)$. That is to say, $\rho(A)$ is an eigenvalue of the matrix A with $x \gneq 0$ being an associated eigenvector.

(2) The vector y can be obtained by applying the same argument on the matrix A^{T}. $\qquad\square$

By Lemma 4.25, we know that $A \geq 0$ has nonnegative **right-** and **left-eigenvectors** associated with the eigenvalue $\lambda = \rho(A)$. However, unlike the **positive matrix**, the spectral radius of a **nonnegative matrix** may be equal to zero. For example, if the matrix A is a strictly lower-triangular nonnegative matrix, then $\rho(A) = 0$.

Lemma 4.26. *Let $A \in \mathbb{R}^{n \times n}$ be nonnegative. If there exist a scalar $\alpha \in \mathbb{R}$ and a vector $x \in \mathbb{R}^n$ such that $x \gneq 0$ and $Ax \geq \alpha x$, then $\rho(A) \geq \alpha$.*

Proof. For any positive scalar $\varepsilon > 0$, define the matrix

$$A(\varepsilon) \triangleq A + \varepsilon e e^{\mathsf{T}}, \quad \text{with} \quad e = [1, 1, \dots, 1]^{\mathsf{T}} \in \mathbb{R}^n.$$

Then $A(\varepsilon) > 0$ and there exists a positive vector $y(\varepsilon)$ such that

$$(y(\varepsilon))^{\mathsf{T}} A(\varepsilon) = \rho(A(\varepsilon)) \, (y(\varepsilon))^{\mathsf{T}}.$$

As $x \gneq 0$ and $Ax \geq \alpha x$, it follows from $A(\varepsilon) > A$ that

$$A(\varepsilon) \, x - \alpha x > Ax - \alpha x \geq 0.$$

Hence

$$0 < (y(\varepsilon))^{\mathsf{T}} \big(A(\varepsilon) \, x - \alpha x \big) = \big(\rho(A(\varepsilon)) - \alpha \big) (y(\varepsilon))^{\mathsf{T}} x.$$

Since $y(\varepsilon) > 0$ and $x \gneq 0$, we have $(y(\varepsilon))^{\mathsf{T}} x > 0$ and $\rho(A(\varepsilon)) - \alpha > 0$. By letting $\varepsilon \to 0$, we obtain $\rho(A) \geq \alpha$. $\quad \square$

Lemma 4.27. *Let $A = [a_{ij}] \in \mathbb{R}^{n \times n}$ be nonnegative. Then*

$$\rho(A) = \max_{\substack{x \in \mathbb{R}^n \\ x \geq 0}} \min_{\substack{1 \leq i \leq n \\ x_i \neq 0}} \frac{1}{x_i} \sum_{j=1}^{n} a_{ij} x_j.$$

Proof. For any $x \gneq 0$, define

$$f_A(x) \triangleq \min_{\substack{1 \leq i \leq n \\ x_i \neq 0}} \frac{1}{x_i} \sum_{j=1}^{n} a_{ij} x_j,$$

which is the so-called **Collatz–Wielandt function**. Then we have

$$Ax \geq f_A(x) \, x \quad \text{and} \quad \rho(A) \geq f_A(x).$$

On the other hand, by Lemma 4.25, there exists a vector $x \gneq 0$ such that $Ax = \rho(A) \, x$ and

$$\rho(A) = \frac{1}{x_i} \sum_{j=1}^{n} a_{ij} x_j, \quad \text{for} \quad x_i \neq 0,$$

or, equivalently,

$$\rho(A) = \min_{\substack{1 \leq i \leq n \\ x_i \neq 0}} \frac{1}{x_i} \sum_{j=1}^{n} a_{ij} x_j.$$

Therefore, the conclusion follows. $\quad \square$

Lemma 4.28. *Let $A \in \mathbb{R}^{n \times n}$ be nonnegative and have a positive left-eigenvector. If there exists a vector $x \gneq 0$ such that either $Ax \geq \rho(A) \, x$ or $Ax \leq \rho(A) \, x$, then $Ax = \rho(A) \, x$.*

Proof. Suppose $Ax \geq \rho(A)\,x$. Let $y > 0$ be the positive **left-eigenvector**. By Corollary 4.13, it holds that $A^\mathsf{T} y = \rho(A)\,y$. Therefore, we have

$$y^\mathsf{T}(Ax - \rho(A)\,x) = \rho(A)\,y^\mathsf{T}x - \rho(A)\,y^\mathsf{T}x = 0.$$

As $y > 0$, it follows from Property (4) in Lemma 4.4 that

$$Ax - \rho(A)\,x = 0$$

or

$$Ax = \rho(A)\,x.$$

The proof for the case $Ax \leq \rho(A)\,x$ is similar.   □

We remark that a nonnegative matrix may not have a positive eigenvector. For example,

$$A = \begin{bmatrix} 1 & 0 \\ 0 & 2 \end{bmatrix}.$$

By Lemma 4.25, we know that if $A \geq 0$, then $\rho(A)$ is an eigenvalue of the matrix A, but it may not be simple. For example, if $A = I$, then $\rho(A) = 1$ is the eigenvalue of the matrix A with algebraic multiplicity n. Therefore, the normalized nonnegative eigenvector of the matrix A associated with the eigenvalue $\rho(A)$ may not be unique.

The following result gives a sufficient condition for $\lambda = \rho(A)$ to be a **simple eigenvalue**.

Theorem 4.29. *Let $A \in \mathbb{R}^{n \times n}$ be nonnegative. If $A^k > 0$ holds for some integer $k \geq 1$, then $\rho(A)$ is a simple eigenvalue of the matrix A.*

Proof. It is easily seen that if λ is an eigenvalue of the matrix A, then λ^k is an eigenvalue of the matrix A^k with the same algebraic multiplicity. Hence, if $\rho(A)$ is a multiple eigenvalue of the matrix A, then $\rho(A)^k = \rho(A^k)$ is a multiple eigenvalue of the matrix A^k. But, since $A^k > 0$, $\rho(A^k)$ must be a simple eigenvalue. Therefore, $\rho(A)$ cannot be a multiple eigenvalue of the matrix A.   □

4.2 ▪ Irreducible Matrices

4.2.1 ▪ Reducible and Irreducible Matrices

Definition 4.30. *Let $A \in \mathbb{C}^{n \times n}$ with $n \geq 2$. Then the matrix A is said to be **reducible** if there exists a **permutation matrix** P such that*

$$PAP^\mathsf{T} = \begin{bmatrix} A_{11} & A_{12} \\ 0 & A_{22} \end{bmatrix}, \tag{4.7}$$

*where $A_{11} \in \mathbb{C}^{r \times r}$ and $A_{22} \in \mathbb{C}^{(n-r) \times (n-r)}$, with $1 \leq r < n$. Otherwise, the matrix A is said to be **irreducible**.*

If A is a 1×1 matrix, then it is irreducible if and only if it is nonzero. If $A \in \mathbb{C}^{n \times n}$ is reducible, then it has at least $n - 1$ zero entries. We can easily see that a positive matrix is irreducible.

If the matrix A is reducible, i.e., there exists a permutation matrix P such that the matrix PAP^T is of the form (4.7), then, for any integer $k \geq 1$, we have

$$PA^k P^\mathsf{T} = (PAP^\mathsf{T})^k = \begin{bmatrix} A_{11}^k & \tilde{A}_{12}^{(k)} \\ 0 & A_{22}^k \end{bmatrix}. \tag{4.8}$$

Therefore, we have the following statements.

Lemma 4.31. *Let $A \in \mathbb{C}^{n \times n}$.*

(1) *If the matrix A is reducible, then the matrix A^k is also reducible for $k = 1, 2, \ldots$.*

(2) *If there exists a positive integer k such that the matrix A^k is irreducible, then the matrix A is irreducible.*

We remark that, in general, the power of an irreducible matrix may not be irreducible.

Example 4.32. Let

$$A = \begin{bmatrix} -1 & 1 \\ 1 & 1 \end{bmatrix}.$$

It is clear that the matrix A is irreducible. But,

$$A^2 = \begin{bmatrix} 2 & 0 \\ 0 & 2 \end{bmatrix}$$

is reducible.

In the following, we introduce some sufficient and necessary conditions for a given matrix to be reducible.

Theorem 4.33. *Let $A = [a_{ij}] \in \mathbb{C}^{n \times n}$ and $\mathcal{Z}_n = \{1, 2, \ldots, n\}$. Then the matrix A is reducible if and only if there exist two disjoint nonempty subsets $\mathcal{S}$ and $\mathcal{T}$ of $\mathcal{Z}_n$ such that $\mathcal{S} \oplus \mathcal{T} = \mathcal{Z}_n$ and $a_{ij} = 0$ for all $i \in \mathcal{S}$ and $j \in \mathcal{T}$.*

Proof. If the matrix A is reducible, then there exists a permutation matrix P such that the matrix PAP^T has the form (4.7). Suppose that the translation $A \to PA$ translates the rows $i_1, i_2, \ldots, i_r$ of the matrix A to the first r rows of the matrix PA. Then $PA \to PAP^\mathsf{T}$ translates the columns $i_1, i_2, \ldots, i_r$ of the matrix PA to the first r columns of the matrix PAP^T. Therefore, if we choose $\mathcal{T} = \{i_1, i_2, \ldots, i_r\}$ and $\mathcal{S} = \mathcal{Z}_n \setminus \mathcal{T}$, it holds that $\mathcal{S} \oplus \mathcal{T} = \mathcal{Z}_n$, $\mathcal{S} \cap \mathcal{T} = \emptyset$, and $a_{ij} = 0$ for all $i \in \mathcal{S}$ and $j \in \mathcal{T}$.

On the other hand, suppose that there exist subsets $\mathcal{T} = \{i_1, i_2, \ldots, i_r\} \subseteq \mathcal{Z}_n$ and $\mathcal{S} = \mathcal{Z}_n \setminus \mathcal{T}$ such that $a_{ij} = 0$ for all $i \in \mathcal{S}$ and $j \in \mathcal{T}$. Then we can construct a permutation matrix P that translates the rows $i_1, i_2, \ldots, i_r$ of the matrix A to the first r rows of the matrix PA, and that translates the columns $i_1, i_2, \ldots, i_r$ of the matrix PA to the first r columns of the matrix PAP^T. Therefore, we must have

$$PAP^\mathsf{T} = \begin{bmatrix} \tilde{A}_{11} & \tilde{A}_{12} \\ 0 & \tilde{A}_{22} \end{bmatrix},$$

where $\tilde{A}_{11} \in \mathbb{C}^{r \times r}$ and $\tilde{A}_{22} \in \mathbb{C}^{(n-r) \times (n-r)}$. That is to say, the matrix A is reducible. $\quad\square$

From Theorem 4.33, we see that the values of the main diagonal entries have no impact on the reducibility of a matrix.

Corollary 4.34. *If $A = [a_{ij}] \in \mathbb{C}^{n \times n}$ is irreducible, then*

$$B \triangleq A - \mathrm{diag}(a_{11}, a_{22}, \dots, a_{nn})$$

is also irreducible.

Theorem 4.35. *Let $A = [a_{ij}] \in \mathbb{C}^{n \times n}$ and $\mathcal{Z}_n = \{1, 2, \dots, n\}$. Then the matrix A is reducible if and only if there exist two integers $k, l \in \mathcal{Z}_n$, with $k \neq l$, such that*

$$a_{ki_1} a_{i_1 i_2} \cdots a_{i_r l} = 0$$

for any $\{i_1, i_2, \dots, i_r\} \subseteq \mathcal{Z}_n$, i.e., the matrix A is irreducible if and only if for any two distinct integers $k, l \in \mathcal{Z}_n$, there exists a sequence of integers $\{i_1, i_2, \dots, i_m\} \subseteq \mathcal{Z}_n$ such that

$$a_{ki_1} a_{i_1 i_2} \cdots a_{i_m l} \neq 0.$$

Proof. Suppose that the matrix A is reducible. Then it follows from Theorem 4.33 that there exist two disjoint nonempty subsets $\mathcal{S}$ and $\mathcal{T}$ of $\mathcal{Z}_n$ such that $\mathcal{S} \oplus \mathcal{T} = \mathcal{Z}_n$ and $a_{ij} = 0$ for all $i \in \mathcal{S}, j \in \mathcal{T}$. Let $k \in \mathcal{S}$ and $l \in \mathcal{T}$. If there exists a sequence of integers $\{i_1, i_2, \dots, i_r\} \subseteq \mathcal{Z}_n$ such that

$$a_{ki_1} a_{i_1 i_2} \cdots a_{i_r l} \neq 0,$$

then $a_{ki_1} \neq 0$, which, together with $k \in \mathcal{S}$, indicates that $i_1 \notin \mathcal{T}$, i.e., $i_1 \in \mathcal{S}$. Analogously, we have $i_2 \in \mathcal{S}, i_3 \in \mathcal{S}, \cdots$, and, finally, we have $l \in \mathcal{S}$, which contradicts with $l \in \mathcal{T}$. Hence,

$$a_{ki_1} a_{i_1 i_2} \cdots a_{i_r l} = 0$$

for any $\{i_1, i_2, \dots, i_r\} \subseteq \mathcal{Z}_n$.

Conversely, suppose that there exist two distinct integers $k, l \in \mathcal{Z}_n$ such that

$$a_{ki_1} a_{i_1 i_2} \cdots a_{i_r l} = 0$$

for any $\{i_1, i_2, \dots, i_r\} \subseteq \mathcal{Z}_n$. Let

$$\mathcal{S} \triangleq \{k\} \bigcup \{j \in \mathcal{Z}_n : a_{ki_1} a_{i_1 i_2} \cdots a_{i_m j} \neq 0, \quad \text{for some} \quad i_1, i_2, \dots, i_m \in \mathcal{Z}_n\}$$

and $\mathcal{T} = \mathcal{Z}_n \setminus \mathcal{S}$. Then $k \in \mathcal{S}, l \in \mathcal{T}$ and $\mathcal{S} \oplus \mathcal{T} = \mathcal{Z}_n, \mathcal{S} \cap \mathcal{T} = \emptyset$. Assume that there exist i, j such that $i \in \mathcal{S}, j \in \mathcal{T}$ and $a_{ij} \neq 0$. As $i \in \mathcal{S}$, there exist $i_1, i_2, \dots, i_m$ such that

$$a_{ki_1} a_{i_1 i_2} \cdots a_{i_m i} \neq 0.$$

Hence,

$$a_{ki_1} a_{i_1 i_2} \cdots a_{i_m i} a_{ij} \neq 0,$$

so that $j \in \mathcal{S}$, which contradicts with $j \in \mathcal{T}$. Therefore, $a_{ij} = 0$ for all $i \in \mathcal{S}$ and $j \in \mathcal{T}$. It follows from Theorem 4.33 that the matrix A is reducible. $\quad\square$

If the submatrices A_{11} and A_{22} in (4.7) are also reducible, we can reduce them in the same way as we have reduced the matrix A. Thus, we can obtain a **permutation matrix** P such that

$$PAP^\mathsf{T} = \begin{bmatrix} A_{11} & A_{12} & \cdots & A_{1k} \\ 0 & A_{22} & \cdots & A_{2k} \\ \vdots & \vdots & \ddots & \vdots \\ 0 & 0 & \cdots & A_{kk} \end{bmatrix}, \tag{4.9}$$

where the diagonal blocks A_{ii} ($i = 1, 2, \ldots, k$) are square and they are either irreducible or zero. The expression (4.9) is called the **normal form** of a reducible matrix A [329].

As we mentioned before, the spectral radius of a nonnegative matrix can be zero. The following theorem gives a necessary and sufficient condition for $\rho(A) = 0$.

Theorem 4.36. *Let $A \in \mathbb{R}^{n \times n}$ be nonnegative. Then $\rho(A) = 0$ if and only if the matrix A is reducible and its normal form is a strictly upper-triangular matrix.*

Proof. The proof is left as Exercise 4.7.   □

The term *irreducible* was introduced by Frobenius [150]. If the matrix A is reducible, i.e., there exists a permutation matrix P such that

$$PAP^{\mathsf{T}} = \begin{bmatrix} \tilde{A}_{11} & \tilde{A}_{12} \\ 0 & \tilde{A}_{22} \end{bmatrix} = \tilde{A},$$

then solving the linear system $Ax = b$ is equivalent to solving the following two smaller linear subsystems

$$\begin{cases} \tilde{A}_{22}\, y_2 = f_2, \\ \tilde{A}_{11}\, y_1 = f_1 - \tilde{A}_{12}\, y_2, \end{cases}$$

where

$$\begin{bmatrix} y_1 \\ y_2 \end{bmatrix} \triangleq Px \quad \text{and} \quad \begin{bmatrix} f_1 \\ f_2 \end{bmatrix} \triangleq Pb.$$

4.2.2 ▪ Irreducible Nonnegative Matrix

It is a useful heuristic principle that if one can prove a result for matrices with nonzero components, then the result can often be generalized to the irreducible matrices.

We first give some useful characterizations of a **nonnegative matrix** to be **irreducible**.

Lemma 4.37. *Let $A \in \mathbb{R}^{n \times n}$ be nonnegative. Then the matrix A is irreducible if and only if*

$$(I + A)^{n-1} > 0.$$

Proof. Suppose that $A \geq 0$ is irreducible. In order to prove $(I + A)^{n-1} > 0$, it is sufficient to show that $(I + A)^{n-1}x > 0$ for any $x \gneq 0$. Let $x \gneq 0$ and define a sequence of nonnegative vectors as follows:

$$\begin{cases} x^{(0)} = x, \\ x^{(k+1)} = (I + A)x^{(k)}, \quad k = 0, 1, \ldots, n - 2. \end{cases}$$

If $x > 0$, then it is clear that $(I + A)^{n-1}x > 0$. Now, we suppose that the vector x has zero entries. For simplicity, we denote the number of zero components of a vector z by $\#_0(z)$. As

$$x^{(k+1)} = (I + A)x^{(k)} = x^{(k)} + Ax^{(k)}$$

and

$$Ax^{(k)} \geq 0,$$

it is clear that

$$\#_0(x^{(k+1)}) \leq \#_0(x^{(k)}).$$

We want to prove that, if

$$\#_0(x^{(k)}) > 0,$$

then

$$\#_0(x^{(k+1)}) < \#_0(x^{(k)}),$$

that is, $x^{(k+1)}$ has fewer zero components than $x^{(k)}$.

Assume

$$\#_0(x^{(k+1)}) = \#_0(x^{(k)}) > 0.$$

Then there exists a **permutation matrix** P such that

$$Px^{(k+1)} = \begin{bmatrix} \tilde{x}^{(k+1)} \\ 0 \end{bmatrix} \quad \text{and} \quad Px^{(k)} = \begin{bmatrix} \tilde{x}^{(k)} \\ 0 \end{bmatrix}, \quad \text{with } \tilde{x}^{(k+1)} > 0 \text{ and } \tilde{x}^{(k)} > 0,$$

where $\tilde{x}^{(k+1)}$ and $\tilde{x}^{(k)}$ are of the same length. By partitioning the matrix PAP^{T} conformally with the vector $Px^{(k)}$, we have

$$
\begin{aligned}
Px^{(k+1)} &= P(I+A)x^{(k)} \\
&= Px^{(k)} + (PAP^{\mathsf{T}})(Px^{(k)}) \\
&= \begin{bmatrix} \tilde{x}^{(k)} \\ 0 \end{bmatrix} + \begin{bmatrix} \tilde{A}_{11} & \tilde{A}_{12} \\ \tilde{A}_{21} & \tilde{A}_{22} \end{bmatrix} \begin{bmatrix} \tilde{x}^{(k)} \\ 0 \end{bmatrix}.
\end{aligned}
$$

Therefore,

$$\begin{bmatrix} \tilde{x}^{(k+1)} \\ 0 \end{bmatrix} = \begin{bmatrix} \tilde{x}^{(k)} + \tilde{A}_{11}\tilde{x}^{(k)} \\ \tilde{A}_{21}\tilde{x}^{(k)} \end{bmatrix}.$$

It follows that

$$\tilde{A}_{21}\tilde{x}^{(k)} = 0,$$

which, together with $\tilde{x}^{(k)} > 0$, implies $\tilde{A}_{21} = 0$. That is to say, the matrix A is reducible, which leads to a contradiction. Hence,

$$\#_0(x^{(k+1)}) < \#_0(x^{(k)})$$

holds true for $\#_0(x^{(k)}) > 0$. As

$$\#_0(x^{(0)}) \le n - 1,$$

it follows that

$$\#_0(x^{(1)}) \le n - 2, \quad \#_0(x^{(2)}) \le n - 3, \ldots,$$

and finally,

$$\#_0(x^{(n-1)}) = 0,$$

that is, $(I + A)^{n-1}x > 0$.

In the following, we show that if $A \ge 0$ and $(I+A)^{n-1} > 0$, then the matrix A is **irreducible**. This is equivalent to show that if the matrix A is **reducible**, then the matrix $(I + A)^{n-1}$ has at least one zero element. Suppose that the matrix A is reducible, that is, there exists a permutation matrix P such that

$$PAP^\mathsf{T} = \begin{bmatrix} \tilde{A}_{11} & \tilde{A}_{12} \\ 0 & \tilde{A}_{22} \end{bmatrix}.$$

By straightforward computations, we know that

$$(I + PAP^\mathsf{T})^{n-1} = P(I + A)^{n-1}P^\mathsf{T}$$

has the same zero block as PAP^T on the lower-left corner, which implies that the matrix $(I + A)^{n-1}$ is reducible and, hence, it cannot be positive.   ☐

Lemma 4.37, together with Lemma 4.31, leads to the following result immediately.

Corollary 4.38. *Let $A \in \mathbb{R}^{n\times n}$ be a nonnegative matrix with positive diagonal entries. Then the matrix A is irreducible if and only if $A^{n-1} > 0$.*

Lemma 4.39 (Neumann Lemma). *Let $A \in \mathbb{C}^{n\times n}$. If $\rho(A) < 1$, then the matrix $I - A$ is nonsingular and*

$$(I - A)^{-1} = I + A + A^2 + \cdots. \tag{4.10}$$

Conversely, if the sequence on the right-hand side of (4.10) converges, then $\rho(A) < 1$.

Proof. Suppose that $\rho(A) < 1$. It is well known that λ is an eigenvalue of the matrix A if and only if $1 - \lambda$ is an eigenvalue of the matrix $I - A$. As $\rho(A) < 1$, all eigenvalues of the matrix $I - A$ have positive real parts, so that $I - A$ is a nonsingular matrix. It is easy to verify that

$$I - (I - A)(I + A + A^2 + \cdots + A^k) = A^{k+1}.$$

Moreover, by Theorem 1.34 we have

$$\lim_{k\to\infty} \left[I - (I - A)(I + A + A^2 + \cdots + A^k) \right] = \lim_{k\to\infty} A^{k+1} = 0.$$

Therefore,

$$I - (I - A)(I + A + A^2 + \cdots) = 0,$$

so that

$$(I - A)^{-1} = I + A + A^2 + \cdots.$$

Conversely, suppose that

$$I + A + A^2 + \cdots$$

is convergent. Let λ be any eigenvalue of the matrix A with the corresponding eigenvector x. Then

$$(I + A + A^2 + \cdots)x = (1 + \lambda + \lambda^2 + \cdots)x.$$

Evidently, the convergence of the matrix series

$$I + A + A^2 + \cdots$$

implies the convergence of the number series

$$1 + \lambda + \lambda^2 + \cdots.$$

Therefore, it holds that

$$\lambda^k \to 0 \quad \text{as} \quad k \to \infty.$$

This shows that $|\lambda| < 1$, or in other words, $\rho(A) < 1$. $\quad\square$

As an immediate corollary of Lemma 4.39, we see that the matrix $I - A$ is invertible whenever $\|A\| < 1$, and from (4.10) that

$$\|(I - A)^{-1}\| \le \sum_{k=0}^{\infty} \|A\|^k = \frac{1}{1 - \|A\|}, \tag{4.11}$$

where $\|\cdot\|$ is any consistent matrix norm. This is a special case of the following, more general, result.

Lemma 4.40 (Perturbation Lemma). *Let $A, B \in \mathbb{C}^{n\times n}$ and $\|\cdot\|$ be any consistent matrix norm. Assume that the matrix A is invertible, with $\|A^{-1}\| \le \alpha$. If $\|A - B\| \le \beta$ and $\alpha\beta < 1$, then the matrix B is also invertible, and*

$$\|B^{-1}\| \le \frac{\alpha}{1 - \alpha\beta}.$$

Proof. Since

$$\|I - A^{-1}B\| = \|A^{-1}(A - B)\| \le \|A^{-1}\|\|A - B\| \le \alpha\beta < 1,$$

it follows from Lemma 4.39 that the matrix $A^{-1}B$ is invertible. Hence, the matrix B is invertible. Moreover, we conclude from (4.11) that

$$\begin{aligned}
\|B^{-1}\| &= \|[I - (I - A^{-1}B)]^{-1}A^{-1}\| \\
&\le \|[I - (I - A^{-1}B)]^{-1}\|\|A^{-1}\| \\
&\le \|A^{-1}\| \sum_{k=0}^{\infty} \|I - A^{-1}B\|^k \\
&\le \alpha \sum_{k=0}^{\infty} (\alpha\beta)^k \\
&= \frac{\alpha}{1 - \alpha\beta}. \quad\square
\end{aligned}$$

Theorem 4.41. *Let $A \in \mathbb{R}^{n\times n}$ be nonnegative such that $\rho(A) < 1$. Then the matrix A is irreducible if and only if $(I - A)^{-1} > 0$.*

Proof. Let

$$B \triangleq \frac{1}{2}(I + A).$$

Then the matrix B is nonnegative and its diagonal entries are all positive. Moreover, as $\rho(A) < 1$, we have

$$\rho(B) \le \frac{1}{2}(1 + \rho(A)) < 1.$$

It follows from Lemma 4.39 and the equality $A = 2B - I$ that

$$(I - A)^{-1} = (2I - 2B)^{-1} = \frac{1}{2}(I - B)^{-1} = \frac{1}{2}\sum_{k=0}^{\infty} B^k. \tag{4.12}$$

If the matrix A is irreducible, then the matrix B is irreducible as well. Since the matrix B has positive diagonal entries, it follows from Corollary 4.38 that $B^{n-1} > 0$, which, together with (4.12), indicates that $(I - A)^{-1} > 0$.

Conversely, if $(I - A)^{-1} > 0$, then the matrix A must be irreducible. Otherwise, if the matrix A is reducible, by (4.8) and (4.10) we know that

$$(I - A)^{-1} = I + A + A^2 + \cdots + A^k + \cdots$$

is reducible, too. This indicates that the matrix $(I - A)^{-1}$ cannot be positive, which leads to a contradiction. □

This result can be generalized as follows.

Corollary 4.42. *Let $A \in \mathbb{R}^{n \times n}$ be nonnegative and α be a real scalar such that $\alpha > \rho(A)$. Then the matrix A is irreducible if and only if $(\alpha I - A)^{-1} > 0$.*

Proof. The proof is left as Exercise 4.8. □

Now we give the Perron–Frobenius theorem for the irreducible nonnegative matrices [150, 274].

Theorem 4.43 (Perron–Frobenius Theorem). *Let $A \in \mathbb{R}^{n \times n}$ be nonnegative and irreducible. Then*

(1) *$\rho(A) > 0$;*

(2) *$\rho(A)$ is a simple eigenvalue of the matrix A;*

(3) *there exists a unique positive vector x with $\|x\|_1 = 1$ such that $Ax = \rho(A)\,x$;*

(4) *there exists a unique positive vector y with $y^\mathsf{T} x = 1$ such that $A^\mathsf{T} y = \rho(A)\,y$;*

(5) *each nonnegative eigenvector of the matrix A is associated with the eigenvalue $\rho(A)$.*

Proof. Statement (1) follows directly from Theorem 4.36.

By Lemma 4.25 we know that $\rho(A)$ is an eigenvalue of the matrix A. Suppose that $\rho(A)$ is a multiple eigenvalue of the matrix A. Then

$$\rho((I + A)^{n-1}) = (1 + \rho(A))^{n-1}$$

is a multiple eigenvalue of the matrix $(I+A)^{n-1}$. As the matrix A is nonnegative and irreducible, it follows from Lemma 4.37 that

$$(I + A)^{n-1} > 0.$$

By Theorem 4.29 we see that $\rho((I + A)^{n-1})$ is a simple eigenvalue, which leads to a contradiction. Therefore, Statement (2) holds true.

It follows from Lemma 4.25 that there exists a vector $x \gneqq 0$ such that $Ax = \rho(A)\,x$. As the matrix A is nonnegative and irreducible, by Lemma 4.37 we have

$$(I + A)^{n-1} > 0.$$

Hence,

$$0 < (I + A)^{n-1}x = (1 + \rho(A))^{n-1}x,$$

which implies that $x > 0$. As $\rho(A)$ is a simple eigenvalue of the matrix A, the normalization condition $\|x\|_1 = 1$ ensures that such a vector x is unique. This proves Statement (3).

Statement (4) can be proved analogously.

We now turn to demonstrate the validity of Statement (5). Suppose that $z \geq 0$ is a nonnegative eigenvector of the matrix A associated with the eigenvalue μ, that is, $Az = \mu z$. Then it follows from Statement (4) that there exists a positive vector y such that $A^\mathsf{T}y = \rho(A)\,y$. Hence $y^\mathsf{T}z > 0$ and

$$\mu y^\mathsf{T}z = y^\mathsf{T}Az = \rho(A)\,y^\mathsf{T}z,$$

which implies $\mu = \rho(A)$. Then Statement (5) follows straightforwardly. □

The positive vectors x and y in Theorem 4.43 are said to be the **right-** and **left-Perron vectors** of the matrix A, respectively.

Corollary 4.44. *Let $A = [a_{ij}] \in \mathbb{R}^{n \times n}$ be nonnegative and irreducible, and $x \in \mathbb{R}^n$ satisfy $x \gneq 0$. Then the following statements hold true:*

(1) *$Ax = \rho(A)\,x$ if either $Ax \geq \rho(A)\,x$ or $Ax \leq \rho(A)\,x$;*

(2) *if $Ax \geq \alpha x$, then $\rho(A) \geq \alpha$, and, in addition, if $Ax \neq \alpha x$, then $\rho(A) > \alpha$;*

(3) *if $Ax \leq \beta x$, then $\rho(A) \leq \beta$ and $x > 0$, and, in addition, if $Ax \neq \beta x$, then $\rho(A) < \beta$.*

Proof. (1) As the matrix A is nonnegative and irreducible, by Theorem 4.43 we know that it has a positive **left-eigenvector**, say, e.g., $y \in \mathbb{R}^n$. The first statement follows from Lemma 4.28 immediately.

(2) If $\alpha x \leq Ax$, then

$$(\rho(A) - \alpha)(y^\mathsf{T}x) = \rho(A)\,y^\mathsf{T}x - \alpha y^\mathsf{T}x = y^\mathsf{T}(\rho(A)\,x - \alpha x) = y^\mathsf{T}(Ax - \alpha x) \geq 0.$$

Because $y^\mathsf{T}x > 0$, we have $\rho(A) - \alpha \geq 0$, or $\rho(A) \geq \alpha$. If $\alpha x \neq Ax$, then

$$y^\mathsf{T}(Ax - \alpha x) > 0.$$

Therefore, $\rho(A) - \alpha > 0$, or $\rho(A) > \alpha$.

(3) This statement can be proved in the same way except that $x > 0$. Suppose that $x = [x_1, x_2, \ldots, x_n]^\mathsf{T} \in \mathbb{R}^n$ is not positive, i.e., there exist two disjoint nonempty subsets $\mathcal{S} = \{i_1, i_2, \ldots, i_k\}$ and $\mathcal{T} = \{i_{k+1}, i_{k+2}, \ldots, i_n\}$ of the positive integer set $\{1, 2, \ldots, n\}$ such that $x_j = 0$ for $j \in \mathcal{S}$ and $x_l > 0$ for $l \in \mathcal{T}$. As $A \geq 0$ and $Ax \leq \beta x$, it holds that

$$0 \leq [Ax]_j = \sum_{l=1}^n a_{jl}x_l = \sum_{l \in \mathcal{T}} a_{jl}x_l \leq \beta x_j = 0, \quad \text{for } j \in \mathcal{S}.$$

This implies that $[Ax]_j = 0$ and, thus,

$$a_{jl} = 0, \quad \text{for } j \in \mathcal{S} \text{ and } l \in \mathcal{T}.$$

It follows from Theorem 4.33 that the matrix A is reducible, which leads to a contradiction. Hence, $x > 0$ holds true. □

A more general result about $\rho(A)$ is as follows.

Theorem 4.45. Let $A \in \mathbb{R}^{n \times n}$ be nonnegative and irreducible, and α be a positive scalar. Then the following statements are equivalent:

(1) $\rho(A) > \alpha$,

(2) there exists a positive vector $x \in \mathbb{R}^n$ such that $Ax > \alpha x$,

(3) there exists $x \in \mathbb{R}^n$ with $x \gneq 0$ such that $Ax > \alpha x$.

We remark that the relationship ">" in Theorem 4.45 can be replaced by "$\geq$", "<", or "$\leq$".

Lemma 4.46. Let $A \in \mathbb{R}^{n \times n}$ be nonnegative. Suppose that $B \in \mathbb{C}^{n \times n}$ satisfies $|B| = A$. If there exists a positive vector $x \in \mathbb{R}^n$ such that $Bx = Ax$, then $B = A$.

Proof. Let

$$B = B_1 + \mathrm{i} B_2, \quad \text{with} \quad B_1, B_2 \in \mathbb{R}^{n \times n}.$$

Then we have

$$\begin{cases} B_1 x = Ax, \\ B_2 x = 0. \end{cases}$$

Since

$$B_1 \leq |B_1| \leq |B| = A$$

and $x > 0$, it follows from Property (4) in Lemma 4.4 that $B_1 = A$. If $B_2 \neq 0$, then

$$|B| = |B_1 + \mathrm{i} B_2| > |B_1| = A,$$

which leads to a contradiction. Hence, $B_2 = 0$. $\square$

Theorem 4.47. Let $A \in \mathbb{R}^{n \times n}$ be nonnegative and irreducible. Suppose that $B \in \mathbb{C}^{n \times n}$ satisfies $|B| \leq A$. If $\rho(B) = \rho(A)$ and $\lambda = e^{\mathrm{i}\phi} \rho(B)$ is an eigenvalue of the matrix B with $\phi \in \mathbb{R}$, then there exist $\theta_1, \theta_2, \ldots, \theta_n \in \mathbb{R}$ such that $B = e^{\mathrm{i}\phi} D A D^{-1}$, where

$$D = \mathrm{diag}(e^{\mathrm{i}\theta_1}, e^{\mathrm{i}\theta_2}, \ldots, e^{\mathrm{i}\theta_n}).$$

Proof. Let $\lambda = e^{\mathrm{i}\phi} \rho(B)$ be an eigenvalue of the matrix B with an associated eigenvector $x \neq 0$, that is, $Bx = \lambda x$. As $\rho(B) = \rho(A)$, we have

$$\rho(A) |x| = \rho(B) |x| = |\lambda| |x| = |\lambda x| = |Bx| \leq |B| |x| \leq A|x|.$$

As $|x| \neq 0$, it follows from Corollary 4.44 that

$$\rho(A) |x| = |B| |x| = A|x|$$

and $|x| > 0$. Hence,

$$(A - |B|)|x| = 0.$$

As $A \geq |B|$, by Property (4) in Lemma 4.4, we have $A = |B|$.

Define θ_k by

$$e^{\mathrm{i}\theta_k} = \frac{x_k}{|x_k|}, \quad k = 1, 2, \ldots, n,$$

and let

$$D = \mathrm{diag}(e^{\mathrm{i}\theta_1}, e^{\mathrm{i}\theta_2}, \ldots, e^{\mathrm{i}\theta_n}).$$

Then we have $x = D|x|$ and

$$\begin{cases} \lambda x = e^{i\phi}\rho(A) \cdot D|x| = e^{i\phi}D\,\rho(A)\,|x| = e^{i\phi}DA|x|, \\ \lambda x = Bx = BD|x|, \end{cases}$$

which implies that

$$BD|x| = e^{i\phi}DA|x|,$$

i.e.,

$$(e^{-i\phi}D^{-1}BD)|x| = A|x|.$$

As

$$|e^{-i\phi}D^{-1}BD| = |D^{-1}BD| = |B| = A$$

and $|x| > 0$, by Lemma 4.46 we have

$$e^{-i\phi}D^{-1}BD = A,$$

i.e.,

$$B = e^{i\phi}DAD^{-1}. \qquad \square$$

A stronger statement is that if $A \in \mathbb{R}^{n\times n}$ is an irreducible nonnegative matrix and $|B| \leq A$, then $\rho(A) = \rho(B)$ if and only if there exist $\phi, \theta_1, \ldots, \theta_n \in \mathbb{R}$ such that $B = e^{i\phi}DAD^{-1}$, where

$$D = \mathrm{diag}(e^{i\theta_1}, e^{i\theta_2}, \ldots, e^{i\theta_n});$$

see [329, 347].

Corollary 4.48. *Let $A \in \mathbb{R}^{n\times n}$ be nonnegative and irreducible.*

(1) *If $B \in \mathbb{C}^{n\times n}$ satisfies $|B| \leq A$ and $|B| \neq A$, then $\rho(B) < \rho(A)$.*

(2) *$\rho(A)$ increases when any entry of the matrix A increases.*

(3) *If $A_k \in \mathbb{R}^{k\times k}$ $(1 \leq k < n)$ is any **principal submatrix** of the matrix A, then $\rho(A_k) < \rho(A)$.*

Corollary 4.49. *Let $A \in \mathbb{R}^{n\times n}$ be nonnegative. Then the matrix A is reducible if and only if $\rho(A)$ is an eigenvalue of one of its principal submatrices.*

A more precise description for the spectral distribution of an irreducible nonnegative matrix is given below.

Theorem 4.50. [199, 329] *Let $A \in \mathbb{R}^{n\times n}$ be nonnegative and irreducible. If the matrix A has exactly k distinct eigenvalues of modulus $\rho(A)$, then they must be*

$$\lambda_p = \rho(A)\,e^{2\pi i p/k}, \quad p = 0, 1, \ldots, k-1,$$

and they are all of algebraic multiplicity 1. Moreover, if λ is any eigenvalue of the matrix A, then $\lambda e^{2\pi i p/k}$ is also an eigenvalue of the matrix A for $p = 1, 2, \ldots, k-1$.

From Theorem 4.50, we know that if $A \geq 0$ is irreducible and has exactly k distinct eigenvalues of modulus $\rho(A)$, then k must be a divisor of the number of the nonzero eigenvalues. In particular, if the matrix A is nonsingular, then k is a divisor of n, and, in addition, if n is a prime, the matrix A must have either 1 or n eigenvalues of module $\rho(A)$.

Corollary 4.51. [329] *Let $A \in \mathbb{R}^{n \times n}$ be nonnegative and irreducible. If the matrix A has exactly $k > 1$ distinct eigenvalues of modulus $\rho(A)$, then there exists a permutation matrix $P \in \mathbb{R}^{n \times n}$ such that*

$$PAP^{\mathsf{T}} = \begin{bmatrix} 0 & A_{12} & 0 & \cdots & 0 \\ 0 & 0 & A_{23} & \cdots & 0 \\ \vdots & \vdots & \vdots & \ddots & \vdots \\ 0 & 0 & 0 & \cdots & A_{(k-1)k} \\ A_{k1} & 0 & 0 & \cdots & 0 \end{bmatrix}, \tag{4.13}$$

where the zero-blocks on the main diagonal are all square.

Obviously, the specific representation (4.13) can be permuted into several different but equivalent forms. One of the most useful forms is

$$PAP^{\mathsf{T}} = \begin{bmatrix} 0 & 0 & \cdots & 0 & A_{1k} \\ A_{21} & 0 & \cdots & 0 & 0 \\ 0 & A_{32} & \cdots & 0 & 0 \\ \vdots & \vdots & \ddots & \vdots & \vdots \\ 0 & 0 & \cdots & A_{k(k-1)} & 0 \end{bmatrix},$$

which is called the **normal form** [329] of the irreducible nonnegative matrix $A \in \mathbb{R}^{n \times n}$.

Theorem 4.52. [199] *Let $A \in \mathbb{R}^{n \times n}$ be nonnegative and irreducible. Then*

$$\lim_{n \to \infty} \frac{1}{n} \sum_{k=1}^{n} \left[\frac{A}{\rho(A)} \right]^k = xy^{\mathsf{T}},$$

*where $x, y \in \mathbb{R}^n$ are positive vectors, which are the **right-** and **left-eigenvectors** of the matrix A corresponding to the eigenvalue $\rho(A)$, i.e.,*

$$Ax = \rho(A)\, x, \quad A^{\mathsf{T}} y = \rho(A)\, y,$$

and $x > 0$ and $y > 0$ satisfying the normalization condition $x^{\mathsf{T}} y = 1$. Moreover, there exists a constant $\delta \triangleq \delta(A) > 0$ such that

$$\left\| \frac{1}{n} \sum_{k=1}^{n} \left[\frac{A}{\rho(A)} \right]^k - xy^{\mathsf{T}} \right\| \leq \frac{\delta}{n},$$

where the norm $\| \cdot \|$ is defined by

$$\|G\| = \max_{1 \leq i,j \leq n} \{ |g_{ij}| \},$$

for $G = [g_{ij}] \in \mathbb{C}^{n \times n}$.

The following result is about bounds for the spectral radius of an irreducible nonnegative matrix.

Lemma 4.53. [329] *Let $A = [a_{ij}] \in \mathbb{R}^{n \times n}$ be nonnegative and irreducible. Then either*

$$\rho(A) = \sum_{j=1}^{n} a_{ij}, \quad \forall\, 1 \leq i \leq n,$$

or

$$\min_{1 \leq i \leq n} \sum_{j=1}^{n} a_{ij} < \rho(A) < \max_{1 \leq i \leq n} \sum_{j=1}^{n} a_{ij}.$$

Proof. If all row sums of the matrix A are equal, then the first equality follows from Lemma 4.8. Otherwise, we can construct an irreducible nonnegative matrix $B = [b_{ij}] \in \mathbb{R}^{n \times n}$ by decreasing certain positive entries of the matrix A so that

$$\sum_{j=1}^{n} b_{kj} = \min_{1 \le i \le n} \sum_{j=1}^{n} a_{ij}, \quad \text{for} \quad k = 1, 2, \dots, n.$$

Thereby, it follows that $B \lneq A$ and

$$\rho(B) = \min_{1 \le i \le n} \sum_{j=1}^{n} a_{ij}.$$

By Corollary 4.48, we have $\rho(B) < \rho(A)$ and, hence,

$$\rho(A) > \min_{1 \le i \le n} \sum_{j=1}^{n} a_{ij}.$$

On the other hand, we can similarly construct an irreducible matrix $C = [c_{ij}] \ge 0$ by increasing certain entries of the matrix A so that all row sums of the matrix C are equal to $\max\limits_{1 \le i \le n} \sum_{j=1}^{n} a_{ij}$ and $A \lneq C$. Hence, it holds that

$$\rho(A) < \rho(C) = \max_{1 \le i \le n} \sum_{j=1}^{n} a_{ij}. \qquad \square$$

Let

$$D_x = \mathrm{diag}(x_1, x_2, \dots, x_n) > 0.$$

Then we have

$$\rho(A) = \rho(D_x^{-1} A D_x).$$

The following result follows immediately.

Theorem 4.54. *Let* $A = [a_{ij}] \in \mathbb{R}^{n \times n}$ *be nonnegative and irreducible. Then, for any vector* $x = [x_1, x_2, \dots, x_n]^{\mathsf{T}} > 0$, *either*

$$\rho(A) = \frac{1}{x_i} \sum_{j=1}^{n} a_{ij} x_j, \quad \forall \, 1 \le i \le n,$$

or

$$\min_{1 \le i \le n} \left\{ \frac{1}{x_i} \sum_{j=1}^{n} a_{ij} x_j \right\} < \rho(A) < \max_{1 \le i \le n} \left\{ \frac{1}{x_i} \sum_{j=1}^{n} a_{ij} x_j \right\}.$$

Let $A = [a_{ij}] \in \mathbb{R}^{n \times n}$ be a nonnegative and irreducible matrix. For any $x \in \mathbb{R}^n$, $x = [x_1, x_2, \dots, x_n]^{\mathsf{T}} \gneq 0$, we define

$$r_A(x) \triangleq \min_{x_i \neq 0} \left\{ \frac{1}{x_i} \sum_{j=1}^{n} a_{ij} x_j \right\}.$$

Obviously, $r_A(x)$ is a nonnegative real number and the supremum of all numbers α for which $Ax \geq \alpha x$. Consider the nonnegative quantity r_A defined by

$$r_A \triangleq \sup_{\substack{x \in \mathbb{R}^n \\ x \geq 0}} \{r_A(x)\}.$$

As $r_A(x) = r_A(\alpha x)$ holds for any positive scalar α, we only need to consider the vectors $x \geq 0$ with $\|x\|_2 = 1$. Multiplying both sides of the inequality

$$Ax \geq r_A(x)\, x$$

by $(I + A)^{n-1}$, we get

$$Ay \geq r_A(x)\, y, \quad y = (I + A)^{n-1}x,$$

and, therefore,

$$r_A(y) \geq r_A(x).$$

Obviously,

$$r_A \geq r_A(y),$$

so it holds that

$$r_A = \sup_{y \in \mathcal{Q}}\{r_A(y)\},$$

where

$$\mathcal{Q} \triangleq \{y = (I + A)^{n-1}x : x \geq 0 \quad \text{and} \quad \|x\|_2 = 1\}.$$

It is easy to see that $\mathcal{Q} \subset \mathbb{R}^n$ is a compact set and $r_A(y)$ is a continuous function on $\mathcal{Q}$. Therefore, there exists at least one positive vector $z \in \mathcal{Q}$ such that

$$r_A = r_A(z).$$

All the nonnegative nonzero vectors satisfying the above equality are called the **extremal vectors** of the matrix $A \in \mathbb{R}^{n \times n}$.

Theorem 4.55. *Let $A \in \mathbb{R}^{n \times n}$ be nonnegative and irreducible. Suppose that $z \in \mathbb{R}^n$ is an extremal vector of the matrix A. Then*

(1) $r_A > 0$;

(2) $Az = r_A z$ *and* $z > 0$, *i.e.,* z *is a positive eigenvector corresponding to the eigenvalue* $\lambda = r_A$;

(3) $r_A = \rho(A)$.

Proof. Denote $e \triangleq [1, 1, \ldots, 1]^{\mathsf{T}} \in \mathbb{R}^n$. Because the matrix A is nonnegative and irreducible, it holds that $Ae > 0$. Hence, $r_A(e) > 0$, and we have

$$r_A \geq r_A(e) > 0.$$

For the second statement, since $z \in \mathbb{R}^n$ is an extremal vector of the matrix A, we have $z \geq 0$,

$$\eta \triangleq Az - r_A z \geq 0 \quad \text{and} \quad w \triangleq (I + A)^{n-1}z > 0.$$

If $\eta \neq 0$, then

$$Aw - r_A w = (I + A)^{n-1}(Az - r_A z) = (I + A)^{n-1}\eta > 0.$$

It shows that

$$r_A < r_A(w),$$

which contradicts with the definition of r_A. Hence, it must hold $\eta = 0$, i.e.,

$$Az = r_A z.$$

If the vector z has zero components, from

$$(I + A)^{n-1} z = (1 + r_A)^{n-1} z$$

and

$$1 + r_A > 0$$

we see that the vector $(I + A)^{n-1} z$ also has zero components, which contradicts with the fact that the matrix $(I + A)^{n-1}$ is positive. Therefore, it holds that $z > 0$.

The last statement follows directly from the second one and Corollary 4.13. $\quad\square$

From the Perron–Frobenius theorem, i.e., Theorem 4.43, we see that the extremal vector $z \gneq 0$, with $\|z\|_2 = 1$, is uniquely determined.

4.2.3 ▪ Primitive Matrix

If the matrix $A \in \mathbb{R}^{n \times n}$ is positive, then there is no eigenvalue of maximum modulus other than the spectral radius. However, this conclusion does not hold true for irreducible nonnegative matrix. This motivates the definition of primitive matrix [193, 274].

Definition 4.56. *Let $A \in \mathbb{R}^{n \times n}$ be nonnegative and irreducible, and k be the number of eigenvalues of the matrix A of modulus $\rho(A)$. If $k = 1$, then the matrix A is said to be **primitive**; and if $k > 1$, then the matrix A is said to be **cyclic**.*

Clearly, all positive matrices are primitive.

Lemma 4.57. *Let $A = [a_{ij}] \in \mathbb{R}^{n \times n}$ be nonnegative and irreducible. If all main diagonal entries of the matrix A are positive, then $A^{n-1} > 0$ and the matrix A is primitive.*

Proof. Denote

$$\alpha \triangleq \min_{1 \leq i \leq n} \{a_{ii}\} > 0,$$

and let

$$B = A - \text{diag}(a_{11}, a_{22}, \ldots, a_{nn}).$$

As the matrix A is nonnegative and irreducible, it follows from Corollary 4.34 that the matrix B is nonnegative and irreducible, too. Clearly,

$$A \geq \alpha I + B = \alpha \left(I + \frac{1}{\alpha} B \right).$$

Therefore, it holds that

$$A^{n-1} \geq \alpha^{n-1} \left(I + \frac{1}{\alpha} B \right)^{n-1} > 0.$$

Then the matrix A^{n-1} is primitive, and $(\rho(A))^{n-1}$ is the unique and simple eigenvalue of the matrix A^{n-1} of modulus $(\rho(A))^{n-1}$. Thus, $\rho(A)$ is the unique and simple eigenvalue of the matrix A of modulus $\rho(A)$, i.e., the matrix A is primitive.   □

Lemma 4.58. *Let $A \in \mathbb{R}^{n \times n}$ be primitive. Then the matrix A^k is primitive for $k = 1, 2, \ldots$.*

Proof. As the matrix A is primitive, $\lambda = \rho(A)$ is its simple and only eigenvalue with modulus $\rho(A)$. Hence, $\lambda = (\rho(A))^k$ is the simple and only eigenvalue of the matrix A^k with modulus $(\rho(A))^k$. Since the matrix A^k is obviously nonnegative, it suffices to show that A^k is irreducible.

Suppose that A^k is reducible, that is, there exists a **permutation matrix** P such that

$$PA^k P^\mathsf{T} = \begin{bmatrix} A_{11}^{(k)} & A_{12}^{(k)} \\ 0 & A_{22}^{(k)} \end{bmatrix},$$

where $A_{11}^{(k)}$ and $A_{22}^{(k)}$ are square matrices. Let $(\rho(A), x)$ be an eigenpair of the matrix A with $x > 0$. Then

$$PA^k P^\mathsf{T}(Px) = (\rho(A))^k(Px),$$

or, equivalently,

$$\begin{bmatrix} A_{11}^{(k)} & A_{12}^{(k)} \\ 0 & A_{22}^{(k)} \end{bmatrix} \begin{bmatrix} \tilde{x}_1 \\ \tilde{x}_2 \end{bmatrix} = (\rho(A))^k \begin{bmatrix} \tilde{x}_1 \\ \tilde{x}_2 \end{bmatrix}, \quad \text{with} \quad \begin{bmatrix} \tilde{x}_1 \\ \tilde{x}_2 \end{bmatrix} \triangleq Px.$$

It follows that

$$A_{22}^{(k)} \tilde{x}_2 = (\rho(A))^k \tilde{x}_2,$$

which indicates that $(\rho(A))^k$ is an eigenvalue of the submatrix $A_{22}^{(k)}$.

Analogously, let $(\rho(A), y)$ be an eigenpair of the matrix A^T with $y > 0$. Then

$$(PA^k P^\mathsf{T})^\mathsf{T}(Py) = (\rho(A))^k(Py).$$

With the similar argument, we can deduce that $(\rho(A))^k$ is an eigenvalue of the matrix $(A_{11}^{(k)})^\mathsf{T}$ and, hence, of the submatrix $A_{11}^{(k)}$ as well. Therefore, $(\rho(A))^k$ is a multiple eigenvalue of the matrix A^k, which is a contradiction. Hence, the matrix A^k must be irreducible.   □

Lemma 4.59. *Let $A = [a_{ij}] \in \mathbb{R}^{n \times n}$ be primitive. Then*

$$\lim_{k \to \infty} \left(\frac{A}{\rho(A)} \right)^k = xy^\mathsf{T},$$

*where x, y are the **right-** and the **left-Perron vectors** of the matrix A, respectively.*

Proof. As the matrix A is nonnegative and irreducible, $\lambda = \rho(A)$ is its simple eigenvalue. Hence, there exists a nonsingular matrix $X = [x, X_1]$ such that

$$A = X \begin{bmatrix} \rho(A) & 0 \\ 0 & B \end{bmatrix} X^{-1}, \tag{4.14}$$

where $B \in \mathbb{R}^{(n-1) \times (n-1)}$. As $\rho(A)$ is the only eigenvalue of the matrix A with modulus $\rho(A)$, we have $\rho(B) < \rho(A)$. Hence, it holds that

$$\rho(\rho(A)^{-1}B) < 1,$$

which implies

$$(\rho(A)^{-1}B)^k \to 0 \quad \text{as} \quad k \to \infty.$$

Therefore,

$$\lim_{k\to\infty} \left(\frac{A}{\rho(A)} \right)^k = X \lim_{k\to\infty} \begin{bmatrix} 1 & 0 \\ 0 & (\rho(A)^{-1}B)^k \end{bmatrix} X^{-1} = X \begin{bmatrix} 1 & 0 \\ 0 & 0 \end{bmatrix} X^{-1}. \tag{4.15}$$

Let $\tilde{y}$ be the first column of $X^{-\mathsf{T}}$. It follows from $X^{-1}X = I$ that $\tilde{y}^\mathsf{T}x = 1$, and the right-hand term of (4.15) is $x\tilde{y}^\mathsf{T}$, that is,

$$\lim_{k\to\infty} \left(\frac{A}{\rho(A)} \right)^k = x\tilde{y}^\mathsf{T}.$$

From (4.14) we have

$$A^\mathsf{T}X^{-\mathsf{T}} = X^{-\mathsf{T}} \begin{bmatrix} \rho(A) & 0 \\ 0 & B^\mathsf{T} \end{bmatrix}.$$

Hence,

$$A^\mathsf{T}\tilde{y} = \rho(A)\,\tilde{y},$$

which implies that $\tilde{y}$ is a **left-eigenvector** of the matrix A corresponding to the eigenvalue $\rho(A)$. As $\rho(A)$ is a simple eigenvalue of the matrix A, there exists a scalar α such that $\tilde{y} = \alpha y$. It follows from

$$1 = \tilde{y}^\mathsf{T}x = \alpha y^\mathsf{T}x = \alpha$$

that $\alpha = 1$, that is, $\tilde{y} = y$. Therefore,

$$\lim_{k\to\infty} \left(\frac{A}{\rho(A)} \right)^k = x\tilde{y}^\mathsf{T} = xy^\mathsf{T}. \qquad \square$$

By Lemma 4.59 we see that $(\rho(A)^{-1}A)^k$ tends to a positive rank-1 matrix as k tends to infinity.

Corollary 4.60. *Let $A \in \mathbb{R}^{n\times n}$ be primitive. Then there exists an integer $k \geq 1$ such that all diagonal entries of the matrix A^k are positive.*

The following important result is a characterization of the primitive matrix [150].

Theorem 4.61. *Let $A = [a_{ij}] \in \mathbb{R}^{n\times n}$ be nonnegative. Then the matrix A is primitive if and only if there exists an integer $m \geq 1$ such that $A^m > 0$.*

Proof. Suppose that $A^m > 0$ holds true for some $m \geq 1$. Then the matrix A^m is primitive and irreducible and, by Lemma 4.31, the matrix A is irreducible. If the matrix A is not primitive, then it has k ($k > 1$) different eigenvalues with modulus $\rho(A)$. Thus, the matrix A^m has k eigenvalues with modulus $(\rho(A))^m$, which contradicts with the statement that the matrix A^m is primitive. Therefore, the matrix A is primitive.

Conversely, if the matrix A is primitive, then it is nonnegative and irreducible. Therefore, there is at least one positive entry in its first column, which can be supposed to be $a_{k_1 1}$. If $k_1 = 1$, then $a_{11} > 0$. Otherwise, by Theorem 4.35 there exists a sequence of positive integers

$\{i_1, i_2, \ldots, i_{m_1}\}$ such that

$$a_{1i_1} a_{i_1 i_2} \cdots a_{i_{m_1} k_1} > 0.$$

Thus,

$$a_{1i_1} a_{i_1 i_2} \cdots a_{i_{m_1} k_1} a_{k_1 1} > 0.$$

This means that the $(1, 1)$ entry of the matrix A^{m_1+1} is positive. It follows from Lemma 4.58 that the matrix A^{m_1+1} is primitive and is, therefore, nonnegative and irreducible.

Again, there exist a positive integer k_2 and a sequence of positive integers $\{i_1, i_2, \ldots, i_{m_2}\}$ such that

$$a_{2i_1} a_{i_1 i_2} \cdots a_{i_{m_2} k_2} a_{k_2 2} > 0.$$

Therefore, the $(1, 1)$ and $(2, 2)$ entries of the matrix $A^{(m_1+1)(m_2+1)}$ are positive. Continuing in this way, we obtain the positive integers $m_1, m_2, \ldots, m_n$ such that the main diagonal entries of the matrix

$$A^{(m_1+1)(m_2+1)\cdots(m_n+1)}$$

are positive. Lemma 4.57 then ensures that

$$A^{(m_1+1)(m_2+1)\cdots(m_n+1)(n-1)} > 0,$$

which completes the proof.   □

As $m_i \leq n - 1$, we see that the integer m in Theorem 4.61 is not larger than $(n - 1)n^n$. A sharper upper bound is given in the following theorem.

Theorem 4.62 (Wielandt Theorem). [199] *Let $A \in \mathbb{R}^{n \times n}$ be nonnegative. Then the matrix A is primitive if and only if*

$$A^{n^2 - 2n + 2} > 0.$$

4.3 ▪ Geršgorin Disc Theorem

It is well known that finding the eigenvalues of a matrix $A \in \mathbb{C}^{n \times n}$ is equivalent to finding the n zeros of its **characteristic polynomial** $\det(\lambda I - A)$. For a large scale matrix, finding the zeros of its characteristic polynomial is very difficult and usually impossible. Hence we may turn to locate its eigenvalues approximately.

Let $A = [a_{ij}] \in \mathbb{C}^{n \times n}$. Define

$$\mathsf{R}_i = \sum_{\substack{j=1 \\ j \neq i}}^{n} |a_{ij}|, \quad i = 1, 2, \ldots, n,$$

and let $\mathcal{D}_i(a_{ii}, \mathsf{R}_i)$ $(i = 1, 2, \ldots, n)$ be the closed discs centered at a_{ii} with radius R_i, i.e.,

$$\mathcal{D}_i(a_{ii}, \mathsf{R}_i) = \{z \in \mathbb{C} : |z - a_{ii}| \leq \mathsf{R}_i\}, \quad i = 1, 2, \ldots, n.$$

Such discs are called the **Geršgorin discs** of the matrix A.

Geršgorin [158] established the following famous result.

Theorem 4.63 (Geršgorin Disc Theorem). *Let* $A = [a_{ij}] \in \mathbb{C}^{n \times n}$ *and* $\mathcal{D}_i(a_{ii}, \mathsf{R}_i)$ $(i = 1, 2, \ldots, n)$ *be the Geršgorin discs of the matrix A. Then every eigenvalue of the matrix A lies in at least one of the Geršgorin discs. That is to say, if* λ *is an eigenvalue of the matrix A, then there exists at least one positive integer i such that* $\lambda \in \mathcal{D}_i(a_{ii}, \mathsf{R}_i)$, *or,*

$$\sigma(A) \subseteq \bigcup_{i=1}^{n} \mathcal{D}_i(a_{ii}, \mathsf{R}_i), \tag{4.16}$$

where $\sigma(A)$ *denotes the spectrum of the matrix A.*

Proof. Let $x = [x_1, x_2, \ldots, x_n]^\mathsf{T} \in \mathbb{C}^n$ be an eigenvector of the matrix A associated with the eigenvalue λ, i.e., $Ax = \lambda x$. Let $i \in \{1, 2, \ldots, n\}$ be chosen so that

$$|x_i| = \max_{1 \le j \le n} |x_j|.$$

Then $|x_i| > 0$ and

$$\lambda x_i - a_{ii} x_i = \sum_{j=1}^{n} a_{ij} x_j - a_{ii} x_i = \sum_{\substack{j=1 \\ j \ne i}}^{n} a_{ij} x_j.$$

Taking absolute values and dividing through both sides by $|x_i|$, we obtain

$$\left| \lambda - a_{ii} \right| = \frac{1}{|x_i|} \cdot \left| \sum_{\substack{j=1 \\ j \ne i}}^{n} a_{ij} x_j \right| \le \sum_{\substack{j=1 \\ j \ne i}}^{n} |a_{ij}| \cdot \frac{|x_j|}{|x_i|} \le \sum_{\substack{j=1 \\ j \ne i}}^{n} |a_{ij}| = \mathsf{R}_i. \qquad \square$$

Geršgorin [158] also presented the following interesting result: If $\bigcup_{i=1}^{n} \mathcal{D}_i(a_{ii}, \mathsf{R}_i)$ consists of two nonempty disjoint sets $\mathcal{D}_\mathcal{S}$ and $\mathcal{D}_\mathcal{T}$, where $\mathcal{D}_\mathcal{S}$ consists of the union of, say, k discs, and $\mathcal{D}_\mathcal{T}$ consists of the union of the remaining $n-k$ discs, then $\mathcal{D}_\mathcal{S}$ contains exactly k eigenvalues (counting multiplicities) of the matrix A, while $\mathcal{D}_\mathcal{T}$ contains exactly the remaining $n-k$ eigenvalues (also counting multiplicities) of the matrix A. The proof of this result depends on the fact that the zeros of the characteristic polynomial vary continuously with the entries a_{ij} $(i, j = 1, 2, \ldots, n)$ of the matrix $A = [a_{ij}] \in \mathbb{C}^{n \times n}$.

By applying the Geršgorin disc theorem on the matrix A^T, we see that the eigenvalues of the matrix A must lie within the union of the Geršgorin discs $\mathcal{D}_j(a_{jj}, \mathsf{C}_j)$, where

$$\mathsf{C}_j = \sum_{\substack{i=1 \\ i \ne j}}^{n} |a_{ij}|, \quad j = 1, 2, \ldots, n.$$

Therefore, we have the following result.

Theorem 4.64. *Let* $A = [a_{ij}] \in \mathbb{C}^{n \times n}$. *Then it holds that*

$$\sigma(A) \subseteq \left(\bigcup_{i=1}^{n} \mathcal{D}_i(a_{ii}, \mathsf{R}_i) \right) \bigcap \left(\bigcup_{j=1}^{n} \mathcal{D}_j(a_{jj}, \mathsf{C}_j) \right).$$

One way to interpret the Geršgorin disc theorem is that if the off-diagonal entries of a square matrix have small moduli, then the eigenvalues of this matrix cannot be "far from" its diagonal entries. Therefore, by reducing the moduli of off-diagonal entries we can attempt to approximate the eigenvalues of a matrix. Of course, diagonal entries may change in the process of minimizing off-diagonal entries. This is the basic idea of some numerical algorithms for computing eigenvalues approximately.

Corollary 4.65. [8] *Let λ be an eigenvalue of the matrix $A = [a_{ij}] \in \mathbb{C}^{n \times n}$. Suppose that $x, y \in \mathbb{C}^n$ are the **right-** and **left-eigenvectors** of the matrix A corresponding to the eigenvalue λ, respectively, i.e., $Ax = \lambda x$ and $A^* y = \lambda y$. Then*

$$\lambda \in \left(\bigcup_{i \in \mathcal{I}} \mathcal{D}_i(a_{ii}, \mathsf{R}_i) \right) \bigcap \left(\bigcup_{j \in \mathcal{J}} \mathcal{D}_j(a_{jj}, \mathsf{C}_j) \right),$$

where

$$\mathcal{I} = \{ i \, : \, |x_i| = \|x\|_\infty \} \quad and \quad \mathcal{J} = \{ j \, : \, |y_j| = \|y\|_\infty \}.$$

As $\mathcal{D}_i(a_{ii}, \mathsf{R}_i)$ is a subset of the disc

$$\{ z \in \mathbb{C} \, : \, |z| \le |a_{ii}| + \mathsf{R}_i \},$$

the following result holds true.

Corollary 4.66. *Let $A = [a_{ij}] \in \mathbb{C}^{n \times n}$. Then*

$$\rho(A) \le \max_{1 \le i \le n} \sum_{j=1}^{n} |a_{ij}|$$

and

$$\rho(A) \le \max_{1 \le j \le n} \sum_{i=1}^{n} |a_{ij}|.$$

Because **similar matrices** have the same spectrum, we immediately have the following result.

Corollary 4.67. *Let $A, X \in \mathbb{C}^{n \times n}$ with the matrix X being nonsingular. If $X^{-1}AX = D + F$, where $D = \mathrm{diag}(d_1, d_2, \ldots, d_n)$ and $F = [f_{ij}] \in \mathbb{C}^{n \times n}$ with all of its main diagonal entries being zero, then*

$$\sigma(A) \subseteq \bigcup_{i=1}^{n} \mathcal{D}_i,$$

where

$$\mathcal{D}_i = \left\{ z \in \mathbb{C} \, : \, |z - d_i| \le \sum_{j=1}^{n} |f_{ij}| \right\}, \quad i = 1, 2, \ldots, n.$$

If we choose $X = \mathrm{diag}(x_1, x_2, \ldots, x_n)$ to be a positive diagonal matrix, then Corollary 4.66 immediately leads to the following bound for $\rho(A)$.

Corollary 4.68. *Let $A = [a_{ij}] \in \mathbb{C}^{n \times n}$ and $x_1, x_2, \ldots, x_n$ be any n positive real numbers. Then*

$$\rho(A) \le \min \left\{ \max_{1 \le i \le n} \frac{1}{x_i} \sum_{i=1}^{n} |a_{ij}| x_j, \ \max_{1 \le j \le n} x_j \sum_{i=1}^{n} \frac{|a_{ij}|}{x_i} \right\}.$$

One of the most useful results, which sharpens the inclusion in (4.16), is due to Taussky [313].

Theorem 4.69. *Let $A = [a_{ij}] \in \mathbb{C}^{n \times n}$ be an irreducible matrix. If λ is an eigenvalue of the matrix A which lies on the boundary of the union of all Geršgorin discs, then λ must lie on the boundary of each Geršgorin discs, i.e., it holds that*

$$|\lambda - a_{ii}| = \mathsf{R}_i, \quad \forall\, i = 1, 2, \ldots, n.$$

Proof. Suppose that λ is an eigenvalue of the matrix A which lies on the boundary of the union of all Geršgorin discs, and let $x = [x_1, x_2, \ldots, x_n]^\mathsf{T}$ be an eigenvector of the matrix A corresponding to the eigenvalue λ with

$$|x_r| = 1 \geq |x_i|, \quad i = 1, 2, \ldots, n.$$

Then it follows from $Ax = \lambda x$ that

$$|\lambda - a_{rr}| \leq \frac{1}{|x_r|} \sum_{\substack{j=1 \\ j \neq r}}^{n} |a_{rj}| \cdot |x_j| = \sum_{\substack{j=1 \\ j \neq r}}^{n} |a_{rj}| \cdot |x_j| \leq \sum_{\substack{j=1 \\ j \neq r}}^{n} |a_{rj}| = \mathsf{R}_r.$$

Because λ is a boundary point of the union $\bigcup\limits_{i=1}^{n} \mathcal{D}_i(a_{ii}, \mathsf{R}_i)$, we have

$$|\lambda - a_{rr}| = \mathsf{R}_r.$$

Therefore,

$$\sum_{\substack{j=1 \\ j \neq r}}^{n} |a_{rj}| \cdot |x_j| = \sum_{\substack{j=1 \\ j \neq r}}^{n} |a_{rj}|.$$

This equality holds true if and only if $|x_l| = 1$ for all $a_{rl} \neq 0$ with $l \neq r$.

As the matrix A is irreducible, from Theorem 4.35 we know that for any integer j with $1 \leq j \leq n$ and $j \neq r$, there exists a sequence of integers $\{i_1, i_2, \ldots, i_m\} \subseteq \{1, 2, \ldots, n\}$ such that

$$a_{r i_1} a_{i_1 i_2} \cdots a_{i_m j} \neq 0.$$

Thus, $a_{r i_1} \neq 0$ and $|x_{i_1}| = 1$. Repeating the above argument with $r = i_1$, we have

$$|\lambda - a_{i_1 i_1}| \leq \frac{1}{|x_{i_1}|} \sum_{\substack{j=1 \\ j \neq i_1}}^{n} |a_{i_1 j}| \cdot |x_j| = \sum_{\substack{j=1 \\ j \neq i_1}}^{n} |a_{i_1 j}| \cdot |x_j| \leq \sum_{\substack{j=1 \\ j \neq i_1}}^{n} |a_{i_1 j}| = \mathsf{R}_{i_1}.$$

By making use of the hypothesis that λ is a boundary point of the union $\bigcup\limits_{i=1}^{n} \mathcal{D}_i(a_{ii}, \mathsf{R}_i)$ and the fact that $a_{i_1 i_2} \neq 0$, we obtain

$$|\lambda - a_{i_1 i_1}| = \mathsf{R}_{i_1} \quad \text{and} \quad |x_{i_2}| = 1.$$

Continuing this argument for $i_2, i_3, \ldots, i_m, j$, we can finally conclude that

$$|\lambda - a_{jj}| = \mathsf{R}_j.$$

This indicates that λ lies on the boundary of any **Geršgorin disc**. $\qquad\square$

From the proof of Theorem 4.69, we see that if an eigenvalue λ of the matrix $A = [a_{ij}] \in \mathbb{C}^{n\times n}$ lies on the boundary of the union $\bigcup_{i=1}^{n} \mathcal{D}_i(a_{ii}, R_i)$, the corresponding eigenvector $x = [x_1, x_2, \ldots, x_n]^{\mathsf{T}}$ satisfies

$$|x_i| = \|x\|_\infty, \quad i = 1, 2, \ldots, n.$$

With this result in hand, we can obtain the following corollary.

Corollary 4.70. *Let $A = [a_{ij}] \in \mathbb{C}^{n\times n}$ be an irreducible matrix and $x_1, x_2, \ldots, x_n$ be any n positive real numbers. If*

$$\frac{1}{x_i} \sum_{j=1}^{n} |a_{ij}| x_j \le \gamma, \quad \forall\, i = 1, 2, \ldots, n,$$

with strict inequality holds for at least one i, then $\rho(A) < \gamma$. Analogously, if

$$x_j \sum_{i=1}^{n} \frac{|a_{ij}|}{x_i} \le \tilde{\gamma}, \quad \forall\, j = 1, 2, \ldots, n,$$

with strict inequality holds for at least one j, then $\rho(A) < \tilde{\gamma}$.

Proof. Left as Exercise 4.14. ◻

The Geršgorin disc theorem can also be made stronger as follows [85, 299].

Theorem 4.71. *Let $A = [a_{ij}] \in \mathbb{C}^{n\times n}$, and let r be an integer satisfying $1 \le r \le n$. Then each eigenvalue of the matrix A is either in one of the discs*

$$\left\{ z \in \mathbb{C} : |z - a_{jj}| \le \mathsf{S}_j^{(r-1)} \right\}, \quad j = 1, 2, \ldots, n,$$

where $\mathsf{S}_j^{(r-1)}$ is the sum of the magnitudes of the $r-1$ largest off-diagonal entries of the matrix A in column j, or in one of the regions

$$\left\{ z \in \mathbb{C} : \sum_{i\in\mathcal{S}} |z - a_{ii}| \le \sum_{i\in\mathcal{S}} R_i \right\},$$

*where $\mathcal{S}$ is any subset of the set $\{1, 2, \ldots, n\}$ satisfying $\#\mathcal{S} = r$, where $\#\mathcal{S}$ denotes the **cardinality**, or the number of entries, of the subset $\mathcal{S}$.*

One worthwhile extension of the Geršgorin disc theorem is due to Brauer [79], who used the **Cassini oval** to determine the regions for the eigenvalues. For $A = [a_{ij}] \in \mathbb{C}^{n\times n}$ with $n \ge 2$, the Cassini ovals of the matrix A are defined by

$$\mathcal{D}_{ij} \triangleq \left\{ z \in \mathbb{C} : |z - a_{ii}|\,|z - a_{jj}| \le R_i R_j \right\}, \quad i, j = 1, 2, \ldots, n, \ i \ne j.$$

Clearly, the matrix A has $\frac{1}{2}n(n-1)$ Cassini ovals.

Theorem 4.72. *Let $A = [a_{ij}] \in \mathbb{C}^{n \times n}$ with $n \geq 2$. Then every eigenvalue of the matrix A lies in at least one of its Cassini ovals. That is to say, if λ is an eigenvalue of the matrix A, then there exist at least one pair (i, j), with $i \neq j$, such that $\lambda \in \mathcal{D}_{ij}$, or*

$$\sigma(A) \subseteq \bigcup_{\substack{i,j=1 \\ i \neq j}}^{n} \mathcal{D}_{ij}. \tag{4.17}$$

Proof. Let λ be an eigenvalue of the matrix A with the corresponding eigenvector $x = [x_1, x_2, \ldots, x_n]^{\mathsf{T}}$ satisfying

$$|x_r| = 1 \geq |x_i|, \quad i = 1, 2, \ldots, n.$$

If all other components of the vector x are zero, then $\lambda = a_{rr}$. Hence, $\lambda \in \mathcal{D}_{rj}$ for any pair (r, j) with $j \neq r$.

If the other components of the vector x are not all zero, let x_q be the component with the second largest modulus, i.e.,

$$1 = |x_r| \geq |x_q| > 0 \quad \text{and} \quad |x_q| \geq |x_i|, \quad \forall i \neq r, q.$$

It follows from $Ax = \lambda x$ that

$$|\lambda - a_{rr}| \leq \frac{1}{|x_r|} \sum_{\substack{j=1 \\ j \neq r}}^{n} |a_{rj}| \, |x_j| \leq |x_q| \sum_{\substack{j=1 \\ j \neq r}}^{n} |a_{rj}| = |x_q| \, \mathsf{R}_r$$

and

$$|\lambda - a_{qq}| \leq \frac{1}{|x_q|} \sum_{\substack{j=1 \\ j \neq q}}^{n} |a_{qj}| \, |x_j| \leq \frac{1}{|x_q|} \sum_{\substack{j=1 \\ j \neq q}}^{n} |a_{qj}| = \frac{\mathsf{R}_q}{|x_q|}.$$

Multiplying these two inequalities side by side leads to

$$|\lambda - a_{rr}| \, |\lambda - a_{qq}| \leq \mathsf{R}_r \mathsf{R}_q,$$

which implies that $\lambda \in \mathcal{D}_{rq}$. $\quad\square$

Note that the eigenvalue inclusions (4.16) and (4.17) use the exact same data of the matrix $A = [a_{ij}] \in \mathbb{C}^{n \times n}$, i.e., a_{ii} and R_i, $i = 1, 2, \ldots, n$. It is easy to see that

$$\bigcup_{\substack{i,j=1 \\ i \neq j}}^{n} \mathcal{D}_{ij} \subseteq \bigcup_{i=1}^{n} \mathcal{D}_i, \quad \text{with} \quad \mathcal{D}_i \triangleq \mathcal{D}_i(a_{ii}, \mathsf{R}_i),$$

which indicates that the Cassini ovals are always at least as good as the Geršgorin discs.

Brauer's extension in Theorem 4.72 depends on the idea of using two different rows at a time, as opposed to Geršgorin who used a single row at a time. That would seem to suggest that one can do even better with three or more different rows at a time. However, this is not the case. Consider the following counterexample [236]:

$$A = \begin{bmatrix} 1 & 1 & 0 & 0 \\ 1 & 1 & 0 & 0 \\ 0 & 0 & 1 & 0 \\ 0 & 0 & 0 & 1 \end{bmatrix} \in \mathbb{R}^{4 \times 4},$$

which has the eigenvalue set $\{0, 1, 1, 2\}$. Consider the sets

$$\mathcal{D}_{ijk} \triangleq \{z \in \mathbb{C} : |z - a_{ii}| \, |z - a_{jj}| \, |z - a_{kk}| \leq \mathsf{R}_i \, \mathsf{R}_j \, \mathsf{R}_k\},$$

where $i, j, k \in \{1, 2, 3, 4\}$ are different from each other. It is easy to see that $\mathsf{R}_1 = \mathsf{R}_2 = 1$ and $\mathsf{R}_3 = \mathsf{R}_4 = 0$. Therefore, each set $\mathcal{D}_{ijk}$ only consists of one point $z = 1$, and they fail to capture the eigenvalues 0 and 2.

For more results about the Geršgorin discs, we refer to the monograph of Varga [330].

4.4 ▪ M-Matrix and Monotone Matrix

4.4.1 ▪ M-Matrix and H-Matrix

In biological, physical, and social sciences, many problems can finally be reduced to the ones involving a matrix A whose off-diagonal entries are nonpositive while diagonal entries are non-negative, i.e., the matrix A is of the form

$$A = sI - B, \quad \text{with some } s > 0 \text{ and } B \geq 0. \tag{4.18}$$

Also, matrices of the form (4.18) often occur in relation to systems of linear or nonlinear equations, and to eigenvalue problems in a wide variety of areas.

Definition 4.73. *A matrix $A \in \mathbb{R}^{n \times n}$ is said to be an (nonsingular) M-matrix if it is of the form (4.18) with $s > \rho(B)$.*

Remark 4.1. *From the definition, we can see that if $A \in \mathbb{R}^{n \times n}$ is an M-matrix, then all of its eigenvalues have positive real parts. Hence, it is nonsingular. In some literature, M-matrix is not required to be nonsingular, i.e., only $s \geq \rho(B)$ is imposed in the definition, which is called a singular M-matrix.*

Definition 4.74. *Let $A = [a_{ij}] \in \mathbb{R}^{n \times n}$. If $a_{ij} \leq 0$ holds for $i \neq j$, $i, j = 1, 2, \ldots, n$, then the matrix A is said to be a Z-matrix.*

Denote by $\mathcal{Z}^{n \times n}$ the set of all Z-matrices, i.e.,

$$\mathcal{Z}^{n \times n} = \{A = [a_{ij}] \in \mathbb{R}^{n \times n} : a_{ij} \leq 0, \ i \neq j, \ i, j = 1, 2, \ldots, n\}.$$

Then it is clear that an M-matrix must be a Z-matrix.

Definition 4.75. *Let $A \in \mathbb{R}^{n \times n}$. If the matrix A is a Z-matrix and all of its diagonal entries are positive, then it is said to be an L-matrix.*

For a given matrix $A = [a_{ij}] \in \mathbb{C}^{n \times n}$, its **comparison matrix** is defined by $\langle A \rangle = [\langle a_{ij} \rangle] \in \mathbb{R}^{n \times n}$, where

$$\langle a_{ii} \rangle = |a_{ii}| \quad \text{and} \quad \langle a_{ij} \rangle = -|a_{ij}|, \quad i \neq j, \quad i, j = 1, 2, \ldots, n.$$

It is clear that $\langle A \rangle$ is a Z-matrix. Let $D \triangleq \text{diag}(A)$ be the diagonal part of the matrix A. Then $\langle A \rangle = |D| - |B|$, where $B = D - A$.

Definition 4.76. *A matrix $A \in \mathbb{C}^{n \times n}$ is said to be an **H-matrix** if its comparison matrix $\langle A \rangle$ is an M-matrix. An H-matrix of all diagonal entries being positive is called an **H_+-matrix** [19].*

Note that the concept of the comparison matrix can be introduced to any rectangular matrix $A \in \mathbb{C}^{m \times n}$ in a straightforward fashion, and the concept of the H_+-matrix was introduced in [19] for analyzing the convergence properties of matrix splitting iteration methods for solving the linear complementarity problems.

Remark 4.2. *Alternatively, for a given matrix $A \in \mathbb{C}^{n \times n}$ we can define its **comparison matrix** through its **Jordan decomposition** or **spectral decomposition**.*

More precisely, if $A = XJX^{-1}$ is the Jordan decomposition of the matrix $A \in \mathbb{C}^{n \times n}$, with the matrix $J \in \mathbb{C}^{n \times n}$ being the Jordan canonical form and the columns of the matrix $X \in \mathbb{C}^{n \times n}$ corresponding to the eigenvectors of the matrix A, then the J-comparison matrix of the matrix A, denoted as $\langle A \rangle_J$, is defined as $\langle A \rangle_J = X \langle J \rangle X^{-1}$, with $\langle J \rangle$ being the comparison matrix of the matrix J. Besides, the J-absolute value of the matrix $A \in \mathbb{C}^{n \times n}$, denoted as $]A[_J$, is defined as $]A[_J = X |J| X^{-1}$.

*In particular, if the matrix $A \in \mathbb{C}^{n \times n}$ is Hermitian and if $A = U \Lambda U^*$ is its spectral decomposition, with the matrix $U \in \mathbb{C}^{n \times n}$ being unitary and the matrix $\Lambda \in \mathbb{C}^{n \times n}$ being diagonal, then the S-comparison matrix of the matrix A, denoted as $\langle A \rangle_S$, is defined as $\langle A \rangle_S = U |\Lambda| U^*$, with $|\Lambda|$ being the **absolute value** of the matrix Λ. Besides, the S-absolute value of the matrix $A \in \mathbb{C}^{n \times n}$, denoted as $]A[_S$, is defined as $]A[_S = U |\Lambda| U^*$. Clearly, it holds that $\langle A \rangle_S =]A[_S$. Similar concepts were introduced and applied by Bai in [21, 22] in the convergence analysis of the additive and multiplicative splitting iteration methods for solving systems of linear equations.*

Theorem 4.77. *Let $A \in \mathbb{R}^{n \times n}$ be nonnegative. Then $\rho(A) < \alpha$ if and only if the matrix $\alpha I - A$ is nonsingular and $(\alpha I - A)^{-1} \geq 0$.*

Proof. Suppose $\rho(A) < \alpha$ and let

$$M \triangleq \frac{1}{\alpha} A.$$

Then we see that $\rho(M) < 1$. It follows from Lemma 4.39 that the matrix $I - M$ is nonsingular and

$$(I - M)^{-1} = I + M + M^2 + \cdots.$$

As the matrix A is nonnegative, it holds that $M \geq 0$. Hence,

$$(I - M)^{-1} \geq 0.$$

From

$$\alpha I - A = \alpha(I - M)$$

we see that the matrix $\alpha I - A$ is nonsingular, and

$$(\alpha I - A)^{-1} = \frac{1}{\alpha}(I - M)^{-1} \geq 0.$$

Conversely, suppose that $(\alpha I - A)^{-1} \geq 0$. It follows from $A \geq 0$ and Lemma 4.25 that there exists a vector $x \gneq 0$ such that $Ax = \rho(A) x$. Thus

$$(\alpha I - A)x = (\alpha - \rho(A))x.$$

Multiplying both sides by $(\alpha I - A)^{-1}$, we have

$$\left(\alpha - \rho(A)\right)(\alpha I - A)^{-1}x = x.$$

Since $(\alpha I - A)^{-1} \geq 0$ and $x \gneq 0$, we see that $\alpha - \rho(A) > 0$, i.e., $\rho(A) < \alpha$. □

As a special case, we have the following result.

Corollary 4.78. *Let $A \in \mathbb{R}^{n \times n}$ be a **nonnegative matrix**. Then $\rho(A) < 1$ if and only if the matrix $I - A$ is nonsingular and $(I - A)^{-1} \geq 0$.*

If $A \in \mathbb{R}^{n \times n}$ is an **irreducible matrix**, then we can further strengthen the conclusion of Theorem 4.77.

Theorem 4.79. *Let $A \in \mathbb{R}^{n \times n}$ be a nonnegative matrix. Then the matrix A is irreducible and $\rho(A) < \alpha$ if and only if the matrix $\alpha I - A$ is nonsingular and $(\alpha I - A)^{-1} > 0$.*

Proof. The proof is left as Exercise 4.17. □

The following theorem gives a sufficient and necessary condition for a real matrix $A \in \mathbb{R}^{n \times n}$ to be an M-**matrix**.

Theorem 4.80. *Let $A \in \mathbb{R}^{n \times n}$. Then the matrix A is an M-matrix if and only if $A \in \mathcal{Z}^{n \times n}$ and it is nonsingular with $A^{-1} \geq 0$.*

Proof. Clearly, if the matrix A is an M-matrix, then $A \in \mathcal{Z}^{n \times n}$ and, by Definition 4.73, it can be written as $A = sI - B$, where $B \geq 0$ and $s > \rho(B)$. Applying Theorem 4.77 to the matrix B, we know that the matrix $A = sI - B$ is nonsingular and

$$A^{-1} = (sI - B)^{-1} \geq 0.$$

Conversely, if $A = [a_{ij}] \in \mathcal{Z}^{n \times n}$, then it can be written as $A = sI - B$, where

$$s = \max_{1 \leq i \leq n} |a_{ii}| \quad \text{and} \quad B = sI - A \geq 0.$$

When the matrix A is nonsingular and $A^{-1} \geq 0$, by Theorem 4.77 we have $s > \rho(B)$ and, hence, by Definition 4.73 we know that the matrix A is an M-matrix. □

Remark 4.3. *In some literature, the M-matrix is also defined by Theorem 4.80, i.e., $A \in \mathbb{R}^{n \times n}$ is said to be an **M-matrix** if $A \in \mathcal{Z}^{n \times n}$ and A is nonsingular with $A^{-1} \geq 0$; see [329].*

4.4.2 ▪ Properties of M-Matrix

In this subsection, we investigate some important properties of an **M-matrix**.

The following result shows that all diagonal entries of an M-matrix must be positive.

Lemma 4.81. *Let $A = [a_{ij}] \in \mathcal{Z}^{n \times n}$ be an M-matrix. Then $a_{ii} > 0$ holds for $i = 1, 2, \ldots, n$.*

Proof. Denote by

$$C = [c_{ij}] \triangleq A^{-1}.$$

Then $AC = I$, which implies

$$\sum_{k=1}^{n} a_{ik} c_{ki} = 1, \quad i = 1, 2, \ldots, n,$$

or equivalently,

$$a_{ii} c_{ii} = 1 - \sum_{\substack{k=1 \\ k \neq i}}^{n} a_{ik} c_{ki}, \quad i = 1, 2, \ldots, n.$$

As the matrix A is an M-matrix, it follows from Theorem 4.80 that $c_{ij} \geq 0$ and $a_{ij} \leq 0$ for $i \neq j$. Therefore, $a_{ik} c_{ki} \leq 0$ holds for $k \neq i$, which indicates that the right-hand side of the above equality is not less than 1 for every $i \in \{1, 2, \ldots, n\}$. Hence, $c_{ii} \geq 0$ implies $a_{ii} > 0$, $i = 1, 2, \ldots, n$. $\quad\Box$

Lemma 4.81 implies that an M-matrix must be an L-matrix.

Let $A \in \mathcal{Z}^{n \times n}$ with all diagonal entries being positive, i.e., the matrix A is an L-matrix. Denote by D the diagonal part of the matrix A. Then D is a nonsingular matrix. Define $B = D - A$. Then the matrix B is nonnegative. By Corollary 4.78, we learn that

$$A^{-1} = (I - D^{-1} B)^{-1} D^{-1}$$

is nonnegative if and only if $\rho(D^{-1} B) < 1$. Therefore, the last condition in Theorem 4.80 can be replaced by $\rho(D^{-1} B) < 1$.

Theorem 4.82. *Let $A \in \mathbb{R}^{n \times n}$ have positive diagonal part. Then the matrix A is an M-matrix if and only if $A \in \mathcal{Z}^{n \times n}$ and $\rho(I - D^{-1} A) < 1$, where D is the diagonal part of the matrix A.*

Proof. Assume that $A \in \mathbb{R}^{n \times n}$ is an M-matrix. Then from Theorem 4.80 we know that $A \in \mathcal{Z}^{n \times n}$, A is nonsingular, and $A^{-1} \geq 0$. For

$$e = [1, 1, \ldots, 1]^{\mathsf{T}} \in \mathbb{R}^n,$$

it holds that

$$u \triangleq A^{-1} e > 0,$$

as each row of the matrix A^{-1} must have at least one positive entry. As D is a positive diagonal matrix, we have

$$(I - D^{-1} A) e = e - D^{-1} u < e.$$

Note that

$$I - D^{-1} A \geq 0.$$

Hence, in accordance with Theorem 4.12 (2) we can obtain

$$\rho(I - D^{-1} A) < 1.$$

Now, assume that $A \in \mathcal{Z}^{n \times n}$ satisfies $\rho(I - D^{-1} A) < 1$. By denoting $B = D - A$, we see that D is a positive diagonal matrix and

$$B \geq 0, \quad \rho(D^{-1} B) < 1.$$

Hence, the matrix

$$I - D^{-1}B = D^{-1}(D - B) = D^{-1}A$$

is nonsingular, which readily implies that the matrix A is nonsingular too. As $D^{-1}B \geq 0$, it holds that

$$A^{-1} = (D - B)^{-1} = (I - D^{-1}B)^{-1}D^{-1} = \sum_{k=0}^{\infty} \left(D^{-1}B\right)^k D^{-1} \geq 0.$$

As a consequence, we know that the matrix A is an M-matrix.   □

Corollary 4.83. *Let $A \in \mathbb{R}^{n \times n}$ be an **H-matrix** and $D = \mathrm{diag}(A)$. Then*

(1) *the matrix D is nonsingular, i.e., all of its diagonal entries are nonzero;*

(2) $\rho(I - |D|^{-1}\langle A\rangle) < 1;$

(3) *the matrix A is nonsingular and $|A^{-1}| \leq \langle A\rangle^{-1}$.*

Proof. Denote by $A = [a_{ij}] = D - B$. Then it holds that

$$\langle A\rangle = |D| - |B|.$$

As the matrix A is an H-matrix, its comparison matrix $\langle A\rangle$ is an M-matrix. By Lemma 4.81 we know that all diagonal entries of the matrix $\langle A\rangle$ are positive, that is,

$$|a_{ii}| > 0, \quad i = 1, 2, \ldots, n.$$

This shows that

$$a_{ii} \neq 0, \quad i = 1, 2, \ldots, n,$$

so that the matrix D is nonsingular.

As the matrix $\langle A\rangle$ is an M-matrix, it follows from Theorem 4.82 that

$$\rho(I - |D|^{-1}\langle A\rangle) < 1. \tag{4.19}$$

Note that the inequality (4.19) is equivalent to

$$\rho(|D|^{-1}|B|) < 1.$$

As

$$|D^{-1}B| = |D|^{-1}|B|,$$

we have

$$\rho(D^{-1}B) \leq \rho(|D^{-1}B|) = \rho(|D|^{-1}|B|) < 1.$$

Therefore, the matrix $I - D^{-1}B$ is nonsingular, and from

$$A = D - B = D(I - D^{-1}B)$$

we see that the matrix A is nonsingular, too. By noticing

$$A^{-1} = (I - D^{-1}B)^{-1}D^{-1} = \sum_{k=0}^{\infty} \left(D^{-1}B\right)^k D^{-1},$$

we can further obtain

$$|A^{-1}| = \left| \sum_{k=0}^{\infty} \left(D^{-1} B \right)^k D^{-1} \right| \leq \sum_{k=0}^{\infty} \left(|D|^{-1} |B| \right)^k |D|^{-1}$$
$$= (I - |D|^{-1} |B|)^{-1} |D|^{-1} = (|D| - |B|)^{-1} = \langle A \rangle^{-1}. \qquad \square$$

If the matrix A is irreducible, then we have the following result.

Theorem 4.84. *Let* $A \in \mathbb{R}^{n \times n}$ *be an* **M-matrix**. *If the matrix* A *is irreducible, then* $A^{-1} > 0$.

Proof. Denote by $A = D - B$ and $\tilde{A} = D^{-1} B$. As the matrix A is an M-matrix, D is a positive diagonal matrix and it holds that

$$\tilde{A} \geq 0, \quad \rho(\tilde{A}) < 1.$$

Moreover, as the matrix A is irreducible, from Theorem 4.34 we know that the matrix $\tilde{A}$ is irreducible too. In light of Theorem 4.41, it holds that $(I - \tilde{A})^{-1} > 0$. Then it follows that

$$A^{-1} = (D - B)^{-1} = (I - \tilde{A})^{-1} D^{-1} > 0. \qquad \square$$

Theorem 4.85. *Let* $A, C \in \mathbb{R}^{n \times n}$ *such that* $C \in \mathcal{Z}^{n \times n}$ *and* $A \leq C$. *If the matrix* A *is an* M-*matrix, then the matrix* C *is an* M-*matrix as well.*

Proof. Denote

$$D_A \triangleq \mathrm{diag}(A) \quad \text{and} \quad D_C \triangleq \mathrm{diag}(C).$$

If $A \in \mathbb{R}^{n \times n}$ is an M-matrix, then $D_A \geq 0$. As $C \in \mathcal{Z}^{n \times n}$ and $A \leq C$, we have

$$0 \leq D_A \leq D_C \quad \text{and} \quad 0 \leq D_C - C \leq D_A - A.$$

Therefore,

$$0 \leq D_C^{-1} \leq D_A^{-1},$$

and

$$0 \leq D_C^{-1}(D_C - C) \leq D_A^{-1}(D_A - A)$$

or, equivalently,

$$0 \leq I - D_C^{-1} C \leq I - D_A^{-1} A.$$

As the matrix A is an M-matrix, it follows from Corollary 4.6 and Theorem 4.82 that

$$\rho(I - D_C^{-1} C) \leq \rho(I - D_A^{-1} A) < 1.$$

Therefore, by Theorem 4.82 we know that the matrix C is an M-matrix. $\qquad \square$

As a consequence, we have a useful way to obtain **M-matrices**.

Corollary 4.86. *Let* $A \in \mathbb{R}^{n \times n}$ *be an M-matrix. If* $C \in \mathbb{R}^{n \times n}$ *is obtained by setting certain off-diagonal entries of the matrix* A *to be zero, then the matrix* C *is an M-matrix as well.*

A similar result is given in the following.

Corollary 4.87. *Let $A \in \mathbb{R}^{n \times n}$ be an M-matrix. Then any **principal submatrix** of the matrix A is also an M-matrix.*

Proof. Left as Exercise 4.18.   □

Theorem 4.88. *Let $A \in \mathbb{R}^{n \times n}$ be an M-matrix and $B \in \mathbb{C}^{n \times n}$. If $\langle B \rangle \geq A$, then*

(1) *the matrix B is an H-matrix;*

(2) *the matrix B is nonsingular;*

(3) *$A^{-1} \geq \langle B \rangle^{-1} \geq |B^{-1}| \geq 0$.*

Proof. Obviously, we have $\langle B \rangle \in \mathcal{Z}^{n \times n}$. As $A \in \mathbb{R}^{n \times n}$ is an M-matrix and $\langle B \rangle \geq A$, from Theorem 4.85 we know that the matrix $\langle B \rangle$ is an M-matrix. Therefore, the matrix B is an H-matrix.

An H-matrix is, of course, nonsingular. So, the matrix B is nonsingular.

In the light of Corollary 4.83 (3), it holds that

$$|B^{-1}| \leq \langle B \rangle^{-1}.$$

As both matrices A and $\langle B \rangle$ are M-matrices, the relation $A \leq \langle B \rangle$ implies $A^{-1} \geq \langle B \rangle^{-1}$. As a result, we have

$$|B^{-1}| \leq \langle B \rangle^{-1} \leq A^{-1}.   □$$

Corollary 4.89. *Let $A, B \in \mathbb{R}^{n \times n}$ be M-matrices. If $A \leq B$, then it holds that $B^{-1} \leq A^{-1}$.*

In the following theorem, we list some equivalent properties for a matrix $A \in \mathcal{Z}^{n \times n}$ to be an **M-matrix**. For more properties, we refer to [72].

Theorem 4.90. *Let $A \in \mathcal{Z}^{n \times n}$. Then the following statements are equivalent:*

(1) *the matrix A is an M-matrix;*

(2) *all diagonal entries of the matrix A are positive, and there exists a positive diagonal matrix D such that the matrix AD is strictly diagonally dominant (see Definition 4.97);*

(3) *there exists a positive diagonal matrix D such that the matrix $AD + DA^{\mathsf{T}}$ is symmetric positive definite;*

(4) *there exists a symmetric positive definite matrix W such that the matrix $AW + WA^{\mathsf{T}}$ is symmetric positive definite;*

(5) *the matrix A is positive stable, i.e., all eigenvalues of the matrix A have positive real parts;*

(6) *every real eigenvalue of the matrix A is positive;*

(7) *for each vector $x \neq 0$, there exists a nonnegative diagonal matrix D such that $x^{\mathsf{T}} A D x > 0$;*

(8) *the matrix $A + D$ is nonsingular for any nonnegative diagonal matrix D.*

The following theorem gives a necessary and sufficient condition for an arbitrary matrix to be a nonsingular M-matrix.

Theorem 4.91. *[72] $A \in \mathbb{R}^{n \times n}$ is an M-matrix if and only if the matrix $A + D$ is nonsingular and $(A + D)^{-1} \geq 0$ for any nonnegative diagonal matrix D.*

Note that in Theorem 4.91 we do not assume that the matrix A is a Z-matrix.

4.4.3 ▪ Monotone Matrix

Suppose that $A \in \mathbb{R}^{n \times n}$ is an M-matrix. If $Ax = f$ holds for some nonnegative vector $f \in \mathbb{R}^n$, then $x = A^{-1}f \geq 0$. In particular, if $Ax \geq 0$, then $x \geq 0$. Any matrix possessing this property is called a **monotone matrix** [96].

Definition 4.92. *A matrix $A \in \mathbb{R}^{n \times n}$ is called monotone if $Ax \geq 0$ implies $x \geq 0$ for any $x \in \mathbb{R}^n$.*

It is easily seen that if $A \in \mathbb{R}^{n \times n}$ is monotone, then $Ax \leq Ay$ implies $x \leq y$.

Lemma 4.93. *$A \in \mathbb{R}^{n \times n}$ is a monotone matrix if and only if it is nonsingular and $A^{-1} \geq 0$.*

Proof. Suppose that $A \in \mathbb{R}^{n \times n}$ is monotone. Let $Ax = 0$. Then $A(-x) = 0$. Therefore, $Ax \geq 0$ and $A(-x) \geq 0$, which imply that $x \geq 0$ and $-x \geq 0$. Hence, $x = 0$. That is to say, $Ax = 0$ has a unique solution $x = 0$, so the matrix A is nonsingular. As

$$A(A^{-1}e_i) = e_i \geq 0, \quad i = 1, 2, \ldots, n,$$

where e_i is the i-th column of the identity matrix, we have

$$A^{-1}e_i \geq 0, \quad i = 1, 2, \ldots, n.$$

Therefore,

$$A^{-1} = A^{-1}[e_1, e_2, \ldots, e_n] \geq 0.$$

The converse statement is trivial. ☐

If $A \in \mathbb{R}^{n \times n}$ is a Z-matrix, then the following result holds immediately.

Theorem 4.94. *$A \in \mathcal{Z}^{n \times n}$ is a monotone matrix if and only if it is an M-matrix.*

In addition, if a Z-matrix is symmetric and positive definite, then it must be monotone.

Theorem 4.95. *Let $A = [a_{ij}] \in \mathcal{Z}^{n \times n}$ be a symmetric positive definite matrix. Then it is monotone and an M-matrix.*

Proof. Let $x \in \mathbb{R}^n$ satisfy $Ax \geq 0$. By the definition of the monotone matrix, we need to show that $x \geq 0$. If $x = 0$, then the conclusion follows immediately. Suppose that $x \neq 0$. Splitting the vector x into its positive and negative parts, i.e.,

$$x = x^+ + x^-,$$

where $x^+ \geq 0$ and $x^- \leq 0$, with

$$x^+ = [x_1^+, x_2^+, \ldots, x_n^+]^\mathsf{T} \quad \text{and} \quad x^- = [x_1^-, x_2^-, \ldots, x_n^-]^\mathsf{T},$$

we then have

$$x_i^+ x_i^- = 0, \quad i = 1, 2, \ldots, n.$$

As $A \in \mathbb{R}^{n \times n}$ is symmetric positive definite, it holds that

$$\langle x^-, Ax^- \rangle \geq 0$$

and

$$
\begin{aligned}
0 \leq \langle x^-, Ax^- \rangle &= \langle x^-, Ax \rangle - \langle x^-, Ax^+ \rangle \\
&= \langle x^-, Ax \rangle - \sum_{i,j=1}^{n} a_{ij} x_i^- x_j^+ \\
&= \langle x^-, Ax \rangle - \sum_{\substack{i,j=1 \\ i \neq j}}^{n} a_{ij} x_i^- x_j^+.
\end{aligned}
$$

Since

$$Ax \geq 0, \quad x^+ \geq 0, \quad x^- \leq 0,$$

and

$$a_{ij} \leq 0, \quad \forall i \neq j, \; i,j = 1, 2, \ldots, n,$$

the right-hand side of the above inequality is nonpositive, and $\langle x^-, Ax^- \rangle$ is nonpositive too. This implies

$$\langle x^-, Ax^- \rangle = 0,$$

so that $x^- = 0$, i.e., $x \geq 0$. Therefore, the matrix A is monotone.   □

If $A \in \mathcal{Z}^{n \times n}$ is symmetric positive definite, then it is said to be a **Stieltjes matrix** [329]. Clearly, a Stieltjes matrix must be an M**-matrix**.

Theorem 4.96. *Let $A \in \mathbb{R}^{n \times n}$ be a Stieltjes matrix. Then the matrix A must be an M-matrix.*

4.5 ▪ Diagonally Dominant Matrix

4.5.1 ▪ Diagonally Dominant and Irreducible Matrix

Definition 4.97. *A matrix $A = [a_{ij}] \in \mathbb{C}^{n \times n}$ is said to be a **weakly diagonally dominant matrix** if*

$$|a_{ii}| \geq \sum_{\substack{j=1 \\ j \neq i}}^{n} |a_{ij}|, \quad i = 1, 2, \ldots, n,$$

*where the strict inequality holds at least for one index i. If the strict inequality holds for all indices i, then the matrix A is said to be a **strictly diagonally dominant matrix**.*

Lemma 4.98. *If $A = [a_{ij}] \in \mathbb{C}^{n \times n}$ is strictly diagonally dominant or irreducibly weakly diagonally dominant, then it is nonsingular.*

Proof. If $A \in \mathbb{C}^{n \times n}$ is strictly diagonally dominant, then the origin is outside the union of its **Geršgorin discs**. It follows from Theorem 4.63 that $\lambda = 0$ cannot be an eigenvalue of the matrix A. Therefore, the matrix A is nonsingular.

If $A \in \mathbb{C}^{n \times n}$ is weakly diagonally dominant with an eigenvalue $\lambda = 0$, then there exists a nonzero vector $x \in \mathbb{C}^n$ such that $Ax = 0$. Suppose $x = [x_1, x_2, \ldots, x_n]^{\mathsf{T}}$ with $\|x\|_\infty = 1$. Let r be the integer such that

$$|x_r| = \|x\|_\infty = 1 \geq |x_j|, \quad j = 1, 2, \ldots, n.$$

Then it holds that

$$|a_{rr}| = |\lambda - a_{rr}| \leq \frac{1}{|x_r|} \sum_{\substack{j=1 \\ j \neq r}}^{n} |a_{rj}| \cdot |x_j| \leq \sum_{\substack{j=1 \\ j \neq r}}^{n} |a_{rj}|,$$

where the equality holds if and only if $|x_j| = 1$ for all $a_{rj} \neq 0$ with $j \neq r$. As the matrix A is weakly diagonally dominant, we have

$$|a_{rr}| = \sum_{\substack{j=1 \\ j \neq r}}^{n} |a_{rj}|.$$

Therefore, $a_{rj} = 0$ for the index j such that $|x_j| \neq 1$. Define the index sets $\mathcal{S}$ and $\mathcal{T}$ by

$$\mathcal{S} = \{1 \leq j \leq n : |x_j| = 1\} \quad \text{and} \quad \mathcal{T} = \{1 \leq j \leq n : j \notin \mathcal{S}\}.$$

Then, we have

$$a_{rj} = 0, \quad \text{for } r \in \mathcal{S} \text{ and } j \in \mathcal{T}.$$

It is obvious that $\mathcal{S}$ is not empty. We claim that $\mathcal{T}$ cannot be empty too. Otherwise, we have

$$|a_{rr}| \leq \sum_{\substack{j=1 \\ j \neq r}}^{n} |a_{rj}|, \quad \text{for } r = 1, 2, \ldots, n,$$

which indicates that the matrix A cannot be weakly diagonally dominant. It follows from Theorem 4.33 that the matrix A is reducible, which leads to a contradiction. Therefore, $\lambda = 0$ cannot be an eigenvalue of the matrix A, which shows that the matrix A is nonsingular. $\qquad \square$

If $A \in \mathbb{C}^{n \times n}$ is a diagonally dominant matrix and all of its diagonal entries are positive, then all Geršgorin discs of the matrix A are located in the right-half part of the complex plane. This result is precisely stated in the following corollary.

Corollary 4.99. *If $A \in \mathbb{C}^{n \times n}$ is strictly diagonally dominant or irreducibly weakly diagonally dominant, with all diagonal entries being positive, then it is positive stable, i.e., all eigenvalues of the matrix A have positive real parts.*

If $A \in \mathbb{C}^{n \times n}$ is Hermitian, then all of its eigenvalues are real. Hence we have the following result.

Corollary 4.100. *Let $A \in \mathbb{C}^{n \times n}$ be a Hermitian matrix with positive diagonal entries. If the matrix A is strictly diagonally dominant or irreducibly weakly diagonally dominant, then it is Hermitian positive definite.*

Lemma 4.101. [201] *Let $A = [a_{ij}] \in \mathbb{C}^{n \times n}$ be a strictly diagonally dominant matrix. Then for any matrix $B = [b_{ij}] \in \mathbb{C}^{n \times n}$, it holds that*

$$\|A^{-1}B\|_\infty \le \max_{1 \le i \le n} \frac{\displaystyle\sum_{j=1}^{n} |b_{ij}|}{|a_{ii}| - \displaystyle\sum_{\substack{j=1 \\ j \ne i}}^{n} |a_{ij}|}.$$

Proof. By definition, we know that there exists a nonzero vector $x = [x_1, x_2, \ldots, x_n]^\mathsf{T} \in \mathbb{C}^n$ such that $\|x\|_\infty = 1$ and

$$\|A^{-1}B\|_\infty = \|A^{-1}Bx\|_\infty.$$

Let

$$y = [y_1, y_2, \ldots, y_n]^\mathsf{T} \triangleq A^{-1}Bx.$$

Then

$$Ay = Bx. \tag{4.20}$$

Let k be the positive integer such that

$$|y_k| = \max_{1 \le i \le n} |y_i| = \|y\|_\infty.$$

Comparing the k-th entry of the vectors on both sides of the equation (4.20) we have

$$\sum_{j=1}^{n} a_{kj} y_j = \sum_{j=1}^{n} b_{kj} x_j.$$

Therefore,

$$
\begin{aligned}
|y_k| \left(|a_{kk}| - \sum_{\substack{j=1 \\ j \ne k}}^{n} |a_{kj}| \right) &= |a_{kk} y_k| - \sum_{\substack{j=1 \\ j \ne k}}^{n} |a_{kj} y_k| \\
&\le |a_{kk} y_k| - \sum_{\substack{j=1 \\ j \ne k}}^{n} |a_{kj} y_j| \\
&\le \left| \sum_{j=1}^{n} a_{kj} y_j \right| = \left| \sum_{j=1}^{n} b_{kj} x_j \right| \\
&\le \sum_{j=1}^{n} |b_{kj}| \cdot |x_j| \\
&\le \sum_{j=1}^{n} |b_{kj}|.
\end{aligned}
$$

It follows that

$$\|A^{-1}B\|_\infty = \|y\|_\infty = |y_k| \le \frac{\displaystyle\sum_{j=1}^n |b_{kj}|}{|a_{kk}| - \displaystyle\sum_{\substack{j=1 \\ j \ne k}}^n |a_{kj}|} \le \max_{1 \le i \le n} \frac{\displaystyle\sum_{j=1}^n |b_{ij}|}{|a_{ii}| - \displaystyle\sum_{\substack{j=1 \\ j \ne i}}^n |a_{ij}|}. \qquad \square$$

4.5.2 ▪ Diagonally Dominant M-Matrix

Let $A = [a_{ij}] \in \mathbb{R}^{n \times n}$ be a **Z-matrix** and $D \in \mathbb{R}^{n \times n}$ be its diagonal part. Denote by

$$B = [b_{ij}] \triangleq D^{-1}(D - A) = I - D^{-1}A.$$

If the matrix A is **strictly diagonally dominant**, then

$$\sum_{j=1}^n |b_{ij}| < 1, \quad \text{for} \quad i = 1, 2, \ldots, n.$$

Hence, $\||B|\|_\infty < 1$, which implies that $\rho(|B|) < 1$. If $A \in \mathbb{R}^{n \times n}$ is **weakly diagonally dominant** and irreducible, then

$$\sum_{j=1}^n |b_{ij}| \le 1, \quad \text{for} \quad i = 1, 2, \ldots, n,$$

and at least one of the strict inequalities holds. We can construct a nonnegative and irreducible matrix $\tilde{B} = [\tilde{b}_{ij}] \in \mathbb{R}^{n \times n}$ such that $|B| \lneqq \tilde{B}$ and

$$\sum_{j=1}^n \tilde{b}_{ij} = 1, \quad \text{for } i = 1, 2, \ldots, n.$$

By Lemma 4.8 we have $\rho(\tilde{B}) = 1$. As $|B| \lneqq \tilde{B}$, it follows from Corollary 4.48 that

$$\rho(|B|) < \rho(\tilde{B}) = 1$$

and

$$\rho(I - D^{-1}A) = \rho(B) \le \rho(|B|) < 1.$$

In accordance with Theorem 4.82, we have demonstrated the following result.

Theorem 4.102. *Let $A = [a_{ij}] \in \mathbb{R}^{n \times n}$ be a Z-matrix with positive diagonal entries. If the matrix A is strictly diagonally dominant or irreducibly weakly diagonally dominant, then it is an M-matrix.*

We immediately have the following result.

Corollary 4.103. *Let $A \in \mathbb{C}^{n \times n}$. If the matrix A is a strictly diagonally dominant matrix or an irreducibly weakly diagonally dominant matrix, then it is an H-matrix.*

Lemma 4.104. [201] *Let $A = [a_{ij}] \in \mathcal{Z}^{n \times n}$ be a **strictly diagonally dominant matrix** with positive diagonal entries, and $B = [b_{ij}] \in \mathbb{R}^{n \times n}$ be a **nonnegative matrix**. Then*

$$\rho(A^{-1}B) \geq \min_{1 \leq i \leq n} \frac{\sum\limits_{j=1}^{n} b_{ij}}{a_{ii} + \sum\limits_{\substack{j=1 \\ j \neq i}}^{n} a_{ij}}.$$

Proof. It follows from Theorem 4.102 that $A \in \mathbb{R}^{n \times n}$ is an M-matrix. Hence, $A^{-1} \geq 0$ and $A^{-1}B \geq 0$. Let

$$y = [y_1, y_2, \ldots, y_n]^\mathsf{T} \triangleq A^{-1}Be,$$

i.e.,

$$Be = Ay, \tag{4.21}$$

where $e = [1, 1, \ldots, 1]^\mathsf{T} \in \mathbb{R}^n$. Then $y \geq 0$ and, by Theorem 4.9, we have

$$\rho(A^{-1}B) \geq \min_{1 \leq i \leq n} y_i,$$

where y_i is equal to the i-th row sum of the matrix $A^{-1}B$. Let k be the index such that

$$y_k = \min_{1 \leq i \leq n} y_i.$$

By comparing the k-th entry of the vectors on both sides of the equation (4.21), we have

$$\sum_{j=1}^{n} b_{kj} = \sum_{j=1}^{n} a_{kj} y_j = a_{kk} y_k - \sum_{\substack{j=1 \\ j \neq k}}^{n} |a_{kj}| \, y_j$$

$$\leq y_k \left(a_{kk} - \sum_{\substack{j=1 \\ j \neq k}}^{n} |a_{kj}| \right) = y_k \left(a_{kk} + \sum_{\substack{j=1 \\ j \neq k}}^{n} a_{kj} \right).$$

Then it follows that

$$\rho(A^{-1}B) \geq \min_{1 \leq i \leq n} y_i = y_k \geq \frac{\sum\limits_{j=1}^{n} b_{kj}}{a_{kk} + \sum\limits_{\substack{j=1 \\ j \neq k}}^{n} a_{kj}} \geq \min_{1 \leq i \leq n} \frac{\sum\limits_{j=1}^{n} b_{ij}}{a_{ii} + \sum\limits_{\substack{j=1 \\ j \neq i}}^{n} a_{ij}}. \qquad \square$$

4.5.3 ▪ Generalized Strictly Diagonally Dominant Matrix

Definition 4.105. *A matrix $A = [a_{ij}] \in \mathbb{C}^{n \times n}$ is said to be a **generalized strictly diagonally dominant matrix** if there exists a positive vector $x = [x_1, x_2, \ldots, x_n]^\mathsf{T} \in \mathbb{R}^n$ such that*

$$|a_{ii}| x_i > \sum_{\substack{j=1 \\ i \neq i}}^{n} |a_{ij}| x_j, \quad i = 1, 2, \ldots, n. \tag{4.22}$$

It is easily seen that $A \in \mathbb{R}^{n \times n}$ is generalized strictly diagonally dominant if and only if there exists a diagonal matrix

$$D = \mathrm{diag}(x_1, x_2, \ldots, x_n) \in \mathbb{R}^{n \times n},$$

with $x_i > 0$ $(i = 1, 2, \ldots, n)$, such that the matrix AD is strictly diagonally dominant. The set of inequalities in (4.22) is also equivalent to $\langle A \rangle x > 0$.

Theorem 4.106. *A matrix $A = [a_{ij}] \in \mathcal{Z}^{n \times n}$ is an **M-matrix** if and only if there exists a positive vector $x \in \mathbb{R}^n$ such that $Ax > 0$.*

Proof. If $A \in \mathcal{Z}^{n \times n}$ is an M-matrix, then the matrix A is nonsingular and $A^{-1} \geq 0$. Let $x = A^{-1}e$, where $e = [1, 1, \ldots, 1]^\mathsf{T} \in \mathbb{R}^n$. Then $x > 0$ and $Ax = e > 0$.

Conversely, if there exists a positive vector $x = [x_1, x_2, \ldots, x_n] \in \mathbb{R}^n$ such that $Ax > 0$, then

$$a_{ii}x_i > -\sum_{\substack{j=1 \\ j \neq i}}^{n} a_{ij}x_j, \quad i = 1, 2, \ldots, n.$$

As $A \in \mathcal{Z}^{n \times n}$ and $x > 0$, it holds that $a_{ii} > 0$ and

$$|a_{ii}x_i| > \left| -\sum_{\substack{j=1 \\ j \neq i}}^{n} a_{ij}x_j \right| = \sum_{\substack{j=1 \\ j \neq i}}^{n} |a_{ij}x_j|, \quad i = 1, 2, \ldots, n.$$

Let

$$D = \mathrm{diag}(x_1, x_2, \ldots, x_n) \in \mathbb{R}^{n \times n}.$$

Then the matrix $AD \in \mathcal{Z}^{n \times n}$, and it is strictly diagonally dominant. It follows from Theorem 4.102 that the matrix AD is an M-matrix, i.e., AD is nonsingular and $(AD)^{-1} \geq 0$. Hence, the matrix A is nonsingular and

$$A^{-1} = D(AD)^{-1} \geq 0,$$

which implies that the matrix A is an M-matrix. □

Theorem 4.107. *A matrix $A = [a_{ij}] \in \mathbb{C}^{n \times n}$ is an **H-matrix** if and only if it is a **generalized strictly diagonally dominant matrix**.*

Proof. Suppose that the matrix A is an H-matrix. Then by definition its comparison matrix $\langle A \rangle$ is an M-matrix. It follows from Theorem 4.106 that there exists a positive vector $x = [x_1, x_2, \ldots, x_n]^\mathsf{T}$ such that $\langle A \rangle x > 0$, that is,

$$|a_{ii}|x_i > \sum_{\substack{j=1 \\ j \neq i}}^{n} |a_{ij}|x_j, \quad i = 1, 2, \ldots, n,$$

which indicates that $A \in \mathbb{C}^{n \times n}$ is a generalized strictly diagonally dominant matrix.

Conversely, if the matrix $A \in \mathbb{C}^{n \times n}$ is generalized strictly diagonally dominant, so is its comparison matrix $\langle A \rangle$. It follows from Theorem 4.106 that the matrix $\langle A \rangle$ is an M-matrix and, hence, the matrix A is an H-matrix. □

4.6 ▪ Exercises

4.1. Let $A \in \mathbb{R}^{n \times n}$. If $A \leq 0$ and $A^k > 0$ for some integer k, show that $\rho(A) > 0$.

4.2. Let $A \in \mathbb{R}^{n \times n}$. If $A \gneq 0$ has a positive eigenvector, show that $\rho(A) > 0$.

4.3. Let $A \in \mathbb{R}^{n \times n}$. If $A \geq 0$ has a positive eigenvector, show that the matrix A is similar to a nonnegative matrix whose row sums are equal to a constant.

4.4. Let $A = [a_{ij}] \in \mathbb{R}^{n \times n}$ be a nonnegative matrix with a positive eigenvector. Show that

$$\rho(A) = \max_{x > 0} \min_{1 \leq i \leq n} \frac{1}{x_i} \sum_{j=1}^{n} a_{ij} x_j = \min_{x > 0} \max_{1 \leq i \leq n} \frac{1}{x_i} \sum_{j=1}^{n} a_{ij} x_j,$$

where $x = [x_1, x_2, \ldots, x_n]^\mathsf{T} \in \mathbb{R}^n$.
(Hint: use the positive eigenvector in (4.4) or (4.5).)

4.5. Show by example that the generalization of Corollary 4.13 is not true: For $A \in \mathbb{R}^{n \times n}$, if $A \geq 0$, $x \gneq 0$ and $Ax = \lambda x$, then $\lambda = \rho(A)$.

4.6. Let $A \in \mathbb{C}^{n \times n}$. Show that the matrix A is irreducible if and only if the matrix A^T is irreducible.

4.7. Prove Theorem 4.36.

4.8. Prove Lemma 4.42.

4.9. Let $A = [a_{ij}] \in \mathbb{R}^{n \times n}$ be nonnegative and irreducible. Show that

$$\rho(A) = \min_{\substack{x \gneq 0 \\ }} \max_{\substack{1 \leq i \leq n \\ x_i > 0}} \frac{1}{x_i} \sum_{1 \leq j \leq n} a_{ij} x_j = \max_{\substack{x \gneq 0 \\ }} \min_{\substack{1 \leq i \leq n \\ x_i > 0}} \frac{1}{x_i} \sum_{1 \leq j \leq n} a_{ij} x_j,$$

where $x = [x_1, x_2, \ldots, x_n]^\mathsf{T} \in \mathbb{R}^n$.

4.10. Let $A \in \mathbb{R}^{n \times n}$ be nonnegative. If the matrix A has a nonnegative eigenvector $x \in \mathbb{R}^n$ with $r \geq 1$ positive entries and $n - r$ zero entries, show that there exists a permutation matrix $P \in \mathbb{R}^{n \times n}$ such that

$$PAP^\mathsf{T} = \begin{bmatrix} A_{11} & A_{12} \\ 0 & A_{22} \end{bmatrix},$$

where $A_{11} \in \mathbb{R}^{r \times r}$, $A_{22} \in \mathbb{R}^{(n-r) \times (n-r)}$, and the submatrix A_{11} has a positive eigenvector. Hence, the matrix A is reducible if $r < n$.

4.11. Let $A \in \mathbb{R}^{n \times n}$ and $\alpha \in \mathbb{R}$. Show that if $A \geq 0$, then $\rho(\alpha I + A) = \alpha + \rho(A)$.

4.12. Let $A \in \mathbb{C}^{n \times n}$ and suppose $\mathcal{D}_S$ consist of the union of k $(1 \leq k \leq n)$ Geršgorin discs. Show that if $\mathcal{D}_S$ is disjoint from the union of the remaining Geršgorin discs, then $\mathcal{D}_S$ contains exactly k eigenvalues (counting multiplicities) of the matrix A.

4.13. Let

$$A = \begin{bmatrix} 1 & -\frac{1}{2} & -\frac{1}{2} & 0 \\ -\frac{1}{2} & \frac{3}{2} & i & 0 \\ 0 & -\frac{i}{2} & 5 & \frac{i}{2} \\ -1 & 0 & 0 & 5i \end{bmatrix}.$$

What is the strongest statement you can make about the eigenvalues of the matrix A?

4.14. Prove Corollary 4.70.

4.15. [132] Let $A \in \mathbb{R}^{n \times n}$ be nonnegative. Show that $\alpha > \rho(A)$ if and only if there exists a vector $x > 0$ such that $(\alpha I - A)x > 0$.

4.16. Let $A \in \mathbb{R}^{n \times n}$ have positive diagonal part. Show that the matrix A is an M-matrix if and only if all of its eigenvalues have positive real parts.

4.17. Prove Theorem 4.79.

4.18. Prove Corollary 4.87.

4.19. [105] Let $A - [a_{ij}] \in \mathbb{C}^{n \times n}$ be a strictly diagonally dominant matrix. Prove that the Schur complement of the entry a_{ii}, $i \in \{1, 2, \ldots, n\}$, in the matrix A is strictly diagonally dominant, too.

Chapter 5

Matrix Splitting Iteration Methods

Consider the system of linear equations

$$Ax = b, \tag{5.1}$$

where $A \in \mathbb{C}^{n \times n}$ is the coefficient matrix, $b \in \mathbb{C}^n$ is the **right-hand side** vector, and $x \in \mathbb{C}^n$ is the unknown vector. It is well known that the **linear system** (5.1) has a unique solution if and only if the matrix A is nonsingular; then the solution is given by $x = A^{-1}b$. In this chapter, we always assume that the coefficient matrix A is nonsingular.

5.1 ▪ Direct Methods

5.1.1 ▪ Cramer Rule

The determinants can be used to solve the system of linear equations (5.1). For

$$A = [a_{ij}] \in \mathbb{C}^{n \times n} \quad \text{and} \quad b = [b_1, b_2, \ldots, b_n]^{\mathsf{T}} \in \mathbb{C}^n,$$

let $B_j \in \mathbb{C}^{n \times n}$ be the matrix obtained by replacing the j-th column of the matrix A by the vector b, i.e.,

$$B_j = \begin{bmatrix} a_{11} & \cdots & a_{1(j-1)} & b_1 & a_{1(j+1)} & \cdots & a_{1n} \\ a_{21} & \cdots & a_{2(j-1)} & b_2 & a_{2(j+1)} & \cdots & a_{2n} \\ \vdots & \vdots & \vdots & \vdots & \vdots & \vdots & \vdots \\ a_{n1} & \cdots & a_{n(j-1)} & b_n & a_{n(j+1)} & \cdots & a_{nn} \end{bmatrix}, \quad j = 1, 2, \ldots, n.$$

Theorem 5.1. *Let $A \in \mathbb{C}^{n \times n}$ be nonsingular. Then the solution $x = [x_1, x_2, \ldots, x_n]^{\mathsf{T}} \in \mathbb{C}^n$ of the linear system* (5.1) *is given by*

$$x_j = \frac{\det(B_j)}{\det(A)}, \quad j = 1, 2, \ldots, n.$$

This theorem is the well-known **Cramer rule** [99]. The Cramer rule can be regarded as a corollary of the following rank-1 update formula.

Lemma 5.2. *Let $A \in \mathbb{C}^{n \times n}$ be nonsingular. Then*

$$\det(A + \alpha uv^*) = (1 + \alpha v^* A^{-1} u) \det(A),$$

where $u, v \in \mathbb{C}^n$ and $\alpha \in \mathbb{C}$.

Proof. Because

$$A + \alpha u v^* = A(I + \alpha A^{-1} u v^*),$$

we have

$$\det(A + \alpha u v^*) = \det(A) \cdot \det(I + \alpha A^{-1} u v^*).$$

By Proposition 2.1, it holds that

$$\det(I + \alpha A^{-1} u v^*) = 1 + \alpha v^* (A^{-1} u).$$

The statement then follows immediately. $\square$

Now, we present a brief proof of the Cramer rule, which was first introduced and shown in [26]. Denote the j-th column of the matrix A by a_j. As $A \in \mathbb{C}^{n \times n}$ is nonsingular and

$$B_j = A + (b - a_j) e_j^{\mathsf{T}},$$

where e_j is the j-th column of the identity matrix I_n, it follows from Lemma 5.2 that

$$\begin{aligned}
\det(B_j) &= \det\left(A + (b - a_j) e_j^{\mathsf{T}} \right) \\
&= \det\left(A \left(I + A^{-1}(b - a_j) e_j^{\mathsf{T}} \right) \right) \\
&= \det(A) \det\left(I + A^{-1}(b - a_j) e_j^{\mathsf{T}} \right) \\
&= \det(A)(1 + e_j^{\mathsf{T}} A^{-1}(b - a_j)).
\end{aligned}$$

Furthermore, as $x = [x_1, x_2, \ldots, x_n]^{\mathsf{T}} \in \mathbb{C}^n$ is the exact solution of the linear system (5.1), we have $x = A^{-1}b$, so that

$$\begin{aligned}
\det(B_j) &= \det(A)(1 + e_j^{\mathsf{T}}(A^{-1}b - A^{-1}a_j)) \\
&= \det(A)(1 + e_j^{\mathsf{T}}(x - e_j)) \\
&= \det(A)(1 + x_j - 1) \\
&= \det(A) \, x_j.
\end{aligned}$$

Therefore,

$$x_j = \frac{\det(B_j)}{\det(A)}.$$

As the total number of operations for computing the determinant of an $n \times n$ matrix is about $n \cdot n! - 1$, the computational cost of the Cramer rule is of the order $n \cdot (n+1)!$. This is unacceptable even for a matrix A of small dimension. Therefore, the Cramer rule is practically of little use.

Note that the above proof of the Cramer rule leads to an equivalent formula

$$x_j = 1 + e_j^{\mathsf{T}} A^{-1}(b - a_j), \quad j = 1, 2, \ldots, n,$$

for the j-th element x_j of the solution x of the linear system (5.1). Therefore, using this formula and the LU decomposition of the matrix A we can describe a modified algorithm, being equivalent to the Cramer rule, for computing the solution x as follows.

Algorithm 5.1: **Modified Cramer Rule**

1: Compute the LU decomposition $A = LU$ of the matrix A
2: **for** $j = 1, 2, \ldots, n$ **do**
3:     solve $Ly = b - a_j$
4:     solve $Uz = y$
5:     compute $x_j = 1 + z_j$ with z_j being the j-th element of the vector z
6: **end for**

The total number of operations of this algorithm is about $\frac{8}{3}n^3 + \mathcal{O}(n^2)$, which is considerably smaller than that of the Cramer rule. For more details, we refer to [26].

5.1.2 ▪ Gaussian Elimination

The basic idea of the **Gaussian elimination** is to reduce the linear system (5.1) to an equivalent linear system $Ux = \tilde{b}$, where $U \in \mathbb{C}^{n \times n}$ is an **upper-triangular matrix**, and then to solve this upper-triangular linear system by **backward substitution**.

In the process of reducing the matrix A to an upper-triangular matrix U, we make use of the **Gauss transformation**; see (2.1). Suppose that $a_{11} \neq 0$. Let

$$l_1 = [0, l_{21}, l_{31}, \ldots, l_{n1}]^\mathsf{T},$$

with

$$l_{i1} = -\frac{a_{i1}}{a_{11}}, \quad i = 2, 3, \ldots, n.$$

Then

$$G_1(l_1)\,A = (I + l_1 e_1^\mathsf{T})A = A + l_1 e_1^\mathsf{T} A = \begin{bmatrix} a_{11} & a_{12} & \cdots & a_{1n} \\ 0 & \tilde{a}_{22} & \cdots & \tilde{a}_{2n} \\ \vdots & \vdots & \ddots & \vdots \\ 0 & \tilde{a}_{n2} & \cdots & \tilde{a}_{nn} \end{bmatrix} \triangleq \tilde{A}.$$

Suppose again that $\tilde{a}_{22} \neq 0$. Let

$$l_2 = [0, 0, l_{32}, l_{42}, \ldots, l_{n2}]^\mathsf{T},$$

with

$$l_{i2} = -\frac{\tilde{a}_{i2}}{\tilde{a}_{22}}, \quad i = 3, 4, \ldots, n.$$

Then

$$G_2(l_2)\,\tilde{A} = (I + l_2 e_2^\mathsf{T})\tilde{A} = \tilde{A} + l_2 e_2^\mathsf{T} \tilde{A} = \begin{bmatrix} a_{11} & a_{12} & a_{13} & \cdots & a_{1n} \\ 0 & \tilde{a}_{22} & \tilde{a}_{23} & \cdots & \tilde{a}_{2n} \\ 0 & 0 & \hat{a}_{33} & \cdots & \hat{a}_{3n} \\ \vdots & \vdots & \vdots & \ddots & \vdots \\ 0 & 0 & \hat{a}_{n3} & \cdots & \hat{a}_{nn} \end{bmatrix}.$$

Continuing this procedure, we can finally reduce the matrix $A \in \mathbb{C}^{n \times n}$ by **forward elimination** to an **upper-triangular matrix** $U \in \mathbb{C}^{n \times n}$.

Remark 5.1. *Note that in the process of reducing the matrix $A \in \mathbb{C}^{n \times n}$ to an upper-triangular matrix $U \in \mathbb{C}^{n \times n}$, we require that the k-th main diagonal entry of the resulting matrix, after k steps of the reduction, is not equal to zero. Otherwise, we may need to adopt the **pivoting technique**; see [105] and [167] for details.*

The computational cost for this reducing process is about $\frac{2}{3}n^3 + \mathcal{O}(n^2)$, and the number of operations for backward substitution is about $n^2 + \mathcal{O}(n)$. Hence, the overall computational cost for the Gaussian elimination is of the order $\mathcal{O}(n^3)$ in magnitude.

In fact, the process of reducing the matrix $A \in \mathbb{C}^{n \times n}$ to an upper-triangular matrix is equivalent to computing the **LU decomposition** of the matrix A; see Section 2.2.1. By Theorem 2.13, we know that the Gaussian elimination fails unless all of the **leading principal submatrices** of the matrix $A \in \mathbb{C}^{n \times n}$ are nonsingular.

One of the main drawbacks of the Gaussian elimination is that it does not make use of sparsity of the coefficient matrix A while, in many practical problems, the matrix A is usually very sparse. Thus, the Gaussian elimination is not suitable for solving large sparse systems of linear equations.

5.2 ▪ Classical Iteration Methods

Iteration methods try to obtain the solution of the linear system (5.1) by modifying one or a few components of an approximate solution at a time. At each step, they require to compute the products of matrices with vectors. In the case of a dense matrix, the computational cost for each iteration step is about $\mathcal{O}(n^2)$. Compared with an overall cost $\mathcal{O}(n^3)$ needed by the **Gaussian elimination method**, iteration methods can, therefore, become competitive with **direct methods**, provided the number of iteration steps that are required to converge is much smaller than n, or is possibly either independent of n, or scales sublinearly with respect to n. In fact, for large sparse matrices, the cost of matrix-vector product is much less than $\mathcal{O}(n^2)$ and, thus, iteration methods become especially much more competitive.

In this section, we consider the classical iteration methods, while the **HSS-type iteration methods** will be introduced in Section 5.5, and the **Krylov subspace iteration methods** will be discussed later in Chapter 6.

In order to obtain an approximate solution of the linear system $Ax = b$ in (5.1), we may turn to solve an approximate linear system $Mx = b$, with $M \in \mathbb{C}^{n \times n}$, that satisfies the following conditions:

(1) the matrix M is nonsingular;

(2) the linear system $Mx = b$ can be solved easily;

(3) the matrix M may be a good approximation to the matrix A.

By solving the linear system $Mx = b$, we obtain $\hat{x} \triangleq M^{-1}b$. If $\hat{x}$ is a good approximation to the exact solution $x_* = A^{-1}b$ of the linear system (5.1), then we can stop. Otherwise, we need to adopt a correction so that the corresponding residual $r \triangleq b - A\hat{x}$ is further reduced and the corresponding approximate solution $\hat{x}$ is made further accurate. Denote by $\Delta x = x_* - \hat{x}$. Then $x_* = \hat{x} + \Delta x$ and it holds that

$$b = Ax_* = A(\hat{x} + \Delta x) = A\hat{x} + A\,\Delta x,$$

or

$$A\,\Delta x = b - A\hat{x} = r.$$

Hence, in order to compute the update increment Δx, we need to solve a linear system with the same coefficient A but a different right-hand side vector r, which is as costly as solving the original linear system. To reduce the computational workload again, we use the matrix M to approximate the matrix A. Then, instead of solving the residual equation $A\,\Delta x = r$ we turn to solve the approximated residual equation $M\,\Delta x = r$, obtaining $\Delta\hat{x} \triangleq M^{-1}r$, which is an approximation to Δx.

Now the approximate solution is updated in the manner

$$\tilde{x} \triangleq \hat{x} + \Delta\hat{x},$$

or

$$\begin{aligned}
\tilde{x} &= \hat{x} + \Delta\hat{x} \\
&= \hat{x} + M^{-1}r \\
&= \hat{x} + M^{-1}(b - A\hat{x}) \\
&= M^{-1}(M - A)\hat{x} + M^{-1}b.
\end{aligned}$$

Denote by $N = M - A$, i.e.,

$$A = M - N,$$

which is a **splitting** of the matrix A. Then the relationship between the next approximate solution $\tilde{x}$ and the current approximate solution $\hat{x}$ is given by

$$\tilde{x} = M^{-1}N\hat{x} + M^{-1}b. \tag{5.2}$$

Taking $\tilde{x}$ as a new approximate solution to x_*, we can then obtain the next approximate solution by the formula (5.2). This procedure can be processed continuously until a good approximate solution is achieved.

To be clearer and more precise, for $A, M, N \in \mathbb{C}^{n \times n}$ we define $A = M - N$ as a splitting of the matrix $A \in \mathbb{C}^{n \times n}$ if the matrix $M \in \mathbb{C}^{n \times n}$ is nonsingular. Note that in some literature the splitting matrix M could be allowed to be singular.

Formula (5.2) leads to the following general form of the ***matrix splitting iteration method***:

$$x^{(k+1)} = M^{-1}Nx^{(k)} + M^{-1}b, \quad k = 0, 1, 2, \ldots, \tag{5.3}$$

where $x^{(0)}$ is a given initial guess and $x^{(k)}$ is the approximate solution obtained at the k-th iteration step. For simplicity, we rewrite the **iteration scheme** (5.3) as

$$x^{(k+1)} = Gx^{(k)} + g, \quad k = 0, 1, 2, \ldots, \tag{5.4}$$

where $G \triangleq M^{-1}N$ is called the **iteration matrix** and $g \triangleq M^{-1}b$.

Actually, the iteration scheme introduced in (5.4) is a special case of iteration methods of the form

$$\begin{aligned}
x^{(0)} &= \phi_0(A, b), \\
x^{(k+1)} &= \phi_{k+1}(x^{(k)}, x^{(k-1)}, \ldots, x^{(1)}, x^{(0)}; A, b), \quad k = 0, 1, 2, \ldots,
\end{aligned}$$

where ϕ_k, $k = 0, 1, 2, \ldots$, are given arbitrary well-defined functions. If there exists a positive integer ℓ such that ϕ_k is independent of k for $k \geq \ell$, then this iteration method is said to be **stationary**; otherwise, it is said to be **nonstationary**. In the stationary case, we let

$$\phi = \phi_\ell = \phi_{\ell+1} = \cdots,$$

so that the stationary iteration method becomes the following one:

$$x^{(0)} = \phi_0(A, b),$$
$$x^{(k+1)} = \phi_{k+1}(x^{(k)}, x^{(k-1)}, \ldots, x^{(1)}, x^{(0)}; A, b), \quad k = 0, 1, \ldots, l - 2,$$
$$x^{(k+1)} = \phi(x^{(k)}, x^{(k-1)}, \ldots, x^{(1)}, x^{(0)}; A, b), \quad k = l - 1, l, \ldots.$$

Besides, if $x^{(k+1)}$ depends only on at most the m vectors

$$x^{(k)}, x^{(k-1)}, \ldots, x^{(k-m+1)},$$

then the iteration method is called an m-step method; in particular, when $m = 1$, it is called a **one-step** or a **single-step** method, while when $m \geq 2$, it is called an **m-step** or a **multistep** method.

The **degree** [358] or **order** [8] of a stationary iteration method is the smallest integer $m \leq \ell$ such that, for $k \geq \ell$, $x^{(k+1)}$ depends on at most the previous m vectors

$$x^{(k)}, x^{(k-1)}, \ldots, x^{(k-m+1)}$$

but not on $x^{(i)}$ for $i \leq k - m$.

Note that the two terminologies "step" and "degree" (or "order") associated with an iteration method have exactly the same meaning.

Finally, if ϕ_k depends linearly on

$$x^{(0)}, x^{(1)}, \ldots, x^{(k-1)},$$

the iteration method is called **linear**; otherwise, it is called **nonlinear**. For more details, we refer to [186, 257].

In the light of these definitions, the method (5.4) is a linear stationary iteration method of single step or of first degree, that is, it is a first-order linear stationary iteration method.

Remark 5.2. *The matrix splitting iteration scheme in* (5.3) *can be equivalently reformulated into the following one:*

$$x^{(k+1)} = x^{(k)} + M^{-1}(b - Ax^{(k)}), \quad k = 0, 1, 2, \ldots. \tag{5.5}$$

As pointed out in [50], *these two iteration schemes are mathematically equivalent, but they are numerically different in actual implementations on aspects of computational complexity, convergence speed, approximate accuracy, numerical stability, etc. In particular, the iteration scheme* (5.3) *is called a **direct-splitting scheme**, and the iteration scheme* (5.5) *is called a **residual-updating scheme**. For more details, we refer to* [50] *and the references therein.*

5.2.1 ▪ Jacobi, Gauss–Seidel, and SOR Iterations

In this subsection, we introduce three classical iteration methods for solving the linear system (5.1). To this end, we first split the coefficient matrix $A \in \mathbb{C}^{n \times n}$ such that

$$A = D - L - U,$$

where D is the diagonal part of the matrix A, and $-L, -U$ are the strictly lower-triangular and strictly upper-triangular parts of the matrix A, respectively.

In this subsection, we always assume that all diagonal entries of the matrix A are nonzero, i.e., the diagonal matrix D is nonsingular.

5.2.1.1 ▪ Jacobi Iteration

If we choose $M = D$, then $N = L + U$; the iteration scheme (5.3) results in

$$x^{(k+1)} = D^{-1}(L + U)x^{(k)} + D^{-1}b, \quad k = 0, 1, 2, \ldots, \tag{5.6}$$

which is known as the **Jacobi iteration method**, or simply, the Jacobi method. Clearly, the **iteration matrix** of the Jacobi method is

$$G_{\mathrm{J}} \triangleq D^{-1}(L + U) = D^{-1}(D - A) = I - D^{-1}A.$$

The componentwise form of the Jacobi iteration method is given by

$$x_i^{(k+1)} = \frac{1}{a_{ii}} \left(b_i - \sum_{j=1}^{i-1} a_{ij}x_j^{(k)} - \sum_{j=i+1}^{n} a_{ij}x_j^{(k)} \right), \quad i = 1, 2, \ldots, n. \tag{5.7}$$

A generalization of the Jacobi iteration method is its extrapolated or relaxed variant, in which, by introducing a **relaxation parameter** $\omega \in \mathbb{R}$, the iteration scheme (5.7) is generalized to the following:

$$x_i^{(k+1)} = \frac{\omega}{a_{ii}} \left(b_i - \sum_{\substack{j=1 \\ j \neq i}}^{n} a_{ij}x_j^{(k)} \right) + (1 - \omega)x_i^{(k)}$$

$$= x_i^{(k)} + \frac{\omega}{a_{ii}} \left(b_i - \sum_{j=1}^{n} a_{ij}x_j^{(k)} \right), \quad i = 1, 2, \ldots, n.$$

This is the so-called *Jacobi overrelaxation* (JOR) or **extrapolated Jacobi iteration method**, and its matrix form is

$$x^{(k+1)} = G_{\mathrm{JOR}}(\omega)\, x^{(k)} + \omega D^{-1}b, \quad k = 0, 1, 2, \ldots, \tag{5.8}$$

where the corresponding JOR **iteration matrix** is

$$G_{\mathrm{JOR}}(\omega) \triangleq \omega D^{-1}(L + U) + (1 - \omega)I = I - \omega D^{-1}A.$$

5.2.1.2 ▪ Gauss–Seidel Iteration

If we choose $M = D - L$, then $N = U$; the iteration scheme (5.3) results in

$$x^{(k+1)} = (D - L)^{-1}Ux^{(k)} + (D - L)^{-1}b, \quad k = 0, 1, 2, \ldots, \tag{5.9}$$

which is the so-called **Gauss–Seidel iteration method**. The corresponding **iteration matrix** is given by

$$G_{\mathrm{GS}} \triangleq (D - L)^{-1}U,$$

and the componentwise form of the Gauss–Seidel iteration method is as follows:

$$x_i^{(k+1)} = \frac{1}{a_{ii}} \left(b_i - \sum_{j=1}^{i-1} a_{ij}x_j^{(k+1)} - \sum_{j=i+1}^{n} a_{ij}x_j^{(k)} \right), \quad i = 1, 2, \ldots, n. \tag{5.10}$$

We can see that the Gauss–Seidel iteration method differs from the Jacobi iteration method in that, at the $(k+1)$-th step, the currently available values $x_j^{(k+1)}$, $j = 1, 2, \ldots, i-1$, are promptly used to update the i-th component $x_i^{(k+1)}$ of the approximate solution $x^{(k+1)}$. Hence, it is expected that the Gauss–Seidel iteration method may converge faster than the Jacobi iteration method.

We can rewrite (5.10) as

$$x_i^{(k+1)} = x_i^{(k)} + \frac{1}{a_{ii}}\left(b_i - \sum_{j=1}^{i-1} a_{ij}x_j^{(k+1)} - \sum_{j=i}^{n} a_{ij}x_j^{(k)}\right), \quad i = 1, 2, \ldots, n, \qquad (5.11)$$

where the second term on the right-hand side can be regarded as a **correction term**.

5.2.1.3 ▪ SOR Iteration

In order to improve the convergence property of the Gauss–Seidel iteration method, we extrapolate $x_i^{(k+1)}$ in (5.11) with $x_i^{(k)}$ by a factor ω, obtaining the following modification of the iteration scheme in (5.11):

$$x_i^{(k+1)} = x_i^{(k)} + \frac{\omega}{a_{ii}}\left(b_i - \sum_{j=1}^{i-1} a_{ij}x_j^{(k+1)} - \sum_{j=i}^{n} a_{ij}x_j^{(k)}\right), \quad i = 1, 2, \ldots, n, \qquad (5.12)$$

where $\omega \in \mathbb{R}$ is called the **relaxation parameter**. The iteration scheme (5.12) defines the *successive overrelaxation* (SOR) iteration method, or briefly, the SOR method; see [144, 357]. In matrix-vector form, the SOR iteration method can be written as

$$x^{(k+1)} = (D - \omega L)^{-1}\big[(1 - \omega)D + \omega U\big]x^{(k)} + \omega(D - \omega L)^{-1}b, \quad k = 0, 1, 2, \ldots.$$

The **iteration matrix** of the SOR method is

$$G_{\mathrm{SOR}}(\omega) \triangleq (D - \omega L)^{-1}[(1 - \omega)D + \omega U],$$

which corresponds to the matrix splitting $A = M(\omega) - N(\omega)$ with

$$M(\omega) = \frac{1}{\omega}(D - \omega L) \quad \text{and} \quad N(\omega) = \frac{1}{\omega}[(1 - \omega)D + \omega U].$$

5.2.2 ▪ SGS and SSOR Iterations

Even if the matrix $A \in \mathbb{C}^{n \times n}$ is Hermitian, the system of linear equations with the coefficient matrix M, which we need to solve at each step of the Gauss–Seidel and SOR iteration methods, is not necessarily Hermitian. To overcome this drawback, we introduce a technique that allows to symmetrize these iteration schemes, obtaining Hermitian matrix splittings correspondingly induced from them.

Note that an analogue of the Gauss–Seidel iteration method can be obtained by simply exchanging the role of the matrix L with that of the matrix U in the iteration scheme (5.9), i.e.,

$$x^{(k+1)} = (D - U)^{-1}Lx^{(k)} + (D - U)^{-1}b, \quad k = 0, 1, 2, \ldots, \qquad (5.13)$$

which is called the **backward Gauss–Seidel iteration method**. The *symmetric Gauss–Seidel* (SGS) iteration method is hence constructed by combining one iteration step of the (**forward**)

Gauss–Seidel method (5.9) with one iteration step of the **backward Gauss–Seidel method** (5.13), i.e.,

$$\begin{cases} x^{(k+\frac{1}{2})} = (D - L)^{-1} U x^{(k)} + (D - L)^{-1} b, \\ x^{(k+1)} = (D - U)^{-1} L x^{(k+\frac{1}{2})} + (D - U)^{-1} b, \end{cases} \quad k = 0, 1, 2, \ldots,$$

which is a kind of **two-step iteration scheme**; see [21, 24]. By eliminating the **auxiliary vector** $x^{(k+\frac{1}{2})}$, we obtain

$$x^{(k+1)} = G_{\mathrm{SGS}} \, x^{(k)} + g_{\mathrm{SGS}}, \quad k = 0, 1, 2, \ldots,$$

where

$$G_{\mathrm{SGS}} = (D - U)^{-1} L (D - L)^{-1} U \quad \text{and} \quad g_{\mathrm{SGS}} = (D - U)^{-1} D (D - L)^{-1} b.$$

The SGS iteration method can be regarded as the **matrix splitting iteration method** corresponding to the **splitting** $A = M - N$ of the matrix A, with

$$M = (D - L) D^{-1} (D - U) \quad \text{and} \quad N = L D^{-1} U.$$

Note that if the matrix A is Hermitian, then $U^* = L$, so that the matrix M is Hermitian too.

In a similar fashion, we can define the **symmetric SOR** (SSOR) iteration method as follows:

$$\begin{cases} x^{(k+\frac{1}{2})} = (D - \omega L)^{-1} \big[(1 - \omega) D + \omega U\big] x^{(k)} + \omega (D - \omega L)^{-1} b, \\ x^{(k+1)} = (D - \omega U)^{-1} \big[(1 - \omega) D + \omega L\big] x^{(k+\frac{1}{2})} + \omega (D - \omega U)^{-1} b, \end{cases} \tag{5.14}$$

$$k = 0, 1, 2, \ldots,$$

or

$$x^{(k+1)} = G_{\mathrm{SSOR}}(\omega) \, x^{(k)} + g_{\mathrm{SSOR}}(\omega), \tag{5.15}$$

where

$$\begin{cases} G_{\mathrm{SSOR}}(\omega) = (D - \omega U)^{-1} [(1 - \omega) D + \omega L] (D - \omega L)^{-1} [(1 - \omega) D + \omega U], \\ g_{\mathrm{SSOR}}(\omega) = \omega (2 - \omega)(D - \omega U)^{-1} D (D - \omega L)^{-1} b. \end{cases} \tag{5.16}$$

The corresponding matrix splitting is $A = M(\omega) - N(\omega)$ with

$$M(\omega) = \frac{\omega}{2 - \omega} \left(\frac{1}{\omega} D - L \right) D^{-1} \left(\frac{1}{\omega} D - U \right) \tag{5.17}$$

and

$$N(\omega) = \frac{\omega}{2 - \omega} \left[\left(1 - \frac{1}{\omega} \right) D - L \right] D^{-1} \left[\left(1 - \frac{1}{\omega} \right) D - U \right]. \tag{5.18}$$

Obviously, if the matrix A is Hermitian, then the matrix $M(\omega)$ is Hermitian too.

Remark 5.3. *By choosing different relaxation parameters ω_1 and ω_2 in the two half-steps of the iteration scheme* (5.14), *respectively, we can obtain the so-called* **unsymmetric SOR** (USOR) *iteration method:*

$$\begin{cases} x^{(k+\frac{1}{2})} = (D - \omega_1 L)^{-1} \big[(1 - \omega_1) D + \omega_1 U\big] x^{(k)} + \omega_1 (D - \omega_1 L)^{-1} b, \\ x^{(k+1)} = (D - \omega_2 U)^{-1} \big[(1 - \omega_2) D + \omega_2 L\big] x^{(k+\frac{1}{2})} + \omega_2 (D - \omega_2 U)^{-1} b, \end{cases}$$

$$k = 0, 1, 2, \ldots.$$

5.2.3 ▪ AOR and SAOR Iterations

One more general iteration scheme is the ***accelerated overrelaxation*** (AOR) iteration method, which is defined as follows [187]:

$$x^{(k+1)} = G_{\text{AOR}}(\omega, \gamma)\, x^{(k)} + g_{\text{AOR}}(\omega, \gamma), \quad k = 0, 1, 2, \ldots,$$

with

$$G_{\text{AOR}}(\omega, \gamma) = (D - \gamma L)^{-1}\big[(1 - \omega)D + (\omega - \gamma)L + \omega U\big] \tag{5.19}$$

and

$$g_{\text{AOR}}(\omega, \gamma) = \omega(D - \gamma L)^{-1}b,$$

where $\omega \in \mathbb{R}$ is a **relaxation parameter** and $\gamma \in \mathbb{R}$ is an **acceleration parameter**. The corresponding **matrix splitting** $A = M(\omega, \gamma) - N(\omega, \gamma)$ is given by

$$M(\omega, \gamma) = \frac{1}{\omega}(D - \gamma L) \quad \text{and} \quad N(\omega, \gamma) = \frac{1}{\omega}\big[(1 - \omega)D + (\omega - \gamma)L + \omega U\big].$$

We can easily verify that the Jacobi, Gauss–Seidel, and SOR iteration methods are special cases of the AOR iteration method when the parameter pair (ω, γ) is chosen to be $(1, 0)$, $(1, 1)$, and (ω, ω), respectively. We remark that for $\gamma \neq 0$ it holds that

$$G_{\text{AOR}}(\omega, \gamma) = \frac{\omega}{\gamma}\, G_{\text{SOR}}(\gamma) + \left(1 - \frac{\omega}{\gamma}\right) I.$$

That is to say, the AOR iteration method is an **extrapolation** of the SOR iteration method corresponding to the **extrapolation factor** $\frac{\omega}{\gamma}$.

Analogously, we can define the ***symmetric AOR*** (SAOR) iteration method as

$$x^{(k+1)} = G_{\text{SAOR}}(\omega, \gamma)\, x^{(k)} + g_{\text{SAOR}}(\omega, \gamma), \quad k = 0, 1, 2, \ldots,$$

with

$$\begin{aligned}
G_{\text{SAOR}}(\omega, \gamma) &= (D - \gamma U)^{-1}\big[(1 - \omega)D + (\omega - \gamma)U + \omega L\big] \\
&\quad \cdot (D - \gamma L)^{-1}\big[(1 - \omega)D + (\omega - \gamma)L + \omega U\big]
\end{aligned}$$

and

$$g_{\text{SAOR}}(\omega, \gamma) = \omega(D - \gamma U)^{-1}\big[(2 - \omega)D + (\omega - \gamma)(L + U)\big](D - \gamma L)^{-1}b.$$

The corresponding matrix splitting $A = M(\omega, \gamma) - N(\omega, \gamma)$ is given by

$$M(\omega, \gamma) = \frac{1}{\omega}(D - \gamma L)\big[(2 - \omega)D + (\omega - \gamma)(L + U)\big]^{-1}(D - \gamma U)$$

and

$$N(\omega, \gamma) = \frac{1}{\omega}(D - \gamma U - \omega A)\, W(\omega, \gamma)^{-1}\, (D - \gamma L - \omega A),$$

where

$$W(\omega, \gamma) = (2 - \omega)D + (\omega - \gamma)(L + U) = (D - \gamma L) + (D - \gamma U) - \omega A.$$

Clearly, the SGS and SSOR iteration methods are special cases of the SAOR iteration method. Here we emphasize that if the matrix A is Hermitian, so is the SAOR splitting matrix $M(\omega, \gamma)$.

We remark that an ***unsymmetric AOR*** or **UAOR** iteration method can be defined in an analogous fashion to the **USOR** iteration method stated in Remark 5.3.

In addition, for simplicity we may omit the relaxation parameter(s) in the notation of the iteration matrices $G_{\text{JOR}}(\omega)$, $G_{\text{SOR}}(\omega)$, $G_{\text{SSOR}}(\omega)$, $G_{\text{AOR}}(\omega, \gamma)$, and $G_{\text{SAOR}}(\omega, \gamma)$, in the sequel, without causing any confusion.

Remark 5.4. *For parallel computing, these classical matrix splitting relaxation iteration methods have been naturally generalized to the* **parallel decomposition-type relaxation** *(PDR) iteration methods and the* **matrix multisplitting relaxation** *iteration methods. We refer to [16, 17, 18, 44, 51, 52, 55, 252] for detailed discussions and comprehensive surveys about algorithmic frameworks and convergence properties with respect to these parallel relaxation iteration methods.*

5.3 ▪ Convergence Analyses

5.3.1 ▪ General Results

Consider the **iteration scheme** (5.3) or (5.4). Let $x_* = A^{-1}b$ be the exact solution of the linear system (5.1). Then it holds that

$$x_* = Gx_* + g. \tag{5.20}$$

We define the **error vector** $\varepsilon^{(k)}$ for the k-th iterate as $\varepsilon^{(k)} \triangleq x^{(k)} - x_*$. If, for any initial guess $x^{(0)}$, $\varepsilon^{(k)}$ tends to zero as k tends to infinity, then the iteration scheme (5.3) is called **convergent**.

Subtracting (5.20) from (5.4), we obtain

$$\varepsilon^{(k+1)} = G\varepsilon^{(k)}, \quad k = 0, 1, 2, \ldots.$$

Therefore,

$$\varepsilon^{(k+1)} = G\varepsilon^{(k)} = G^2\varepsilon^{(k-1)} = \cdots = G^{k+1}\varepsilon^{(0)}. \tag{5.21}$$

It follows that $\varepsilon^{(k)} \to 0$ ($k \to \infty$) if and only if $G^k \to 0$ ($k \to \infty$), i.e., the iteration matrix G is convergent. By Theorem 1.34, we know that $G^k \to 0$ ($k \to \infty$) if and only if $\rho(G) < 1$. As a result, we have the following **basic convergence theorem**.

Theorem 5.3. *Let $A = M - N$ be a matrix splitting of $A \in \mathbb{C}^{n \times n}$ with $M \in \mathbb{C}^{n \times n}$ being nonsingular. Then, for any initial guess $x^{(0)} \in \mathbb{C}^n$, the iteration scheme (5.4) converges to the exact solution x_* of the linear system (5.1) if and only if $\rho(G) < 1$.*

Proof. If $\rho(G) < 1$, then $G^k \to 0$ as $k \to \infty$. Hence,

$$\varepsilon^{(k)} = G^k\varepsilon^{(0)} \to 0 \quad \text{as} \quad k \to \infty.$$

Conversely, suppose that the iteration scheme (5.4) is convergent. We prove $\rho(G) < 1$ by contradiction. If $\rho(G) \geq 1$, then there exists an eigenvalue λ of the matrix G with $|\lambda| = \rho(G) \geq 1$. Let $z \neq 0$ be the corresponding eigenvector. Choosing $x^{(0)} = x_* + z$ as the initial guess, we have

$$\varepsilon^{(k)} = G^k\varepsilon^{(0)} = G^kz = \lambda^kz,$$

which cannot tend to zero as k tends to infinity. This contradicts with the hypothesis that the iteration scheme (5.4) is convergent. Hence, $\rho(G)$ must be less than 1. □

Theorem 5.3 indicates that whether or not the iteration scheme (5.4) asymptotically converges to the exact solution x_* of the linear system (5.1) depends on the eigenvalues of the **iteration matrix** G, in particular, on its **spectral radius**. However, the actual **convergence rate** of this iteration should depend on not only the eigenvalues, but also the eigenvectors, of the corresponding iteration matrix.

In general, it is difficult to compute the spectral radius of a matrix. So, sufficient conditions that guarantee the convergence can be useful in practice.

As $\rho(G) \leq \|G\|$ holds true for any **consistent matrix norm,** we have the following result immediately.

Theorem 5.4. *Let $A = M - N$ be a **splitting** of the matrix $A \in \mathbb{C}^{n \times n}$ with the splitting matrix $M \in \mathbb{C}^{n \times n}$ being nonsingular. Denote by $G = M^{-1}N$. If there exists a consistent matrix norm $\| \cdot \|$ such that $\|G\| < 1$, then the iteration scheme (5.4) converges to the exact solution x_* of the linear system (5.1) for any initial guess $x^{(0)} \in \mathbb{C}^n$.*

From (5.21) we have

$$\|\varepsilon^{(k)}\| \leq \|G^k\| \cdot \|\varepsilon^{(0)}\|.$$

Thus, $\|G^k\|$ gives an upper bound for the ratio $\|\varepsilon^{(k)}\|/\|\varepsilon^{(0)}\|$ after k steps of iteration.

Definition 5.5. *Let $G \in \mathbb{C}^{n \times n}$ be the iteration matrix. Then, for a given consistent matrix norm $\| \cdot \|$, we call*

(1) $\|G^k\|$ *the **convergence factor** after k steps of iteration,*

(2) $\|G^k\|^{\frac{1}{k}}$ *the **average convergence factor** after k steps of iteration,*

(3) $R_k(G) \triangleq -\dfrac{1}{k} \log \|G^k\|$ *the **average convergence rate** after k steps of iteration, and*

(4) $R(G) \triangleq \lim\limits_{k \to \infty} R_k(G) = -\log \rho(G)$ *the **asymptotic convergence rate** of the iteration.*

For stationary iteration methods, the quantity $R(G)$, or equivalently, $\rho(G)$, serves as a basis in comparisons for the convergence rates of different iteration schemes. Roughly speaking, the smaller the $\rho(G)$ is, the faster the iteration scheme will be. Note that $R(G)$ is completely determined by $\rho(G)$, and vice versa. So, sometimes, $\rho(G)$ is also called the asymptotic convergence rate, or the **asymptotic convergence factor**, of the iteration, instead of $R(G)$.

We mention that the quantity $\|G\|$ is also termed the **contraction factor** of the associated iteration method.

If the matrix $A \in \mathbb{C}^{n \times n}$ is **Hermitian positive definite**, we have the following convergence result.

Theorem 5.6. *Let $A \in \mathbb{C}^{n \times n}$ be Hermitian positive definite, and $A = M - N$ be a splitting of the matrix A. Denote by $G = M^{-1}N$. If the matrix $M + M^* - A$ is Hermitian positive definite, then the splitting matrix $M \in \mathbb{C}^{n \times n}$ is invertible and $\rho(G) < 1$, i.e., the iteration scheme (5.4) asymptotically converges to the exact solution x_* of the linear system (5.1) for any initial guess $x^{(0)} \in \mathbb{C}^n$.*

Proof. We first prove the invertibility of the matrix M. Suppose that $M \in \mathbb{C}^{n \times n}$ is singular. Then there exists a nonzero vector $x \in \mathbb{C}^n$ such that $Mx = 0$. It follows that

$$x^*Mx = 0 \quad \text{and} \quad x^*M^*x = (x^*Mx)^* = 0.$$

As the matrix A is Hermitian positive definite, we have

$$x^*(M + M^* - A)x = -x^*Ax < 0,$$

which contradicts with the condition that the matrix $M + M^* - A$ is Hermitian positive definite. Therefore, the splitting matrix M must be nonsingular.

Because the matrix A is Hermitian positive definite, there exists a unique Hermitian positive-definite matrix B such that $B^2 = A$, which is denoted by $A^{\frac{1}{2}}$; see Theorem 1.55. We have

$$\begin{aligned}
\rho(G) &= \rho(A^{\frac{1}{2}}GA^{-\frac{1}{2}}) \\
&\leq \|A^{\frac{1}{2}}GA^{-\frac{1}{2}}\|_2 \\
&= \|A^{\frac{1}{2}}(M^{-1}N)A^{-\frac{1}{2}}\|_2 \\
&= \|A^{\frac{1}{2}}(I - M^{-1}A)A^{-\frac{1}{2}}\|_2 \\
&= \|I - A^{\frac{1}{2}}M^{-1}A^{\frac{1}{2}}\|_2.
\end{aligned} \tag{5.22}$$

Denote by

$$W = I - A^{\frac{1}{2}}M^{-1}A^{\frac{1}{2}}.$$

Then

$$\begin{aligned}
W^*W &= \left(I - A^{\frac{1}{2}}(M^{-1})^*A^{\frac{1}{2}}\right)\left(I - A^{\frac{1}{2}}M^{-1}A^{\frac{1}{2}}\right) \\
&= I - A^{\frac{1}{2}}(M^{-1})^*A^{\frac{1}{2}} - A^{\frac{1}{2}}M^{-1}A^{\frac{1}{2}} + A^{\frac{1}{2}}(M^{-1})^*AM^{-1}A^{\frac{1}{2}} \\
&= I - A^{\frac{1}{2}}(M^{-1})^*(M + M^* - A)M^{-1}A^{\frac{1}{2}}.
\end{aligned}$$

As the matrix $M + M^* - A$ is Hermitian positive definite, the matrix

$$A^{\frac{1}{2}}(M^{-1})^*(M + M^* - A)M^{-1}A^{\frac{1}{2}}$$

is Hermitian positive definite, too. Therefore, the matrix $I - W^*W$ is Hermitian positive definite, which implies $\rho(W^*W) < 1$. Hence,

$$\|W\|_2 = \sqrt{\rho(W^*W)} < 1,$$

which, together with (5.22), yields $\rho(G) < 1$.   □

If we choose the splitting matrix $M \in \mathbb{C}^{n \times n}$ to be Hermitian, then Theorem 5.6 results in the following.

Corollary 5.7. *Let $A \in \mathbb{C}^{n \times n}$ be Hermitian positive definite, and $A = M - N$ be a splitting of the matrix A. Denote by $G = M^{-1}N$. If the splitting matrix $M \in \mathbb{C}^{n \times n}$ is Hermitian and the matrix $2M - A$ is Hermitian positive definite, then $\rho(G) < 1$, i.e., the iteration scheme (5.4) asymptotically converges to the exact solution x_* of the linear system (5.1) for any initial guess $x^{(0)} \in \mathbb{C}^n$.*

Lemma 5.8. *Let $A = M - N$ be a splitting of the matrix $A \in \mathbb{C}^{n \times n}$. If the matrix A is Hermitian, then, for any $x \in \mathbb{C}^n$, it holds that*

$$x^*Ax - \tilde{x}^*A\tilde{x} = u^*(M + M^* - A)u,$$

where $\tilde{x} = M^{-1}Nx$ and $u = x - \tilde{x}$.

Proof. It follows from $\tilde{x} = M^{-1}Nx$ that $M\tilde{x} = Nx$. Thus

$$Mu = Mx - M\tilde{x} = Mx - Nx = Ax,$$
$$Nu = Nx - N\tilde{x} = M\tilde{x} - N\tilde{x} = A\tilde{x}.$$

By straightforward manipulations, we have

$$
\begin{aligned}
x^*Ax - \tilde{x}^*A\tilde{x} &= x^*Mu - \tilde{x}^*Nu \\
&= x^*(M - A + A^*)u - \tilde{x}^*(M - A)u \\
&= (x^* - \tilde{x}^*)(M - A)u + x^*A^*u \\
&= u^*(M - A)u + (Ax)^*u \\
&= u^*(M - A)u + (Mu)^*u \\
&= u^*(M + M^* - A)u. \quad \square
\end{aligned}
$$

Theorem 5.9. *Let $A \in \mathbb{C}^{n \times n}$ be Hermitian, and $A = M - N$ be a splitting of the matrix A. Denote by $G = M^{-1}N$. If the matrix $M + M^* - A$ is Hermitian positive definite and $\rho(G) < 1$, then the matrix A is Hermitian positive definite.*

Proof. We prove this statement by contradiction. Suppose that the matrix A is not positive definite. As $\rho(G) < 1$, it holds that $A = M(I - G)$ is nonsingular. Thus, there exists a nonzero vector $x^{(0)} \in \mathbb{C}^n$ such that

$$\eta \triangleq \left(x^{(0)}\right)^* Ax^{(0)} < 0.$$

Taking this vector $x^{(0)}$ as the initial guess, we consider the iteration sequence $\{x^{(k)}\}_{k=0}^{\infty}$ defined by

$$x^{(k)} = M^{-1}Nx^{(k-1)}, \quad k = 1, 2, \ldots.$$

As $\rho(M^{-1}N) = \rho(G) < 1$, it holds that

$$\lim_{k \to \infty} x^{(k)} = \lim_{k \to \infty} (M^{-1}N)^k x^{(0)} = 0. \tag{5.23}$$

Denote by $u^{(k)} = x^{(k-1)} - x^{(k)}$. It follows from Lemma 5.8 that

$$\left(x^{(k-1)}\right)^* Ax^{(k-1)} - \left(x^{(k)}\right)^* Ax^{(k)} = \left(u^{(k)}\right)^* (M + M^* - A)u^{(k)}.$$

Since the matrix $M + M^* - A$ is Hermitian positive definite, the quantity on the **right-hand side** of this equality is nonnegative. Hence,

$$\left(x^{(k)}\right)^* Ax^{(k)} \leq \left(x^{(k-1)}\right)^* Ax^{(k-1)}.$$

It follows that

$$\left(x^{(k)}\right)^* Ax^{(k)} \leq \left(x^{(0)}\right)^* Ax^{(0)} = \eta < 0,$$

which shows that the vector series $\{x^{(k)}\}_{k=0}^{\infty}$ cannot be convergent to 0. This contradicts with (5.23). Therefore, the matrix A must be positive definite. $\quad \square$

5.3.2 ▪ Convergence of Jacobi and Gauss–Seidel Iterations

We first give some convergence results for the **Jacobi iteration method**.

Theorem 5.10. *Let $A \in \mathbb{C}^{n \times n}$. If both matrices A and $2D - A$ are Hermitian positive definite, then the Jacobi iteration method (5.6) is convergent, i.e., $\rho(G_{\mathrm{J}}) < 1$. Conversely, assume that the matrix A is Hermitian, then it must be positive definite provided the matrix $2D - A$ is Hermitian positive definite and $\rho(G_{\mathrm{J}}) < 1$.*

Proof. The result follows immediately from Corollary 5.7 and Theorem 5.9. $\quad\square$

For the **JOR** iteration method (5.8), the assumption that the matrix $2D - A$ is **Hermitian positive definite** can be removed.

Theorem 5.11. *Let $A \in \mathbb{C}^{n \times n}$ be a Hermitian positive definite matrix. Then the JOR iteration method is convergent for*

$$0 < \omega < \frac{2}{\rho(D^{-1}A)}.$$

Proof. The result follows from the fact that

$$G_{\mathrm{JOR}}(\omega) = I - \omega D^{-1}A. \quad\square$$

As

$$G_{\mathrm{JOR}}(\omega) = \omega G_{\mathrm{J}} + (1 - \omega)I,$$

we have the following result immediately.

Theorem 5.12. *If the Jacobi iteration is convergent, then the JOR iteration is convergent for $0 < \omega \le 1$.*

In the following, we discuss the convergence properties of the **Gauss–Seidel iteration method**. If the matrix A is Hermitian, then $U = L^*$ and

$$(D - L) - A + (D - L)^* = D.$$

By Theorem 5.6, we have the following result.

Theorem 5.13. *Let $A \in \mathbb{C}^{n \times n}$ be Hermitian positive definite. Then the Gauss–Seidel iteration method (5.9) is convergent, i.e., $\rho(G_{\mathrm{GS}}) < 1$.*

Denote by

$$\tilde{L} \triangleq D^{-1}L \quad \text{and} \quad \tilde{U} \triangleq D^{-1}U.$$

As the matrix $\tilde{L}$ is strictly lower-triangular, we have

$$\tilde{L}^n = 0 \quad \text{and} \quad |\tilde{L}|^n = 0.$$

It follows that

$$(I - \tilde{L})^{-1} = I + \tilde{L} + \tilde{L}^2 + \cdots + \tilde{L}^{n-1}$$

and
$$(I - |\tilde{L}|)^{-1} = I + |\tilde{L}| + |\tilde{L}|^2 + \cdots + |\tilde{L}|^{n-1} \geq 0.$$

Moreover, it holds that
$$\begin{aligned}
|(I - \tilde{L})^{-1}| &= |I + \tilde{L} + \tilde{L}^2 + \cdots + \tilde{L}^{n-1}| \\
&\leq I + |\tilde{L}| + |\tilde{L}|^2 + \cdots + |\tilde{L}|^{n-1} \\
&= (I - |\tilde{L}|)^{-1}.
\end{aligned} \tag{5.24}$$

Analogously, we can obtain
$$|(I - \tilde{U})^{-1}| \leq (I - |\tilde{U}|)^{-1}.$$

Theorem 5.14. *If $A \in \mathbb{C}^{n \times n}$ is a strictly diagonally dominant matrix, then both Jacobi and Gauss–Seidel iteration methods are convergent. Moreover, it holds that $\|G_{GS}\|_\infty \leq \|G_J\|_\infty < 1$.*

Proof. We first prove $\|G_J\|_\infty < 1$. As the matrix A is strictly diagonally dominant, that is,
$$|a_{ii}| > \sum_{\substack{j=1 \\ j \neq i}}^{n} |a_{ij}|, \quad i = 1, 2, \ldots, n,$$

it holds that
$$\sum_{\substack{j=1 \\ j \neq i}}^{n} \frac{|a_{ij}|}{|a_{ii}|} < 1, \quad i = 1, 2, \ldots, n. \tag{5.25}$$

Hence
$$\|G_J\|_\infty = \|D^{-1}(L + U)\|_\infty = \max_{1 \leq i \leq n} \sum_{\substack{j=1 \\ j \neq i}}^{n} \frac{|a_{ij}|}{|a_{ii}|} < 1.$$

In the following, we prove $\|G_{GS}\|_\infty \leq \|G_J\|_\infty$. It suffices to show that $|G_{GS}|e \leq |G_J|e$, where $e = [1, 1, \ldots, 1]^\mathsf{T} \in \mathbb{R}^n$. By straightforward computations, we have
$$|G_{GS}|e = |(D - L)^{-1}U|e = |(I - \tilde{L})^{-1}\tilde{U}|e \leq |(I - \tilde{L})^{-1}||\tilde{U}|e \leq (I - |\tilde{L}|)^{-1}|\tilde{U}|e. \tag{5.26}$$

Here the last inequality is valid due to (5.24). It follows from (5.25) that
$$(I - |\tilde{L}| - |\tilde{U}|)e > 0. \tag{5.27}$$

Multiplying both sides of (5.27) from the left by $|\tilde{L}|$ and observing $|\tilde{L}| \geq 0$, we obtain
$$\begin{aligned}
0 \leq |\tilde{L}|(I - |\tilde{L}| - |\tilde{U}|)e &= (|\tilde{L}| - |\tilde{L}|^2 + |\tilde{U}| - |\tilde{L}| \cdot |\tilde{U}| - |\tilde{U}|)e \\
&= \left[(I - |\tilde{L}|)(|\tilde{L}| + |\tilde{U}|) - |\tilde{U}| \right] e,
\end{aligned}$$

which implies
$$|\tilde{U}|e \leq (I - |\tilde{L}|)(|\tilde{L}| + |\tilde{U}|)e.$$

Then, by multiplying both sides of this inequality from the left by the matrix $(I - |\tilde{L}|)^{-1}$ and noticing that $(I - |\tilde{L}|)^{-1} \geq 0$, we have
$$(I - |\tilde{L}|)^{-1}|\tilde{U}|e < (|\tilde{L}| + |\tilde{U}|)e, \tag{5.28}$$

As

$$|\tilde{L}| + |\tilde{U}| = |D^{-1}(L + U)| = |G_J|,$$

it follows from (5.26) and (5.28) that $|G_{\mathrm{GS}}|e \leq |G_J|e$, which completes the proof. □

The result in Theorem 5.14 also holds if the matrix A is irreducibly weakly diagonally dominant.

Theorem 5.15. *If $A \in \mathbb{C}^{n \times n}$ is an **irreducibly weakly diagonally dominant matrix**, then both Jacobi and Gauss–Seidel iteration methods are convergent for any initial guess $x^{(0)} \in \mathbb{C}^n$.*

Proof. The proof is left as Exercise 5.4. □

Corollary 5.16. *If $A \in \mathbb{C}^{n \times n}$ is **strictly diagonal dominant** or **irreducibly weakly diagonally dominant**, then the JOR iteration method is convergent for $0 < \omega \leq 1$.*

5.3.3 ▪ Convergence of SOR and SSOR Iterations

We first give a necessary condition for guaranteeing the convergence of the **SOR iteration method**, which was established in Kahan [214].

Lemma 5.17. *Let $A \in \mathbb{C}^{n \times n}$. Then, for any $\omega \in \mathbb{R}$, we have $\rho(G_{\mathrm{SOR}}(\omega)) \geq |1 - \omega|$. Therefore, if the **SOR** iteration method is convergent, it must hold $0 < \omega < 2$.*

Proof. We can rewrite the **iteration matrix** $G_{\mathrm{SOR}} \triangleq G_{\mathrm{SOR}}(\omega)$ as

$$G_{\mathrm{SOR}} = (D - \omega L)^{-1}[(1 - \omega)D + \omega U] = (I - \omega \tilde{L})^{-1}[(1 - \omega)I + \omega \tilde{U}],$$

with

$$\tilde{L} = D^{-1}L \quad \text{and} \quad \tilde{U} = D^{-1}U.$$

Therefore, it holds that

$$\begin{aligned}
\det(G_{\mathrm{SOR}}) &= \det\left((I - \omega \tilde{L})^{-1}[(1 - \omega)I + \omega \tilde{U}]\right) \\
&= \det\left((I - \omega \tilde{L})^{-1}\right) \cdot \det\left((1 - \omega)I + \omega \tilde{U}\right) \\
&= (1 - \omega)^n.
\end{aligned}$$

Let $\lambda_1, \lambda_2, \ldots, \lambda_n$ be the n eigenvalues of the matrix G_{SOR}. Then it follows that

$$\lambda_1 \lambda_2 \cdots \lambda_n = \det(G_{\mathrm{SOR}}) = (1 - \omega)^n.$$

Hence,

$$\rho(G_{\mathrm{SOR}}) = \max_{1 \leq i \leq n} |\lambda_i| \geq |\lambda_1 \lambda_2 \cdots \lambda_n|^{\frac{1}{n}} = |1 - \omega|.$$

If $\rho(G_{\mathrm{SOR}}) < 1$, then it must hold $|1 - \omega| < 1$, i.e., $0 < \omega < 2$. □

In an analogous fashion, we can establish the following necessary condition for guaranteeing the convergence of the **SSOR iteration method**.

Lemma 5.18. *Let $A \in \mathbb{C}^{n \times n}$. Then, for any $\omega \in \mathbb{R}$, we have $\rho(G_{\mathrm{SSOR}}(\omega)) \geq |1 - \omega|^2$. Therefore, if the **SSOR** iteration method is convergent, it must hold $0 < \omega < 2$.*

Proof. We can rewrite the **iteration matrix** $G_{\text{SSOR}} \triangleq G_{\text{SSOR}}(\omega)$ in (5.16) as

$$G_{\text{SSOR}} = G_{\text{SOR}}^{(B)} G_{\text{SOR}}^{(F)},$$

where $G_{\text{SOR}}^{(B)}$ is the backward SOR iteration matrix given by

$$G_{\text{SOR}}^{(B)} = (D - \omega U)^{-1}[(1 - \omega)D + \omega L] = (I - \omega \tilde{U})^{-1}[(1 - \omega)I + \omega \tilde{L}],$$

and $G_{\text{SOR}}^{(F)}$ is the forward SOR iteration matrix given by

$$G_{\text{SOR}}^{(F)} = (D - \omega L)^{-1}[(1 - \omega)D + \omega U] = (I - \omega \tilde{L})^{-1}[(1 - \omega)I + \omega \tilde{U}],$$

with

$$\tilde{L} = D^{-1}L \quad \text{and} \quad \tilde{U} = D^{-1}U.$$

Since

$$\begin{aligned}
\det(G_{\text{SOR}}^{(B)}) &= \det\left((I - \omega \tilde{U})^{-1}[(1 - \omega)I + \omega \tilde{L}]\right) \\
&= \det\left((I - \omega \tilde{U})^{-1}\right) \cdot \det\left((1 - \omega)I + \omega \tilde{L}\right) \\
&= (1 - \omega)^n
\end{aligned}$$

and

$$\begin{aligned}
\det(G_{\text{SOR}}^{(F)}) &= \det\left((I - \omega \tilde{L})^{-1}[(1 - \omega)I + \omega \tilde{U}]\right) \\
&= \det\left((I - \omega \tilde{L})^{-1}\right) \cdot \det\left((1 - \omega)I + \omega \tilde{U}\right) \\
&= (1 - \omega)^n,
\end{aligned}$$

we have

$$\det(G_{\text{SSOR}}) = \det(G_{\text{SOR}}^{(B)} G_{\text{SOR}}^{(F)}) = \det(G_{\text{SOR}}^{(B)}) \det(G_{\text{SOR}}^{(F)}) = (1 - \omega)^{2n}.$$

Let $\lambda_1, \lambda_2, \ldots, \lambda_n$ be the n eigenvalues of the matrix G_{SSOR}. Then it follows that

$$\lambda_1 \lambda_2 \cdots \lambda_n = \det(G_{\text{SSOR}}) = (1 - \omega)^{2n}.$$

Hence,

$$\rho(G_{\text{SSOR}}) = \max_{1 \le i \le n} |\lambda_i| \ge |\lambda_1 \lambda_2 \cdots \lambda_n|^{\frac{1}{n}} = |1 - \omega|^2.$$

If $\rho(G_{\text{SSOR}}) < 1$, then it must hold $|1 - \omega| < 1$, i.e., $0 < \omega < 2$. $\square$

Now we turn to discuss sufficient conditions for guaranteeing the convergence of the SOR and SSOR iteration methods in terms of the diagonally dominant matrices.

Theorem 5.19. *Let $A \in \mathbb{C}^{n \times n}$ be strictly diagonally dominant. Then the SOR iteration method converges if $0 < \omega \le 1$.*

Proof. We prove this result by contradiction. For $G_{\text{SOR}} \triangleq G_{\text{SOR}}(\omega)$, suppose that $\rho(G_{\text{SOR}}) \ge 1$. Let λ be an eigenvalue of the matrix G_{SOR} such that $|\lambda| \ge 1$. As

$$\det(\lambda I - G_{\text{SOR}}) = 0 \quad \text{and} \quad \det(I - \omega \tilde{L}) = 1,$$

it holds that

$$\det(\lambda(I - \omega\tilde{L}) - (1-\omega)I - \omega\tilde{U}) = 0.$$

Since $0 < \omega \leq 1$ and $|\lambda| \geq 1$, we have $\lambda + \omega - 1 \neq 0$. It follows that $\det(\tilde{G}) = 0$, where

$$\tilde{G} = I - \frac{\lambda\omega}{\lambda + \omega - 1}\tilde{L} - \frac{\omega}{\lambda + \omega - 1}\tilde{U}.$$

Let $\lambda = \alpha + \beta i$ with $\alpha, \beta \in \mathbb{R}$. Then, from $0 < \omega \leq 1$ and $|\lambda| \geq 1$, we know that

$$\begin{aligned}
|\lambda + \omega - 1|^2 - |\lambda\omega|^2 &= (\alpha + \omega - 1)^2 + \beta^2 - \omega^2(\alpha^2 + \beta^2) \\
&= (1 - \omega)[(\alpha - 1)^2 + \omega(\alpha^2 + \beta^2 - 1) + \beta^2] \\
&\geq 0
\end{aligned}$$

and

$$\frac{|\omega|}{|\lambda + \omega - 1|} \leq \frac{|\lambda\omega|}{|\lambda + \omega - 1|} \leq 1.$$

As the matrix A is strictly diagonally dominant, the matrix $\tilde{G}$ is also strictly diagonally dominant. This indicates that $\det(\tilde{G}) \neq 0$, which leads to a contradiction. $\quad\square$

Theorem 5.20. *Let $A \in \mathbb{C}^{n \times n}$ be strictly diagonally dominant. Then the SSOR iteration method converges if $0 < \omega \leq 1$.*

Proof. As the matrix A is strictly diagonally dominant, from the proof of Theorem 5.14 we can obtain the inequalities in (5.25), that is, in matrix-vector form,

$$(I - |\tilde{L}| - |\tilde{U}|)e > 0,$$

where

$$\tilde{L} = D^{-1}L, \quad \tilde{U} = D^{-1}U, \quad \text{and} \quad e = [1, 1, \dots, 1]^{\mathsf{T}} \in \mathbb{R}^n.$$

Evidently, this inequality is equivalent to

$$[(1-\omega)I + \omega|\tilde{U}|]e < (I - \omega|\tilde{L}|)e.$$

Note that $I - \omega|\tilde{L}|$ is an M-matrix, since it is an L-matrix satisfying $\rho(\omega|\tilde{L}|) = 0$. Hence, we have

$$(I - \omega|\tilde{L}|)^{-1} \geq 0.$$

As a result, it holds that

$$(I - \omega|\tilde{L}|)^{-1}[(1-\omega)I + \omega|\tilde{U}|]e < e,$$

which implies

$$\|(I - \omega|\tilde{L}|)^{-1}[(1-\omega)I + \omega|\tilde{U}|]\|_\infty < 1.$$

By switching the roles of the matrices $\tilde{L}$ and $\tilde{U}$, in an analogous fashion we can obtain

$$\|(I - \omega|\tilde{U}|)^{-1}[(1-\omega)I + \omega|\tilde{L}|]\|_\infty < 1.$$

For the forward SOR iteration matrix

$$G_{\text{SOR}}^{(F)} = (D - \omega L)^{-1}[(1 - \omega)D + \omega U] = (I - \omega \tilde{L})^{-1}[(1 - \omega)I + \omega \tilde{U}],$$

by straightforward computations we have

$$
\begin{aligned}
|G_{\text{SOR}}^{(F)}| &= \left| (I - \omega \tilde{L})^{-1}[(1 - \omega)I + \omega \tilde{U}] \right| \\
&\leq \left| (I - \omega \tilde{L})^{-1} \right| \left| (1 - \omega)I + \omega \tilde{U} \right| \\
&= \left| I + (\omega \tilde{L}) + (\omega \tilde{L})^2 + \cdots + (\omega \tilde{L})^{n-1} \right| \left| (1 - \omega)I + \omega \tilde{U} \right| \\
&\leq \left[I + (\omega |\tilde{L}|) + (\omega |\tilde{L}|)^2 + \cdots + (\omega |\tilde{L}|)^{n-1} \right] \left[(1 - \omega)I + \omega |\tilde{U}| \right] \\
&= (I - \omega |\tilde{L}|)^{-1} \left[(1 - \omega)I + \omega |\tilde{U}| \right].
\end{aligned}
$$

It then follows that

$$\|G_{\text{SOR}}^{(F)}\|_{\infty} = \| |G_{\text{SOR}}^{(F)}| e\|_{\infty} \leq \|(I - \omega |\tilde{L}|)^{-1}[(1 - \omega)I + \omega |\tilde{U}|] e\|_{\infty} < 1. \qquad (5.29)$$

Similarly, for the backward SOR iteration matrix

$$G_{\text{SOR}}^{(B)} = (D - \omega U)^{-1}[(1 - \omega)D + \omega L] = (I - \omega \tilde{U})^{-1}[(1 - \omega)I + \omega \tilde{L}],$$

we can also demonstrate the validity of the inequality

$$|G_{\text{SOR}}^{(B)}| \leq (I - \omega |\tilde{U}|)^{-1}[(1 - \omega)I + \omega |\tilde{L}|],$$

obtaining the estimate

$$\|G_{\text{SOR}}^{(B)}\|_{\infty} = \| |G_{\text{SOR}}^{(B)}| e\|_{\infty} \leq \|(I - \omega |\tilde{U}|)^{-1}[(1 - \omega)I + \omega |\tilde{L}|] e\|_{\infty} < 1. \qquad (5.30)$$

Therefore, it follows from the relation $G_{\text{SSOR}} = G_{\text{SOR}}^{(B)} G_{\text{SOR}}^{(F)}$ as well as the estimates in (5.29) and (5.30) that

$$\|G_{\text{SSOR}}\|_{\infty} = \|G_{\text{SOR}}^{(B)} G_{\text{SOR}}^{(F)}\|_{\infty} \leq \|G_{\text{SOR}}^{(B)}\|_{\infty} \|G_{\text{SOR}}^{(F)}\|_{\infty} < 1,$$

which straightforwardly implies

$$\rho(G_{\text{SSOR}}) \leq \|G_{\text{SSOR}}\|_{\infty} < 1.$$

Hence, the SSOR iteration method is convergent.　　　□

Analogously, we can show that these results also hold true for **irreducibly weakly diagonally dominant matrices**.

Theorem 5.21. *Let $A \in \mathbb{C}^{n \times n}$ be irreducibly weakly diagonally dominant. Then the SOR and SSOR iteration methods converge if $0 < \omega \leq 1$.*

As the **matrix splitting** $A = M(\omega) - N(\omega)$ corresponding to the SOR iteration method is given by

$$M \triangleq M(\omega) = \frac{1}{\omega} D - L, \quad N \triangleq N(\omega) = \left(\frac{1}{\omega} - 1 \right) D + U,$$

we see that

$$M + M^* - A = \frac{1}{\omega}(D + D^*) - L - L^* - A$$
$$= \frac{1}{\omega}[(1 - \omega)D + D^*] - L^* + U.$$

If the matrix A is Hermitian positive definite, so is the diagonal matrix D. Hence, from Theorem 5.6 and Lemma 5.17, we can obtain the following result [258, 279].

Theorem 5.22 (Ostrowski–Reich Theorem). *Let $A \subset \mathbb{C}^{n \times n}$ be Hermitian positive definite. Then the SOR iteration method is convergent if and only if $0 < \omega < 2$.*

Conversely, we have the following result.

Theorem 5.23. *Let $A \in \mathbb{C}^{n \times n}$ be Hermitian. If the diagonal matrix D is positive definite, and if there exists a parameter $\omega \in (0, 2)$ such that $\rho(G_{\mathrm{SOR}}(\omega)) < 1$, then the matrix A must be positive definite.*

Proof. The proof is left as Exercise 5.5.   □

In particular, for $\omega = 1$ we can get the following result.

Corollary 5.24. *Let $A \in \mathbb{C}^{n \times n}$ be Hermitian. If the diagonal matrix D is positive definite and $\rho(G_{\mathrm{GS}}) < 1$, then the matrix A must be positive definite.*

When the matrix A is Hermitian, we have the following convergence result for the SSOR iteration method.

Theorem 5.25. *Let $A \in \mathbb{C}^{n \times n}$ be Hermitian positive definite. Then the SSOR iteration method is convergent if and only if $0 < \omega < 2$.*
    Conversely, let $A \in \mathbb{C}^{n \times n}$ be Hermitian. If the diagonal matrix D is positive definite, and if there exists a parameter $\omega \in (0, 2)$ such that $\rho(G_{\mathrm{SSOR}}(\omega)) < 1$, then the matrix A must be positive definite.

Proof. The proof is left as Exercise 5.6.   □

The above results show that the convergence of the **SOR** iteration method is dependent on the **relaxation parameter** ω. The question of how to determine the optimal value ω_{opt} for the relaxation parameter ω such that $\rho(G_{\mathrm{SOR}}(\omega))$ is minimized is theoretically very important, but usually very difficult. However, in some special cases, we can give satisfactory answers. For instance, see [8, 329, 358]. Here we consider the matrices which possess **Property A**.

5.3.4 ▪ Property A and Consistent Ordering

In this subsection, we consider a special kind of block two-by-two matrices.

Definition 5.26. [358] *A matrix $A \in \mathbb{C}^{n \times n}$ is said to be of **Property A** if there exists a **permutation matrix** $P \in \mathbb{R}^{n \times n}$ such that*

$$PAP^{\mathsf{T}} = \begin{bmatrix} D_1 & A_{12} \\ A_{21} & D_2 \end{bmatrix}, \tag{5.31}$$

where D_1 and D_2 are diagonal matrices.

Clearly, Property A is invariant under symmetric permutations. For simplicity, in the following, if we say a matrix has Property A, we mean that it is of the form (5.31).

Note that if the matrix A is of the form (5.31), then the corresponding Jacobi iteration matrix has the same structure except that the diagonal blocks vanish. These Jacobi iteration matrices satisfy an important property stated in the following lemma.

Lemma 5.27. *Let B be a matrix of the block two-by-two structure as follows:*

$$B = \begin{bmatrix} 0 & B_{12} \\ B_{21} & 0 \end{bmatrix},$$

with its diagonal blocks, i.e., the two zero submatrices, being both square. Let L and U be the strictly lower- and the strictly upper-triangular parts of the matrix B, respectively. Then

(1) *if μ is an eigenvalue of the matrix B, so is $-\mu$;*

(2) *the eigenvalues of the matrix*

$$B(\alpha) = \alpha L + \frac{1}{\alpha} U, \quad \forall \alpha \neq 0,$$

are independent of the parameter α.

Proof. The first property is shown by simply observing that if $[x^\mathsf{T}, \, y^\mathsf{T}]^\mathsf{T}$ is an eigenvector of the matrix B associated with the eigenvalue μ, then $[x^\mathsf{T}, \, -y^\mathsf{T}]^\mathsf{T}$ is also an eigenvector of the matrix B associated with the eigenvalue $-\mu$.

Consider the second property. For any $\alpha \neq 0$, we have

$$\begin{bmatrix} I & 0 \\ 0 & \alpha I \end{bmatrix}^{-1} B(\alpha) \begin{bmatrix} I & 0 \\ 0 & \alpha I \end{bmatrix} = \begin{bmatrix} I & 0 \\ 0 & \frac{1}{\alpha} I \end{bmatrix} \begin{bmatrix} 0 & \frac{1}{\alpha} B_{12} \\ \alpha B_{21} & 0 \end{bmatrix} \begin{bmatrix} I & 0 \\ 0 & \alpha I \end{bmatrix} = \begin{bmatrix} 0 & B_{12} \\ B_{21} & 0 \end{bmatrix},$$

which means that the matrix $B(\alpha)$ is similar to the matrix B. This proves the desired result. □

A definition which generalizes this important property is the so-called **consistently ordered matrix**. Let

$$A = D - L - U$$

and

$$\tilde{L} = D^{-1} L, \quad \tilde{U} = D^{-1} U,$$

where $D, -L, -U$ are the diagonal, strictly lower-triangular, and strictly upper-triangular parts of the matrix A, respectively.

Definition 5.28. [358] *A matrix A of order n is **consistently ordered** if the eigenvalues of the matrix*

$$G_\mathtt{J}(\alpha) \triangleq \alpha \tilde{L} + \frac{1}{\alpha} \tilde{U}$$

are independent of the parameter α for any $\alpha \neq 0$.

It is easily seen that $G_\mathtt{J}(1) = G_\mathtt{J}$ is the Jacobi **iteration matrix** corresponding to the matrix A. It follows from Lemma 5.27 that if the matrix A has Property A, then it is consistently ordered.

Consistently ordered matrices satisfy an important property which relates the eigenvalues of the corresponding SOR iteration matrix to those of the Jacobi iteration matrix. The main theorem regarding the convergence theory for the SOR method is a consequence of the following result proved by Young in [358].

Remember that the iteration matrix of the SOR method is

$$G_{\mathrm{SOR}} \triangleq G_{\mathrm{SOR}}(\omega) = (D - \omega L)^{-1}[(1 - \omega)D + \omega U] = (I - \omega \tilde{L})^{-1}[(1 - \omega)I + \omega \tilde{U}].$$

Theorem 5.29. *Let $A = [a_{ij}] \in \mathbb{C}^{n \times n}$ be a consistently ordered matrix with $a_{ii} \neq 0$ for $i = 1, 2, \ldots, n$, and let $\omega \neq 0$. If λ is a nonzero eigenvalue of the SOR iteration matrix G_{SOR}, then any scalar μ such that*

$$(\lambda + \omega - 1)^2 = \lambda \omega^2 \mu^2 \tag{5.32}$$

is an eigenvalue of the Jacobi iteration matrix G_{J}. Conversely, if μ is an eigenvalue of the Jacobi iteration matrix G_{J} and λ is a scalar satisfying (5.32), then λ is an eigenvalue of the SOR iteration matrix G_{SOR}.

Proof. Let λ be a nonzero eigenvalue of the SOR iteration matrix G_{SOR}. Then

$$\det \left(\lambda I - (I - \omega \tilde{L})^{-1}[(1 - \omega)I + \omega \tilde{U}] \right) = 0, \tag{5.33}$$

which is equivalent to

$$\det \left(\lambda (I - \omega \tilde{L}) - [(1 - \omega)I + \omega \tilde{U}] \right) = 0$$

or

$$\det \left((\lambda + \omega - 1)I - \omega(\lambda \tilde{L} + \tilde{U}) \right) = 0.$$

Since $\omega \neq 0$ and $\lambda \neq 0$, we have

$$\det \left(\frac{\lambda + \omega - 1}{\omega \sqrt{\lambda}} I - \left(\sqrt{\lambda} \tilde{L} + \frac{1}{\sqrt{\lambda}} \tilde{U} \right) \right) = 0. \tag{5.34}$$

Define

$$\mu = \frac{\lambda + \omega - 1}{\omega \sqrt{\lambda}}.$$

Then μ is an eigenvalue of the matrix

$$\sqrt{\lambda} \tilde{L} + \frac{1}{\sqrt{\lambda}} \tilde{U}.$$

As the matrix A is consistently ordered, the eigenvalues of the matrix

$$\sqrt{\lambda} \tilde{L} + \frac{1}{\sqrt{\lambda}} \tilde{U}$$

are the same as those of the Jacobi iteration matrix

$$G_{\mathrm{J}} = \tilde{L} + \tilde{U}.$$

Hence, μ is an eigenvalue of the Jacobi iteration matrix G_{J}, too. In the same fashion, we can show that $-\mu$ is also an eigenvalue of the Jacobi iteration matrix G_{J}.

Conversely, let μ be an eigenvalue of the Jacobi iteration matrix G_{J} and assume that λ satisfies (5.32). If $\lambda = 0$, then $\omega = 1$ and

$$G_{\mathrm{SOR}} = (D - L)^{-1} U = G_{\mathrm{GS}}.$$

Hence $\det(G_{\mathrm{SOR}}) = 0$, which implies that $\lambda = 0$ is an eigenvalue of the SOR iteration matrix G_{SOR}. Now, suppose $\lambda \neq 0$. Then

$$\mu = \frac{\lambda + \omega - 1}{\omega\sqrt{\lambda}} \quad \text{or} \quad \mu = -\frac{\lambda + \omega - 1}{\omega\sqrt{\lambda}}.$$

As the matrix A is consistently ordered, we know that

$$\frac{\lambda + \omega - 1}{\omega\sqrt{\lambda}}$$

is an eigenvalue of the matrix

$$\sqrt{\lambda}\tilde{L} + \frac{1}{\sqrt{\lambda}}\tilde{U},$$

which implies that (5.34) holds true, and so does (5.33). Therefore, λ is an eigenvalue of the SOR iteration matrix G_{SOR}.

The proof is completed.   □

If $\omega = 1$, then (5.32) reduces to

$$\lambda^2 = \lambda\mu^2,$$

or

$$\lambda = \mu^2$$

for $\lambda \neq 0$. Therefore, we have the following result.

Corollary 5.30. *Let the matrix $A \in \mathbb{C}^{n \times n}$ be consistently ordered. Then $\rho(G_{\mathrm{GS}}) = \rho(G_{\mathrm{J}})^2$.*

From Corollary 5.30, we see that both Jacobi and Gauss–Seidel iteration methods converge or fail to converge at the same time. Furthermore, if they are convergent, the **Gauss–Seidel iteration** converges more rapidly than the **Jacobi iteration**, and the **asymptotic convergence rate** of the Gauss–Seidel iteration is twice that of the Jacobi iteration.

To get the most benefit from an overrelaxation, we would like to find the optimal value ω_{opt} of the relaxation parameter ω, which minimizes $\rho(G_{\mathrm{SOR}}(\omega))$.

Theorem 5.31. *Let the matrix $A \in \mathbb{C}^{n \times n}$ be consistently ordered, and suppose all eigenvalues of the Jacobi iteration matrix G_{J} are real. If $\rho(G_{\mathrm{J}}) < 1$, then*

$$\omega_{opt} = \frac{2}{1 + \sqrt{1 - \rho(G_{\mathrm{J}})^2}}$$

and the corresponding spectral radius of the SOR iteration matrix $G_{\mathrm{SOR}}(\omega)$ is given by

$$\rho(G_{\mathrm{SOR}}(\omega_{opt})) = \omega_{opt} - 1 = \frac{\rho(G_{\mathrm{J}})^2}{\left(1 + \sqrt{1 - \rho(G_{\mathrm{J}})^2}\right)^2}.$$

Proof. This result can be derived from the relationship (5.32).   □

5.3.5 ▪ Block Relaxation Iterations

The iteration methods in the previous sections are also referred to as **pointwise iteration methods**, since they act on single entries of the coefficient matrix A. It is also possible to construct **block versions** of these iteration methods.

Suppose that the matrix $A \in \mathbb{C}^{n \times n}$ is partitioned into the **block form**

$$A = \begin{bmatrix} A_{11} & A_{12} & \cdots & A_{1p} \\ A_{21} & A_{22} & \cdots & A_{2p} \\ \vdots & \vdots & \ddots & \vdots \\ A_{p1} & A_{p2} & \cdots & A_{pp} \end{bmatrix},$$

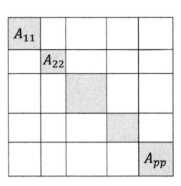

where all of the diagonal matrices A_{ii}, $i = 1, 2, \ldots, p$, are square and nonsingular. Let x_i and b_i be vectors whose lengths are consistent with the size of the submatrix A_{ii}, for $i = 1, 2, \ldots, p$. Then we can define the block Jacobi, block Gauss–Seidel, and block SOR iteration methods as follows.

- **Block Jacobi iteration method**:

$$A_{ii} x_i^{(k+1)} = b_i - \sum_{\substack{j=1 \\ j \neq i}}^{p} A_{ij} x_j^{(k)}, \quad i = 1, 2, \ldots, p.$$

- **Block Gauss–Seidel iteration method**:

$$A_{ii} x_i^{(k+1)} = b_i - \sum_{j=1}^{i-1} A_{ij} x_j^{(k+1)} - \sum_{j=i+1}^{p} A_{ij} x_j^{(k)}, \quad i = 1, 2, \ldots, p.$$

- **Block SOR iteration method**:

$$x_i^{(k+1)} = (1 - \omega) x_i^{(k)} + \omega A_{ii}^{-1} \left(b_i - \sum_{j=1}^{i-1} A_{ij} x_j^{(k+1)} - \sum_{j=i+1}^{p} A_{ij} x_j^{(k)} \right),$$
$$i = 1, 2, \ldots, p.$$

In an analogous fashion, we can define the block AOR, block SSOR, and block SAOR iteration methods, etc.

These blockwise **relaxation iteration methods** are much more suitable and effective than their pointwise counterparts when being implemented in the parallel computing environments. See [16, 243, 255].

5.4 ▪ Regular Splitting

As we have known, the convergence property of the classical iteration methods depends on the spectrum of the iteration matrix $M^{-1}N$. If $\rho(M^{-1}N) < 1$, that is, the iteration matrix $M^{-1}N$ is convergent, then we call the corresponding splitting $A = M - N$ of the matrix $A \in \mathbb{C}^{n \times n}$ a convergent splitting. Roughly speaking, the smaller the spectral radius $\rho(M^{-1}N)$ of the iteration matrix $M^{-1}N$ is, the faster the corresponding **iteration scheme** will converge. In this section, we will investigate some typical **matrix splittings** and their convergence properties.

5.4.1 ▪ Regular, Weakly Regular, and Nonnegative Splittings

Definition 5.32. *Let $A \in \mathbb{R}^{n \times n}$. Then $A = M - N$ is called*

  (1) *a **regular splitting** if the matrix M is nonsingular and $M^{-1} \geq 0$, $N \geq 0$;* [329]
  (2) *a **weak regular splitting** if the matrix M is nonsingular and $M^{-1} \geq 0$, $M^{-1}N \geq 0$;* [257]
  (3) *a **nonnegative splitting** if the matrix M is nonsingular and $M^{-1}N \geq 0$.* [60, 300]

Clearly, a regular splitting must be a weak regular splitting, and a weak regular splitting must be a nonnegative splitting.

Aiming at the Z-matrix class, we additionally introduce the concept of the **M-splitting**; see, e.g., [72].

Definition 5.33. *Let $A \in \mathbb{R}^{n \times n}$. Then $A = M - N$ is called an M-splitting if $M \in \mathbb{R}^{n \times n}$ is an M-matrix and $N \in \mathbb{R}^{n \times n}$ is a nonnegative matrix, that is, $N \geq 0$.*

We remark that an M-splitting must be a regular splitting. In addition, if $A = M - N$ is an M-splitting of the matrix $A \in \mathbb{R}^{n \times n}$, then the matrix A must be a Z-matrix, it is, however, not necessarily an L-matrix.

If both matrices A and M are nonsingular, then

$$M^{-1}N = (A + N)^{-1}N = (I + A^{-1}N)^{-1}A^{-1}N.$$

Let τ be an eigenvalue of the matrix $A^{-1}N$ and x be the corresponding eigenvector. Then $1 + \tau \neq 0$ and

$$M^{-1}Nx = (I + A^{-1}N)^{-1}A^{-1}Nx = \frac{\tau}{1+\tau}x.$$

Clearly, $\mu = \frac{\tau}{1+\tau}$ is an eigenvalue of the matrix $M^{-1}N$ and x is the corresponding eigenvector.

Conversely, let μ be an eigenvalue of the matrix $M^{-1}N$ with the associated eigenvector x. Then we have

$$(I + A^{-1}N)^{-1}A^{-1}Nx = \mu x,$$

or equivalently,

$$\mu(I + A^{-1}N)x = A^{-1}Nx.$$

As $x \neq 0$, it holds that $\mu \neq 1$. Thus, it follows that

$$A^{-1}Nx = \frac{\mu}{1-\mu}x.$$

We can obtain the following conclusion.

Lemma 5.34. *Let $A = M - N$ with both matrices $A \in \mathbb{R}^{n \times n}$ and $M \in \mathbb{R}^{n \times n}$ being nonsingular. Then τ is an eigenvalue of the matrix $A^{-1}N$ if and only if $\mu = \frac{\tau}{1+\tau}$ is an eigenvalue of the matrix $M^{-1}N$. Moreover, the matrices $A^{-1}N$ and $M^{-1}N$ have the same corresponding eigenvectors.*

Now we consider the spectral properties of the matrix $M^{-1}N$ for the **regular splitting** $A = M - N$.

Theorem 5.35. *Let $A = M - N$ be a regular splitting of the matrix $A \in \mathbb{R}^{n \times n}$. Then the matrix A is nonsingular with $A^{-1} \geq 0$ if and only if*

$$\rho(M^{-1}N) = \frac{\rho(A^{-1}N)}{1 + \rho(A^{-1}N)} < 1.$$

Proof. Suppose that $A^{-1} \geq 0$. As $A = M - N$ is a regular splitting, we have $M^{-1}N \geq 0$ and $A^{-1}N \geq 0$. By the property of **nonnegative matrices**, we know that $\rho(M^{-1}N)$ is an eigenvalue of the matrix $M^{-1}N$ and the corresponding eigenvector $x \geq 0$. It follows from Lemma 5.34 that the vector x is also an eigenvector of the matrix $A^{-1}N$. Let τ be the eigenvalue of the matrix $A^{-1}N$ associated with the eigenvector x. Then

$$\rho(M^{-1}N) = \frac{\tau}{1 + \tau} \quad \text{and} \quad \tau x = A^{-1}Nx \geq 0.$$

Hence $\tau \geq 0$. As $\frac{\tau}{1+\tau}$ is a strictly monotonically increasing function with respect to τ for $\tau \geq 0$, its maximum is achieved at $\tau = \rho(A^{-1}N)$. Therefore, we see that

$$\rho(M^{-1}N) = \frac{\rho(A^{-1}N)}{1 + \rho(A^{-1}N)} < 1.$$

Conversely, suppose that $\rho(M^{-1}N) < 1$. As $M^{-1}N \geq 0$, from Corollary 4.78 we know that the matrix $I - M^{-1}N$ is nonsingular and $(I - M^{-1}N)^{-1} \geq 0$. So

$$A = M - N = M(I - M^{-1}N)$$

is nonsingular and

$$A^{-1} = (I - M^{-1}N)^{-1}M^{-1} \geq 0.$$

Here we have used the fact that both $(I - M^{-1}N)^{-1}$ and M^{-1} are nonnegative matrices. □

Corollary 5.36. *Let $A \in \mathbb{R}^{n \times n}$ be an **M-matrix**.*

(1) *If $A = M - N$ is a regular splitting, then $\rho(M^{-1}N) < 1$;*

(2) *If $A = M - N$ is an M-splitting, then $\rho(M^{-1}N) < 1$.*

The following result gives a mean for generating a regular splitting, in particular, an M-splitting, of an M-matrix.

Theorem 5.37. *Let $A \in \mathbb{R}^{n \times n}$ be an M-matrix. If $M \in \mathbb{R}^{n \times n}$ is obtained by setting certain off-diagonal entries of the matrix A to be zero, then $A = M - N$ is an M-splitting. Thus, it is a regular splitting and it is convergent, that is, $\rho(M^{-1}N) < 1$.*

Proof. The proof is direct from Corollary 4.86 and Theorem 5.35. □

Furthermore, if the matrix $A \in \mathbb{R}^{n \times n}$ is **symmetric positive definite**, we have the following result.

Corollary 5.38. *Let $A \in \mathbb{R}^{n \times n}$ be a monotone matrix, and $A = M - N$ be a regular splitting. If the matrix A is symmetric positive definite and the matrix N is symmetric, then*

$$\rho(M^{-1}N) \leq \frac{\rho(A^{-1})\,\rho(N)}{1 + \rho(A^{-1})\,\rho(N)} < 1.$$

Proof. As the matrix A is a monotone matrix, we have $A^{-1} \geq 0$. Thus, the statement in Theorem 5.35 is valid. Since both matrices A^{-1} and N are symmetric, it holds that $\rho(A^{-1}) = \|A^{-1}\|_2$ and $\rho(N) = \|N\|_2$. Hence,

$$\rho(A^{-1}N) \leq \|A^{-1}N\|_2 \leq \|A^{-1}\|_2\|N\|_2 = \rho(A^{-1})\,\rho(N).$$

It follows from the strictly monotonically increasing property of the function $\frac{\tau}{1+\tau}$ for $\tau \geq 0$ that

$$\rho(M^{-1}N) = \frac{\rho(A^{-1}N)}{1 + \rho(A^{-1}N)} \leq \frac{\rho(A^{-1})\,\rho(N)}{1 + \rho(A^{-1})\,\rho(N)} < 1. \qquad \square$$

Suppose that we have two regular splittings

$$A = M_1 - N_1 = M_2 - N_2.$$

Then the following result, known as the **comparison theorem**, gives a relationship between $\rho(M_1^{-1}N_1)$ and $\rho(M_2^{-1}N_2)$.

Theorem 5.39. *Let $A = M_1 - N_1 = M_2 - N_2$ be two regular splittings of the matrix $A \in \mathbb{R}^{n \times n}$. If $A^{-1} \geq 0$ and $N_2 \geq N_1 \geq 0$, then*

$$0 \leq \rho(M_1^{-1}N_1) \leq \rho(M_2^{-1}N_2) < 1. \tag{5.35}$$

Moreover, if $A^{-1} > 0$ and $N_2 \gneq N_1 \gneq 0$, then

$$0 < \rho(M_1^{-1}N_1) < \rho(M_2^{-1}N_2) < 1. \tag{5.36}$$

Proof. As $A^{-1} \geq 0$ and $N_2 \geq N_1 \geq 0$, it holds that

$$A^{-1}N_2 \geq A^{-1}N_1 \geq 0.$$

By Corollary 4.6 we have

$$\rho(A^{-1}N_2) \geq \rho(A^{-1}N_1).$$

Then (5.35) follows directly from

$$\rho(M_i^{-1}N_i) = \frac{\rho(A^{-1}N_i)}{1 + \rho(A^{-1}N_i)}, \quad i = 1, 2,$$

and from the strictly monotonically increasing property of the function $\frac{\tau}{1+\tau}$ for $\tau \geq 0$.

To prove the strict inequalities of (5.36), it suffices to prove that

$$\rho(A^{-1}N_2) > \rho(A^{-1}N_1) > 0.$$

As $N_1 \gneq 0$, there exists at least one index pair (i, j) such that the (i, j)-entry $N_1(i, j)$ of the matrix N_1 is positive. It follows from $A^{-1} > 0$ that the j-th column of the matrix $A^{-1}N_1$ is positive too. Thus, by Corollary 4.10 we have $\rho(A^{-1}N_1) > 0$.

As $A^{-1} > 0$, for any nonnegative vector $x \in \mathbb{R}^n$ we claim that $A^{-1}x > 0$ if and only if $x \neq 0$. Then each column of the matrix $A^{-1}N_2$ must be either positive or zero. It follows that there exists a **permutation matrix** P such that

$$PA^{-1}N_2P^{\mathsf{T}} = \begin{bmatrix} 0 & G \\ 0 & H \end{bmatrix},$$

where $G \in \mathbb{R}^{(n-k) \times k}$, $H \in \mathbb{R}^{k \times k}$ are positive matrices with $1 \leq k \leq n$. As $N_2 \gneq N_1 \gneq 0$, it holds that

$$PA^{-1}N_1P^{\mathsf{T}} = \begin{bmatrix} 0 & \tilde{G} \\ 0 & \tilde{H} \end{bmatrix},$$

where $\tilde{G} \in \mathbb{R}^{(n-k)\times k}$, $\tilde{H} \in \mathbb{R}^{k\times k}$ are nonnegative matrices and $G \gneqq \tilde{G}$, $H \gneqq \tilde{H}$. It is clear that

$$\rho(A^{-1}N_2) = \rho(H) \quad \text{and} \quad \rho(A^{-1}N_1) = \rho(\tilde{H}).$$

From Corollary 4.48 we have $\rho(H) > \rho(\tilde{H})$ and, hence,

$$\rho(A^{-1}N_2) > \rho(A^{-1}N_1),$$

which completes the proof. $\quad\square$

In particular, if the matrix $A \in \mathbb{R}^{n\times n}$ is an **M-matrix**, the following result holds true.

Corollary 5.40. *Let $A \in \mathbb{R}^{n\times n}$ be an irreducible M-matrix. If the matrices M_1 and M_2 are obtained by setting certain off-diagonal entries of the matrix A to be zero, and the two splittings $A = M_1 - N_1 = M_2 - N_2$ satisfy $N_2 \gneqq N_1 \gneqq 0$, then*

$$0 < \rho(M_1^{-1}N_1) < \rho(M_2^{-1}N_2) < 1.$$

Lemma 5.41. *Let $A = M_1 - N_1 = M_2 - N_2$ be two splittings of the matrix $A \in \mathbb{R}^{n\times n}$, satisfying $M_1^{-1} \geq 0$ and $M_2^{-1} \geq 0$. If $N_2 \geq N_1$, then $M_1^{-1} \geq M_2^{-1}$.*

Proof. It follows from $N_2 \geq N_1$ that

$$M_1(M_1^{-1} - M_2^{-1})M_2 = M_2 - M_1 = (A + N_2) - (A + N_1) = N_2 - N_1 \geq 0,$$

which, together with the hypotheses $M_1^{-1} \geq 0$ and $M_2^{-1} \geq 0$, leads to

$$M_1^{-1} - M_2^{-1} \geq 0 \quad \text{or} \quad M_1^{-1} \geq M_2^{-1}. \quad\square$$

For two regular splittings, we have the following **comparison theorem** under weaker conditions. For a proof, see [100, 351].

Theorem 5.42. *Let $A = M_1 - N_1 = M_2 - N_2$ be two regular splittings of the matrix $A \in \mathbb{R}^{n\times n}$. If $A^{-1} \geq 0$ and $M_1^{-1} \geq M_2^{-1}$, then*

$$0 \leq \rho(M_1^{-1}N_1) \leq \rho(M_2^{-1}N_2) < 1.$$

In particular, if $A^{-1} > 0$ and $M_1^{-1} > M_2^{-1}$, then

$$0 < \rho(M_1^{-1}N_1) < \rho(M_2^{-1}N_2) < 1.$$

Lemma 5.41 shows that the assumption $M_1^{-1} \geq M_2^{-1}$ is weaker than the assumption $N_2 \geq N_1 \geq 0$.

Theorem 5.43. *[329] Let $A = M - N$ be a weak regular splitting of the matrix $A \in \mathbb{R}^{n\times n}$. Then the matrix A is nonsingular with $A^{-1} \geq 0$ if and only if $\rho(M^{-1}N) < 1$.*

Proof. Suppose that $\rho(M^{-1}N) < 1$. Then we can show that $A^{-1} \geq 0$ in the way similar to the proof in Theorem 5.35.

Conversely, suppose that $A^{-1} \geq 0$. We first prove the following equality by induction:

$$\left(I - (M^{-1}N)^{k+1}\right) A^{-1} = \left(I + M^{-1}N + \cdots + (M^{-1}N)^k\right) M^{-1}, \quad k = 0, 1, 2, \ldots. \tag{5.37}$$

In fact, it holds that

$$(I - M^{-1}N)A^{-1} = M^{-1}(M - N)A^{-1} = M^{-1}.$$

Hence, (5.37) holds for $k = 0$. Assume that (5.37) holds for $k \leq \ell - 1$. Then we have

$$
\begin{aligned}
\left(I - (M^{-1}N)^{\ell+1}\right) A^{-1} &= M^{-1} \left(M - N(M^{-1}N)^{\ell}\right) A^{-1} \\
&= M^{-1} \left(A + N(I - (M^{-1}N)^{\ell})\right) A^{-1} \\
&= M^{-1} + M^{-1}N \left(I + M^{-1}N + \cdots + (M^{-1}N)^{\ell-1}\right) M^{-1} \\
&= \left(I + M^{-1}N + \cdots + (M^{-1}N)^{\ell}\right) M^{-1}.
\end{aligned}
$$

That is to say, (5.37) holds true for $k = \ell$, too. Therefore, by induction we see that (5.37) is valid for all nonnegative integer k.

As $A^{-1} \geq 0$ and $M^{-1}N \geq 0$, we have

$$(I - (M^{-1}N)^{k+1})A^{-1} \leq A^{-1},$$

so that

$$\left(I + M^{-1}N + \cdots + (M^{-1}N)^{k}\right) M^{-1} \leq A^{-1}$$

is true for any integer $k \geq 0$, which readily shows that

$$\left(I + M^{-1}N + \cdots + (M^{-1}N)^{k} + \cdots\right) M^{-1} \leq A^{-1}.$$

As $M^{-1} \geq 0$ and $M^{-1}N \geq 0$, the above matrix inequality implies that the sum on its **left-hand side** is nonnegative and uniformly bounded from the above, which further implies that this sum of matrices is convergent. Hence, the general term $(M^{-1}N)^{k}$ must be convergent to 0 as $k \to \infty$. It then follows from Lemma 4.39 that $\rho(M^{-1}N) < 1$. □

As a consequence, Corollary 5.38 is also valid when the assumption "regular splitting" is replaced by "weak regular splitting." However, Theorem 5.42 does not hold for weak regular splittings.

Example 5.44. [8] Let

$$A = \begin{bmatrix} 1 & -1 \\ -\frac{1}{2} & 1 \end{bmatrix}$$

and

$$A = M_1 - N_1 = M_2 - N_2$$

be two splittings of the matrix A, where

$$M_1 = \begin{bmatrix} 1 & -(1+\alpha) \\ -\frac{1}{2} & 1-\alpha \end{bmatrix}, \quad N_1 = \begin{bmatrix} 0 & -\alpha \\ 0 & -\alpha \end{bmatrix},$$

with $0 < \alpha < \frac{1}{3}$, and

$$M_2 = A, \quad N_2 = 0.$$

Then

$$M_1^{-1} = \frac{2}{1 - 3\alpha} \begin{bmatrix} 1-\alpha & 1+\alpha \\ \frac{1}{2} & 1 \end{bmatrix} \quad \text{and} \quad M_2^{-1} = A^{-1} = 2 \begin{bmatrix} 1 & 1 \\ \frac{1}{2} & 1 \end{bmatrix}.$$

We can then easily verify that $M_1^{-1} > M_2^{-1}$, but

$$\rho(M_1^{-1}N_1) = \frac{3\alpha}{1 - 3\alpha} > \rho(M_2^{-1}N_2) = 0.$$

Theorem 5.45. [60, 300, 352] *Let* $A = M - N$ *be a* ***nonnegative splitting*** *of the matrix* $A \in \mathbb{R}^{n \times n}$. *Then the following statements are equivalent:*

(1) $\rho(M^{-1}N) < 1$;

(2) *the matrix* $I - M^{-1}N$ *is monotone;*

(3) *the matrix* A *is nonsingular and* $A^{-1}N \geq 0$;

(4) *the matrix* A *is nonsingular and*

$$\rho(M^{-1}N) = \frac{\rho(A^{-1}N)}{1 + \rho(A^{-1}N)}.$$

By enlarging the real matrix class to the complex matrix class, we introduce the concepts of ***H*-splitting** and ***H*-compatible splitting**; see [152].

Definition 5.46. *Let* $A \in \mathbb{C}^{n \times n}$ *and* $A = M - N$ *be its splitting. Then, this splitting is said to be an H-splitting if* $\langle M \rangle - |N|$ *is an M-matrix, and this splitting is called an H-compatible splitting if it satisfies* $\langle A \rangle = \langle M \rangle - |N|$.

H-splittings were used in the context of interval matrices by Neumaier [246, 247, 248] and Mayer [239], where they are called strong splittings. H-compatible splittings are used implicitly in Neumaier [246, Lemma 8] and in Frommer and Mayer [151, Theorem 4.1].

Note that an M-splitting must be an H-splitting. However, it is possible that an M-splitting is not an H-compatible splitting, an H-compatible splitting is not an H-splitting, and an H-splitting of an H-matrix is also not necessarily an H-compatible splitting.

If $A = M - N$ is an H-splitting, then M is an H-matrix, and so is the matrix A.

Theorem 5.47. [152] *Let* $A \in \mathbb{C}^{n \times n}$ *and* $A = M - N$ *be its splitting.*

(i) *If the splitting is an H-splitting, then* A *and* M *are H-matrices and* $\rho(M^{-1}N) \leq \rho(\langle M \rangle^{-1}|N|) < 1$.

(ii) *If the splitting is an M-splitting and* A *is an M-matrix, then it is an H-splitting and also an H-compatible splitting.*

(iii) *If the splitting is an H-compatible splitting and* A *is an H-matrix, then it is an H-splitting and thus convergent.*

Proof. We first prove the validity of Statement (i). As $A = M - N$ is an H-splitting, we know that $\langle M \rangle - |N|$ is an M-matrix and, hence, $\langle M \rangle$ is an L-matrix. Since

$$\langle M \rangle - |N| \leq \langle A \rangle$$

and

$$\langle M \rangle - |N| \leq \langle M \rangle,$$

according to Theorem 4.85 we see that both $\langle A \rangle$ and $\langle M \rangle$ are M-matrices. Therefore, A and M are H-matrices. The inequality for the spectral radii follows by repeated application of Corollary 4.48 (1) and Corollary 4.83 (3) to obtain

$$\rho(M^{-1}N) \leq \rho(|M^{-1}N|) \leq \rho(|M^{-1}| |N|) \leq \rho(\langle M \rangle^{-1}|N|),$$

and from the fact that $\langle M \rangle - |N|$ is an M-splitting, whence by Corollary 5.36 it holds that $\rho(\langle M \rangle^{-1}|N|) < 1$.

To show (ii), just note that for an M-splitting of an M-matrix we have

$$A = \langle A \rangle = \langle M \rangle - |N| = M - N.$$

Finally, if we have an H-compatible splitting and the matrix A is an H-matrix, we see from $\langle M \rangle - |N| = \langle A \rangle$ that $\langle M \rangle - |N|$ is an M-matrix. This proves (iii). $\square$

5.4.2 ▪ Convergence of Classical Iteration Methods

If $A \in \mathbb{R}^{n \times n}$ is an **M-matrix**, then we always have $A^{-1} \geq 0$. Therefore, by Theorem 5.35, the following result holds true.

Theorem 5.48. *Let $A \in \mathbb{R}^{n \times n}$ be an M-matrix. If $A = M - N$ is a regular splitting, then the iteration scheme* (5.4) *converges to the exact solution $x_* \in \mathbb{R}^n$ of the linear system $Ax = b$ in* (5.1) *for any initial guess $x^{(0)} \in \mathbb{R}^n$.*

Let $A \in \mathbb{R}^{n \times n}$ be an M-matrix, and $A = D - L - U$, with D, $-L$, and $-U$ being its diagonal, strictly lower-triangular, and strictly upper-triangular parts, respectively. Then all of the diagonal entries of the matrices A and D are positive, and $L + U \geq 0$. Hence, $A = M - N$, with $M = D$ and $N = L + U$, is a regular splitting of the matrix A. This readily leads to the following result based on Theorem 5.48.

Theorem 5.49. *Let $A \in \mathbb{R}^{n \times n}$ be an M-matrix. Then the **Jacobi iteration method** is convergent.*

Before moving further on, we introduce the following basic result, which is fundamentally useful in the convergence analysis of the classical relaxation iteration methods.

Lemma 5.50. *Let $D \in \mathbb{C}^{n \times n}$ be a nonsingular diagonal matrix. Let $E \in \mathbb{C}^{n \times n}$ be either a strictly lower-triangular matrix, or a strictly upper-triangular matrix. Then $|D| - |E|$ is an M-matrix, and it holds that*

$$|(D - E)^{-1}| \leq (|D| - |E|)^{-1}.$$

Proof. Without loss of generality, we only prove this result for the case that the matrix $E \in \mathbb{C}^{n \times n}$ is a strictly lower-triangular matrix.

Denote by $\tilde{E} \triangleq D^{-1}E$. As $\tilde{E}$ and $|\tilde{E}|$ are strictly lower-triangular matrices, we have

$$\rho(\tilde{E}) = 0 < 1, \quad \rho(|\tilde{E}|) = 0 < 1,$$

and

$$\tilde{E}^k = 0, \quad |\tilde{E}|^k = 0, \quad \forall k \geq n.$$

It follows from the definition of the M-matrix that $I - |\tilde{E}|$ is an M-matrix. As

$$|D| - |E| = |D|(I - |D|^{-1}|E|) = |D|(I - |\tilde{E}|),$$

we see that $|D| - |E|$ is an M-matrix, too.

Besides, according to Lemma 4.39 (i.e., the Neumann lemma), we have

$$(D - E)^{-1} = (I - \tilde{E})^{-1}D^{-1} = (I + \tilde{E} + \tilde{E}^2 + \cdots + \tilde{E}^{n-1})D^{-1}.$$

Hence, it holds that

$$|(D - E)^{-1}| = \left| \sum_{k=0}^{n-1} \tilde{E}^k D^{-1} \right| \le \sum_{k=0}^{n-1} |\tilde{E}|^k |D|^{-1} = (I - |\tilde{E}|)^{-1} |D|^{-1} = (|D| - |E|)^{-1}. \qquad \square$$

If $A \in \mathbb{C}^{n \times n}$ is an **H-matrix**, then its **comparison matrix**

$$\langle A \rangle = |D| - |L| - |U|$$

is an M-matrix.

Frequently, we have the following simple, but very useful facts.

Lemma 5.51. *For $A \in \mathbb{C}^{n \times n}$, let D, $-L$, and $-U$ be its diagonal, strictly lower-triangular, and strictly upper-triangular parts, respectively, so that $A = D - L - U$. Let $\omega \in (0, 1)$. Then the following three splittings of the type $A = M - N$ are all M-splittings:*

  (i) $M = |D|$ *and* $N = |L| + |U|$,
  (ii) $M = |D| - |L|$ *and* $N = |U|$,
  (iii) $M = \frac{1}{\omega}(|D| - \omega|L|)$ *and* $N = \frac{1}{\omega}[(1 - \omega)|D| + \omega|U|]$.

In addition, if $A \in \mathbb{C}^{n \times n}$ is an H-matrix, then all of these three splittings are convergent, that is, it holds that

$$\rho(|D|^{-1}(|L| + |U|)) < 1, \quad \rho((|D| - |L|)^{-1}|U|) < 1$$

and

$$\rho((|D| - \omega|L|)^{-1}[(1 - \omega)|D| + \omega|U|]) < 1.$$

As the Jacobi iteration matrix corresponding to the matrix A is given by

$$G_{\mathrm{J}} = D^{-1}(L + U),$$

we see that

$$|G_{\mathrm{J}}| = |D^{-1}(L + U)| = |D|^{-1}(|L| + |U|)$$

and

$$\rho(G_{\mathrm{J}}) \le \rho(|G_{\mathrm{J}}|) < 1.$$

Theorem 5.52. *Let $A \in \mathbb{C}^{n \times n}$ be an H-matrix. Then the Jacobi iteration method is convergent.*

If $A \in \mathbb{R}^{n \times n}$ is an M-matrix, we can show that $(D - L)^{-1} \ge 0$; see Exercise 5.8. Hence, the matrix splitting corresponding to the **Gauss–Seidel iteration method** is an **M-splitting**, and is also a **regular splitting**.

Theorem 5.53. *Let $A \in \mathbb{R}^{n \times n}$ be an M-matrix. Then the Gauss–Seidel iteration method is convergent.*

In accordance with Lemma 5.50 we have

$$|(D - L)^{-1}U| \le |(D - L)^{-1}||U| \le (|D| - |L|)^{-1}|U|,$$

and in the light of Lemma 5.51 we know that the matrix $(|D| - |L|)^{-1}|U|$ is convergent, that is,

$$\rho((|D| - |L|)^{-1}|U|) < 1.$$

This demonstrates the convergence of the Gauss–Seidel iteration method.

Theorem 5.54. *Let $A \in \mathbb{C}^{n \times n}$ be an H-matrix. Then the Gauss–Seidel iteration method is convergent.*

The following theorem demonstrates the asymptotic convergence of the SOR iteration method for the H-matrix class.

Theorem 5.55. *Let $A \in \mathbb{C}^{n \times n}$ be an H-matrix. Then the SOR iteration method is convergent, provided the relaxation parameter ω satisfies*

$$0 < \omega < \frac{2}{1 + \rho(|G_J|)}.$$

Proof. Recalling again that the SOR iteration matrix is

$$G_{\text{SOR}} \triangleq G_{\text{SOR}}(\omega) = (D - \omega L)^{-1}[(1 - \omega)D + \omega U],$$

by making use of Lemma 5.50 we have

$$
\begin{aligned}
|G_{\text{SOR}}| &\leq |(D - \omega L)^{-1}| \, |(1 - \omega)D + \omega U| \\
&\leq (|D| - \omega |L|)^{-1} \left(|1 - \omega| |D| + \omega |U| \right) \\
&\triangleq M_\omega^{-1} N_\omega,
\end{aligned}
$$

where

$$M_\omega = \frac{1}{\omega}(|D| - \omega |L|) \quad \text{and} \quad N_\omega = \frac{1}{\omega}(|1 - \omega| |D| + \omega |U|).$$

Also, by Lemma 5.50 we know that M_ω is an M-matrix. Obviously, N_ω is a nonnegative matrix. If we denote by

$$A_\omega \triangleq M_\omega - N_\omega,$$

then this constitutes an M-splitting.

Furthermore, by straightforward computations we can obtain

$$
\begin{aligned}
A_\omega &= M_\omega - N_\omega \\
&= \frac{1}{\omega}(|D| - \omega |L|) - \frac{1}{\omega}(|1 - \omega| |D| + \omega |U|) \\
&= \frac{1 - |1 - \omega|}{\omega}|D| - |L| - |U| \\
&\triangleq D_\omega - B_\omega,
\end{aligned}
$$

with

$$D_\omega = \frac{1 - |1 - \omega|}{\omega}|D| \quad \text{and} \quad B_\omega = |L| + |U|.$$

Note that for $\omega \in (0, 2)$ it holds that

$$\frac{1 - |1 - \omega|}{\omega} > 0.$$

Hence, A_ω is an L-matrix. As the condition

$$0 < \omega < \frac{2}{1 + \rho(|G_J|)}$$

is equivalent to the inequality

$$|1 - \omega| + \omega\,\rho(|G_{\mathsf{J}}|) < 1,$$

we have

$$\rho(D_\omega^{-1}B_\omega) = \frac{\omega}{1 - |1 - \omega|}\rho(|D|^{-1}(|L| + |U|))$$

$$= 1 + \frac{|1 - \omega| + \omega\,\rho(|G_{\mathsf{J}}|) - 1}{1 - |1 - \omega|}$$

$$< 1.$$

In accordance with Theorem 4.82, we see that A_ω is an M-matrix.

Up to now, we have demonstrated that A_ω is an M-matrix and $A_\omega = M_\omega - N_\omega$ is an M-splitting. As a consequence, this splitting is a convergent splitting, that is, it holds that $\rho(M_\omega^{-1}N_\omega) < 1$. It then follows that

$$\rho(G_{\mathrm{SOR}}) \leq \rho(|G_{\mathrm{SOR}}|) \leq \rho(M_\omega^{-1}N_\omega) < 1.$$

That is to say, the SOR iteration method is convergent. □

We can also establish the asymptotic convergence theory for the AOR iteration method in the H-matrix class.

Theorem 5.56. *Let $A \in \mathbb{C}^{n \times n}$ be an H-matrix. Then the AOR iteration method is convergent, provided the relaxation parameter ω and the acceleration parameter γ satisfy*

$$0 \leq \gamma \leq \omega \quad and \quad 0 < \omega < \frac{2}{1 + \rho(|G_{\mathsf{J}}|)}.$$

Proof. As $A \in \mathbb{C}^{n \times n}$ is an H-matrix, it holds that $\rho(|G_{\mathsf{J}}|) < 1$. For any positive real ε, we define the matrix

$$J_\varepsilon \triangleq |D|^{-1}(|L| + |U| + \varepsilon e e^{\mathsf{T}}) = |G_{\mathsf{J}}| + \varepsilon|D|^{-1}e e^{\mathsf{T}},$$

with $e = [1, 1, \ldots, 1]^{\mathsf{T}} \in \mathbb{R}^n$. Then $J_\varepsilon \in \mathbb{R}^{n \times n}$ is a nonnegative and irreducible matrix. In the light of the Perron–Frobenius theorem (i.e., Theorem 4.43), there exists a unique positive vector $x_\varepsilon \in \mathbb{R}^n$ such that

$$J_\varepsilon x_\varepsilon = \rho(J_\varepsilon)\,x_\varepsilon. \tag{5.38}$$

In addition, from the definition of the matrix J_ε we know that it is monotonically increasing with respect to ε. Because any eigenvalue of a square matrix is a continuous function of the elements of this matrix, and because the spectral radius of a nonnegative matrix is a monotonically increasing function with respect to the matrix (see Corollary 4.6), we see that $\rho(J_\varepsilon)$ is a monotonically increasing function with respect to ε. Therefore, we can let the positive number ε be small enough such that $\rho_\varepsilon \triangleq \rho(J_\varepsilon) < 1$. Noticing that the condition

$$0 < \omega < \frac{2}{1 + \rho(|G_{\mathsf{J}}|)}$$

is equivalent to the inequality

$$|1 - \omega| + \omega\,\rho(|G_{\mathsf{J}}|) < 1,$$

we can further restrict the positive real ε so small that

$$\eta_\varepsilon \triangleq |1 - \omega| + \omega\,\rho_\varepsilon < 1. \tag{5.39}$$

As $D \in \mathbb{C}^{n \times n}$ is diagonal and $L \in \mathbb{C}^{n \times n}$ is strictly lower triangular, by Lemma 5.50 we have

$$\left|(D - \gamma L)^{-1}\right| \leq (|D| - \gamma|L|)^{-1}.$$

From the definition of the AOR iteration matrix in (5.19), under the condition $0 \leq \gamma \leq \omega$ we can obtain

$$
\begin{aligned}
|G_{\text{AOR}}(\omega, \gamma)| &= \left|(D - \gamma L)^{-1}\left[(1 - \omega)D + (\omega - \gamma)L + \omega U\right]\right| \\
&\leq \left|(D - \gamma L)^{-1}\right| |(1 - \omega)D + (\omega - \gamma)L + \omega U| \\
&\leq (|D| - \gamma|L|)^{-1}[|1 - \omega||D| + (\omega - \gamma)|L| + \omega|U|] \\
&= (|D| - \gamma|L|)^{-1}[(|1 - \omega| - 1)|D| + (|D| - \gamma|L|) + \omega(|L| + |U|)] \\
&= I + (|D| - \gamma|L|)^{-1}[(|1 - \omega| - 1)|D| + \omega(|L| + |U|)] \\
&\leq I + (|D| - \gamma|L|)^{-1}[(|1 - \omega| - 1)|D| + \omega(|L| + |U| + \varepsilon e e^\mathsf{T})] \\
&= I + (|D| - \gamma|L|)^{-1}|D|[(|1 - \omega| - 1)I + \omega J_\varepsilon].
\end{aligned}
$$

It then follows from (5.38) and (5.39) that

$$
\begin{aligned}
|G_{\text{AOR}}(\omega, \gamma)|\, x_\varepsilon &\leq \left\{I + (|D| - \gamma|L|)^{-1}|D|[(|1 - \omega| - 1)I + \omega J_\varepsilon]\right\} x_\varepsilon \\
&= \left[I + (|D| - \gamma|L|)^{-1}|D|(|1 - \omega| - 1 + \omega\rho_\varepsilon)\right] x_\varepsilon \\
&= \left[I - (|D| - \gamma|L|)^{-1}|D|(1 - \eta_\varepsilon)\right] x_\varepsilon. \tag{5.40}
\end{aligned}
$$

As

$$|D| - \gamma|L| \leq |D|$$

and $|D| - \gamma|L|$ is an M-matrix, it holds that

$$(|D| - \gamma|L|)^{-1}|D| \geq I.$$

Hence, based upon (5.40) we can further obtain the inequality

$$|G_{\text{AOR}}(\omega, \gamma)|\, x_\varepsilon \leq [1 - (1 - \eta_\varepsilon)]\, x_\varepsilon = \eta_\varepsilon\, x_\varepsilon.$$

Note that the matrix $|G_{\text{AOR}}(\omega, \gamma)|$ is nonnegative and the vector x_ε is positive, in accordance with Theorem 4.12 we see that

$$\rho(|G_{\text{AOR}}(\omega, \gamma)|) \leq \eta_\varepsilon,$$

so that

$$\rho(G_{\text{AOR}}(\omega, \gamma)) \leq \rho(|G_{\text{AOR}}(\omega, \gamma)|) < 1.$$

As a result, the AOR iteration method is convergent. $\quad\square$

Evidently, Theorem 5.55 is a special case of Theorem 5.56 when $\gamma = \omega$. Even so, we have given the proofs of these two theorems by making use of different techniques and knowledge. The proof of Theorem 5.55 mainly uses matrix operations based on the M-splitting property in the M-matrix theory, while the proof of Theorem 5.56 largely utilizes algebraic analysis based on the Perron–Frobenius theorem in the nonnegative matrix theory.

For $A = [a_{ij}] \in \mathbb{C}^{n \times n}$, we define

$$\Omega(A) \triangleq \left\{ B = [b_{ij}] \in \mathbb{C}^{n \times n} : |b_{ij}| = |a_{ij}|, \ 1 \leq i, j \leq n \right\}$$

to be the set of **equimodular matrices** associated with the matrix A [72].

Theorem 5.57. [355] *Let $A \in \mathbb{C}^{n \times n}$ be a matrix with all of its diagonal entries being nonzero, and let the relaxation parameter ω and the acceleration parameter γ satisfy $0 \leq \gamma \leq \omega$. Then the matrix A is an H-matrix if and only if the SAOR **iteration matrix** $G_{\text{SAOR}}(\omega, \gamma)$ with respect to any matrix $B \in \Omega(A)$ satisfies $\rho(G_{\text{SAOR}}(\omega, \gamma)) < 1$ and*

$$0 < \omega < \frac{2}{1 + \rho(|G_{\text{J}}|)}. \tag{5.41}$$

In particular, the matrix A is an H-matrix if and only if the SSOR iteration matrix $G_{\text{SSOR}}(\omega)$ with respect to any matrix $B \in \Omega(A)$ satisfies $\rho(G_{\text{SSOR}}(\omega)) < 1$ and the relaxation parameter ω satisfies (5.41).

Corollary 5.58. *Let $A \in \mathbb{C}^{n \times n}$ be **strictly diagonally dominant** or **irreducibly weakly diagonally dominant**. Then the **SOR** and **SSOR** iteration methods are convergent if*

$$0 < \omega < \frac{2}{1 + \rho(|G_J|)}.$$

This corollary provides a larger convergence domain for the SOR and SSOR iteration methods with respect to the **relaxation parameter** ω than those in Theorems 5.19, 5.20, and 5.21.

5.4.3 ▪ P-Regular Splitting

Definition 5.59. [254] *Let $A \in \mathbb{C}^{n \times n}$. Then $A = M - N$ is called a **P-regular splitting** of the matrix A if the matrix $M + N$ is **positive definite**.*

It is clear that the matrix $M + N$ is positive definite if and only if the matrix $M^* + N$ is positive definite. In particular, if the matrix A is Hermitian, then $A = M - N$ is a P-regular splitting if and only if the matrix $M + M^* - A$ is Hermitian positive definite.

The following result, called the Householder–John theorem, is stated in [256] and re-proved in [342]. In fact, it is a straightforward integration of Theorems 5.6 and 5.9, but with a different proof.

Theorem 5.60 (Householder–John Theorem). *Let $A \in \mathbb{C}^{n \times n}$ be a Hermitian and nonsingular matrix. If $A = M - N$ is a P-regular splitting, then $\rho(M^{-1}N) < 1$ if and only if the matrix A is positive definite.*

Proof. Let

$$G \triangleq M^{-1}N = I - M^{-1}A$$

and

$$C \triangleq A - G^* A G.$$

Then

$$C = A - (I - M^{-1}A)^* A(I - M^{-1}A)$$
$$= (M^{-1}A)^* A + AM^{-1}A - (M^{-1}A)^* AM^{-1}A$$
$$= (M^{-1}A)^* \left[A(M^{-1}A)^{-1} + ((M^{-1}A)^*)^{-1}A - A \right] M^{-1}A$$
$$= (M^{-1}A)^* (M + M^* - A) M^{-1}A.$$

As $A = M - N$ is a P-regular splitting and A is a Hermitian matrix, the matrix $M + M^* - A$ is Hermitian positive definite. Hence, the matrix $C = A - G^* AG$ is Hermitian positive definite, too. If the matrix A is Hermitian positive definite, then it follows from Theorem 1.61 that $\rho(G) < 1$.

Conversely, we suppose that $\rho(G) < 1$. As the matrix $C = A - G^* AG$ is Hermitian positive definite, we know that the matrices

$$(G^*)^i CG^i, \quad i = 1, 2, \ldots,$$

are Hermitian positive semidefinite and the equalities

$$(G^*)^i CG^i = (G^*)^i AG^i - (G^*)^{i+1}AG^{i+1}$$
$$= (M^{-1}AG^i)^*(M + M^* - A)(M^{-1}AG^i), \quad i = 1, 2, \ldots,$$

hold true. Note that

$$A - (G^*)^k AG^k = C + G^* AG - (G^*)^k AG^k$$
$$= C + \sum_{i=1}^{k-1} \left[(G^*)^i AG^i - (G^*)^{i+1}AG^{i+1} \right]$$
$$= C + \sum_{i=1}^{k-1} (G^*)^i CG^i.$$

Then, by using $\rho(G) < 1$ and letting $k \to \infty$ we have

$$A = C + \sum_{i=1}^{\infty} (G^*)^i CG^i.$$

Recalling that the matrix C is Hermitian positive definite and the matrices

$$(G^*)^i CG^i, \quad i = 1, 2, \ldots,$$

are Hermitian positive semidefinite, the above equality then shows that the matrix A is Hermitian positive definite. □

Theorem 5.60 can be used to prove the **Ostrowski–Reich theorem**, i.e., if the matrix $A \in \mathbb{C}^{n \times n}$ is Hermitian positive definite, then the SOR iteration method converges for $\omega \in (0, 2)$; see Theorem 5.22. A more general result is stated in the following theorem.

Theorem 5.61 (Ostrowski Theorem). [258] *Let $A = D - E - E^* \in \mathbb{C}^{n \times n}$ be a Hermitian matrix, where the matrix D is Hermitian positive definite and the matrix $D - \omega E$ is nonsingular for $0 < \omega < 2$. Then $\rho(\mathcal{L}(\omega)) < 1$ if and only if the matrix A is positive definite and the parameter ω satisfies $0 < \omega < 2$, where*

$$\mathcal{L}(\omega) \triangleq (D - \omega E)^{-1}[(1 - \omega)D + \omega E^*]$$

Note that in Theorem 5.61 the matrix $D \in \mathbb{C}^{n \times n}$ need not be diagonal, and the matrix $E \in \mathbb{C}^{n \times n}$ need not be strictly lower- or strictly upper-triangular; and Theorem 5.22, that is, the Ostrowski–Reich theorem, is a special case of this theorem.

A stronger version of Theorem 5.61, due to Kuznetsov [218], can be similarly established; see Exercise 5.10.

The special case $\omega = 1$ of Theorem 5.61, first proved by Reich [279], is given as the following corollary.

Corollary 5.62. *Let* $A = D - E - E^* \in \mathbb{C}^{n \times n}$ *be a Hermitian matrix, where the matrix D is Hermitian positive definite and the matrix $D - E$ is nonsingular. Then the iteration method of the Gauss–Seidel type is convergent, i.e.,* $\rho((D - E)^{-1}E^*) < 1$, *if and only if the matrix A is positive definite.*

From Theorem 5.60, we know that a P-regular splitting of a Hermitian positive definite matrix is convergent. However, a convergent splitting of a Hermitian positive definite matrix may not be P-regular.

Example 5.63. [89] Let $A = M - N$, where

$$A = \begin{bmatrix} 1 & 0 \\ 0 & 1 \end{bmatrix}, \quad M = \begin{bmatrix} \dfrac{1}{\varepsilon} & -\dfrac{m}{\varepsilon^2} \\ 0 & \dfrac{1}{\varepsilon} \end{bmatrix}, \quad N = \begin{bmatrix} \dfrac{1}{\varepsilon} - 1 & -\dfrac{m}{\varepsilon^2} \\ 0 & \dfrac{1}{\varepsilon} - 1 \end{bmatrix}, \quad 0 < \varepsilon < 1.$$

Then

$$M^{-1} = \begin{bmatrix} \varepsilon & m \\ 0 & \varepsilon \end{bmatrix} \quad \text{and} \quad M^{-1}N = \begin{bmatrix} 1 - \varepsilon & -m \\ 0 & 1 - \varepsilon \end{bmatrix},$$

which leads to

$$\rho(M^{-1}N) = 1 - \varepsilon < 1.$$

On the other hand, we have

$$M + M^* - A = \begin{bmatrix} \dfrac{2}{\varepsilon} - 1 & -\dfrac{m}{\varepsilon^2} \\ -\dfrac{m}{\varepsilon^2} & \dfrac{2}{\varepsilon} - 1 \end{bmatrix},$$

which is not positive definite if $m > \varepsilon(2 - \varepsilon)$. Therefore, $A = M - N$ is not a P-regular splitting when $m > \varepsilon(2 - \varepsilon)$.

Theorem 5.64. *Let* $A \in \mathbb{C}^{n \times n}$ *be a Hermitian positive definite matrix, and $A = M - N$ be a splitting of the matrix A. Then* $\|M^{-1}N\|_{A^{1/2}} < 1$ *if and only if the matrix splitting $A = M - N$ is P-regular.*

Proof. Let $G = M^{-1}N$. Then

$$A - G^*AG = (M^{-1}A)^*(M + M^* - A)(M^{-1}A).$$

Multiplying both sides of this matrix equality by $A^{-\frac{1}{2}}$ from both left and right, we have

$$I - (A^{\frac{1}{2}}GA^{-\frac{1}{2}})^*(A^{\frac{1}{2}}GA^{-\frac{1}{2}}) = (M^{-1}A^{\frac{1}{2}})^*(M + M^* - A)(M^{-1}A^{\frac{1}{2}}).$$

Since

$$\|A^{\frac{1}{2}} G A^{-\frac{1}{2}}\|_2 = \|G\|_{A^{1/2}},$$

the conclusion follows immediately.   □

Theorem 5.65. [255, 336] *Let* $A \in \mathbb{C}^{n \times n}$ *be positive definite. If* $A = M - N$ *is a P-regular splitting such that* $N \in \mathbb{C}^{n \times n}$ *is Hermitian, then* $\rho(M^{-1}N) < 1$. *See also* [335, 360].

Proof. Let

$$\mathscr{H}(A) = \frac{1}{2}(A + A^*) \quad \text{and} \quad \mathscr{S}(A) = \frac{1}{2}(A - A^*)$$

be the Hermitian and skew-Hermitian parts of the matrix A, respectively, and let

$$\mathscr{H}(M) = \frac{1}{2}(M + M^*)$$

be the Hermitian part of the matrix M. Since the matrix N is Hermitian,

$$\mathscr{S}(M) = \frac{1}{2}(M - M^*) = \frac{1}{2}[(M - N) - (M - N)^*] = \frac{1}{2}(A - A^*) = \mathscr{S}(A).$$

So, the skew-Hermitian part of the matrix M coincides with the skew-Hermitian part of the matrix A, and

$$\mathscr{H}(A) = \mathscr{H}(M) - N$$

is Hermitian positive definite.

In addition, that $A = M - N$ is a P-regular splitting implies that the matrix $M^* + N$ is positive definite. Consequently, the matrix $\mathscr{H}(M) + N$ is Hermitian positive definite. In the light of Theorem 5.60 we have $\rho((\mathscr{H}(M))^{-1}N) < 1$. Since the matrix $\mathscr{H}(M)$ is Hermitian positive definite, with $D \triangleq (\mathscr{H}(M))^{\frac{1}{2}}$ it holds that

$$\rho((\mathscr{H}(M))^{-1}N) = \rho(D^{-1}ND^{-1}) = \max_{y \neq 0} \left| \frac{y^* D^{-1} N D^{-1} y}{y^* y} \right| < 1. \tag{5.42}$$

Let λ be an eigenvalue of the matrix $M^{-1}N$ satisfying $|\lambda| = \rho(M^{-1}N)$ and x be a corresponding eigenvector. Then from

$$M^{-1}N = (\mathscr{H}(M) + \mathscr{S}(M))^{-1}N = D^{-1} \left(I + D^{-1} \mathscr{S}(M) D^{-1}\right)^{-1} D^{-1}N,$$

with the variable replacement $y = Dx$ we have

$$D^{-1}ND^{-1}y = \lambda \left(I + D^{-1} \mathscr{S}(M) D^{-1}\right) y,$$

which straightforwardly leads to

$$\lambda = \frac{y^* D^{-1} N D^{-1} y}{y^*(I + D^{-1} \mathscr{S}(M) D^{-1})y}.$$

Since the matrix $\mathscr{S}(M)$ is skew-Hermitian, so is the matrix $\left(D^{-1} \mathscr{S}(M) D^{-1}\right)$. As a result, the quantity

$$y^* D^{-1} \mathscr{S}(M) D^{-1} y$$

is purely imaginary. Therefore, by making use of (5.42) we can obtain

$$|\lambda| = \frac{|y^* D^{-1} N D^{-1} y|}{|y^*(I + D^{-1} \mathscr{S}(M) D^{-1}) y|} < \frac{\|y\|_2^2}{\sqrt{\|y\|_2^4 + |y^* D^{-1} \mathscr{S}(M) D^{-1} y|^2}} \leq 1,$$

that is, $\rho(M^{-1} N) < 1$. ☐

For a more general version of this theorem, we refer to [336].

5.5 ▪ HSS-Type Iteration Methods

For any matrix $A \in \mathbb{C}^{n \times n}$, it naturally possesses a **Hermitian and skew-Hermitian** (HS) splitting [9, 97, 118, 166, 169, 335, 346]

$$A = H + S, \tag{5.43}$$

where

$$H = \frac{1}{2}(A + A^*) \quad \text{and} \quad S = \frac{1}{2}(A - A^*)$$

are the Hermitian and skew-Hermitian parts of the matrix A, respectively. Bai, Golub, and Ng [36] presented and studied an efficient iteration method based on this **matrix splitting** for solving the system of linear equations (5.1).

5.5.1 ▪ HSS Iteration

Based on the HS splitting (5.43), Bai, Golub, and Ng [36] presented the following **Hermitian and skew-Hermitian splitting** (HSS) iteration method:

$$\begin{cases} (\alpha I + H) x^{(k+\frac{1}{2})} = (\alpha I - S) x^{(k)} + b, \\ (\alpha I + S) x^{(k+1)} = (\alpha I - H) x^{(k+\frac{1}{2})} + b, \end{cases} \quad k = 0, 1, 2, \ldots, \tag{5.44}$$

where $\alpha \in \mathbb{R}$ is a given positive parameter.

Evidently, each iterate of the **HSS** iteration alternates between the Hermitian part H and the skew-Hermitian part S of the matrix A, analogously to the classical *alternating direction implicit* (ADI) iteration for solving partial differential equations; see Peaceman and Rachford [273] and Douglas and Rachford [115].

Note that we can reverse roles of the matrices H and S in the above HSS iteration method, so that we may first solve the system of linear equations with coefficient matrix $\alpha I + S$ and then solve the system of linear equations with coefficient matrix $\alpha I + H$.

In order to establish the convergence theory for the HSS iteration method (5.44), we eliminate the intermediate vector $x^{(k+\frac{1}{2})}$ and write this iteration as a standard stationary iteration scheme of the form

$$x^{(k+1)} = G_{\text{HSS}}(\alpha) x^{(k)} + g_{\text{HSS}}(\alpha), \tag{5.45}$$

where

$$G_{\text{HSS}}(\alpha) \triangleq (\alpha I + S)^{-1}(\alpha I - H)(\alpha I + H)^{-1}(\alpha I - S) \tag{5.46}$$

is the HSS **iteration matrix**, and

$$g_{\text{HSS}}(\alpha) \triangleq 2\alpha(\alpha I + S)^{-1}(\alpha I + H)^{-1} b.$$

In fact, by letting

$$\begin{cases} M_{\text{HSS}}(\alpha) & = & \frac{1}{2\alpha}(\alpha I + H)(\alpha I + S), \\ N_{\text{HSS}}(\alpha) & = & \frac{1}{2\alpha}(\alpha I - H)(\alpha I - S), \end{cases}$$

we have

$$A = M_{\text{HSS}}(\alpha) - N_{\text{HSS}}(\alpha) \tag{5.47}$$

and

$$G_{\text{HSS}}(\alpha) = M_{\text{HSS}}(\alpha)^{-1} N_{\text{HSS}}(\alpha), \quad g_{\text{HSS}}(\alpha) = M_{\text{HSS}}(\alpha)^{-1} b.$$

As a consequence, the HSS iteration scheme (5.44) can also be regarded as a matrix splitting iteration induced by the splitting (5.47) of the coefficient matrix A.

Note that the fixed-point iteration scheme (5.45) converges asymptotically for arbitrary initial guesses and right-hand sides to the exact solution of the linear system (5.1) if and only if the corresponding iteration matrix $G_{\text{HSS}}(\alpha)$ in (5.46) is convergent, that is, $\rho(G_{\text{HSS}}(\alpha)) < 1$, where $\rho(G_{\text{HSS}}(\alpha))$ denotes the spectral radius of the HSS iteration matrix $G_{\text{HSS}}(\alpha)$.

For the convergence property of the HSS iteration, we have the following theorem.

Theorem 5.66. [36] *Let $A \in \mathbb{C}^{n \times n}$ be a positive definite matrix, $H = \frac{1}{2}(A + A^*)$ and $S = \frac{1}{2}(A - A^*)$ be its Hermitian and skew-Hermitian parts, respectively, and $\alpha \in \mathbb{R}$ be a positive scalar. Then the spectral radius $\rho(G_{\text{HSS}}(\alpha))$ of the HSS iteration matrix $G_{\text{HSS}}(\alpha)$ is bounded by*

$$\varsigma_{\text{HSS}}(\alpha) \triangleq \max_{\lambda_i \in \sigma(H)} \frac{|\alpha - \lambda_i|}{\alpha + \lambda_i},$$

*where $\sigma(H)$ is the **spectral set** of the matrix H. Therefore, it holds that*

$$\rho(G_{\text{HSS}}(\alpha)) \leq \varsigma_{\text{HSS}}(\alpha) < 1, \quad \forall \alpha > 0,$$

i.e., the HSS iteration converges unconditionally to the unique solution $x_* \in \mathbb{C}^n$ of the system of linear equations (5.1).

Proof. By the **similarity invariance** of the **matrix spectrum**, we have

$$\begin{aligned} \rho(G_{\text{HSS}}(\alpha)) &= \rho((\alpha I - H)(\alpha I + H)^{-1}(\alpha I - S)(\alpha I + S)^{-1}) \\ &\leq \|(\alpha I - H)(\alpha I + H)^{-1}(\alpha I - S)(\alpha I + S)^{-1}\|_2 \\ &\leq \|(\alpha I - H)(\alpha I + H)^{-1}\|_2 \|(\alpha I - S)(\alpha I + S)^{-1}\|_2. \end{aligned}$$

Letting

$$Q(\alpha) = (\alpha I - S)(\alpha I + S)^{-1}$$

and noting that $S^* = -S$, we see that

$$\begin{aligned} Q(\alpha)^* Q(\alpha) &= (\alpha I - S)^{-1}(\alpha I + S)(\alpha I - S)(\alpha I + S)^{-1} \\ &= (\alpha I - S)^{-1}(\alpha I - S)(\alpha I + S)(\alpha I + S)^{-1} \\ &= I. \end{aligned}$$

That is to say, $Q(\alpha)$ is a unitary matrix. ($Q(\alpha)$ is also called the **Cayley transform** of the matrix S.) Therefore, $\|Q(\alpha)\|_2 = 1$. It then follows that

$$\rho(G_{\text{HSS}}(\alpha)) \leq \|(\alpha I - H)(\alpha I + H)^{-1}\|_2 = \max_{\lambda_i \in \sigma(H)} \frac{|\alpha - \lambda_i|}{\alpha + \lambda_i}.$$

Since $\lambda_i > 0$ $(i = 1, 2, \ldots, n)$ and α is a positive constant, it is easy to see that

$$\rho(G_{\mathrm{HSS}}(\alpha)) \leq \varsigma_{\mathrm{HSS}}(\alpha) < 1. \qquad \square$$

Theorem 5.66 shows that the **convergence speed** of the HSS iteration is bounded by $\varsigma_{\mathrm{HSS}}(\alpha)$, which only depends on the spectrum of the Hermitian part H, but depends neither on the spectrum of the skew-Hermitian part S and the coefficient matrix A, nor on the eigenvectors of the matrices H, S, and A.

Now, if we introduce a vector norm

$$|||x||| \triangleq \|(\alpha I + S)x\|_2, \quad \text{for} \quad x \in \mathbb{C}^n,$$

and denote the induced matrix norm by

$$|||X||| \triangleq \|(\alpha I + S)X(\alpha I + S)^{-1}\|_2,$$

then from the proof of Theorem 5.66 we see that

$$|||G_{\mathrm{HSS}}(\alpha)||| = \|(\alpha I - H)(\alpha I + H)^{-1}(\alpha I - S)(\alpha I + S)^{-1}\|_2 \leq \varsigma_{\mathrm{HSS}}(\alpha).$$

It follows that

$$|||x^{(k+1)} - x_*||| \leq \varsigma_{\mathrm{HSS}}(\alpha) |||x^{(k)} - x_*|||, \qquad k = 0, 1, 2, \ldots.$$

Therefore, $\varsigma_{\mathrm{HSS}}(\alpha)$ is also an upper bound of the **contraction factor** of the HSS iteration in the sense of the norm $||| \cdot |||$. See [36].

We remark that if the lower and the upper bounds of the eigenvalues of the Hermitian part H are known, then an approximate optimal parameter α_* for $\varsigma_{\mathrm{HSS}}(\alpha)$ (or an upper bound of $\rho(G_{\mathrm{HSS}}(\alpha))$ or $|||G_{\mathrm{HSS}}(\alpha)|||$) can be obtained. This fact is precisely stated in the following corollary.

Corollary 5.67. [36] *Let $A \in \mathbb{C}^{n \times n}$ be positive definite, $A = H + S$ be the HS splitting of the matrix A, and α be a positive scalar. Denote by $\gamma_{\min}$ and $\gamma_{\max}$ the minimum and the maximum eigenvalues of the matrix H. Then*

$$\alpha_* \equiv \operatorname*{argmin}_{\alpha} \left\{ \max_{\gamma_{\min} \leq \lambda \leq \gamma_{\max}} \frac{|\alpha - \lambda|}{\alpha + \lambda} \right\} = \sqrt{\gamma_{\min}\gamma_{\max}}$$

and

$$\varsigma_{\mathrm{HSS}}(\alpha_*) = \frac{\sqrt{\gamma_{\max}} - \sqrt{\gamma_{\min}}}{\sqrt{\gamma_{\max}} + \sqrt{\gamma_{\min}}} = \frac{\sqrt{\kappa(H)} - 1}{\sqrt{\kappa(H)} + 1},$$

*where $\kappa(H)$ is the **spectral condition number** of the matrix H.*

Proof. Now,

$$\varsigma_{\mathrm{HSS}}(\alpha) = \max \left\{ \frac{|\alpha - \gamma_{\min}|}{\alpha + \gamma_{\min}}, \quad \frac{|\alpha - \gamma_{\max}|}{\alpha + \gamma_{\max}} \right\}.$$

To compute an approximate optimal $\alpha > 0$ such that the **convergence factor** $\rho(G_{\mathrm{HSS}}(\alpha))$ of the HSS iteration is minimized, we can minimize the upper bound $\varsigma_{\mathrm{HSS}}(\alpha)$ of $\rho(G_{\mathrm{HSS}}(\alpha))$ instead. If α_* is such a minimum point, then it must satisfy

$$\alpha_* - \gamma_{\min} > 0, \quad \alpha_* - \gamma_{\max} < 0,$$

and

$$\frac{\alpha_\star - \gamma_{\min}}{\alpha_\star + \gamma_{\min}} = \frac{\gamma_{\max} - \alpha_\star}{\gamma_{\max} + \alpha_\star}.$$

Therefore,

$$\alpha_\star = \sqrt{\gamma_{\min}\gamma_{\max}},$$

and the result follows.   □

Remark 5.5. *Note that in Corollary 5.67 we minimize $\varsigma_{\mathrm{HSS}}(\alpha)$ over the interval $[\gamma_{\min}, \gamma_{\max}]$ instead of on the spectral set $\sigma(H)$. However, it can be easily shown that*

$$\max_{\lambda_i \in \sigma(H)} \frac{|\alpha - \lambda_i|}{\alpha + \lambda_i} = \max_{\gamma_{\min} \leq \lambda \leq \gamma_{\max}} \frac{|\alpha - \lambda|}{\alpha + \lambda}.$$

Also, $\gamma_{\min}$ and $\gamma_{\max}$ can be replaced by the lower and the upper bounds for the eigenvalues of the matrix H, respectively.

Remark 5.6. *We emphasize that in Corollary 5.67 the optimal parameter $\alpha_\star$ only minimizes the upper bound $\varsigma_{\mathrm{HSS}}(\alpha)$ of the spectral radius of the iteration matrix, but does not minimize the spectral radius itself.*

Corollary 5.67 shows that when the approximate optimal parameter $\alpha_\star$ is employed, the upper bound of the convergence rate of the HSS iteration is about the same as that of the ***conjugate gradient*** (CG) method applied to linear systems with their coefficient matrices being the Hermitian positive definite matrix H, and it does become the same when, in particular, the coefficient matrix A is Hermitian. It should be mentioned that when the coefficient matrix A is **normal**, we have $HS = SH$ and, therefore,

$$\rho(G_{\mathrm{HSS}}(\alpha)) = |||G_{\mathrm{HSS}}(\alpha)||| = \varsigma_{\mathrm{HSS}}(\alpha).$$

The optimal parameter $\alpha_\star$ then minimizes all of these three quantities.

For further results about the optimal iteration parameter α_{opt} of the HSS iteration method which minimizes the spectral radius $\rho(G_{\mathrm{HSS}}(\alpha))$ of the HSS iteration matrix $G_{\mathrm{HSS}}(\alpha)$, we refer to [33, 64]; for in-depth convergence theory on the HSS iteration method, we refer to [24, 34, 74]; and for applications of the HSS technique to **saddle-point problems**, we refer to [31, 32, 38, 65, 68, 295]. See also [267] and [268] for other applications.

5.5.2 ▪ NSS Iteration

We can extend the HS splitting (5.43) to obtain the ***normal and skew-Hermitian*** (NS) splitting [37]

$$A = N + S,$$

where N is a normal matrix and S is a skew-Hermitian matrix. Based on this NS splitting, Bai, Golub, and Ng [37] established the following ***normal and skew-Hermitian splitting*** (NSS) iteration method for solving the system of linear equations (5.1):

$$\begin{cases} (\alpha I + N)x^{(k+\frac{1}{2})} = (\alpha I - S)x^{(k)} + b, \\ (\alpha I + S)x^{(k+1)} = (\alpha I - N)x^{(k+\frac{1}{2})} + b, \end{cases} \qquad k = 0, 1, 2, \ldots,$$

where $\alpha \in \mathbb{R}$ is a given positive parameter.

The **NSS** iteration method can be equivalently rewritten as

$$x^{(k+1)} = G_{\text{NSS}}(\alpha)\, x^{(k)} + g_{\text{NSS}}(\alpha), \quad k = 0, 1, 2, \ldots, \tag{5.48}$$

where

$$G_{\text{NSS}}(\alpha) \triangleq (\alpha I + S)^{-1}(\alpha I - N)(\alpha I + N)^{-1}(\alpha I - S)$$

is the NSS **iteration matrix**, and

$$g_{\text{NSS}}(\alpha) \triangleq 2\alpha(\alpha I + S)^{-1}(\alpha I + N)^{-1}b.$$

In fact, the iteration scheme (5.48) may also result from the splitting

$$A = M_{\text{NSS}}(\alpha) - N_{\text{NSS}}(\alpha)$$

of the coefficient matrix A, with

$$\begin{cases} M_{\text{NSS}}(\alpha) &= \frac{1}{2\alpha}(\alpha I + N)(\alpha I + S), \\ N_{\text{NSS}}(\alpha) &= \frac{1}{2\alpha}(\alpha I - N)(\alpha I - S). \end{cases}$$

Then it holds that

$$G_{\text{NSS}}(\alpha) = M_{\text{NSS}}(\alpha)^{-1} N_{\text{NSS}}(\alpha) \quad \text{and} \quad g_{\text{NSS}}(\alpha) = M_{\text{NSS}}(\alpha)^{-1} b.$$

For the convergence property of the NSS iteration, we have the following theorem.

Theorem 5.68. [37, 47] *Let $A \in \mathbb{C}^{n \times n}$ be a positive definite matrix, $A = N + S$ be the NS splitting of the matrix A, and $\alpha \in \mathbb{R}$ be a positive scalar. Then the spectral radius $\rho(G_{\text{NSS}}(\alpha))$ of the NSS iteration matrix $G_{\text{NSS}}(\alpha)$ is bounded by*

$$\varsigma_{\text{NSS}}(\alpha) = \max_{\lambda_j \in \sigma(N)} \frac{|\alpha - \lambda_j|}{|\alpha + \lambda_j|} = \max_{\gamma_j + i\eta_j \in \sigma(N)} \sqrt{\frac{(\alpha - \gamma_j)^2 + \eta_j^2}{(\alpha + \gamma_j)^2 + \eta_j^2}}.$$

Therefore, it holds that

$$\rho(G_{\text{NSS}}(\alpha)) \leq \varsigma_{\text{NSS}}(\alpha) < 1, \quad \forall \alpha > 0,$$

i.e., the NSS iteration converges unconditionally to the exact solution $x_* \in \mathbb{C}^n$ of the system of linear equations (5.1).

Moreover, if $\gamma_{\min}$ and $\gamma_{\max}$, $\eta_{\min}$ and $\eta_{\max}$ are the lower and the upper bounds of the real, the absolute values of the imaginary parts of the eigenvalues of the matrix N, respectively, and $\Omega = [\gamma_{\min}, \gamma_{\max}] \times [\eta_{\min}, \eta_{\max}]$, then

$$\alpha_\star \triangleq \underset{\alpha}{\arg\min} \left\{ \max_{(\gamma, \eta) \in \Omega} \sqrt{\frac{(\alpha - \gamma)^2 + \eta^2}{(\alpha + \gamma)^2 + \eta^2}} \right\}$$

$$= \begin{cases} \sqrt{\gamma_{\min} \gamma_{\max} - \eta_{\max}^2}, & \text{for } \eta_{\max} < \sqrt{\gamma_{\min} \gamma_{\max}}, \\ \sqrt{\gamma_{\min}^2 + \eta_{\max}^2}, & \text{for } \eta_{\max} \geq \sqrt{\gamma_{\min} \gamma_{\max}}, \end{cases}$$

and

$$\varsigma_{\text{NSS}}(\alpha_\star) = \begin{cases} \left(\dfrac{\gamma_{\min} + \gamma_{\max} - 2\sqrt{\gamma_{\min} \gamma_{\max} - \eta_{\max}^2}}{\gamma_{\min} + \gamma_{\max} + 2\sqrt{\gamma_{\min} \gamma_{\max} - \eta_{\max}^2}} \right)^{\frac{1}{2}}, & \text{for } \eta_{\max} < \sqrt{\gamma_{\min} \gamma_{\max}}, \\[4mm] \left(\dfrac{\sqrt{\gamma_{\min}^2 + \eta_{\max}^2} - \gamma_{\min}}{\sqrt{\gamma_{\min}^2 + \eta_{\max}^2} + \gamma_{\min}} \right)^{\frac{1}{2}}, & \text{for } \eta_{\max} \geq \sqrt{\gamma_{\min} \gamma_{\max}}. \end{cases}$$

Proof. By the **similarity invariance** of the **matrix spectrum**, we have

$$
\begin{aligned}
\rho(G_{\text{NSS}}(\alpha)) &= \rho((\alpha I - N)(\alpha I + N)^{-1}(\alpha I - S)(\alpha I + S)^{-1}) \\
&\leq \|(\alpha I - N)(\alpha I + N)^{-1}(\alpha I - S)(\alpha I + S)^{-1}\|_2 \\
&\leq \|(\alpha I - N)(\alpha I + N)^{-1}\|_2 \|(\alpha I - S)(\alpha I + S)^{-1}\|_2.
\end{aligned}
$$

Letting

$$
Q(\alpha) = (\alpha I - S)(\alpha I + S)^{-1},
$$

we see that $Q(\alpha)$ is the **Cayley transform** of the matrix S and is, thus, a unitary matrix. Therefore, $\|Q(\alpha)\|_2 = 1$. It then follows that

$$
\rho(G_{\text{NSS}}(\alpha)) \leq \|(\alpha I - N)(\alpha I + N)^{-1}\|_2.
$$

Because $N \in \mathbb{C}^{n \times n}$ is a **normal matrix**, there exist a unitary matrix $U \in \mathbb{C}^{n \times n}$ and a complex diagonal matrix $\Lambda = \text{diag}(\lambda_1, \lambda_2, \dots, \lambda_n) \in \mathbb{C}^{n \times n}$ such that $N = U\Lambda U^*$. Hence, we can further get

$$
\begin{aligned}
\rho(G_{\text{NSS}}(\alpha)) &\leq \max_{\lambda_j \in \sigma(N)} \left| \frac{\alpha - \lambda_j}{\alpha + \lambda_j} \right| = \max_{\lambda_j = \gamma_j + i\eta_j \in \sigma(N)} \left| \frac{\alpha - (\gamma_j + i\eta_j)}{\alpha + (\gamma_j + i\eta_j)} \right| \\
&= \max_{\gamma_j + i\eta_j \in \sigma(N)} \sqrt{\frac{(\alpha - \gamma_j)^2 + \eta_j^2}{(\alpha + \gamma_j)^2 + \eta_j^2}},
\end{aligned}
$$

where $\sigma(N)$ indicates the **spectral set** of the matrix N. Since the real parts γ_j of λ_j, $j = 1, 2, \dots, n$, are positive and α is a positive constant, it is easy to see that

$$
\rho(G_{\text{NSS}}(\alpha)) \leq \varsigma_{\text{NSS}}(\alpha) < 1.
$$

We now compute the optimal parameter $\alpha_\star$ that minimizes the upper bound $\varsigma_{\text{NSS}}(\alpha)$ of the **convergence factor** $\rho(G_{\text{NSS}}(\alpha))$ of the NSS iteration.

Noticing that

$$
\frac{(\alpha - \gamma)^2 + \eta^2}{(\alpha + \gamma)^2 + \eta^2}
$$

is an increasing function with respect to the variable η, we have

$$
\begin{aligned}
&\max_{(\gamma, \eta) \in \Omega} \left\{ \frac{(\alpha - \gamma)^2 + \eta^2}{(\alpha + \gamma)^2 + \eta^2} \right\} \\
&= \max_{\gamma_{\min} \leq \gamma \leq \gamma_{\max}} \left\{ \frac{(\alpha - \gamma)^2 + \eta_{\max}^2}{(\alpha + \gamma)^2 + \eta_{\max}^2} \right\} \\
&= \begin{cases} \max \left\{ \frac{(\alpha - \gamma_{\min})^2 + \eta_{\max}^2}{(\alpha + \gamma_{\min})^2 + \eta_{\max}^2}, \frac{(\alpha - \gamma_{\max})^2 + \eta_{\max}^2}{(\alpha + \gamma_{\max})^2 + \eta_{\max}^2} \right\}, & \text{for } \eta_{\max} < \sqrt{\gamma_{\min}\gamma_{\max}}, \\ \frac{(\alpha - \gamma_{\min})^2 + \eta_{\max}^2}{(\alpha + \gamma_{\min})^2 + \eta_{\max}^2}, & \text{for } \eta_{\max} \geq \sqrt{\gamma_{\min}\gamma_{\max}}. \end{cases}
\end{aligned}
$$

If $\alpha_\star$ is the minimum point of $\varsigma_{\text{NSS}}(\alpha)$, then it must satisfy

$$
\frac{(\alpha - \gamma_{\min})^2 + \eta_{\max}^2}{(\alpha + \gamma_{\min})^2 + \eta_{\max}^2} = \frac{(\alpha - \gamma_{\max})^2 + \eta_{\max}^2}{(\alpha + \gamma_{\max})^2 + \eta_{\max}^2}
$$

when $\eta_{\max} < \sqrt{\gamma_{\min}\gamma_{\max}}$, and

$$
\frac{d}{d\alpha} \left(\frac{(\alpha - \gamma_{\min})^2 + \eta_{\max}^2}{(\alpha + \gamma_{\min})^2 + \eta_{\max}^2} \right) = 0
$$

when $\eta_{\max} \geq \sqrt{\gamma_{\min}\gamma_{\max}}$. Therefore,

$$\alpha_\star = \begin{cases} \sqrt{\gamma_{\min}\gamma_{\max} - \eta_{\max}^2}, & \text{for } \eta_{\max} < \sqrt{\gamma_{\min}\gamma_{\max}}, \\ \sqrt{\gamma_{\min}^2 + \eta_{\max}^2}, & \text{for } \eta_{\max} \geq \sqrt{\gamma_{\min}\gamma_{\max}}, \end{cases}$$

and straightforward derivations yield

$$\begin{aligned} \varsigma_{\text{NSS}}(\alpha_\star) &= \sqrt{\frac{(\alpha_\star - \gamma_{\min})^2 + \eta_{\max}^2}{(\alpha_\star + \gamma_{\min})^2 + \eta_{\max}^2}} \\ &= \begin{cases} \left(\frac{(\sqrt{\gamma_{\min}\gamma_{\max} - \eta_{\max}^2} - \gamma_{\min})^2 + \eta_{\max}^2}{(\sqrt{\gamma_{\min}\gamma_{\max} - \eta_{\max}^2} + \gamma_{\min})^2 + \eta_{\max}^2}\right)^{\frac{1}{2}}, & \text{for } \eta_{\max} < \sqrt{\gamma_{\min}\gamma_{\max}}, \\ \left(\frac{(\sqrt{\gamma_{\min}^2 + \eta_{\max}^2} - \gamma_{\min})^2 + \eta_{\max}^2}{(\sqrt{\gamma_{\min}^2 + \eta_{\max}^2} + \gamma_{\min})^2 + \eta_{\max}^2}\right)^{\frac{1}{2}}, & \text{for } \eta_{\max} \geq \sqrt{\gamma_{\min}\gamma_{\max}}, \end{cases} \\ &= \begin{cases} \left(\frac{\gamma_{\min} + \gamma_{\max} - 2\sqrt{\gamma_{\min}\gamma_{\max} - \eta_{\max}^2}}{\gamma_{\min} + \gamma_{\max} + 2\sqrt{\gamma_{\min}\gamma_{\max} - \eta_{\max}^2}}\right)^{\frac{1}{2}}, & \text{for } \eta_{\max} < \sqrt{\gamma_{\min}\gamma_{\max}}, \\ \left(\frac{\gamma_{\min}^2 + \eta_{\max}^2 - \gamma_{\min}\sqrt{\gamma_{\min}^2 + \eta_{\max}^2}}{\gamma_{\min}^2 + \eta_{\max}^2 + \gamma_{\min}\sqrt{\gamma_{\min}^2 + \eta_{\max}^2}}\right)^{\frac{1}{2}}, & \text{for } \eta_{\max} \geq \sqrt{\gamma_{\min}\gamma_{\max}}, \end{cases} \\ &= \begin{cases} \left(\frac{\gamma_{\min} + \gamma_{\max} - 2\sqrt{\gamma_{\min}\gamma_{\max} - \eta_{\max}^2}}{\gamma_{\min} + \gamma_{\max} + 2\sqrt{\gamma_{\min}\gamma_{\max} - \eta_{\max}^2}}\right)^{\frac{1}{2}}, & \text{for } \eta_{\max} < \sqrt{\gamma_{\min}\gamma_{\max}}, \\ \left(\frac{\sqrt{\gamma_{\min}^2 + \eta_{\max}^2} - \gamma_{\min}}{\sqrt{\gamma_{\min}^2 + \eta_{\max}^2} + \gamma_{\min}}\right)^{\frac{1}{2}}, & \text{for } \eta_{\max} \geq \sqrt{\gamma_{\min}\gamma_{\max}}. \end{cases} \end{aligned} \qquad \square$$

Theorem 5.68 shows that the **convergence speed** of the NSS iteration is bounded by $\varsigma_{\text{NSS}}(\alpha)$. Analogously, we have

$$|||x^{(k+1)} - x_*||| \leq \varsigma_{\text{NSS}}(\alpha)\,|||x^{(k)} - x_*|||, \qquad k = 0, 1, 2, \ldots.$$

If the lower and the upper bounds $\gamma_{\min}$, $\eta_{\min}$ and $\gamma_{\max}$, $\eta_{\max}$ are known, then the optimal parameter $\alpha_\star$ for $\varsigma_{\text{NSS}}(\alpha)$ can be obtained. By employing this optimal parameter $\alpha_\star$, we particularly have

$$|||G_{\text{NSS}}(\alpha_\star)||| \leq \varsigma_{\text{NSS}}(\alpha_\star)$$

and

$$|||x^{(k+1)} - x_*||| \leq \varsigma_{\text{NSS}}(\alpha_\star)\,|||x^{(k)} - x_*|||, \qquad k = 0, 1, 2, \ldots,$$

in the light of Theorem 5.68.

We remark that when $\eta_{\max} < \sqrt{\gamma_{\min}\gamma_{\max}}$, it holds that

$$\left(\frac{\gamma_{\min} + \gamma_{\max} - 2\sqrt{\gamma_{\min}\gamma_{\max} - \eta_{\max}^2}}{\gamma_{\min} + \gamma_{\max} + 2\sqrt{\gamma_{\min}\gamma_{\max} - \eta_{\max}^2}}\right)^{\frac{1}{2}} \geq \frac{\sqrt{\gamma_{\max}} - \sqrt{\gamma_{\min}}}{\sqrt{\gamma_{\max}} + \sqrt{\gamma_{\min}}},$$

and when $\eta_{\max} \geq \sqrt{\gamma_{\min}\gamma_{\max}}$, it holds that

$$\left(\frac{\sqrt{\gamma_{\min}^2 + \eta_{\max}^2} - \gamma_{\min}}{\sqrt{\gamma_{\min}^2 + \eta_{\max}^2} + \gamma_{\min}}\right)^{\frac{1}{2}} \geq \frac{\sqrt{\gamma_{\max}} - \sqrt{\gamma_{\min}}}{\sqrt{\gamma_{\max}} + \sqrt{\gamma_{\min}}}.$$

By Theorems 5.66 and 5.68, the above inequalities imply that among all NSS iterations for solving the non-Hermitian positive definite linear system (5.1), the optimal upper bound of the contraction factor of the HSS iteration is the smallest. However, since the upper bound may be much overestimated and may reflect only the worst case of the asymptotic convergence behavior, and the actual **convergence factor** may be far from the corresponding upper bound of the **contraction factor**, we could not assert that the HSS iteration is the fastest among all NSS iterations for solving the non-Hermitian positive definite linear system (5.1).

We remark that when the coefficient matrix A is normal, we have $NS = SN$ and, therefore,

$$\rho(G_{\mathrm{NSS}}(\alpha)) = |||G_{\mathrm{NSS}}(\alpha)||| = \varsigma_{\mathrm{NSS}}(\alpha).$$

The optimal parameter $\alpha_\star$ then minimizes all of these three quantities. For applications of the NSS technique to solve other practical problems, we refer to [197, 249].

5.5.3 ▪ PSS Iteration

Moreover, the HS splitting can be naturally generalized to the *positive-definite and skew-Hermitian* (PS) splitting [35]

$$A = P + S, \tag{5.49}$$

where $P \in \mathbb{C}^{n \times n}$ is a positive definite matrix and $S \in \mathbb{C}^{n \times n}$ is a skew-Hermitian matrix.

By applying the technique of constructing HSS and NSS iterations to the PS splitting (5.49), we can establish the *positive-definite and skew-Hermitian splitting* (PSS) iteration method for solving the positive definite system of linear equations (5.1) as follows:

$$\begin{cases} (\alpha I + P)x^{(k+\frac{1}{2})} = (\alpha I - S)x^{(k)} + b, \\ (\alpha I + S)x^{(k+1)} = (\alpha I - P)x^{(k+\frac{1}{2})} + b, \end{cases} \quad k = 0, 1, 2, \ldots,$$

where $\alpha \in \mathbb{R}$ is a given positive scalar; see [35].

We easily see that when $P \in \mathbb{C}^{n \times n}$ is normal or Hermitian, the PSS iteration method reduces to the NSS or the HSS iteration method, accordingly.

The **PSS** iteration method can be equivalently rewritten as

$$x^{(k+1)} = G_{\mathrm{PSS}}(\alpha)\, x^{(k)} + g_{\mathrm{PSS}}(\alpha), \tag{5.50}$$

where

$$G_{\mathrm{PSS}}(\alpha) \triangleq (\alpha I + S)^{-1}(\alpha I - P)(\alpha I + P)^{-1}(\alpha I - S) \tag{5.51}$$

is the PSS **iteration matrix**, and

$$g_{\mathrm{PSS}}(\alpha) \triangleq 2\alpha(\alpha I + S)^{-1}(\alpha I + P)^{-1}b.$$

In fact, the iteration scheme (5.50) may also result from the splitting

$$A = M_{\mathrm{PSS}}(\alpha) - N_{\mathrm{PSS}}(\alpha)$$

of the coefficient matrix A, with

$$\begin{cases} M_{\mathrm{PSS}}(\alpha) &= \frac{1}{2\alpha}(\alpha I + P)(\alpha I + S), \\ N_{\mathrm{PSS}}(\alpha) &= \frac{1}{2\alpha}(\alpha I - P)(\alpha I - S). \end{cases}$$

Then it holds that

$$G_{\mathrm{PSS}}(\alpha) = M_{\mathrm{PSS}}(\alpha)^{-1}N_{\mathrm{PSS}}(\alpha) \quad \text{and} \quad g_{\mathrm{PSS}}(\alpha) = M_{\mathrm{PSS}}(\alpha)^{-1}b.$$

For the convergence property of the PSS iteration, we have the following theorem.

Theorem 5.69. [35] *Let $A \in \mathbb{C}^{n \times n}$ be a positive definite matrix, $A = P + S$ be the PS splitting of the matrix A, and $\alpha \in \mathbb{R}$ be a positive scalar. Denote by*

$$V(\alpha) = (\alpha I + P)^{-1}(\alpha I - P).$$

Then the spectral radius $\rho(G_{\mathrm{PSS}}(\alpha))$ of the PSS iteration matrix $G_{\mathrm{PSS}}(\alpha)$ in (5.51) is bounded by $\|V(\alpha)\|_2$. Therefore, it holds that

$$\rho(G_{\mathrm{PSS}}(\alpha)) \le \|V(\alpha)\|_2 < 1, \quad \forall \alpha > 0,$$

i.e., the PSS iteration converges unconditionally to the exact solution $x_* \in \mathbb{C}^n$ of the system of linear equations (5.1).

Proof. Because $S \in \mathbb{C}^{n \times n}$ is a skew-Hermitian matrix, from the definition of the PS splitting (5.49) we know that

$$P^* + P = A^* + A.$$

Hence, $P \in \mathbb{C}^{n \times n}$ is also a positive definite matrix, i.e., $\frac{1}{2}(P^* + P)$, the Hermitian part of the matrix P, is a Hermitian positive definite matrix. As a result, for any $y \in \mathbb{C}^n$ with $y \ne 0$, we have

$$2\alpha \langle (P^* + P)y, \, y \rangle > 0$$

or

$$\langle (\alpha P^* + \alpha P)y, \, y \rangle > \langle (-\alpha P^* - \alpha P)y, \, y \rangle.$$

Here $\langle \cdot, \cdot \rangle$ denotes the inner product in $\mathbb{C}^n$. It then straightforwardly follows that

$$\langle (\alpha^2 I + \alpha P^* + \alpha P + P^* P)y, \, y \rangle > \langle (\alpha^2 I - \alpha P^* - \alpha P + P^* P)y, \, y \rangle,$$

or equivalently,

$$\langle (\alpha I + P)y, \, (\alpha I + P)y \rangle > \langle (\alpha I - P)y, \, (\alpha I - P)y \rangle. \tag{5.52}$$

Let $x = (\alpha I + P)y$. We have $x \ne 0$, since the matrix $\alpha I + P$ is nonsingular and the vector $y \ne 0$. Now, the inequality in (5.52) can be equivalently written as

$$\langle x, x \rangle > \langle V(\alpha)\, x, \, V(\alpha)\, x \rangle.$$

Hence, it holds that

$$\frac{\|V(\alpha)\, x\|_2}{\|x\|_2} < 1, \quad \forall \alpha > 0, \, \forall x \in \mathbb{C}^n \setminus \{0\},$$

or in other words,

$$\|V(\alpha)\|_2 < 1, \quad \forall \alpha > 0.$$

Moreover, let

$$Q(\alpha) \triangleq (\alpha I - S)(\alpha I + S)^{-1}.$$

Then $Q(\alpha)$ is the **Cayley transform** of the matrix S and is, thus, unitary. It follows that $\|Q(\alpha)\|_2 = 1$ for any $\alpha > 0$.

Define
$$\hat{G}(\alpha) = V(\alpha)\,Q(\alpha).$$

Then the matrix $\hat{G}(\alpha)$ is similar to the PSS iteration matrix $G_{\mathrm{PSS}}(\alpha)$. It follows directly from the above argument that

$$\rho(G_{\mathrm{PSS}}(\alpha)) = \rho(\hat{G}(\alpha)) \le \|\hat{G}(\alpha)\|_2 = \|V(\alpha)\,Q(\alpha)\|_2$$
$$\le \|V(\alpha)\|_2 \|Q(\alpha)\|_2 = \|V(\alpha)\|_2 < 1. \qquad \square$$

Theorem 5.69 shows that the upper bound of the contraction factor of the PSS iteration method is only dependent on the spectrum of the positive definite part P, but is independent of the spectrum of the skew-Hermitian part S as well as the eigenvectors of the matrices P, S, and A.

We point out that two important problems need to be further studied for the PSS iteration method. One is the choice of the skew-Hermitian matrix S, or the splitting of the matrix A, and another is the choice of the **acceleration parameter** α. For the latter, the optimal value $\alpha_\star$ of the parameter α that minimizes the function $\|V(\alpha)\|_2$, and the corresponding value $\|V(\alpha_\star)\|_2$, were analytically derived by Bai and Hadjidimos in [39].

Theoretically, due to Theorem 5.69 we can choose S to be any skew-Hermitian matrix such that the matrix $P = A - S$ is positive definite, and α to be any positive scalar. However, practically, besides the above requirements we have to choose S to be the skew-Hermitian matrix such that the linear systems with the coefficient matrices $\alpha I + P$ and $\alpha I + S$ can be solved easily and effectively, and to choose the positive constant α such that the PSS iteration converges very fast. Evidently, these two problems may be very difficult and, usually, their solutions strongly depend on the concrete structures and properties of the coefficient matrix A as well as the splitting matrices P and S.

We give two practical choices of the PS splitting in the following. These two special kinds of PS splittings are very basic; technical combinations of them can yield various and new positive-definite and skew-Hermitian splittings and, hence, many practical PSS iteration methods.

We first write the matrix A into a **block form**, i.e.,

$$A = \begin{bmatrix} A_{11} & A_{12} & \cdots & A_{1m} \\ A_{21} & A_{22} & \cdots & A_{2m} \\ \vdots & \vdots & \ddots & \vdots \\ A_{m1} & A_{m2} & \cdots & A_{mm} \end{bmatrix} \in \mathbb{C}^{n \times n},$$

where the diagonal blocks A_{jj}, $j = 1, 2, \ldots, m$, are square matrices. Let D, L, and U be the block diagonal, the strictly block lower-triangular, and the strictly block upper-triangular part of the matrix A, respectively. Then we have

$$A = (L + D + U^*) + (U - U^*) \triangleq T_1 + S_1$$
$$= (L^* + D + U) + (L - L^*) \triangleq T_2 + S_2. \tag{5.53}$$

Clearly, T_1 and T_2 are block lower-triangular and block upper-triangular matrices, respectively, and both S_1 and S_2 are skew-Hermitian matrices. We will call the two splittings in (5.53) as **block triangular and skew-Hermitian** (BTS) splittings of the matrix A. We remark that these two splittings are both PS splittings, because

$$T_\ell + T_\ell^* = A + A^*, \quad \ell = 1, 2,$$

and $A \in \mathbb{C}^{n \times n}$ is positive definite.

If we make technical combinations of the **BTS** splitting with the HS or the NS splitting, other interesting and practical cases of the PS splitting can be obtained. For example,

$$A = \left(L + \frac{1}{2}(D + D^*) + U^* \right) + \left(\frac{1}{2}(D - D^*) + U - U^* \right) \triangleq T_3 + S_3$$
$$= \left(L^* + \frac{1}{2}(D + D^*) + U \right) + \left(\frac{1}{2}(D - D^*) + L - L^* \right) \triangleq T_4 + S_4 \qquad (5.54)$$

arc two BTS splittings, which come from combinations of BTS splittings of the matrix A in (5.53) and HS splitting of the matrix D.

Now, with the choices

$$P = T_\ell, \quad S = S_\ell, \qquad \ell = 1, 2, 3, 4,$$

we can immediately define the corresponding **block triangular and skew-Hermitian splitting** (BTSS) iteration methods for solving the positive definite system of linear equations (5.1).

We note that for these four **BTSS** iteration methods, we only need to solve block-triangular linear subsystems, rather than to inverse **shifted positive definite matrices** as in the PSS iteration method or **shifted Hermitian (normal) positive definite matrices** as in the HSS (NSS) iteration method. Moreover, the block-triangular linear subsystems can be solved recursively through solutions of the systems of linear equations

$$(\alpha I + A_{jj})x_j = r_j, \qquad j = 1, 2, \dots, m, \qquad (5.55)$$

for the BTSS iteration methods associated with the splittings in (5.53), and

$$\left(\alpha I + \frac{1}{2}(A_{jj} + A_{jj}^*) \right) x_j = r_j, \qquad j = 1, 2, \dots, m, \qquad (5.56)$$

for those associated with the splittings in (5.54). Because the matrix A is positive definite, the submatrices A_{jj} $(j = 1, 2, \dots, m)$ are positive definite; in particular, $\frac{1}{2}(A_{jj} + A_{jj}^*)$ $(j = 1, 2, \dots, m)$ are all Hermitian positive definite matrices. Moreover, as mentioned above, the splitting matrices T_ℓ $(\ell = 1, 2, 3, 4)$ are positive definite. Therefore, we may employ another BTSS iteration to solve the linear subsystems (5.55) and the **conjugate gradient iteration** to solve the linear subsystems (5.56) if necessary. In addition, the matrices T_ℓ, $\ell = 1, 2, 3, 4$, may be much more sparse than the matrices H and N in the HSS and NSS iteration methods. For instance, when the matrix A is an **upper Hessenberg matrix**, T_ℓ and S_ℓ, $\ell = 1, 2, 3, 4$, in the BTSS (or TSS) splittings are still very sparse, but H, S, and N, S in the HS and the NS splitting may be very dense. Therefore, the **BTSS** iteration methods may save computational costs considerably more than both HSS and NSS iteration methods. Another advantage of the BTSS iteration methods is that they can be used to solve both Hermitian and strongly non-Hermitian positive definite system of linear equations more effectively than both HSS and NSS iteration methods. For example, consider the non-Hermitian positive definite system of linear equations

$$(\alpha I + \widehat{S})z = r$$

arising from the HSS, NSS, and TSS iteration methods, where $\widehat{S} \in \mathbb{C}^{n \times n}$ is a skew-Hermitian matrix, α is a positive constant, and $r \in \mathbb{C}^n$ is a given right-hand side vector. Both HSS and NSS iteration methods cannot be used to solve it; however, the BTSS iteration method may solve it very efficiently. This shows that the BTSS iteration methods have a considerably large application area.

When D, L, and U are the (pointwise) diagonal, the (pointwise) strictly lower-triangular, and the (pointwise) strictly upper-triangular part of the matrix A, we particularly call the BTS splitting as *triangular and skew-Hermitian* (TS) splitting and the BTSS iteration method as *triangular and skew-Hermitian splitting* (TSS) iteration method.

We remark that both BTSS and TSS iteration methods are, in general, different from the HSS and the NSS iteration methods. Only when the diagonal matrix D is Hermitian (normal) and $L + U^* = 0$, the BTSS and the TSS iteration methods give the same scheme as the HSS (NSS) iteration method.

5.5.4 ▪ Several Examples Leading to the Splittings

Here we give two practical examples that can naturally lead to HS, NS, and PS splittings. In fact, there are many such examples in the areas of scientific computing and engineering applications.

Example 5.70. Consider the system of linear equations (5.1) with the complex coefficient matrix

$$A = G + iW,$$

where $G, W \in \mathbb{R}^{n \times n}$ are real matrices.

Linear systems of this form may arise from electromagnetics and chemistry computations. We consider the splitting

$$A = M + K, \quad \text{with} \quad M = G \quad \text{and} \quad K = iW. \tag{5.57}$$

When the matrix G is symmetric positive definite and the matrix W is symmetric, the splitting (5.57) gives an **HS** splitting of the matrix A, with $H = M$ and $S = K$; when the matrix G is normal and positive definite and the matrix W is symmetric, the splitting (5.57) gives an **NS** splitting of the matrix A, with $N = M$ and $S = K$; and when the matrix G is positive definite and the matrix W is symmetric, the splitting (5.57) gives a **PS** splitting of the matrix A, with $P = M$ and $S = K$.

Example 5.71. Consider the system of linear equations (5.1) with the block two-by-two coefficient matrix

$$A = \begin{bmatrix} G & E \\ -E^* & C \end{bmatrix},$$

where $G \in \mathbb{C}^{p \times p}$, $C \in \mathbb{C}^{q \times q}$, and $E \in \mathbb{C}^{p \times q}$, with p and q being positive integers satisfying $p \geq q$ and $n = p + q$.

Linear systems of this **saddle-point form** may arise from Stokes problem, mixed finite element method for partial differential equations, structural analysis, electrical networks, image processing, etc.

We consider the splitting

$$A = M + K, \quad \text{with} \quad M = \begin{bmatrix} G & 0 \\ 0 & C \end{bmatrix} \quad \text{and} \quad K = \begin{bmatrix} 0 & E \\ -E^* & 0 \end{bmatrix}. \tag{5.58}$$

When the matrices G and C are Hermitian positive definite, the splitting (5.58) gives an **HS** splitting of the matrix A, with $H = M$ and $S = K$; when the matrices G and C are normal and positive definite, the splitting (5.58) gives an **NS** splitting of the matrix A, with $N = M$

and $S = K$; and when the matrices G and C are positive definite, the splitting (5.58) gives a **PS** splitting of the matrix A, with $P = M$ and $S = K$.

The HSS, NSS, BTSS, and PSS methods are effective iteration solvers for solving large sparse non-Hermitian positive definite system of linear equations, especially, when good **preconditioners** and optimal iteration parameters are easily available; see, e.g., [32, 33, 34, 38, 74]. Also, they can naturally lead to high-quality preconditioners for **Krylov subspace iteration methods**, such as **GMRES** and **BiCGSTAB**, for solving this class of linear systems; see, e.g., [35, 65, 268, 295]. The iteration parameter α considerably affects the effectiveness of the corresponding iteration scheme, although its practical and optimal choice is a challenging task from the viewpoint of both theory and applications. In addition, the convergence theory of these HSS-type iteration methods for singular and positive-semidefinite linear systems is an important problem that deserves further in-depth study.

5.6 ▪ Richardson Iteration and Chebyshev Semi-Iteration

5.6.1 ▪ Richardson Iteration

In the early part of the 20th century, simple iteration methods were predominantly applied to solve discretized self-adjoint elliptic partial differential equations, together with an arbitrary parameter for accelerating the iteration process. The first and simplest of these methods is the **Richardson iteration method** [280].

Let $x^{(k)} \in \mathbb{C}^n$ be an approximate solution of the linear system (5.1) and $r_k \triangleq b - Ax^{(k)}$ be the corresponding residual vector after k steps of iteration. Then the next iterate $x^{(k+1)}$ of the **Richardson iteration** is given by

$$x^{(k+1)} = x^{(k)} + \omega r_k = (I - \omega A)x^{(k)} + \omega b, \tag{5.59}$$

where $\omega \in \mathbb{R} \setminus \{0\}$ is a **relaxation parameter**. Clearly, the iteration scheme (5.59) can be viewed as a **matrix splitting iteration** associated with the splitting

$$A = M - N$$

of the coefficient matrix $A \in \mathbb{C}^{n \times n}$ of the linear system (5.1), with

$$M = \frac{1}{\omega}I \quad \text{and} \quad N = \frac{1}{\omega}I - A.$$

For the $(k + 1)$-th **residual**, we have

$$r_{k+1} = b - Ax^{(k+1)} = (I - \omega A)r_k = \cdots = (I - \omega A)^{k+1} r_0,$$

where $r_0 = b - Ax^{(0)}$ is the initial residual.

It follows from Theorem 5.3 that the Richardson iteration (5.59) converges if and only if $\rho(I - \omega A) < 1$. It is clear that the eigenvalues of the matrix $I - \omega A$ are given by $1 - \omega \lambda_i$, $i = 1, 2, \ldots, n$, where $\lambda_i \in \mathbb{C}$, $i = 1, 2, \ldots, n$, are the eigenvalues of the coefficient matrix A. Thus we have the following convergence result for the Richardson iteration (5.59).

Theorem 5.72. *The Richardson iteration method* (5.59) *converges if and only if*

$$\omega \left(2 \Re(\lambda_i) - \omega |\lambda_i|^2 \right) > 0, \quad i = 1, 2, \ldots, n,$$

where $\lambda_i \in \mathbb{C}$, $i = 1, 2, \ldots, n$, are the eigenvalues of the matrix $A \in \mathbb{C}^{n \times n}$.

Corollary 5.73. *If the sign of the real parts of the eigenvalues of the matrix A is not constant, then the Richardson iteration method (5.59) cannot converge.*

If the eigenvalues of the matrix A are all real and positive, then we have the following result.

Theorem 5.74. *Assume that the eigenvalues of the matrix $A \in \mathbb{C}^{n \times n}$ are all real and positive, which are ordered as $\lambda_1 \geq \lambda_2 \geq \cdots \geq \lambda_n > 0$. Then the Richardson iteration method (5.59) converges if and only if*

$$0 < \omega < \frac{2}{\lambda_1}.$$

Moreover, the optimal parameter ω_{opt} is given by

$$\omega_{opt} = \frac{2}{\lambda_1 + \lambda_n}.$$

If the matrix A is Hermitian positive definite, then the Richardson iteration converges for all ω satisfying

$$0 < \omega < \frac{2}{\rho(A)},$$

and the optimal parameter is given by [329]

$$\omega_{opt} = \frac{2}{\lambda_{\min}(A) + \lambda_{\max}(A)},$$

where $\lambda_{\min}(A)$ and $\lambda_{\max}(A)$ denote the smallest and the largest eigenvalues of the matrix A, respectively.

The Richardson iteration (5.59) is readily generalized by taking a different **relaxation parameter** ω for each iteration step, which leads to the **generalized Richardson iteration**:

$$x^{(k+1)} = x^{(k)} + \omega_k r_k = (I - \omega_k A)x^{(k)} + \omega_k b.$$

Note that this iteration method is a first-order (or one-step), linear, and nonstationary iteration scheme. The sequence $\{\omega_k\}_{k=0}^{\infty}$ can be selected in a number of different ways, leading to different classes of iteration methods, for example, the Chebyshev semi-iteration methods and the Krylov subspace iteration methods, for solving the linear system (5.1).

Note that now the **residual vector** is given by

$$r_{k+1} = (I - \omega_k A)(I - \omega_{k-1}A) \cdots (I - \omega_0 A)r_0 \triangleq p_{k+1}(A)\, r_0,$$

where $p_{k+1}(t)$ is a polynomial of degree $k + 1$ defined by

$$p_{k+1}(t) = (1 - \omega_k t)(1 - \omega_{k-1}t) \cdots (1 - \omega_0 t).$$

Clearly, $p_{k+1}(0) = 1$. This process is, in general, referred to as a **polynomial acceleration**. Hence, the choice of the iteration parameters $\{\omega_k\}_{k=0}^{\infty}$ is, in some sense, equivalent to the choice of the polynomials $\{p_k(t)\}_{k=0}^{\infty}$.

Let $A = M - N$ be a splitting of the matrix A. By applying (5.59) to the **preconditioned linear system**

$$M^{-1}Ax = M^{-1}b,$$

we can obtain the **preconditioned Richardson iteration**

$$x^{(k+1)} = x^{(k)} + \omega_k M^{-1} r_k.$$

The Jacobi and Gauss–Seidel iterations can be regarded as the preconditioned Richardson iterations with

$$\omega_k = 1, \quad M = D,$$

and with

$$\omega_k = 1, \quad M = D - L,$$

respectively, where D and $-L$ are the diagonal and the strictly lower-triangular part of the matrix A.

It is pointed out in [329] that the Richardson iteration has the disadvantage of being numerically unstable.

In fact, the **Chebyshev semi-iteration method** [168] can, in exact arithmetic, be obtained from these polynomial acceleration methods by choosing the acceleration parameters involved in the successive Richardson iterations properly. But this approach is numerically unstable, too. In the **Chebyshev semi-iteration**, exploiting the **three-term recurrence** relation for the **Chebyshev polynomials** can lead to a stable **three-term recurrence iteration method**.

5.6.2 ▪ Real Chebyshev Polynomial

We first introduce the **real Chebyshev polynomial**, which is defined by

$$
\begin{aligned}
T_n(t) &= \frac{1}{2}\left[\left(t + \sqrt{t^2 - 1}\right)^n + \left(t + \sqrt{t^2 - 1}\right)^{-n}\right] \\
&= \frac{1}{2}\left[\left(t + \sqrt{t^2 - 1}\right)^n + \left(t - \sqrt{t^2 - 1}\right)^n\right], \quad n = 0, 1, 2, \ldots,
\end{aligned}
\tag{5.60}
$$

where $t \in \mathbb{R}$. It is easily seen that $T_n(t)$ is a polynomial of degree n with respect to the variable t.

If $|t| \leq 1$, then we can make a transformation $t = \cos(\theta)$ $(0 \leq \theta \leq \pi)$ so that (5.60) can be rewritten as

$$
\begin{aligned}
T_n(t) &= \frac{1}{2}\left[(\cos(\theta) + \mathrm{i}\sin(\theta))^n + (\cos(\theta) - \mathrm{i}\sin(\theta))^n\right] \\
&= \cos(n\theta) = \cos(n \arccos(t)).
\end{aligned}
\tag{5.61}
$$

If $|t| > 1$, then we may take the transformation $t = \cosh(\theta)$ $(\theta > 0)$, where cosh denotes the hyperbolic **cosine function** which is one of the basic **hyperbolic functions**.

We briefly introduce some properties of the hyperbolic functions here. The hyperbolic functions are analogues of the ordinary trigonometric functions. The basic hyperbolic functions include the **hyperbolic sine**: "sinh," the **hyperbolic cosine**: "cosh," and the **hyperbolic tangent**: "tanh," and so on. Their inverses are the **inverse hyperbolic sine**: "arcsinh," the **inverse hyperbolic cosine**: "arccosh," and the **inverse hyperbolic tangent**: "arctanh," and so on.

Analogously to the definitions of $\cos(t)$ and $\sin(t)$, $\cosh(t)$ and $\sinh(t)$ can be defined by

$$\cosh(t) = \frac{1}{2}\left(e^t + e^{-t}\right) \quad \text{and} \quad \sinh(t) = \frac{1}{2}\left(e^t - e^{-t}\right).$$

The following theorem presents some basic properties of sinh and cosh. For more details about the hyperbolic functions, we refer to [192].

Theorem 5.75. *For the hyperbolic functions* sinh *and* cosh, *the following statements hold true:*

(1) $\sinh(t) = -i\sin(it)$, $\cosh(t) = \cos(it)$;

(2) $\sinh(-t) = -\sinh(t)$, $\cosh(-t) = \cosh(t)$;

(3) $\cosh^2(t) - \sinh^2(t) = 1$;

(4) $e^t = \cosh(t) + \sinh(t)$, $e^{-t} = \cosh(t) - \sinh(t)$;

(5) $\cosh(t) \geq 1$, *and the equality holds if and only if* $t = 0$.

When $|t| > 1$, we let $t = \cosh(\theta)$. The **Chebyshev polynomial** can be rewritten as

$$T_n(t) = \frac{1}{2}\left[(\cosh(\theta) + \sinh(\theta))^n + (\cosh(\theta) - \sinh(\theta))^n\right]$$
$$= \cosh(n\theta) = \cosh(n\operatorname{arccosh}(t)). \tag{5.62}$$

Hence we have

$$T_n(t) = \begin{cases} \cos(n\arccos(t)), & \text{for } |t| \leq 1, \\ \cosh(n\operatorname{arccosh}(t)), & \text{for } |t| > 1, \end{cases}$$

which is an alternative definition of the Chebyshev polynomials [288].

In the following theorem, we list some basic properties of the Chebyshev polynomials.

Theorem 5.76. *Let* T_n *be the Chebyshev polynomial defined in* (5.60).

(1) $\{T_n\}_{n\geq 0}$ *satisfies the* **three-term recurrence relationship:**

$$T_0(t) = 1, \ T_1(t) = t, \ T_{n+1}(t) = 2t\,T_n(t) - T_{n-1}(t), \quad n = 1, 2, \ldots. \tag{5.63}$$

(2) *If* $|t| \leq 1$, *then* $|T_n(t)| \leq 1$ *and* $\max_{-1\leq t\leq 1} |T_n(t)| = 1$; *this maximum is achieved at the* $n+1$ *points:*

$$t = \cos\left(\frac{k\pi}{n}\right), \quad k = 0, 1, \ldots, n.$$

(3) *If* $|t| > 1$, *then* $T_n(t) > 1$.

(4) $T_n(-t) = (-1)^n\,T_n(t)$.

(5) *The roots of* $T_n(t) = 0$ *are given by*

$$t = \cos\left(\frac{(2k+1)\pi}{2n}\right), \quad k = 0, 1, \ldots, n-1.$$

(6) $\{T_n\}_{n\geq 0}$ *has the orthogonal property:*

$$\int_{-1}^{1} \frac{T_k(t)\,T_l(t)}{\sqrt{1-t^2}}\,dt = \begin{cases} 0 & \text{if } k \neq l, \\ \frac{\pi}{2} & \text{if } k = l > 0, \\ \pi & \text{if } k = l = 0 \end{cases}$$

Proof. (1) It is obvious that $T_0(t) = 1$ and $T_1(t) = t$. By (5.60) we have

$$
\begin{aligned}
T_{n+1}(t) + T_{n-1}(t) &= \frac{1}{2}\left[\left(t + \sqrt{t^2 - 1}\right)^{n+1} + \left(t + \sqrt{t^2 - 1}\right)^{n-1} \right. \\
&\quad \left. + \left(t - \sqrt{t^2 - 1}\right)^{n+1} + \left(t - \sqrt{t^2 - 1}\right)^{n-1}\right] \\
&= \frac{1}{2}\left[\left(t + \sqrt{t^2 - 1}\right)^{n-1}\left(2t^2 + 2t\sqrt{t^2 - 1}\right) \right. \\
&\quad \left. + \left(t - \sqrt{t^2 - 1}\right)^{n-1}\left(2t^2 - 2t\sqrt{t^2 - 1}\right)\right] \\
&= 2t \cdot \frac{1}{2}\left[\left(t + \sqrt{t^2 - 1}\right)^{n} + \left(t - \sqrt{t^2 - 1}\right)^{n}\right] \\
&= 2t\, T_n(t).
\end{aligned}
$$

Therefore, (5.63) holds true.

(2) As $|t| \leq 1$, it is easily seen from (5.61) that $|T_n(t)| \leq 1$ and the equality holds if and only if

$$
n \arccos(t) = k\pi, \quad k = 0, \pm 1, \pm 2, \ldots,
$$

i.e.,

$$
t = \cos\left(\frac{k\pi}{n}\right), \quad k = 0, 1, 2, \ldots, n,
$$

which are the extremum points of $T_n(t)$ in $[-1, 1]$.

(3) It follows from (5.62) and Theorem 5.75 that $|T_n(t)| \geq 1$ as $|t| > 1$, and the equality holds if and only if

$$
n \operatorname{arccosh}(t) = 0,
$$

i.e., $t = \cosh(0) = 1$. As $|t| > 1$, we have $|T_n(t)| > 1$.

(4) This is a straightforward consequence of the definition (5.60).

(5) By Statements (2) and (3) we know that all roots of $T_n(t) = 0$ must lie in $[-1, 1]$. Hence, $T_n(t) = 0$ is equivalent to $\cos(n \arccos(t)) = 0$, i.e.,

$$
t = \cos\left(\frac{(2k+1)\pi}{2n}\right), \quad k = 0, 1, 2, \ldots, n - 1.
$$

(6) Left as Exercise 5.11. $\quad\square$

Let $\mathcal{P}_n$ denote the set of all real polynomials $p(t)$ with $\deg(p) \leq n$, where $\deg(p)$ denotes the **degree** of the polynomial $p(t)$. Given a scalar $\eta \in \mathbb{R}$, we denote the set of all polynomials $p(t)$ with $\deg(p) \leq n$ and $p(\eta) = 1$ by $\mathcal{P}_n^{(\eta)}$, i.e.,

$$
\mathcal{P}_n^{(\eta)} \triangleq \{p(t) : p(t) \in \mathcal{P}_n \quad \text{and} \quad p(\eta) = 1\}.
$$

The following result is an important approximation property of the **Chebyshev polynomials**.

Theorem 5.77. *Let $\eta \in \mathbb{R}$ be a real scalar with $|\eta| > 1$. Then the unique solution of the **min-max** problem*

$$
\min_{p(t) \in \mathcal{P}_n^{(\eta)}} \max_{-1 \leq t \leq 1} |p(t)|
$$

is given by

$$
\tilde{T}_n(t) \triangleq \frac{T_n(t)}{T_n(\eta)},
$$

where $T_n(t)$ is the Chebyshev polynomial defined in (5.60).

Proof. We first consider the case when $\eta > 1$. Suppose that there exists a polynomial $\tilde{p}(t) \in \mathcal{P}_n^{(\eta)}$ such that

$$\max_{-1 \leq t \leq 1} |\tilde{p}(t)| \leq \max_{-1 \leq t \leq 1} |\tilde{T}_n(t)|.$$

Let

$$r(t) = \tilde{p}(t) - \tilde{T}_n(t) \quad \text{and} \quad t_k = \cos\left(\frac{k\pi}{n}\right), \qquad k = 0, 1, 2, \ldots, n.$$

Then $\deg(r) \leq n$ and

$$r(t_k) = \tilde{p}(t_k) - \tilde{T}_n(t_k) = \tilde{p}(t_k) - \frac{(-1)^k}{T_n(\eta)}.$$

As $\eta > 1$, we have $T_n(\eta) > 1$ and

$$\max_{-1 \leq t \leq 1} |\tilde{p}(t)| \leq \max_{-1 \leq t \leq 1} |\tilde{T}_n(t)| = \frac{\displaystyle\max_{-1 \leq t \leq 1} |T_n(t)|}{|T_n(\eta)|} = \frac{1}{T_n(\eta)}. \tag{5.64}$$

This shows that $r(t_k) \leq 0$ for even k and $r(t_k) \geq 0$ for odd k, which leads to

$$r(t_k)\, r(t_{k-1}) \leq 0, \quad k = 1, 2, \ldots, n.$$

If

$$r(t_k)\, r(t_{k-1}) < 0,$$

then $r(t)$ has at least one zero point in (t_k, t_{k-1}). If

$$r(t_k)\, r(t_{k-1}) = 0,$$

then either $r(t_k) = 0$ or $r(t_{k-1}) = 0$. Suppose that $r(t_k) = 0$, where k satisfies $1 \leq k \leq n - 1$. Then

$$\tilde{p}(t_k) = \tilde{T}_n(t_k) = \frac{(-1)^k}{T_n(\eta)}.$$

It follows from (5.64) that t_k must be one extremum point of $\tilde{p}(t)$ and, hence, $\tilde{p}'(t_k) = 0$. Here and in the sequel we use $f'(t)$ to indicate the first-order derivative of the differentiable function $f(t)$ with respect to the variable t. As t_k is also an extremum point of $T_n(t)$ as well as $\tilde{T}_n(t)$, it holds that t_k is an extremum point of $r(t)$, i.e., $r'(t_k) = 0$. Therefore, t_k is a zero point of $r(t)$ of multiplicity at least 2.

Now we consider the number of zero points of $r(t)$ in $[-1, 1]$. We first consider the interval $[t_1, t_0]$. As

$$r(t_0)\, r(t_1) \leq 0,$$

we may consider the following three cases:

(a) $r(t_0)\, r(t_1) < 0$. In this case, it is easily seen that $r(t)$ has at least one zero point in (t_1, t_0).

(b) $r(t_0) = 0$. We may regard t_0 as a zero point of $r(t)$ in $(t_1, t_0]$.

(c) $r(t_1) = 0$. By the above discussion, we know that t_1 is a zero point of $r(t)$ with multiplicity at least 2. Hence, we may regard t_1 as two overlapped zero points of $r(t)$ with one located in $[t_1, t_0)$ and another in $(t_2, t_1]$.

Therefore, we may conclude that $r(t)$ has at least one zero point in $[t_1, t_0]$. Analogously, we can see that $r(t)$ has at least one zero point in $[t_k, t_{k-1}]$, $k = 2, 3, \ldots, n$. So, $r(t)$ has at least n zero points (including the multiplicities) in $[-1, 1]$. It is clear that

$$r(\eta) = \tilde{p}(\eta) - \tilde{T}_n(\eta) = 1 - 1 = 0.$$

As $\eta > 1$ and $\deg(r(t)) \leq n$, we have $r(t) \equiv 0$, which implies that $\tilde{p}(t) \equiv \tilde{T}_n(t)$.

The proof for the case when $\eta < -1$ is similar. $\qquad$ □

Theorem 5.77 can be easily generalized to any interval $[\alpha, \beta]$.

Theorem 5.78. *Let $\alpha, \beta, \eta \in \mathbb{R}$ be real scalars with $\alpha < \beta$ and $|\eta| \notin [\alpha, \beta]$. Then the unique solution of the **min-max problem***

$$\min_{p(t) \in \mathcal{P}_n^{(\eta)}} \max_{\alpha \leq t \leq \beta} |p(t)|$$

is given by

$$\tilde{T}_n(t) \triangleq \frac{T_n\left(\frac{2t - (\beta+\alpha)}{\beta - \alpha}\right)}{T_n\left(\frac{2\eta - (\beta+\alpha)}{\beta - \alpha}\right)},$$

where $T_n(t)$ is the Chebyshev polynomial defined in (5.61).

Proof. The proof is left as Exercise 5.12. $\qquad$ □

5.6.3 ▪ Complex Chebyshev Polynomial

The **complex Chebyshev polynomial** can be defined in the same way as in (5.60), i.e.,

$$T_n(z) = \frac{1}{2}\left[\left(z + \sqrt{z^2 - 1}\right)^n + \left(z + \sqrt{z^2 - 1}\right)^{-n}\right], \quad z \in \mathbb{C}, \ n = 0, 1, 2, \ldots. \quad (5.65)$$

Let

$$w = z + \sqrt{z^2 - 1}.$$

Then

$$w^{-1} = z - \sqrt{z^2 - 1} \quad \text{and} \quad w + w^{-1} = 2z.$$

An alternative definition of the complex Chebyshev polynomial is given in [288] as

$$T_n(z) = \frac{1}{2}\left(w^n + w^{-n}\right), \quad \text{where} \quad z = \frac{1}{2}\left(w + w^{-1}\right).$$

Note that

$$w + w^{-1} = 2z$$

has two solutions for w, but they are inverses of each other. As a result, the definition of $T_n(z)$ does not depend on which solution is chosen.

Analogous to the real **Chebyshev polynomial**, the complex Chebyshev polynomial $T_n(z)$ also satisfies the **three-term recurrence**

$$T_0(z) = 1, \quad T_1(z) = z, \quad T_{n+1}(z) = 2z\, T_n(z) - T_{n-1}(z), \quad n = 1, 2, \ldots.$$

The complex Chebyshev polynomials are intimately related to ellipses in the complex plane. Let $\mathcal{C}_r$ be the disc of radius $r > 0$ centered at the origin 0, i.e.,

$$\mathcal{C}_r = \{z \in \mathbb{C} : |z| \leq r\}.$$

Then the **Joukowski mapping**

$$J(w) = \frac{1}{2}(w + w^{-1})$$

transforms $\mathcal{C}_r$ into an ellipse centered at the origin, with foci -1 and 1, semi-major axis $\frac{1}{2}|r + r^{-1}|$, and semi-minor axis $\frac{1}{2}|r - r^{-1}|$. We denote such an ellipse by $\mathcal{E}_r$, i.e.,

$$\mathcal{E}_r \triangleq \left\{z \in \mathbb{C} : |z - 1| + |z + 1| \leq r + \frac{1}{r}\right\}. \tag{5.66}$$

A geometrical illustration of this mapping is shown in the following figure:

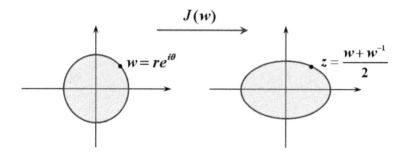

Remark 5.7. *There are two discs with the same image under the mapping $J(w)$, one with radius r and the other with radius r^{-1}. So, here, we only consider the disc with radius $r > 1$. Note that the case $r = 1$ is a degenerate case in which the ellipse $\mathcal{E}_r$ reduces to the interval $[-1, 1]$ traversed through twice.*

Now we consider the **min-max problem**

$$\min_{p(z) \in \mathcal{P}_n^{(\eta)}} \max_{z \in \mathcal{E}_r} |p(z)|, \tag{5.67}$$

where $\mathcal{E}_r$ is the ellipse defined in (5.66), $\eta \in \mathbb{C}$ is a point outside $\mathcal{E}_r$, and $\mathcal{P}_n^{(\eta)}$ is the set of all complex polynomials $p(z)$ with $\deg(p) \leq n$ and $p(\eta) = 1$. As η is not contained in $\mathcal{E}_r$, the **Haar condition** is satisfied, which implies that there always exists a unique solution $p_\star(z)$ to the min-max problem (5.67) [138].

One of the most important problem we concerned is that whether the optimal polynomial $p_\star(z)$ can be formulated by the complex **Chebyshev polynomial** as in Theorem 5.77, that is, whether $p_\star(z)$ is the same as

$$\tilde{T}_n(z) = \frac{T_n(z)}{T_n(\eta)}, \quad \text{where} \quad T_n(z) = \frac{1}{2}\left(w^n + w^{-n}\right), \quad \text{with } z = \frac{1}{2}\left(w + w^{-1}\right). \tag{5.68}$$

Unfortunately, the answer is no.

Fischer and Freund [139] considered the case where η is located on the real axis, i.e., $\eta \in \mathbb{R}$. In this case, the optimal polynomial $p_\star(z)$ is a real polynomial; see, e.g., [241].

Theorem 5.79. [139] *Let the polynomial $\tilde{T}_n(z)$ be defined in (5.68).*

(1) *Let $r > 1$ and $\eta \in \mathbb{R}$ satisfy $|\eta| > r + r^{-1}$. Then, for $n = 1, 2, 3, 4$, $\tilde{T}_n(z)$ is the unique solution to the min-max problem (5.67).*

(2) *For any integer $n \geq 5$, there exists a real number $\tilde{r} = \tilde{r}(n) > 1$ such that $\tilde{T}_n(z)$ is not the solution to the min-max problem (5.67) for all $r > \tilde{r}$ and $\eta \in \mathbb{R}$ satisfying $a_r < |\eta| < a_r + a_r^{-2}$, where $a_r = r + r^{-1}$.*

They also pointed out that, in most cases, however, there holds $p_\star(z) = \tilde{T}_n(z)$.

Theorem 5.80. [139] *Let $n \geq 5$ be an integer, $r > 1$ and $\eta \in \mathbb{R}$. Then the polynomial $\tilde{T}_n(z)$ defined in (5.68) is the unique solution to the min-max problem (5.67) if one of the following conditions are satisfied:*

(1) $|\eta| \geq \dfrac{1}{2}\left(r^{\sqrt{2}} + r^{-\sqrt{2}}\right)$;

(2) $|\eta| \geq \dfrac{2a_r^2 - 1 + \sqrt{2a_r^4 - a_r^2 + 1}}{2a_r}$, *where $a_r = r + r^{-1}$.*

When η is a complex number, we can show that the Chebyshev polynomials are asymptotically optimal, which is all that is needed in practice. We first introduce a lemma due to Zarantonello, which deals with the particular case where the ellipse reduces to a disc.

Lemma 5.81 (Zarantonello Lemma). *Let $\mathcal{C}_r$ be a complex disc centered at the origin with radius $r > 0$. Suppose that η is a point outside of the disc $\mathcal{C}_r$. Then*

$$\min_{p(z) \in \mathcal{P}_n^{(\eta)}} \max_{z \in \mathcal{C}_r} |p(z)| = \left(\frac{r}{|\eta|}\right)^n,$$

and the minimum is achieved for the polynomial $p(z) = \left(\frac{z}{\eta}\right)^n$.

Proof. For the proof, we refer to [281]. □

This result can be generalized to any disc, say, e.g., $\mathcal{C}(c, r)$ in the complex plane with center $c \in \mathbb{C}$ and radius $r > 0$. Let $\eta \in \mathbb{C}$ be any point in the complex plane that is outside of the disc $\mathcal{C}(c, r)$, i.e., $|\eta - c| > r$. Then, by shifting the variable and scaling the polynomial, we can obtain the following min-max result:

$$\min_{p(z) \in \mathcal{P}_n^{(\eta)}} \max_{z \in \mathcal{C}(c, r)} |p(z)| = \left(\frac{r}{|\eta - c|}\right)^n.$$

Now we consider the case of the ellipse $\mathcal{E}_r$ centered at the origin, with foci -1 and 1, and semi-major axis $a_r = r + r^{-1}$. The ellipse $\mathcal{E}_r$ can be considered as mapped by J from the circle $\mathcal{C}_r$ with $r > 1$.

Theorem 5.82. *Consider the ellipse $\mathcal{E}_r$ mapped from the disc $\mathcal{C}_r$ by the mapping J. Let $\eta \in \mathbb{C}$ be a point outside of the ellipse $\mathcal{E}_r$. Then*

$$\frac{r^n}{|w_\eta|^n} \leq \min_{p(z) \in \mathcal{P}_n^{(\eta)}} \max_{z \in \mathcal{E}_r} |p(z)| \leq \frac{r^n + r^{-n}}{|w_\eta^n + w_\eta^{-n}|}, \tag{5.69}$$

where w_η is the dominant root of the equation $J(w) = \eta$.

Proof. For the proof, we refer to [288]. □

As n increases to infinity, the difference between the left and the right bounds in (5.69) tends to zero. Thus, the important point made by Theorem 5.82 is that, for large n, the **normalized Chebyshev polynomial**

$$\tilde{T}_n(z) = \frac{T_n(z)}{T_n(\eta)}, \quad \text{where} \quad T_n(z) = \frac{1}{2}\left(w^n + w^{-n}\right), \text{ with } z = \frac{1}{2}\left(w + w^{-1}\right),$$

is close to the optimal polynomial. This indicates that $\tilde{T}_n(z)$ is asymptotically optimal for the min-max problem (5.67).

For a more general ellipse $\mathcal{E}(c, d, a)$ centered at c, with focal length d and semi-major axis a, a simple change of variables shows that the asymptotically optimal polynomial is given by

$$\tilde{T}_n(z) = \frac{T_n\left(\frac{c-z}{d}\right)}{T_n\left(\frac{c-\eta}{d}\right)}. \tag{5.70}$$

In addition, by examining the expression $\frac{1}{2}\left(w^n + w^{-n}\right)$ for $w = re^{i\theta}$, we easily see that the maximum modulus of $\tilde{T}_n(z)$, i.e., the infinity norm of this polynomial over the ellipse, is reached at the point $c + a$ located on the real axis [288]. This results in the conclusion

$$\max_{z \in \mathcal{E}(c,d,a)} |\tilde{T}_n(z)| = \frac{T_n\left(\frac{a}{d}\right)}{|T_n\left(\frac{c-\eta}{d}\right)|}. \tag{5.71}$$

We remark that if the foci of the ellipse $\mathcal{E}(c, d, a)$ are located on the imaginary axis, i.e., d and a are both purely imaginary, then $\frac{a}{d}$ is still positive and the numerator in the above expression is real. So the formula (5.71) still holds true.

By the definition of the complex Chebyshev polynomial $T_n(z)$, we have the following useful approximation:

$$\frac{T_n\left(\frac{a}{d}\right)}{T_n\left(\frac{c-\eta}{d}\right)} = \frac{\left(\frac{a}{d} + \sqrt{\left(\frac{a}{d}\right)^2 - 1}\right)^n + \left(\frac{a}{d} + \sqrt{\left(\frac{a}{d}\right)^2 - 1}\right)^{-n}}{\left(\frac{c-\eta}{d} + \sqrt{\left(\frac{c-\eta}{d}\right)^2 - 1}\right)^n + \left(\frac{c-\eta}{d} + \sqrt{\left(\frac{c-\eta}{d}\right)^2 - 1}\right)^{-n}}$$

$$= \frac{\left(a + \sqrt{a^2 - d^2}\right)^n + \left(a - \sqrt{a^2 - d^2}\right)^n}{\left(c - \eta + \sqrt{(c - \eta)^2 - d^2}\right)^n + \left(c - \eta - \sqrt{(c - \eta)^2 - d^2}\right)^n}$$

$$\approx \left(\frac{a + \sqrt{a^2 - d^2}}{c - \eta + \sqrt{(c - \eta)^2 - d^2}}\right)^n. \tag{5.72}$$

Remark 5.8. *For the min-max problem (5.67), the optimal polynomials were found for some certain cases. Opfer and Schober [253] considered the case where $n = 1$, and they obtained a complete solution for a more general version of (5.67) with $\mathcal{E}_r \subset \mathbb{C}$ being any compact set excluding η. Freund and Ruscheweyh [148] investigated the **min-max problem** (5.67) for the line segment $\mathcal{E}_r = [-1, 1]$. Fischer [135] showed that for the case $r > 1$ and η being purely imaginary, the **normalized Chebyshev polynomial** (5.68) is optimal if n is even and $|\eta|$ is sufficiently large compared to r. Fischer and Freund [138] presented the necessary and sufficient condition for the polynomials of the form*

$$\frac{T_n(z) + \alpha}{T_n(\eta) + \alpha}, \quad \alpha \in \mathbb{C},$$

to be the solution of the min-max problem (5.67).

5.6.4 ▪ Chebyshev Semi-Iteration

Consider the general **matrix splitting iteration scheme**

$$x^{(k+1)} = Gx^{(k)} + g, \quad k = 0, 1, 2, \ldots, \tag{5.73}$$

where $G \in \mathbb{C}^{n \times n}$ and $\rho(G) < 1$. It is easily seen that the **error vector** $\varepsilon^{(k)} = x^{(k)} - x_*$ satisfies

$$\varepsilon^{(k)} = G\varepsilon^{(k-1)} = \cdots = G^k \varepsilon^{(0)},$$

where $x_* \in \mathbb{C}^n$ is the exact fixed point, that is, it satisfies

$$x_* = Gx_* + g.$$

Let $\tilde{x}^{(k)}$ be a **linear combination** of

$$x^{(0)}, x^{(1)}, \ldots, x^{(k)},$$

i.e.,

$$\tilde{x}^{(k)} = \alpha_{k0}x^{(0)} + \alpha_{k1}x^{(1)} + \cdots + \alpha_{kk}x^{(k)} = \sum_{j=0}^{k} \alpha_{kj}x^{(j)},$$

where $\alpha_{kj} \in \mathbb{C}$ $(j = 0, 1, \ldots, k)$ are such that $\sum_{j=0}^{k} \alpha_{kj} = 1$. Then it holds that

$$\tilde{\varepsilon}^{(k)} = \tilde{x}^{(k)} - x_* = \sum_{j=0}^{k} \alpha_{kj}x^{(j)} - x_* = \sum_{j=0}^{k} \alpha_{kj}(x^{(j)} - x_*)$$

$$= \sum_{j=0}^{k} \alpha_{kj}\varepsilon^{(j)} = \sum_{j=0}^{k} \alpha_{kj}G^j\varepsilon^{(0)}.$$

It is expected that the error series $\{\tilde{\varepsilon}^{(k)}\}_{k=0}^{\infty}$ will tend to zero faster than the error series $\{\varepsilon^{(k)}\}_{k=0}^{\infty}$, i.e., the iteration sequence $\{\tilde{x}^{(k)}\}_{k=0}^{\infty}$ may converge to the vector x_* faster than the iteration sequence $\{x^{(k)}\}_{k=0}^{\infty}$. In this way, we can accelerate the **convergence speed** of the iteration scheme (5.73). This kind of acceleration technique is called the **polynomial acceleration method** or the **semi-iteration method** [329].

Let

$$q_k(t) = \sum_{j=0}^{k} \alpha_{kj}t^j$$

be a polynomial of degree not greater than k, i.e., $\deg(q_k) \leq k$. Then it holds that

$$q_k(1) = 1 \quad \text{and} \quad \tilde{\varepsilon}^{(k)} = q_k(G)\,\varepsilon^{(0)}.$$

Thus, for any consistent matrix norm $\|\cdot\|$ we have

$$\|\tilde{\varepsilon}^{(k)}\| \leq \|q_k(G)\| \cdot \|\varepsilon^{(0)}\|.$$

In order to make the norm of $\tilde{\varepsilon}^{(k)}$ as small as possible, we are naturally led to the minimization problem

$$\min_{q_k(1)=1} \|q_k(G)\|. \tag{5.74}$$

In a certain sense, this problem has a trivial solution for k sufficiently large, i.e., $k \geq n$. In fact, if we let

$$q(t) \triangleq \det(tI - G)$$

be the **characteristic polynomial** of the matrix G, it follows from the **Cayley–Hamilton theorem** [75] that $q(G) = 0$. Define $\tilde{q}(t)$ to be the **normalized polynomial** of $q(t)$ as

$$\tilde{q}(t) \triangleq \frac{q(t)}{q(1)},$$

where $q(1) \neq 0$ as $\rho(G) < 1$, we see that $\tilde{q}(G) = 0$, which leads to

$$\|\tilde{\varepsilon}^{(n)}\| = \|\tilde{q}(G)\,\varepsilon^{(0)}\| = 0.$$

In other words, we can find the exact fixed-point solution x_* at most in n steps. However, determining the characteristic polynomial of the matrix $G \in \mathbb{C}^{n \times n}$ is very difficult and considerably time-consuming, especially when n is very large.

In general, it is difficult to solve the minimization problem (5.74) for $k < n$. Here we particularly assume that the polynomial $q_k(t)$ has real coefficients and the matrix $G \in \mathbb{C}^{n \times n}$ is Hermitian. Thus, there exists a unitary matrix $U \in \mathbb{C}^{n \times n}$ such that

$$G = U \Lambda U^*,$$

where $\Lambda = \mathrm{diag}(\lambda_1, \lambda_2, \dots, \lambda_n) \in \mathbb{R}^{n \times n}$ is a real diagonal matrix. Denote by

$$\mathcal{P}_k^{(1)} = \left\{ p(t) \,:\, p(t) \text{ is a polynomial in } t \text{ with } p(1) = 1 \text{ and } \deg(p) \leq k \right\}.$$

Then it follows that

$$\begin{aligned}
\min_{q_k \in \mathcal{P}_k^{(1)}} \|\tilde{\varepsilon}^{(k)}\|_2 &\leq \min_{q_k \in \mathcal{P}_k^{(1)}} \left\{ \|q_k(G)\|_2 \, \|\varepsilon^{(0)}\|_2 \right\} \\
&= \min_{q_k \in \mathcal{P}_k^{(1)}} \left\{ \|q_k(\Lambda)\|_2 \, \|\varepsilon^{(0)}\|_2 \right\} \\
&= \|\varepsilon^{(0)}\|_2 \min_{q_k \in \mathcal{P}_k^{(1)}} \max_{1 \leq i \leq n} \left\{ |q_k(\lambda_i)| \right\} \\
&\leq \|\varepsilon^{(0)}\|_2 \min_{q_k \in \mathcal{P}_k^{(1)}} \max_{\lambda \in [\lambda_{\min}, \lambda_{\max}]} \left\{ |q_k(\lambda)| \right\},
\end{aligned}$$

where $\lambda_{\min}$ and $\lambda_{\max}$ are the smallest and largest eigenvalues of the matrix $G \in \mathbb{C}^{n \times n}$, that is,

$$\lambda_{\min} = \min_{1 \leq i \leq n} \{\lambda_i\} \quad \text{and} \quad \lambda_{\max} = \max_{1 \leq i \leq n} \{\lambda_i\}.$$

Instead, we turn to solve the following **min-max problem**:

$$\min_{q_k \in \mathcal{P}_k^{(1)}} \max_{\lambda \in [\lambda_{\min}, \lambda_{\max}]} \left\{ |q_k(\lambda)| \right\}. \tag{5.75}$$

Recalling again that $\rho(G) < 1$, we have $1 \notin [\lambda_{\min}, \lambda_{\max}]$. From Theorem 5.78 we know that the unique solution of (5.75) is given by

$$q_k^{\star}(t) \equiv \tilde{T}_k(t) \triangleq \frac{T_k \left(\frac{2t - (\lambda_{\max} + \lambda_{\min})}{\lambda_{\max} - \lambda_{\min}} \right)}{T_k \left(\frac{2 - (\lambda_{\max} + \lambda_{\min})}{\lambda_{\max} - \lambda_{\min}} \right)}. \tag{5.76}$$

Concludingly, if bounds for the extreme eigenvalues of the matrix G are available, the Chebyshev polynomials can be adopted in accelerating the convergence speed of the matrix splitting iteration scheme (5.73). This is the so-called **Chebyshev semi-iteration** or **Chebyshev acceleration**.

However, the unique solution defined through the Chebyshev polynomials given in (5.76) is not easily computed in practice. The reason is that all currently available iterates

$$x^{(0)}, x^{(1)}, \ldots, x^{(k)}$$

and all coefficients of the Chebyshev polynomial $\tilde{T}_k(t)$ need to be stored and called in the computation of the next iterate $x^{(k+1)}$, which will occupy much more computer memory and cost a lot of computing time. Also, computing the smallest and largest eigenvalues $\lambda_{\min}$ and $\lambda_{\max}$ of the matrix $G \in \mathbb{C}^{n \times n}$ is a challenging problem, especially when n is sufficiently large.

Below we conduct an alternative reformulation for simply and economically realizing this Chebyshev acceleration, which calculates the iterate $\tilde{x}^{(k+1)}$ by a **three-term recurrence** only depending on the previous two iterates $\tilde{x}^{(k)}$ and $\tilde{x}^{(k-1)}$.

To this end, we denote by

$$\eta(t) = \frac{2t - (\lambda_{\max} + \lambda_{\min})}{\lambda_{\max} - \lambda_{\min}} \quad \text{and} \quad \eta_o \triangleq \eta(1) = \frac{2 - (\lambda_{\max} + \lambda_{\min})}{\lambda_{\max} - \lambda_{\min}}.$$

Then it holds that

$$
\begin{aligned}
\tilde{T}_{k+1}(t) &= \frac{T_{k+1}(\eta(t))}{T_{k+1}(\eta_o)} = \frac{2\,\eta(t)\,T_k(\eta(t)) - T_{k-1}(\eta(t))}{T_{k+1}(\eta_o)} \\
&= \frac{2\,T_k(\eta_o)}{T_{k+1}(\eta_o)} \cdot \eta(t) \cdot \frac{T_k(\eta(t))}{T_k(\eta_o)} - \frac{T_{k-1}(\eta_o)}{T_{k+1}(\eta_o)} \cdot \frac{T_{k-1}(\eta(t))}{T_{k-1}(\eta_o)} \\
&= \frac{2\,T_k(\eta_o)}{T_{k+1}(\eta_o)} \cdot \eta(t) \cdot \tilde{T}_k(t) - \frac{T_{k-1}(\eta_o)}{T_{k+1}(\eta_o)} \cdot \tilde{T}_{k-1}(t).
\end{aligned}
$$

It follows that

$$
\begin{aligned}
\tilde{\varepsilon}^{(k+1)} &= q_{k+1}^\star(G)\,\varepsilon^{(0)} = \tilde{T}_{k+1}(G)\,\varepsilon^{(0)} \\
&= \frac{2\,T_k(\eta_o)}{T_{k+1}(\eta_o)} \cdot \eta(G) \cdot \tilde{T}_k(G)\,\varepsilon^{(0)} - \frac{T_{k-1}(\eta_o)}{T_{k+1}(\eta_o)} \cdot \tilde{T}_{k-1}(G)\,\varepsilon^{(0)} \\
&= \frac{2\,T_k(\eta_o)}{T_{k+1}(\eta_o)}\,\eta(G)\,\tilde{\varepsilon}^{(k)} - \frac{T_{k-1}(\eta_o)}{T_{k+1}(\eta_o)}\,\tilde{\varepsilon}^{(k-1)}.
\end{aligned}
$$

As

$$\tilde{\varepsilon}^{(k)} = \tilde{x}^{(k)} - x_*$$

with x_* being the convergent point of the fixed-point iteration (5.73), that is, x_* satisfies

$$x_* = Gx_* + g,$$

we have

$$
\begin{aligned}
\eta(G)\,x_* &= \frac{1}{\lambda_{\max} - \lambda_{\min}}\,[2G - (\lambda_{\max} + \lambda_{\min})I]\,x_* \\
&= \eta_o x_* - \frac{2}{\lambda_{\max} - \lambda_{\min}}\,g
\end{aligned}
$$

and

$$\tilde{x}^{(k+1)} - x_* = \frac{2\,T_k(\eta_o)}{T_{k+1}(\eta_o)}\,\eta(G)\left(\tilde{x}^{(k)} - x_*\right) - \frac{T_{k-1}(\eta_o)}{T_{k+1}(\eta_o)}\left(\tilde{x}^{(k-1)} - x_*\right)$$

$$= \left[\frac{2\,T_k(\eta_o)}{T_{k+1}(\eta_o)}\,\eta(G)\,\tilde{x}^{(k)} - \frac{T_{k-1}(\eta_o)}{T_{k+1}(\eta_o)}\,\tilde{x}^{(k-1)}\right]$$

$$- \left[\frac{2\,T_k(\eta_o)}{T_{k+1}(\eta_o)}\,\eta(G)\,x_* - \frac{T_{k-1}(\eta_o)}{T_{k+1}(\eta_o)}\,x_*\right].$$

Note that the subtracted term satisfies

$$\frac{2\,T_k(\eta_o)}{T_{k+1}(\eta_o)}\,\eta(G)\,x_* - \frac{T_{k-1}(\eta_o)}{T_{k+1}(\eta_o)}\,x_* = \frac{2\,T_k(\eta_o)}{T_{k+1}(\eta_o)}\left(\eta_o x_* - \frac{2}{\lambda_{\max} - \lambda_{\min}}g\right) - \frac{T_{k-1}(\eta_o)}{T_{k+1}(\eta_o)}\,x_*$$

$$= \frac{2\eta_o\,T_k(\eta_o) - T_{k-1}(\eta_o)}{T_{k+1}(\eta_o)}\,x_* - \frac{2}{\lambda_{\max} - \lambda_{\min}}\,\frac{2\,T_k(\eta_o)}{T_{k+1}(\eta_o)}\,g$$

$$= x_* - \frac{2}{\lambda_{\max} - \lambda_{\min}}\,\frac{2\,T_k(\eta_o)}{T_{k+1}(\eta_o)}\,g,$$

where the last equality is valid since

$$\frac{2\eta_o\,T_k(\eta_o) - T_{k-1}(\eta_o)}{T_{k+1}(\eta_o)} = \tilde{T}_{k+1}(1) = 1.$$

Consequently, it holds that

$$\tilde{x}^{(k+1)} - x_* = \left[\frac{2\,T_k(\eta_o)}{T_{k+1}(\eta_o)}\,\eta(G)\,\tilde{x}^{(k)} - \frac{T_{k-1}(\eta_o)}{T_{k+1}(\eta_o)}\,\tilde{x}^{(k-1)}\right] - \left[x_* - \frac{2}{\lambda_{\max} - \lambda_{\min}}\,\frac{2\,T_k(\eta_o)}{T_{k+1}(\eta_o)}\,g\right],$$

which straightforwardly leads to the three-term recurrence formula

$$\tilde{x}^{(k+1)} = \frac{2\,T_k(\eta_o)}{T_{k+1}(\eta_o)}\,\eta(G)\,\tilde{x}^{(k)} - \frac{T_{k-1}(\eta_o)}{T_{k+1}(\eta_o)}\,\tilde{x}^{(k-1)} + \frac{4}{\lambda_{\max} - \lambda_{\min}}\,\frac{T_k(\eta_o)}{T_{k+1}(\eta_o)}\,g. \qquad (5.77)$$

By letting

$$\nu = \frac{2}{2 - (\lambda_{\max} + \lambda_{\min})} \quad \text{and} \quad \mu_{k+1} = 2\eta_o\,\frac{T_k(\eta_o)}{T_{k+1}(\eta_o)}, \quad k = 0, 1, 2, \ldots,$$

we can rewrite the **three-term recurrence formula** (5.77) as

$$\tilde{x}^{(k+1)} = \mu_{k+1}\left[\nu(G\tilde{x}^{(k)} + g) + (1 - \nu)\tilde{x}^{(k)}\right] + (1 - \mu_{k+1})\tilde{x}^{(k-1)}. \qquad (5.78)$$

Besides, we can prove that μ_{k+1} satisfies

$$\mu_{k+1}\left(1 - \frac{1}{4\eta_o^2}\,\mu_k\right) = 1,$$

with the initial value being given by $\mu_1 = 2$. Hence, μ_{k+1} can be obtained by updating μ_k according to the rule

$$\mu_{k+1} = \left(1 - \frac{1}{4\eta_o^2}\,\mu_k\right)^{-1}. \qquad (5.79)$$

Now, the combination of (5.78) and (5.79) readily gives a precise description of the **Chebyshev semi-iteration scheme** associated with the fixed-point iteration (5.73).

In practical implementations, the extreme eigenvalues $\lambda_{\min}$ and $\lambda_{\max}$ of the matrix G are often not easily computable. If there exist constants α and β such that

$$-1 < \alpha \leq \lambda_{\min} < \lambda_{\max} \leq \beta < 1,$$

we can use α and β instead of $\lambda_{\min}$ and $\lambda_{\max}$ in the Chebyshev semi-iteration scheme defined through (5.78) and (5.79). This then results in the following practical version of the **Chebyshev semi-iteration method**:

- Give an initial guess $x^{(0)}$, and set $\tilde{x}^{(0)} = x^{(0)}$, $\mu_1 = 2$;

- Compute $\tilde{x}^{(1)} = Gx^{(0)} + g$, with $\eta_o = \frac{2-(\alpha+\beta)}{\beta-\alpha}$ and $\nu = \frac{2}{2-(\alpha+\beta)}$;

- Iterate the following steps for $k = 1, 2, \ldots$ until the error satisfies the prescribed stopping criterion:

$$\mu_{k+1} = \left(1 - \frac{1}{4\eta_o^2}\mu_k\right)^{-1},$$

$$\tilde{x}^{(k+1)} = \mu_{k+1}\left[\nu(G\tilde{x}^{(k)} + g) + (1-\nu)\tilde{x}^{(k)}\right] + (1 - \mu_{k+1})\tilde{x}^{(k-1)}.$$

We remark that the above argument equally holds true when the matrix G is symmetrically diagonalizable, that is, there exist a nonsingular matrix $X \in \mathbb{C}^{n\times n}$ and a Hermitian matrix $\tilde{G} \in \mathbb{C}^{n\times n}$ such that $GX = X\tilde{G}$.

Theorem 5.83. *The Chebyshev semi-iteration method defined in (5.78) and (5.79) is convergent, with the convergence factor being bounded by*

$$\frac{1}{T_k(\eta_o)} = \frac{2}{\left(\eta_o + \sqrt{\eta_o^2 - 1}\right)^k + \left(\eta_o + \sqrt{\eta_o^2 - 1}\right)^{-k}}. \tag{5.80}$$

Proof. Define the **pseudospectral radius** of the **Chebyshev semi-iteration method** as

$$\rho_s(G) \triangleq \max_{\alpha \leq t \leq \beta} |\tilde{T}_k(t)| = \max_{\alpha \leq t \leq \beta} \left|\frac{T_k(\eta(t))}{T_k(\eta_o)}\right|.$$

Since for all $t \in [\alpha, \beta] \subset (-1, 1)$ it holds that

$$|\eta(t)| = \frac{|2t - (\alpha + \beta)|}{\beta - \alpha} < 1,$$

we see that $|T_k(\eta(t))| \leq 1$. From the definition of the real Chebyshev polynomial $T_k(t)$ in (5.60) we have

$$T_k(\eta_o) = \frac{1}{2}\left[\left(\eta_o + \sqrt{\eta_o^2 - 1}\right)^k + \left(\eta_o + \sqrt{\eta_o^2 - 1}\right)^{-k}\right] > 1$$

due to

$$\eta_o = \frac{2 - (\alpha + \beta)}{\beta - \alpha} > 1.$$

Hence,

$$\rho_s(G) \leq \frac{1}{T_k(\eta_o)} < 1.$$

The conclusion then follows immediately.   □

We remark that the upper bound of the **convergence factor** in (5.80) can be further bounded sharply from above by the quantity $\frac{1}{\eta_o^k}$, since it follows from

$$\left(\eta_o + \sqrt{\eta_o^2 - 1}\right)^{-k} = \left(\eta_o - \sqrt{\eta_o^2 - 1}\right)^k$$

that

$$T_k(\eta_o) = \frac{1}{2} \cdot 2 \sum_{i=0}^{\lfloor k/2 \rfloor} \binom{k}{2i} \eta_o^{k-2i} (\eta_o^2 - 1)^i > \eta_o^k.$$

Denote by

$$T_k(\eta_o) = \frac{1 + \tau^k}{2\tau^{k/2}}, \quad \text{with} \quad \tau \triangleq \left(\eta_o + \sqrt{\eta_o^2 - 1}\right)^{-2} < 1.$$

Then, for the **Chebyshev semi-iteration method**, we can define its **average convergence rate** after k steps as

$$R_k(\tilde{T}_k(G)) \triangleq -\frac{1}{k} \log(\rho_s(G)) = \frac{1}{k} \log(T_k(\eta_o)) = -\frac{1}{2} \log \tau - \frac{1}{k} \log \frac{2}{1 + \tau^k},$$

and its **asymptotic convergence rate** as

$$R(G) = \lim_{k \to \infty} R_k(\tilde{T}_k(G)) = -\frac{1}{2} \log \tau = \log(\eta_o + \sqrt{\eta_o^2 - 1}).$$

We see that the average and the asymptotic **convergence rate** of the Chebyshev semi-iteration method are both dependent on the constant

$$\eta_o = \frac{2 - (\alpha + \beta)}{\beta - \alpha};$$

see [189].

Now, we turn to deal with the case that the matrix $G \in \mathbb{C}^{n \times n}$ is diagonalizable but has some complex eigenvalues. To this end, we suppose that all eigenvalues of the matrix G are contained in an ellipse, say, e.g., $\mathcal{E}(c, d, a)$, which is centered at $c \in \mathbb{R}$ with focal length d and semi-major axis a (see also the definition in Section 5.6.3). Note that each eigenvalue λ of the matrix G satisfies $\Re(\lambda) < 1$, and the point $\eta = 1$ is outside of the ellipse $\mathcal{E}(c, d, a)$.

Similar to (5.75), we need to solve the following complex **min-max problem**:

$$\min_{q_k \in \mathcal{P}_k^{(1)}} \max_{z \in \mathcal{E}(c,d,a)} \{|q_k(z)|\}.$$

From the **complex Chebyshev polynomial** defined in (5.70), or in Remark 5.8, we know that the unique solution of this problem is given by

$$q_k^\star(z) \equiv \tilde{T}_k(z) \triangleq \frac{T_k\left(\frac{c-z}{d}\right)}{T_k\left(\frac{c-1}{d}\right)}.$$

Analogously, by making use of the **three-term recurrence** of the complex Chebyshev polynomial $T_k(z)$ we have

$$\tilde{T}_0(z) = 1, \quad \tilde{T}_1(z) = \nu z - \nu + 1,$$

and

$$\tilde{T}_{k+1}(z) = \mu_{k+1}(\nu z - \nu + 1)\tilde{T}_k(z) + (1 - \mu_{k+1})\tilde{T}_{k-1}(z), \quad k = 1, 2, \ldots,$$

where
$$\nu = \frac{1}{1-c}, \quad \eta_o = \frac{1-c}{d},$$

and
$$\mu_{k+1} = \frac{2\eta_o \, T_k(\eta_o)}{T_{k+1}(\eta_o)}, \quad k = 1, 2, \ldots,$$

with $\mu_1 = 2$. Correspondingly, the **Chebyshev semi-iteration scheme** is of the following form:

$$\tilde{z}^{(k)} = Gz^{(k)} + g,$$
$$z^{(k+1)} = \mu_{k+1}\left[\nu\tilde{z}^{(k)} + (1-\nu)z^{(k)}\right] + (1-\mu_{k+1})z^{(k-1)}, \quad k = 1, 2, \ldots.$$

In algorithmic description, it reads as follows:

- Give an initial guess $z^{(0)}$ and set $\mu_1 = 2$;

- Compute $z^{(1)} = Gz^{(0)} + g$, with $\eta_o = \frac{1-c}{d}$ and $\nu = \frac{1}{1-c}$;

- Iterate the following steps for $k = 1, 2, \ldots$ until the error satisfies the prescribed stopping criterion:

$$\mu_{k+1} = \left(1 - \frac{1}{4\eta_o^2}\mu_k\right)^{-1},$$
$$z^{(k+1)} = \mu_{k+1}\left[\nu(Gz^{(k)} + g) + (1-\nu)z^{(k)}\right] + (1-\mu_{k+1})z^{(k-1)}.$$

Note that the point $\eta = 1$ is outside of the ellipse $\mathcal{E}(c, d, a)$. Hence, from (5.71) and (5.72) we have

$$\rho_s(G) \triangleq \max_{z \in \mathcal{E}(c,d,a)} |\tilde{T}_k(z)| = \left|\frac{T_k(\frac{a}{d})}{T_k(\frac{c-1}{d})}\right| \approx \left(\frac{a + \sqrt{a^2 - d^2}}{1 - c + \sqrt{(1-c)^2 - d^2}}\right)^k < 1.$$

This indicates that the **Chebyshev semi-iteration method** is convergent with the **asymptotic convergence rate** being at least

$$R(G) = \lim_{k\to\infty}\left(-\frac{1}{k}\log(\rho_s(G))\right) \approx -\log\left(\frac{a + \sqrt{a^2 - d^2}}{1 - c + \sqrt{(1-c)^2 - d^2}}\right).$$

Admittedly, in practice, the main difficulty for applying the Chebyshev semi-iteration method is how to find an ellipse $\mathcal{E}(c, d, a)$ that can tightly contain all eigenvalues of the matrix G; see [189].

5.7 ▪ Sensitivity Analysis

Solving a linear system by a numerical method inevitably leads to the introduction of **numerical errors**. Hence, what we can obtain is an approximate solution $\hat{x}$ to the analytic solution $x_* = A^{-1}b$ of the system of linear equations (5.1).

Suppose that the approximate solution $\hat{x} = x_* + \delta x$ satisfies the following **perturbed linear system**:

$$(A + \delta A)(x_* + \delta x) = (b + \delta b), \tag{5.81}$$

where δA and δb are small **perturbations** of the matrix A and the right-hand side vector b, respectively. In order to ensure that the linear system (5.81) admits a unique solution, we may assume that the matrix $A + \delta A$ is nonsingular, which can be guaranteed by $\|A^{-1}\| \cdot \|\delta A\| < 1$, with $\|\cdot\|$ being any **consistent matrix norm**.

The following result provides an estimate of the perturbation δx in terms of the perturbations δA and δb.

Theorem 5.84. *Let $A \in \mathbb{C}^{n \times n}$ be a nonsingular matrix, and let $\delta A \in \mathbb{C}^{n \times n}$ satisfy $\|A^{-1}\| \|\delta A\| < 1$. Assume that x_* and $x_* + \delta x$ are the exact solutions of the linear system (5.1) and the corresponding perturbed linear system (5.81), respectively. Then it holds that*

$$\frac{\|\delta x\|}{\|x_*\|} \leq \frac{\kappa(A)}{1 - \kappa(A) \|\delta A\| / \|A\|} \left(\frac{\|\delta b\|}{\|b\|} + \frac{\|\delta A\|}{\|A\|} \right), \tag{5.82}$$

*where $\|\cdot\|$ denotes any consistent matrix norm and $\kappa(\cdot)$ denotes the corresponding **matrix condition number**, i.e., $\kappa(A) = \|A\| \|A^{-1}\|$.*

Proof. As $\|A^{-1}\| \|\delta A\| < 1$, it holds that

$$\rho(-A^{-1} \delta A) \leq \| - A^{-1} \delta A\| \leq \|A^{-1}\| \|\delta A\| < 1.$$

It follows from Lemma 4.39 that the matrix $I + A^{-1} \delta A$ is nonsingular and

$$(I + A^{-1} \delta A)^{-1} = I + \sum_{k=1}^{\infty} (-A^{-1} \delta A)^k.$$

Hence,

$$\begin{aligned}
\|(I + A^{-1} \delta A)^{-1}\| &= \left\| I + \sum_{k=1}^{\infty} (-A^{-1} \delta A)^k \right\| \\
&\leq \|I\| + \sum_{k=1}^{\infty} \|A^{-1} \delta A\|^k \\
&= \frac{1}{1 - \|A^{-1} \delta A\|}.
\end{aligned}$$

Solving the linear system (5.81) for the vector δx, we obtain

$$\delta x = (A + \delta A)^{-1} (\delta b - \delta A \, x_*).$$

It then follows that

$$\begin{aligned}
\|\delta x\| &= \|(A + \delta A)^{-1} (\delta b - \delta A \, x_*)\| \\
&\leq \|A^{-1}\| \|(I + A^{-1} \delta A)^{-1}\| \left(\|\delta b\| + \|\delta A\| \|x_*\| \right) \\
&\leq \frac{\|A^{-1}\|}{1 - \|A^{-1} \delta A\|} \|A\| \|x_*\| \left(\frac{\|\delta b\|}{\|A\| \|x_*\|} + \frac{\|\delta A\|}{\|A\|} \right) \\
&\leq \frac{\|A^{-1}\| \|A\|}{1 - \|A^{-1}\| \|\delta A\|} \|x_*\| \left(\frac{\|\delta b\|}{\|A x_*\|} + \frac{\|\delta A\|}{\|A\|} \right) \\
&= \|x_*\| \frac{\kappa(A)}{1 - \kappa(A) \|\delta A\| / \|A\|} \left(\frac{\|\delta b\|}{\|b\|} + \frac{\|\delta A\|}{\|A\|} \right).
\end{aligned}$$

So, the estimate in (5.82) follows immediately. ☐

Corollary 5.85. *Let $A \in \mathbb{C}^{n \times n}$ be a nonsingular matrix and $\delta A = 0$. Assume that x_* and $x_* + \delta x$ are the exact solutions of the linear system (5.1) and the corresponding perturbed linear system (5.81), respectively. Then it holds that*

$$\frac{1}{\kappa(A)} \frac{\|\delta b\|}{\|b\|} \leq \frac{\|\delta x\|}{\|x_*\|} \leq \kappa(A) \frac{\|\delta b\|}{\|b\|}. \tag{5.83}$$

Proof. We only need to prove the first inequality. As $\delta A = 0$, we have

$$\delta b = A \, \delta x \quad \text{and} \quad \|\delta b\| \leq \|A\| \, \|\delta x\|.$$

Multiplying both sides of this inequality by $\|x_*\|$ and making use of the inequality

$$\|x_*\| \leq \|A^{-1}\| \, \|b\|,$$

we obtain

$$\|\delta b\| \, \|x_*\| \leq \kappa(A) \, \|b\| \, \|\delta x\|,$$

which proves the desired inequality in (5.83). □

Example 5.86. Consider the linear system $Ax = b$ with

$$A = \begin{bmatrix} 1000 & 999 \\ 999 & 998 \end{bmatrix}, \quad b = \begin{bmatrix} 1999 \\ 1997 \end{bmatrix}.$$

It has a unique solution $x_* = [1, 1]^\mathsf{T}$. As

$$A^{-1} = \begin{bmatrix} -998 & 999 \\ 999 & -1000 \end{bmatrix},$$

we have

$$\kappa_1(A) = \|A\|_1 \|A^{-1}\|_1 = 1999^2 \approx 3.996 \times 10^6$$

and

$$\kappa_\infty(A) = \|A\|_\infty \|A^{-1}\|_\infty = 1999^2 \approx 3.996 \times 10^6,$$

which indicate that the matrix A is ill-conditioned.

For a small perturbation $\delta b = [-0.01, 0.01]^\mathsf{T}$ for the right-hand side vector b, the solution of the perturbed linear system $Ax = b + \delta b$ is given by $\hat{x} = [20.97, 18.99]^\mathsf{T}$, which is far from the exact solution x_* of the original linear system $Ax = b$.

5.8 ▪ Exercises

5.1. Prove that the corresponding matrix splitting of the SSOR iteration method (5.15) is given by (5.17) and (5.18).

5.2. Let D be a nonsingular diagonal matrix, and L and U be strictly lower-triangular and strictly upper-triangular matrices, respectively. When is the following matrix invertible?

$$(2 - \omega)D + (\omega - \gamma)(L + U).$$

5.3. Let $G \in \mathbb{C}^{n \times n}$ satisfy $\rho(G) < 1$. Then the average convergence rate and the asymptotic convergence rate of the matrix G satisfy the relationship

$$\lim_{k \to \infty} R_k(G) = -\log \rho(G).$$

5.4. Prove the result in Theorem 5.15.

5.5. Prove the result in Theorem 5.23.

5.6. Prove the result in Theorem 5.25.

5.7. Let the iteration matrix G_{J} of the Jacobi method be nonnegative, i.e., $G_{\text{J}} \geq 0$. Then one and only one of the following mutually exclusive relations holds true:

    (1) $\rho(G_{\text{J}}) = \rho(G_{\text{GS}}) = 0$,

    (2) $0 < \rho(G_{\text{GS}}) < \rho(G_{\text{J}}) < 1$,

    (3) $1 = \rho(G_{\text{J}}) = \rho(G_{\text{GS}})$,

    (4) $1 < \rho(G_{\text{J}}) < \rho(G_{\text{GS}})$.

Thus the Jacobi iteration method and the Gauss–Seidel iteration method are either both convergent, or both divergent.

This result is called the **Stein–Rosenberg theorem**; see [329].

5.8. Let $A \in \mathbb{R}^{n \times n}$ be an M-matrix, and let D and $-L$ be its diagonal and strictly lower-triangular parts, respectively. Show that $(D - L)^{-1} \geq 0$.

5.9. Let $A \in \mathbb{C}^{n \times n}$ be Hermitian positive definite, with D being its diagonal part. Prove that the matrix D is also Hermitian positive definite.

5.10. [218] Let $A = D - E - E^* \in \mathbb{C}^{n \times n}$ be a Hermitian matrix, where the matrix $D \in \mathbb{C}^{n \times n}$ is Hermitian positive definite. Let the parameter ω be real and the matrix $D - \omega E$ be nonsingular. For

$$\mathcal{L}(\omega) = (D - \omega E)^{-1}[(1 - \omega)D + \omega E^*],$$

prove that $\rho(\mathcal{L}(\omega)) < 1$ if and only if

    (1) the matrix A is positive definite and $0 < \omega < 2$, or

    (2) the matrix A is negative definite and $\omega \notin [0, 2]$.

5.11. Prove Property (6) of the Chebyshev polynomials in Theorem 5.76.

5.12. Prove the result in Theorem 5.78.

5.13. Prove that when both are convergent, the Chebyshev semi-iteration method possesses faster convergence rate than the Richardson iteration method.

Chapter 6

Krylov Subspace Methods

Consider the system of linear equations

$$Ax = b, \quad A \in \mathbb{R}^{n \times n}, \ b \in \mathbb{R}^n, \tag{6.1}$$

where $x \in \mathbb{R}^n$ is the solution we need to compute. One of the most useful and popular iteration methods for solving the large sparse linear system (6.1) is the **subspace method**. Instead of solving the potentially very large linear system, this class of iteration methods approximates the solution in a subspace $\mathcal{K} \subset \mathbb{R}^n$ of small dimension. Mathematically, subspace methods are based on projection process.

6.1 ▪ Projection Technique

6.1.1 ▪ Projector and Its Properties

Let $P : \mathbb{R}^n \to \mathbb{R}^n$ be a linear mapping. If

$$P^2 = P,$$

then we call P a **projection operator** or a **projector**. The following are some basic properties of a projector.

Proposition 6.1. *Let $P : \mathbb{R}^n \to \mathbb{R}^n$ be a projector. Then*

(1) *$I - P$ is a projector and $\mathrm{Ker}(P) = \mathrm{Ran}(I - P)$,*

(2) *P^T is a projector.*

Proposition 6.2. *Let $P : \mathbb{R}^n \to \mathbb{R}^n$ be a projector. Then we have*

$$\mathbb{R}^n = \mathrm{Ran}(P) \oplus \mathrm{Ker}(P).$$

Conversely, if $\mathbb{V}$ and $\mathbb{L}$ are two subspaces of $\mathbb{R}^n$ with $\mathbb{R}^n = \mathbb{V} \oplus \mathbb{L}$, then there exists a unique projector P such that

$$\mathrm{Ran}(P) = \mathbb{V} \quad and \quad \mathrm{Ker}(P) = \mathbb{L},$$

that is, for any vector $x \in \mathbb{R}^n$, it holds that

$$Px \in \mathbb{V} \quad and \quad x - Px \in \mathbb{L}.$$

We call P a projector onto $\mathbb{V}$ along $\mathbb{L}$.

This property tells us that a projector is uniquely determined by its range and kernel (null space).

Let $\mathbb{W} = \mathbb{L}^{\perp}$. Then $\mathbb{W}$ has the same dimension as $\mathbb{V}$ and $x - Px \in \mathbb{L}$ is equivalent to

$$x - Px \perp \mathbb{W}.$$

Hence, we call P a projector onto $\mathbb{V}$ and orthogonal to $\mathbb{W}$.

Proposition 6.3. *Let $\mathbb{V}$ and $\mathbb{W}$ be two subspaces of $\mathbb{R}^n$ with the same dimension. If $\mathbb{V} \cap \mathbb{W}^{\perp} = \{0\}$ (or $\mathbb{R}^n = \mathbb{V} \oplus \mathbb{W}^{\perp}$), then there exists a unique projector P such that*

$$\mathrm{Ran}(P) = \mathbb{V} \quad and \quad \mathrm{Ker}(P) = \mathbb{W}^{\perp},$$

that is, P is a projector onto $\mathbb{V}$ and orthogonal to $\mathbb{W}$. Furthermore, we have

$$Px = 0 \quad if and only if \quad x \perp \mathbb{W}.$$

Suppose that the subspaces $\mathbb{V}$ and $\mathbb{W}$ are of the same dimension m and $\mathbb{R}^n = \mathbb{V} \oplus \mathbb{W}^{\perp}$.

Proposition 6.4. *Let $v_1, v_2, \ldots, v_m$ and $w_1, w_2, \ldots, w_m$ be the bases of the subspaces $\mathbb{V}$ and $\mathbb{W}$, respectively. Let P be the projector onto $\mathbb{V}$ and orthogonal to $\mathbb{W}$. Then the matrix representation of the projector P is given by*

$$P = V(W^{\mathsf{T}}V)^{-1}W^{\mathsf{T}},$$

where $V = [v_1, v_2, \ldots, v_m]$ and $W = [w_1, w_2, \ldots, w_m]$.

Proof. We first prove that the matrix $W^{\mathsf{T}}V \in \mathbb{R}^{m \times m}$ is nonsingular. Let $\tilde{W} \in \mathbb{R}^{n \times (n-m)}$ be a matrix whose columns form a basis of the subspace $\mathbb{W}^{\perp}$. As $\mathbb{R}^n = \mathbb{V} \oplus \mathbb{W}^{\perp}$, the columns of the matrix $[V, \tilde{W}] \in \mathbb{R}^{n \times n}$ form a basis of $\mathbb{R}^n$. Therefore, the matrix $[V, \tilde{W}]$ is nonsingular and

$$\mathrm{rank}(W^{\mathsf{T}}) = \mathrm{rank}(W^{\mathsf{T}}[V, \tilde{W}]) = \mathrm{rank}([W^{\mathsf{T}}V, 0]) = \mathrm{rank}(W^{\mathsf{T}}V).$$

Since $\mathrm{rank}(W^{\mathsf{T}}) = m$, we have $\mathrm{rank}(W^{\mathsf{T}}V) = m$, which shows that the matrix $W^{\mathsf{T}}V$ is nonsingular.

If P is the projector onto the subspace $\mathbb{V}$ and orthogonal to the subspace $\mathbb{W}$, then we have $Px \in \mathbb{V}$ and $x - Px \perp \mathbb{W}$. Hence, there exists a vector $y \in \mathbb{R}^m$ such that

$$Px = Vy \quad and \quad W^{\mathsf{T}}(x - Vy) = 0.$$

It follows that $y = (W^{\mathsf{T}}V)^{-1}W^{\mathsf{T}}x$. Therefore,

$$Px = Vy = V(W^{\mathsf{T}}V)^{-1}W^{\mathsf{T}}x$$

holds for all $x \in \mathbb{R}^n$, which implies that $P = V(W^{\mathsf{T}}V)^{-1}W^{\mathsf{T}}$.   □

We remark that although the projector P is uniquely determined by the subspaces $\mathbb{V}$ and $\mathbb{W}$, its matrix representation is not unique.

Let P be a projector. If

$$\mathrm{Ker}(P) = \mathrm{Ran}(P)^{\perp},$$

then P is an **orthogonal projector** onto $\mathrm{Ran}(P)$. A projector that is not orthogonal is **oblique**.

Proposition 6.5. *Let $P : \mathbb{R}^n \to \mathbb{R}^n$ be a projector. Then the projector P is orthogonal if and only if $P^{\mathsf{T}} = P$.*

Proof. If $P^\mathsf{T} = P$, then it follows from Proposition 1.8 that

$$\mathrm{Ker}(P) = \mathrm{Ran}(P^\mathsf{T})^\perp = \mathrm{Ran}(P)^\perp,$$

which implies that the projector P is orthogonal.

Conversely, if the projector P is orthogonal, then $\mathrm{Ker}(P) = \mathrm{Ran}(P)^\perp$. Hence

$$\mathrm{Ran}(P^\mathsf{T}) = \mathrm{Ker}(P)^\perp = \mathrm{Ran}(P), \quad \mathrm{Ker}(P^\mathsf{T}) = \mathrm{Ran}(P)^\perp = \mathrm{Ker}(P),$$

which indicates that the projectors P^T and P have the same range and kernel. It follows from Proposition 6.2 that a projector is uniquely determined by its range and kernel, so we have $P^\mathsf{T} = P$. $\square$

Let $\mathbb{V} = \mathrm{Ran}(P)$. If P is an orthogonal projector, then for any vector $x \in \mathbb{R}^n$ we have

$$Px \in \mathbb{V} \quad \text{and} \quad x - Px \in \mathbb{V}^\perp. \tag{6.2}$$

Proposition 6.6. *Let $P : \mathbb{R}^n \to \mathbb{R}^n$ be an orthogonal projector onto the subspace $\mathbb{V}$. Then $I - P$ is an orthogonal projector onto the subspace $\mathbb{V}^\perp$.*

Let V be the matrix whose columns form an orthonormal basis of the subspace $\mathbb{V}$. Then it follows from Proposition 6.4 that
$$P = VV^\mathsf{T}.$$

Proposition 6.7. *Let $P : \mathbb{R}^n \to \mathbb{R}^n$ be an orthogonal projector. Then*

(1) $\|x\|_2^2 = \|Px\|_2^2 + \|(I - P)x\|_2^2, \ \forall\, x \in \mathbb{R}^n$;

(2) $\|P\|_2 = 1$.

Proof. Let $\mathbb{V} = \mathrm{Ran}(P)$. As the projector P is orthogonal, it follows from (6.2) that $Px \perp (I - P)x$. Therefore,
$$\|x\|_2^2 = \|Px\|_2^2 + \|(I - P)x\|_2^2.$$
This identity immediately gives $\|Px\|_2 \leq \|x\|_2$, leading to $\|P\|_2 \leq 1$. Let $y \in \mathbb{V}$ be a nonzero vector. Then $Py = y$, which indicates that

$$\|P\|_2 = \max_{x \neq 0} \frac{\|Px\|_2}{\|x\|_2} \geq \frac{\|Py\|_2}{\|y\|_2} = 1.$$

Hence, $\|P\|_2 = 1$. $\square$

Given a vector $z \in \mathbb{R}^n$ and a subspace $\mathbb{V} \subseteq \mathbb{R}^n$, we consider the following minimization problem:
$$\min_{x \in \mathbb{V}} \|z - x\|_2, \tag{6.3}$$
that is, to find the best approximation of the vector z in the subspace $\mathbb{V}$ in the sense of the 2-norm.

Proposition 6.8. *Let P be the orthogonal projector onto the subspace $\mathbb{V}$. Then the solution of the minimization problem (6.3) is given by*

$$x_* = Pz.$$

Moreover, as the projector P is uniquely determined by the subspace $\mathbb{V}$, this solution is unique.

Proof. Since P is an orthogonal projector onto the subspace $\mathbb{V}$, it holds that $Pz \in \mathbb{V}$ and $(I - P)z \in \mathbb{V}^{\perp}$. For any vector $x \in \mathbb{V}$, we have $(I - P)z \perp (Pz - x)$ and

$$
\begin{aligned}
\|z - x\|_2^2 &= \|(I - P)z + Pz - x\|_2^2 \\
&= \|(I - P)z\|_2^2 + \|Pz - x\|_2^2 \\
&\geq \|(I - P)z\|_2^2,
\end{aligned}
$$

where the inequality becomes equality if and only if $x = Pz$. $\square$

Corollary 6.9. *Let $x_* \in \mathbb{V}$. Then the vector x_* is the solution of the minimization problem (6.3) if and only if*

$$
z - x_* \perp \mathbb{V}.
$$

Corollary 6.10. *Given a vector $z \in \mathbb{R}^n$ and a subspace $\mathbb{V} \subseteq \mathbb{R}^n$, for the symmetric positive-definite matrix $A \in \mathbb{R}^{n \times n}$ we consider the minimization problem in terms of the $\|\cdot\|_A$-norm as follows:*

$$
\min_{x \in \mathbb{V}} \|z - x\|_A.
$$

Then $x_* \in \mathbb{V}$ is its unique solution if and only if

$$
A(z - x_*) \perp \mathbb{V},
$$

where the norm $\|\cdot\|_A$ is defined as

$$
\|z - x\|_A = \|A^{\frac{1}{2}}(z - x)\|_2.
$$

Proof. The proof is left as Exercise 6.2. $\square$

6.1.2 ▪ General Framework of Projection Methods

Let $\mathcal{K}$ be a subspace of $\mathbb{R}^n$ with dimension m, that is, $\mathcal{K} \subseteq \mathbb{R}^n$ and $m = \dim(\mathcal{K})$, and let $m \ll n$. We now seek the "best" approximate solution of the linear system (6.1) in the subspace $\mathcal{K}$. Because of the m degrees of freedom, m constraints must be imposed to uniquely extract such an approximation. Let $\tilde{x} \in \mathcal{K}$ be the approximate solution of the linear system (6.1) in the subspace $\mathcal{K}$. A typical way is to impose m independent orthogonality conditions on the **residual vector** $r \triangleq b - A\tilde{x}$, that is,

$$
r = b - A\tilde{x} \perp \mathcal{L}, \tag{6.4}
$$

where $\mathcal{L}$ is another subspace of $\mathbb{R}^n$ and of dimension m. The subspace $\mathcal{L}$ is called the **constraint subspace** or **left subspace**. It can be the same as the subspace $\mathcal{K}$, or can be different from the subspace $\mathcal{K}$, and may be even totally unrelated to the subspace $\mathcal{K}$. Condition (6.4) is common for many different mathematical methods and is known as the **Petrov–Galerkin condition**. If $\mathcal{K} = \mathcal{L}$, it is called the **Galerkin condition**.

Obviously, different choices of the left subspace $\mathcal{L}$ may result in different methods. In general, there are two broad classes of projection processes: **orthogonal projection** where $\mathcal{L} = \mathcal{K}$, and **oblique projection** where $\mathcal{L} \neq \mathcal{K}$.

A projection technique onto the subspace $\mathcal{K}$ and orthogonal to the left subspace $\mathcal{L}$ is a process which seeks an approximate solution $\tilde{x} \in \mathcal{K}$ by imposing Condition (6.4), that is,

$$
\text{find } \tilde{x} \in \mathcal{K} \quad \text{such that} \quad b - A\tilde{x} \perp \mathcal{L}. \tag{6.5}
$$

For a given initial guess $x^{(0)} \in \mathbb{R}^n$, if we wish to exploit the knowledge of the vector $x^{(0)}$ to the solution, then the approximation should be sought in the **affine subspace** $x^{(0)} + \mathcal{K}$, and the problem (6.5) can be rewritten as

$$\text{find } \tilde{x} \in x^{(0)} + \mathcal{K} \quad \text{such that} \quad b - A\tilde{x} \perp \mathcal{L}. \tag{6.6}$$

If we write the approximate solution $\tilde{x}$ in the form $\tilde{x} = x^{(0)} + \hat{x}$ with $\hat{x} \in \mathcal{K}$, then the problem (6.6) is the same as the following problem:

$$\text{find } \hat{x} \in \mathcal{K} \quad \text{such that} \quad r_0 - A\hat{x} \perp \mathcal{L}, \tag{6.7}$$

where $r_0 \triangleq b - Ax^{(0)}$ is the initial residual vector.

This is a basic projection step which forms a unified framework for many of the well-known iteration methods in scientific computing.

We can solve the problem (6.7) in matrix form. Let $V = [v_1, v_2, \ldots, v_m]$ and $W = [w_1, w_2, \ldots, w_m]$ be two real $n \times m$ matrices whose column vectors form bases of the subspaces $\mathcal{K}$ and $\mathcal{L}$, respectively. As $\tilde{x} \in x^{(0)} + \mathcal{K}$, there exists a vector $y \in \mathbb{R}^m$ such that

$$\tilde{x} = x^{(0)} + Vy.$$

It follows from the **orthogonality condition** (6.7) that

$$r_0 - AVy \perp w_i, \quad i = 1, 2, \ldots, m,$$

that is,

$$W^\mathsf{T} AVy = W^\mathsf{T} r_0.$$

If the matrix $W^\mathsf{T} AV$ is nonsingular, then we have

$$y = (W^\mathsf{T} AV)^{-1} W^\mathsf{T} r_0$$

and the approximate solution $\tilde{x}$ is given by

$$\tilde{x} = x^{(0)} + V(W^\mathsf{T} AV)^{-1} W^\mathsf{T} r_0.$$

We remark that the matrix $W^\mathsf{T} AV$ does not have to be formed explicitly, since it is always available as a by-product in many methods.

Note that the approximate solution $\tilde{x}$ is defined only when the matrix $W^\mathsf{T} AV$ is nonsingular. It is easy to see that this matrix is nonsingular if and only if no vector of the subspace $A\mathcal{K}$ is orthogonal to the subspace $\mathcal{L}$. There are two important particular cases where the nonsingularity of the matrix $W^\mathsf{T} AV$ is automatically guaranteed.

Theorem 6.11. [288] *If the matrix $A \in \mathbb{R}^{n \times n}$, and the subspaces $\mathcal{K} \subseteq \mathbb{R}^n$ and $\mathcal{L} \subseteq \mathbb{R}^n$ satisfy either of the following conditions:*

(1) *the matrix A is positive definite and $\mathcal{L} = \mathcal{K}$,*

(2) *the matrix A is nonsingular and $\mathcal{L} = A\mathcal{K}$,*

then the matrix $W^\mathsf{T} AV$ is nonsingular for any basis matrices V and W of the subspaces $\mathcal{K}$ and $\mathcal{L}$, respectively.

In practical implementations of the projection process, we need to consider the following problems:

- How to choose the subspaces $\mathcal{K}$ and $\mathcal{L}$.
- If an approximate solution is not good enough, how to find a new subspace in a realistic and economical way.

The above two problems can be solved through the famous Krylov subspace.

6.2 ▪ Krylov Subspace and Arnoldi Process

6.2.1 ▪ Krylov Subspace

Consider the linear system (6.1) and let $A = M - N$ be a splitting of the coefficient matrix $A \in \mathbb{R}^{n \times n}$. Then we can obtain the **matrix splitting iteration scheme**

$$
\begin{aligned}
x^{(m)} &= M^{-1}Nx^{(m-1)} + M^{-1}b \\
&= M^{-1}(M - A)x^{(m-1)} + M^{-1}b \\
&= x^{(m-1)} + M^{-1}(b - Ax^{(m-1)}), \quad m = 1, 2, \ldots.
\end{aligned}
$$

If we choose $M = I$, then this iteration scheme reduces to the **Richardson iteration**:

$$
x^{(m)} = (I - A)x^{(m-1)} + b, \quad m = 1, 2, \ldots;
$$

and if we choose $M = \frac{1}{\omega}I$, then it results in the **extrapolated Richardson iteration** or the **Richardson extrapolation iteration**:

$$
x^{(m)} = (I - \omega A)x^{(m-1)} + \omega b, \quad m = 1, 2, \ldots.
$$

In particular, letting $x^{(0)} = 0$ we have

$$
\begin{aligned}
x^{(m)} &= (I - \omega A)x^{(m-1)} + \omega b \\
&= (I - \omega A)\big[(I - \omega A)x^{(m-2)} + \omega b\big] + \omega b \\
&= (I - \omega A)^2 x^{(m-2)} + \big[(I - \omega A) + I\big]\omega b \\
&= \cdots \\
&= (I - \omega A)^m x^{(0)} + \big[(I - \omega A)^{m-1} + \cdots + (I - \omega A) + I\big]\omega b \\
&= \big[(I - \omega A)^{m-1} + \cdots + (I - \omega A) + I\big]\omega b \\
&\in \text{span}\{b, Ab, \ldots, A^{m-1}b\}.
\end{aligned}
$$

In general, if $x^{(0)} \neq 0$, we can make a transformation $y = x - x^{(0)}$ so that $y^{(0)} = 0$ and

$$
Ay = Ax - Ax^{(0)} = b - Ax^{(0)} = r_0.
$$

By applying either the Richardson extrapolation iteration to this new linear system, or the Richardson iteration to the scaled linear system $\omega Ay = \omega r_0$, we obtain

$$
y^{(m)} = \big[(I - \omega A)^{m-1} + \cdots + (I - \omega A) + I\big]\omega r_0 \in \text{span}\{r_0, Ar_0, \ldots, A^{m-1}r_0\}.
$$

The subspace

$$
\mathcal{K}_m(A, r_0) \triangleq \text{span}\{r_0, Ar_0, \ldots, A^{m-1}r_0\} \subseteq \mathbb{R}^n
$$

is the so-called **Krylov subspace** generated by the matrix A and the vector r_0. For simplicity, we usually denote it by $\mathcal{K}_m$ if there is no ambiguity. The Krylov subspaces form a nested sequence, i.e.,

$$
\mathcal{K}_1(A, r_0) \subseteq \mathcal{K}_2(A, r_0) \subseteq \cdots \subseteq \mathcal{K}_m(A, r_0) \subseteq \cdots.
$$

It is clear that $\mathcal{K}_m(A, r_0)$ is the subspace of all vectors in $\mathbb{R}^n$ which can be written as $x = p(A)r_0$, where $p(\cdot)$ is a polynomial of degree not exceeding $m - 1$. The dimension of the Krylov subspace $\mathcal{K}_m$ does not exceed m. For a more detailed discussion about motivations leading to construction of the Krylov subspace, we refer the reader to [26].

A Krylov subspace method is a projection method based on the subspace $\mathcal{K}_m$. Different choices of a left subspace $\mathcal{L}_m$ may lead to different kinds of Krylov subspace methods. It is desired to choose the subspace $\mathcal{L}_m$ such that the approximate solution may possess some **optimality properties**, such as minimizing the residual norm or the norm of error. Some widely used Krylov subspace methods are proposed based on the choices $\mathcal{L}_m = \mathcal{K}_m(A, r_0)$, $\mathcal{L}_m = A\mathcal{K}_m(A, r_0)$ and $\mathcal{L}_m = \mathcal{K}_m(A^\mathsf{T}, r_0)$.

6.2.2 ▪ Arnoldi Process

The **Arnoldi process** is a procedure to build an orthogonal basis of the Krylov subspace $\mathcal{K}$. It was introduced in 1951 as a means of reducing a dense matrix into the Hessenberg form with unitary transformations [4]. The procedure is described as follows.

Algorithm 6.1: Arnoldi Algorithm

1: Let r_0 be a nonzero vector and set $v_1 = r_0/\|r_0\|_2$
2: **for** $j = 1, 2, \ldots, m$ **do**
3:      $w_j = Av_j$
4:      **for** $i = 1, 2, \ldots, j$ **do**
5:          $h_{ij} = \langle w_j, v_i \rangle$
6:      **end for**
7:      $w_j := w_j - \sum\limits_{i=1}^{j} h_{ij} v_i$
8:      $h_{j+1,j} = \|w_j\|_2$
9:      **if** $h_{j+1,j} = 0$, **then**
10:          stop
11:      **end if**
12:      $v_{j+1} = w_j/h_{j+1,j}$
13: **end for**

We remark that Algorithm 6.1 may break down if $h_{j+1,j} = 0$, i.e., the vector w_j vanishes after the orthonormalization. In this case, the vector Av_j is linearly dependent with the vectors $v_1, v_2, \ldots, v_j$.

In Algorithm 6.1, the vectors v_i's are called the **Arnoldi vectors**. At each step, the algorithm multiplies the previous Arnoldi vector v_j by the matrix A from the left and then orthonormalizes the resulting vector w_j against all previous Arnoldi vectors with the standard Gram–Schmidt procedure.

If the algorithm does not break down, then the Arnoldi vectors $v_1, v_2, \ldots, v_m$ form an **orthonormal basis** of the Krylov subspace $\mathcal{K}_m(A, r_0)$.

Lemma 6.12. *Assume that Algorithm 6.1 does not break down before the first $m - 1$ steps. Then we have*
$$v_j \in \mathcal{K}_j(A, r_0), \quad \text{for} \quad j = 1, 2, \ldots, m.$$

Proof. We prove this result by induction.

As $v_1 = r_0/\|r_0\|_2$, it is clear that $v_1 \in \mathcal{K}_1(A, r_0)$.

Assume that the conclusion holds for all $j \leq k$ ($1 \leq k < m$) and consider the vector v_{k+1}. By the assumption $v_j \in \mathcal{K}_j(A, r_0)$ for $j \leq k$ and the fact $\mathcal{K}_j(A, r_0) \subseteq \mathcal{K}_{j+1}(A, r_0)$, we have

$$Av_k \in \mathcal{K}_{k+1}(A, r_0) \tag{6.8}$$

and

$$v_j \in \mathcal{K}_j(A, r_0) \subseteq \mathcal{K}_{k+1}(A, r_0), \quad \text{for} \quad j = 1, 2, \ldots, k. \tag{6.9}$$

It follows from Algorithm 6.1 that

$$v_{k+1} = \left(Av_k - \sum_{i=1}^{k} h_{ik} v_i \right) \Big/ h_{k+1,k},$$

which, together with (6.8) and (6.9), implies that $v_{k+1} \in \mathcal{K}_{k+1}(A, r_0)$. By induction, the conclusion is true for $j = 1, 2, \ldots, m$. $\square$

As the vectors $v_1, v_2, \ldots, v_m$ are orthonormal and $\dim(\mathcal{K}_m(A, r_0)) \leq m$, the following result holds true.

Theorem 6.13. *Assume that Algorithm 6.1 does not break down before the first $m - 1$ steps. Then the vectors $v_1, v_2, \ldots, v_m$ form an orthonormal basis of the Krylov subspace*

$$\mathcal{K}_m(A, r_0) = \text{span}\{r_0, Ar_0, \ldots, A^{m-1} r_0\}.$$

By Algorithm 6.1, we have

$$h_{j+1,j} v_{j+1} = Av_j - \sum_{i=1}^{j} h_{ij} v_i,$$

that is,

$$Av_j = h_{j+1,j} v_{j+1} + \sum_{i=1}^{j} h_{ij} v_i$$

$$= [v_1, v_2, \ldots, v_{j+1}] \begin{bmatrix} h_{1j} \\ h_{2j} \\ \vdots \\ h_{j+1,j} \end{bmatrix} = [v_1, \ldots, v_{j+1}, v_{j+2}, \ldots, v_{m+1}] \begin{bmatrix} h_{1j} \\ \vdots \\ h_{j+1,j} \\ 0 \\ \vdots \\ 0 \end{bmatrix}$$

$$= V_{m+1} H_{m+1,m}(:, j),$$

where $V_{m+1} = [v_1, v_2, \ldots, v_{m+1}]$ and

$$H_{m+1,m} = \begin{bmatrix} h_{11} & h_{12} & h_{13} & h_{14} & \cdots & h_{1,m-1} & h_{1,m} \\ h_{21} & h_{22} & h_{23} & h_{24} & \cdots & h_{2,m-1} & h_{2,m} \\ 0 & h_{32} & h_{33} & h_{34} & \cdots & h_{3,m-1} & h_{3,m} \\ 0 & 0 & h_{43} & h_{44} & \cdots & h_{4,m-1} & h_{4,m} \\ \vdots & \vdots & \vdots & \vdots & \ddots & \vdots & \vdots \\ 0 & 0 & 0 & 0 & \cdots & h_{m,m-1} & h_{m,m} \\ 0 & 0 & 0 & 0 & \cdots & 0 & h_{m+1,m} \end{bmatrix} \in \mathbb{R}^{(m+1) \times m},$$

with the entries h_{ij} ($i = 1, 2, \ldots, m + 1$, $j = 1, 2, \ldots, m$) being defined by Algorithm 6.1. Therefore, we have the following result.

Theorem 6.14. *Let $V_m = [v_1, v_2, \ldots, v_m]$. Then we have the following relationships:*

$$AV_m = V_{m+1}H_{m+1,m} = V_m H_m + h_{m+1,m} v_{m+1} e_m^{\mathsf{T}}, \qquad (6.10)$$
$$V_m^{\mathsf{T}} AV_m = H_m,$$

where $e_m = [0, \ldots, 0, 1]^{\mathsf{T}} \in \mathbb{R}^m$ and $H_m = H_{m+1,m}(1 : m, 1 : m) \in \mathbb{R}^{m \times m}$, i.e., H_m is the upper Hessenberg matrix obtained from the matrix $H_{m+1,m}$ by deleting its last row.

The result of Theorem 6.14 can be illustrated by the following figure:

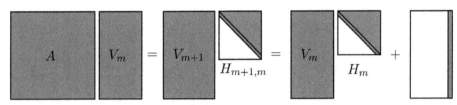

As we remarked before, the Arnoldi algorithm may break down before the step $j = m$. If the **breakdown** happens, we can obtain an **invariant subspace**.

Proposition 6.15. *If Algorithm 6.1 breaks down at step k $(k \leq m)$, i.e., $h_{k+1,k} = 0$, then we have $AV_k = V_k H_k$, which implies that the subspace $\mathcal{K}_k$ is invariant under the linear operator A.*

In practical implementations, considering the numerical stability we always employ the ***modified Gram–Schmidt*** (MGS) algorithm instead of the standard Gram–Schmidt algorithm. This leads to the following algorithm.

Algorithm 6.2: Arnoldi Algorithm with MGS

1: Let r_0 be a nonzero vector and set $v_1 = r_0/\|r_0\|_2$
2: **for** $j = 1, 2, \ldots, m$ **do**
3:     $w_j = Av_j$
4:     **for** $i = 1, 2, \ldots, j$ **do**
5:         $h_{ij} = \langle w_j, v_i \rangle$
6:         $w_j := w_j - h_{ij} v_i$
7:     **end for**
8:     $h_{j+1,j} = \|w_j\|_2$
9:     **if** $h_{j+1,j} = 0$, **then**
10:         stop
11:     **end if**
12:     $v_{j+1} = w_j/h_{j+1,j}$
13: **end for**

It is easy to see that Algorithm 6.2 is mathematically equivalent to Algorithm 6.1. But in **finite precision arithmetic**, Algorithm 6.2 is much more stable. In particular, it was shown that the modified Gram–Schmidt implementation is backward stable in the sense that the **backward error** is proportional to the **machine precision** [262].

However, there are some cases, especially for ill-conditioned matrices, that even Algorithm 6.2 may be unreliable due to the severe cancellations. In those cases, we need more accurate implementations. In general, there are two improvements we can utilize: one is to do MGS twice at each step (see, e.g., [103]), and another is to replace the MGS by the Householder transformation (see, e.g., [334]).

6.3 ▪ Methods for General Linear Systems

Given an initial guess $x^{(0)} \in \mathbb{R}^n$. Let $\mathcal{K}_m$ be the **Krylov subspace** defined by

$$\mathcal{K}_m = \text{span}\{r_0, Ar_0, A^2 r_0, \ldots, A^{m-1} r_0\},$$

where $r_0 = b - Ax^{(0)}$. We consider the iteration methods based on the Krylov subspace $\mathcal{K}_m$ for solving the linear system (6.1). Here we introduce two kinds of **Krylov subspace methods** which are based on taking $\mathcal{L}_m = \mathcal{K}_m$ and $\mathcal{L}_m = A\mathcal{K}_m$, respectively.

6.3.1 ▪ Full Orthogonalization Method

Let $\mathcal{L}_m = \mathcal{K}_m$. Then, to find an approximate solution $\tilde{x} \in \mathbb{R}^n$ for the linear system (6.1) in the Krylov subspace $\mathcal{K}_m$ is equivalent to solving the following problem:

$$\text{find } \tilde{x} \in x^{(0)} + \mathcal{K}_m \quad \text{such that} \quad b - A\tilde{x} \perp \mathcal{K}_m.$$

By applying Algorithm 6.2 on the Krylov subspace $\mathcal{K}_m$, we obtain

$$V_m^{\mathsf{T}} A V_m = H_m \quad \text{and} \quad V_m^{\mathsf{T}} r_0 = V_m^{\mathsf{T}}(\beta v_1) = \beta e_1,$$

where $\beta = \|r_0\|_2$ and $e_1 = [1, 0, \ldots, 0]^{\mathsf{T}} \in \mathbb{R}^m$. As the columns of the matrix V_m form an orthonormal basis of the Krylov subspace $\mathcal{K}_m$ and as $\tilde{x} \in x^{(0)} + \mathcal{K}_m$, there exists a vector $\tilde{y} \in \mathbb{R}^m$ such that

$$\tilde{x} = x^{(0)} + V_m \tilde{y}.$$

The **orthogonality condition** $b - A\tilde{x} \perp \mathcal{K}_m$ leads to

$$V_m^{\mathsf{T}}(b - A\tilde{x}) = 0,$$

or equivalently,

$$0 = V_m^{\mathsf{T}}(b - Ax^{(0)} - AV_m \tilde{y}) = V_m^{\mathsf{T}} r_0 - V_m^{\mathsf{T}} A V_m \tilde{y} = \beta e_1 - H_m \tilde{y}.$$

If the upper Hessenberg matrix H_m is nonsingular, we can compute the vector $\tilde{y} \in \mathbb{R}^m$ by solving the linear system

$$H_m \tilde{y} = \beta e_1, \tag{6.11}$$

leading to $\tilde{y} = \beta H_m^{-1} e_1$. Therefore, the approximate solution $\tilde{x} \in \mathbb{R}^n$ is given by

$$\tilde{x} = x^{(0)} + \beta V_m H_m^{-1} e_1.$$

The algorithm based on this approach is called the ***full orthogonalization method*** (FOM) [288].

Algorithm 6.3: Full Orthogonalization Method (FOM)

1: Given an initial guess $x^{(0)}$, compute $r_0 = b - Ax^{(0)}$
2: $\beta = \|r_0\|_2$
3: $v_1 = r_0/\beta$
4: **for** $j = 1, 2, \ldots, m$ **do**
5: $\quad w_j = Av_j$
6: $\quad$ **for** $i = 1, 2, \ldots, j$ **do**
7: $\quad\quad h_{ij} = \langle w_j, v_i \rangle$

8:           $w_j := w_j - h_{ij} v_i$
9:     **end for**
10:        $h_{j+1,j} = \|w_j\|_2$
11:    **if** $h_{j+1,j} = 0$, **then**
12:        set $m = j$ and stop
13:    **end if**
14:        $v_{j+1} = w_j / h_{j+1,j}$
15: **end for**
16: solve the linear system $H_m \tilde{y} = \beta e_1$ for the vector $\tilde{y}$
17: compute the approximate solution $\tilde{x} = x^{(0)} + V_m \tilde{y}$

In most situations, the dimension of the Krylov subspace $\mathcal{K}_m$ is much smaller than n. Hence we can solve the linear system (6.11) by **direct methods**, such as the **Gaussian elimination**. In fact, as $H_m \in \mathbb{R}^{m \times m}$ is an upper Hessenberg matrix, we usually employ the **QR decomposition**, which is much more robust.

One of the difficulties for FOM is how to choose the dimension m of the Krylov subspace $\mathcal{K}_m$. If m is too small, the approximate solution $\tilde{x}$ may be far away from the true solution; and if m is too large, it may cause a redundant workload. In practice, it is desirable to select m in a dynamic fashion. This would be possible if the residual norm of the approximate solution is available inexpensively.

Theorem 6.16. *Let $\tilde{x} \in x^{(0)} + \mathcal{K}_m$ be the approximate solution for the linear system (6.1) computed by Algorithm 6.3. Then the residual vector is given by*

$$\tilde{r} = b - A\tilde{x} = -h_{m+1,m} \left(e_m^{\mathsf{T}} \tilde{y} \right) v_{m+1},$$

where $\tilde{y} = \beta H_m^{-1} e_1$, and $e_1 = [1, 0, \ldots, 0]^{\mathsf{T}} \in \mathbb{R}^m$, $e_m = [0, \ldots, 0, 1]^{\mathsf{T}} \in \mathbb{R}^m$. Therefore, it holds that

$$\|\tilde{r}\|_2 = h_{m+1,m} |e_m^{\mathsf{T}} \tilde{y}|. \tag{6.12}$$

Proof. It follows from (6.10) that

$$\begin{aligned}
\tilde{r} = b - A\tilde{x} &= b - A(x^{(0)} + V_m \tilde{y}) \\
&= r_0 - A V_m \tilde{y} \\
&= r_0 - V_m H_m \tilde{y} - h_{m+1,m} v_{m+1} e_m^{\mathsf{T}} \tilde{y} \\
&= r_0 - V_m (\beta e_1) - h_{m+1,m} (e_m^{\mathsf{T}} \tilde{y}) v_{m+1} \\
&= r_0 - \beta v_1 - h_{m+1,m} (e_m^{\mathsf{T}} \tilde{y}) v_{m+1}.
\end{aligned}$$

By Algorithm 6.3 we know that $v_1 = r_0 / \beta$. Hence, $r_0 - \beta v_1 = 0$ and

$$\tilde{r} = -h_{m+1,m} \left(e_m^{\mathsf{T}} \tilde{y} \right) v_{m+1}.$$

which straightforwardly leads to the equality in (6.12).   □

By Theorem 6.16, we can check the norm of the residual $\tilde{r}$ without computing the approximate solution $\tilde{x}$. Therefore, in real applications, we can enlarge the dimension m of the Krylov subspace $\mathcal{K}_m$ step by step until the desirable approximate solution is finally obtained. Obviously, $\|\tilde{r}\|_2$ must be zero when $m = n$. This leads to the following **practical FOM**.

Algorithm 6.4: Practical FOM

1: Given an initial guess $x^{(0)}$ and a stopping tolerance $\varepsilon > 0$
2: compute $r_0 = b - Ax^{(0)}$
3: $\beta = \|r_0\|_2$
4: $v_1 = r_0/\beta$
5: **for** $j = 1, 2, \ldots,$ **do**
6: $\quad w_j = Av_j$
7: $\quad$ **for** $i = 1, 2, \ldots, j$ **do**
8: $\quad\quad h_{ij} = \langle w_j, v_i \rangle$
9: $\quad\quad w_j := w_j - h_{ij}v_i$
10: $\quad$ **end for**
11: $\quad h_{j+1,j} = \|w_j\|_2$
12: $\quad$ solve $H_j \tilde{y} = \beta e_1$ for $\tilde{y}$
13: $\quad$ **if** $h_{j+1,j}|e_j^{\mathsf{T}} \tilde{y}| < \varepsilon,$ **then**
14: $\quad\quad$ stop
15: $\quad$ **end if**
16: $\quad v_{j+1} = w_j/h_{j+1,j}$
17: **end for**
18: compute the approximate solution $\tilde{x} = x^{(0)} + V_j \tilde{y}$

If the Arnoldi process breaks down at step j, i.e., $h_{j+1,j} = 0$, then the residual at step j vanishes and we obtain the exact solution of the linear system (6.1).

6.3.2 ▪ Generalized Minimal Residual Method

One of the most popular iteration methods for solving the linear system (6.1) is the ***generalized minimal residual*** (GMRES) method, which is the projection method based on taking $\mathcal{L} = A\mathcal{K}$, that is, based on the solution of the problem:

$$\text{find } \tilde{x} \in x^{(0)} + \mathcal{K} \quad \text{such that} \quad b - A\tilde{x} \perp A\mathcal{K}. \tag{6.13}$$

We derive the **GMRES method** in a different way, which is based on the following **optimality property** of the approximate solution $\tilde{x}$.

Theorem 6.17. *Let* $A \in \mathbb{R}^{n \times n}$ *and* $\mathcal{K} \triangleq \mathcal{K}(A, r_0)$. *Then* $\tilde{x} \in \mathbb{R}^n$ *is the solution of the problem* (6.13) *if and only if it minimizes the residual norm* $\|b - Ax\|_2$ *over the affine subspace* $x^{(0)} + \mathcal{K}$, *i.e.,* $\tilde{x} \in \mathbb{R}^n$ *is the solution of the* ***constraint linear least-squares problem***

$$\min_{x \in x^{(0)} + \mathcal{K}} \|b - Ax\|_2. \tag{6.14}$$

Proof. For any vector

$$x \in x^{(0)} + \mathcal{K},$$

we have

$$x = x^{(0)} + y, \quad \text{with} \quad y \in \mathcal{K}.$$

Therefore, the minimization problem (6.14) can be rewritten as

$$\min_{y \in \mathcal{K}} \|b - A(x^{(0)} + y)\|_2 = \min_{y \in \mathcal{K}} \|r_0 - Ay\|_2 = \min_{z \in A\mathcal{K}} \|r_0 - z\|_2 \tag{6.15}$$

It follows from Corollary 6.9 that $\tilde{z} \in A\mathcal{K}$ is the solution of the minimization problem (6.15) if and only if

$$r_0 - \tilde{z} \perp A\mathcal{K}.$$

Assume that $\tilde{x}$ is the solution of (6.13). Let

$$\tilde{z} = A(\tilde{x} - x^{(0)}).$$

Then $\tilde{z} \in A\mathcal{K}$ and

$$r_0 - \tilde{z} = b - A\tilde{x},$$

which is orthogonal to the subspace $A\mathcal{K}$. Hence, the vector $\tilde{z}$ is the solution of the minimization problem (6.15), which indicates that the vector $\tilde{x}$ is the solution of the constraint linear least-squares problem (6.14).

On the other hand, assume that $\tilde{x} \in \mathbb{R}^n$ is the solution of the constraint linear least-squares problem (6.14). Then the vector

$$\tilde{z} \triangleq A(\tilde{x} - x^{(0)})$$

minimizes $\|r_0 - z\|_2$ over the subspace $A\mathcal{K}$. Hence,

$$r_0 - \tilde{z} \perp A\mathcal{K},$$

i.e.,

$$b - A\tilde{x} \perp A\mathcal{K}. \qquad \square$$

Let the Krylov subspace $\mathcal{K}$ be of dimension m, i.e., $\mathcal{K} = \mathcal{K}_m$, and the columns of the matrix $V_m \in \mathbb{R}^{n \times m}$ form an orthonormal basis of the subspace $\mathcal{K}_m$. It follows from Theorem 6.17 that the GMRES method seeks the solution of the minimization problem (6.14) over the affine subspace $x^{(0)} + \mathcal{K}_m$. For any vector $x \in x^{(0)} + \mathcal{K}_m$, there exists a vector $y \in \mathbb{R}^m$ such that

$$x = x^{(0)} + V_m y.$$

Then from (6.10) it holds that

$$\begin{aligned}
b - Ax &= b - A(x^{(0)} + V_m y) \\
&= r_0 - AV_m y \\
&= \beta v_1 - V_{m+1} H_{m+1,m} y \\
&= V_{m+1}(\beta e_1 - H_{m+1,m} y),
\end{aligned}$$

where

$$e_1 = [1, 0, \ldots, 0]^\mathsf{T} \in \mathbb{R}^{m+1}.$$

As the columns of the matrix V_{m+1} are orthonormal, we have

$$\|b - Ax\|_2 = \|V_{m+1}(\beta e_1 - H_{m+1,m} y)\|_2 = \|\beta e_1 - H_{m+1,m} y\|_2.$$

Consequently, the solution of the minimization problem (6.14) is given by

$$\tilde{x} = x^{(0)} + V_m \tilde{y},$$

where $\tilde{y}$ is the solution of the **(reduced) linear least-squares problem**

$$\min_{y \in \mathbb{R}^m} \|\beta e_1 - H_{m+1,m} y\|_2. \tag{6.16}$$

Instead of solving a linear system with the coefficient matrix H_m in FOM, here we need to solve a least-squares problem with the coefficient matrix $H_{m+1,m} \in \mathbb{R}^{(m+1) \times m}$. A standard method for solving this linear least-squares problem is by using the QR decomposition, which is not expensive provided the dimension m of the Krylov subspace $\mathcal{K}_m$ is not very large.

Let $H_{m+1,m} = Q_{m+1}^\mathsf{T} R_{m+1,m}$ be the QR decomposition of the matrix $H_{m+1,m}$, where $Q_{m+1} \in \mathbb{R}^{(m+1) \times (m+1)}$ is an orthogonal matrix and $R_{m+1,m} \in \mathbb{R}^{(m+1) \times m}$ is an upper-triangular matrix. Then

$$\begin{aligned}
\|\beta e_1 - H_{m+1,m} y\|_2 &= \|\beta e_1 - Q_{m+1}^\mathsf{T} R_{m+1,m} y\|_2 \\
&= \|\beta Q_{m+1} e_1 - R_{m+1,m} y\|_2 \\
&= \left\| \beta q_1 - \begin{bmatrix} R_m \\ 0 \end{bmatrix} y \right\|_2,
\end{aligned}$$

where $q_1 \in \mathbb{R}^{m+1}$ is the first column of the matrix Q_{m+1} and $R_m = R_{m+1,m}(1 : m, 1 : m) \in \mathbb{R}^{m \times m}$ is the top m-by-m block of the matrix $R_{m+1,m}$. Hence, the solution of the linear least-squares problem (6.16) can be obtained by solving the upper-triangular linear system

$$R_m \tilde{y} = \beta \, q_1(1 : m), \tag{6.17}$$

where $q_1(1 : m)$ denotes the vector formed by the first m entries of the vector q_1.

Analogously to FOM, we can check the norm of the residual without computing the approximate solution $\tilde{x}$.

Theorem 6.18. *Let $\tilde{x} \in x^{(0)} + \mathcal{K}_m$ be the approximate solution for the linear system (6.1) computed by the GMRES method. Then the residual vector $\tilde{r} = b - A\tilde{x}$ satisfies*

$$\|\tilde{r}\|_2 = \beta \, |q_1(m + 1)|,$$

where $q_1(m + 1)$ denotes the last entry of the vector $q_1 \in \mathbb{R}^{m+1}$.

Proof. In fact, we have

$$\|\tilde{r}\|_2 = \|\beta e_1 - H_{m+1,m} \tilde{y}\|_2 = \left\| \beta q_1 - \begin{bmatrix} R_m \\ 0 \end{bmatrix} \tilde{y} \right\|_2 = \beta \, |q_1(m + 1)|. \qquad \square$$

The **GMRES method** can be described as follows.

Algorithm 6.5: Generalized Minimal Residual (GMRES) Method

1: Given an initial guess $x^{(0)}$ and a stopping tolerance $\varepsilon > 0$
2: compute $r_0 = b - Ax^{(0)}$, $\beta = \|r_0\|_2$, and set $v_1 = r_0/\beta$
3: **for** $j = 1, 2, \ldots,$ **do**
4:    $w_j = Av_j$
5:    **for** $i = 1, 2, \ldots, j$ **do**   % Arnoldi process
6:      $h_{ij} = \langle w_j, v_i \rangle$
7:      $w_j := w_j - h_{ij} v_i$
8:    **end for**

9:     $h_{j+1,j} = \|w_j\|_2$

10:    **if** $h_{j+1,j} = 0$, **then**

11:       set $m = j$ and stop

12:    **end if**

13:     $v_{j+1} = w_j/h_{j+1,j}$

14:    **if** $\|\tilde{r}\|_2 < \varepsilon$, **then**   % check convergence

15:       set $m = j$ and stop

16:    **end if**

17: **end for**

18: solve the upper-triangular linear system (6.17) for $\tilde{y}$

19: compute the approximate solution $\tilde{x} = x^{(0)} + V_m\tilde{y}$

As in FOM, the only possibility of **breakdown** in GMRES is in the Arnoldi process. If $h_{k+1,k} = 0$ at step $k < n$, we have

$$AV_k = V_k H_k \quad \text{and} \quad \tilde{y} = H_k^{-1}(\beta e_1).$$

Hence,

$$\begin{aligned}
\|\tilde{r}\|_2 = \|b - A\tilde{x}\|_2 &= \|b - Ax^{(0)} - AV_k\tilde{y}\|_2 \\
&= \|r_0 - V_k H_k\tilde{y}\|_2 \\
&= \|\beta v_1 - V_k(\beta e_1)\|_2 = 0,
\end{aligned}$$

which implies that the vector $\tilde{x} \in \mathbb{R}^n$ is the exact solution. Therefore, this kind of breakdown is a **welcome breakdown**.

In fact, the converse is also true, i.e., if the GMRES method stops at step $k < n$ with $\tilde{r} = b - A\tilde{x} = 0$, then $h_{k+1,k} = 0$.

Theorem 6.19. *Let $A \in \mathbb{R}^{n \times n}$ be a nonsingular matrix. Then the GMRES method breaks down at step k if and only if the approximate solution for the linear system (6.1) becomes the exact one.*

6.3.3 ▪ Implementation Details of GMRES

Note that at Step 14 of the GMRES method, in order to compute the norm of the residual vector $\tilde{r}$, we need to compute the **QR decomposition** of the matrix $H_{j+1,j}$. In the following, we show that this can be done inexpensively with one step of the **Givens rotation** if we already have the QR decomposition of the matrix $H_{j,j-1}$.

For $j = 1$, we can easily apply a Givens rotation G_1 to obtain the QR decomposition of the matrix $H_{2,1} \in \mathbb{R}^{2 \times 1}$.

Suppose that we have obtained the QR decomposition of the matrix $H_{j,j-1} \in \mathbb{R}^{j \times (j-1)}$ by a series of Givens rotations. We now turn to consider how to compute the QR decomposition of the matrix $H_{j+1,j} \in \mathbb{R}^{(j+1) \times j}$ with as little work as possible. It is clear that

$$H_{j+1,j} = \begin{bmatrix} H_{j,j-1} & h_j \\ 0 & h_{j+1,j} \end{bmatrix},$$

where $h_j = [h_{1,j}, h_{2,j}, \ldots, h_{j,j}]^{\mathsf{T}}$ is the vector formed by the first j entries of the last column of the matrix $H_{j+1,j}$. Assume that

$$H_{j,j-1} = (G_{j-1}G_{j-2}\cdots G_1)^{\mathsf{T}} R_{j,j-1} = Q_j \begin{bmatrix} R_{j-1} \\ 0 \end{bmatrix}_{j \times (j-1)}$$

is the QR decomposition of the matrix $H_{j,j-1}$, where $R_{j-1} \in \mathbb{R}^{(j-1)\times(j-1)}$ is an upper-triangular matrix, G_k ($k = 1, 2, \ldots, j-1$) are Givens rotations, and

$$Q_j = G_1^\mathsf{T} G_2^\mathsf{T} \cdots G_{j-1}^\mathsf{T}.$$

In order to make the matrix products be consistent, here we suppose that the dimension of the Givens rotation G_i is expanded automatically if necessary. Then we have

$$\begin{bmatrix} Q_j^\mathsf{T} & 0 \\ 0 & 1 \end{bmatrix} H_{j+1,j} = \begin{bmatrix} Q_j^\mathsf{T} & 0 \\ 0 & 1 \end{bmatrix} \begin{bmatrix} H_{j,j-1} & h_j \\ 0 & h_{j+1,j} \end{bmatrix} = \begin{bmatrix} R_{j,j-1} & Q_j^\mathsf{T} h_j \\ 0 & h_{j+1,j} \end{bmatrix} = \begin{bmatrix} R_{j-1} & \tilde{h}_{j-1} \\ 0 & \hat{h}_{j,j} \\ 0 & h_{j+1,j} \end{bmatrix},$$

with

$$Q_j^\mathsf{T} h_j = \begin{bmatrix} \tilde{h}_{j-1} \\ \hat{h}_{j,j} \end{bmatrix},$$

where $\tilde{h}_{j-1}$ is constituted by the first $j-1$ entries and $\hat{h}_{j,j}$ is the last entry of the vector $Q_j^\mathsf{T} h_j$. Now we use the Givens rotation to eliminate the entry $h_{j+1,j}$. Let

$$\tilde{h}_{j,j} = \left(\hat{h}_{j,j}^2 + h_{j+1,j}^2 \right)^{\frac{1}{2}}$$

and

$$c_j = \frac{\hat{h}_{j,j}}{\tilde{h}_{j,j}}, \quad s_j = \frac{h_{j+1,j}}{\tilde{h}_{j,j}}.$$

Define

$$Q_{j+1} = \begin{bmatrix} Q_j & 0 \\ 0 & 1 \end{bmatrix} G_j^\mathsf{T} \in \mathbb{R}^{(j+1)\times(j+1)},$$

where G_j is the Givens rotation

$$G_j = \begin{bmatrix} I_{j-1} & 0 & 0 \\ 0 & c_j & s_j \\ 0 & -s_j & c_j \end{bmatrix} \in \mathbb{R}^{(j+1)\times(j+1)}.$$

Then it holds that

$$Q_{j+1}^\mathsf{T} H_{j+1,j} = G_j \begin{bmatrix} R_{j-1} & \tilde{h}_{j-1} \\ 0 & \hat{h}_{j,j} \\ 0 & h_{j+1,j} \end{bmatrix} = \begin{bmatrix} R_{j-1} & \tilde{h}_{j-1} \\ 0 & \tilde{h}_{j,j} \\ 0 & 0 \end{bmatrix} \triangleq R_{j+1,j},$$

that is to say, $H_{j+1,j} = Q_{j+1} R_{j+1,j}$ is the QR decomposition of the matrix $H_{j+1,j}$. Note that in the above process we only modify the values of the last column of the matrix $H_{j+1,j}$ and then combine it with the previous upper-triangular matrix R_{j-1} to obtain the upper-triangular matrix

$$R_j = \begin{bmatrix} R_{j-1} & \tilde{h}_{j-1} \\ 0 & \tilde{h}_{j,j} \end{bmatrix}.$$

When the residual norm is sufficiently small, we can stop the iteration and solve the upper-triangular linear system (6.17) for the solution vector $\tilde{y}$. The coefficient matrix $R_m \in \mathbb{R}^{m\times m}$ can be obtained by the QR decomposition of the matrix $H_{m+1,m}$ with Givens rotation and the right-hand side vector $\beta q_1 (1:m) \in \mathbb{R}^m$ can be obtained by applying the corresponding Givens rotations $G_1, G_2, \ldots, G_m$ to the vector $\beta e_1 \in \mathbb{R}^{m+1}$. In detail, we can describe the **GMRES method** as follows, where we store the matrix R_m in the matrix $H_{m+1,m}$.

Algorithm 6.6: Practical Implementation of GMRES

1: Given an initial guess $x^{(0)}$ and a stopping tolerance $\varepsilon > 0$
2: compute $r_0 = b - Ax^{(0)}$ and $\beta = \|r_0\|_2$
3: set $v_1 = r_0/\beta$ and $\xi = \beta e_1$
4: **for** $j = 1, 2, \ldots,$ **do**
5:     $w_j = Av_j$
6:     **for** $i = 1, 2, \ldots, j$ **do**   % Arnoldi process
7:         $h_{ij} = \langle w_j, v_i \rangle$
8:         $w_j := w_j - h_{ij} v_i$
9:     **end for**
10:    $h_{j+1,j} = \|w_j\|_2$
11:    **for** $i = 1, 2, \ldots, j-1$ **do**   % apply $G_{j-1}, \ldots, G_1$ to the last column of $H_{j+1,j}$

12:
$$\begin{bmatrix} h_{i,j} \\ h_{i+1,j} \end{bmatrix} := \begin{bmatrix} c_i & s_i \\ -s_i & c_i \end{bmatrix} \begin{bmatrix} h_{i,j} \\ h_{i+1,j} \end{bmatrix}$$

13:    **end for**
14:    **if** $h_{j+1,j} = 0$, **then**
15:        set $m = j$ and stop
16:    **end if**
17:    $v_{j+1} = w_j / h_{j+1,j}$
18:    **if** $|h_{j,j}| > |h_{j+1,j}|$, **then**   % form the Givens rotation G_j
19:        set $c_j = \frac{1}{\sqrt{1+\tau^2}}, s_j = c_j \tau$, where $\tau = \frac{h_{j+1,j}}{h_{j,j}}$
20:    **else**
21:        set $s_j = \frac{1}{\sqrt{1+\tau^2}}, c_j = s_j \tau$, where $\tau = \frac{h_{j,j}}{h_{j+1,j}}$
22:    **end if**
23:    $h_{j,j} := c_j h_{j,j} + s_j h_{j+1,j}, h_{j+1,j} := 0$ % apply G_j to the last column of $H_{j+1,j}$

24:
$$\begin{bmatrix} \xi_j \\ \xi_{j+1} \end{bmatrix} := \begin{bmatrix} c_j & s_j \\ -s_j & c_j \end{bmatrix} \begin{bmatrix} \xi_j \\ 0 \end{bmatrix} \quad \text{% apply } G_j \text{ to the right-hand side}$$

25:    **if** $|\xi_{j+1}| < \varepsilon$, **then**   % check convergence: $\|\tilde{r}\|_2 = |\xi_{j+1}|$
26:        set $m = j$ and stop
27:    **end if**
28: **end for**
29: compute $\tilde{y} = R_m^{-1} \xi_m$ with $R_m = H(1:m, 1:m)$ and $\xi_m = \xi(1:m)$
30: compute the approximate solution $\tilde{x} = x^{(0)} + V_m \tilde{y}$

We remark that in FOM and GMRES, MGS is employed to build the orthonormal basis of the Krylov subspace. In those severe cases where MGS is inadequate, we can adopt Householder transformations instead. For more details, we refer to [334].

The GMRES method is guaranteed to converge in at most n steps, but this would be impractical if j becomes large, because of the memory requirement and computational costs as j increases. A typical way to overcome this drawback is based on a restarting strategy.

Let $m \ll n$ be a fixed positive integer. If GMRES does not converge at m steps, then we compute the approximate solution $x^{(m)} \in x^{(0)} + \mathcal{K}_m$, set $x^{(0)} := x^{(m)}$, and restart the method. We repeat this procedure until convergence is achieved. This leads to the following **restarted GMRES method**.

Algorithm 6.7: GMRES(m): Restarted GMRES Method

1: Given an integer $m \ll n$, an initial guess $x^{(0)}$, and a stopping tolerance $\varepsilon > 0$
2: compute $r_0 = b - Ax^{(0)}$, $\beta = \|r_0\|_2$, and set $v_1 = r_0/\beta$, $\xi = \beta e_1$
3: **for** $j = 1, 2, \ldots, m$ **do**
4:     execute the GMRES method (i.e., Algorithm 6.6) from Step 5 to Step 27
5: **end for**
6: compute $\tilde{y} = R_m^{-1}\xi_m$ with $R_m = H(1:m, 1:m)$ and $\xi_m = \xi(1:m)$
7: compute the approximate solution $x^{(m)} = x^{(0)} + V_m\tilde{y}$
8: **if** $\|\xi_{m+1}\|_2 < \varepsilon$, **then**
9:     stop
10: **end if**
11: set $x^{(0)} := x^{(m)}$ and go to Step 2

The prominent advantage of the restarted GMRES method is to save the memory storage and computational costs. However, the convergence of GMRES(m) is expected to be slower than the full GMRES, as some information is discarded at each restart. Moreover, GMRES(m) can stagnate when the coefficient matrix $A \in \mathbb{R}^{n \times n}$ of the linear system (6.1) is not positive definite, and the convergence cannot be guaranteed even when the number of iterations is equal to or larger than n.

One difficulty of GMRES(m) is how to choose the number of the restarting steps, that is, the positive integer m. If m is "too small," GMRES(m) may be very slow to converge, or even fail to converge entirely. On the other hand, a value of m that is larger than necessary involves excessive work and uses more storage. Unfortunately, there is no definite rule to govern the choice of this positive integer m, which is highly problem-dependent and is also a matter of experience; see also [221, 302].

6.4 • Methods for Symmetric Linear Systems

In this section, we consider the special case of the linear system (6.1) where the coefficient matrix $A \in \mathbb{R}^{n \times n}$ is symmetric.

6.4.1 • Lanczos Process

If the matrix $A \in \mathbb{R}^{n \times n}$ is symmetric, the Arnoldi process, i.e., Algorithm 6.2, can be simplified to a **three-term recurrence**, which is known as the **Lanczos process**.

Recall that in the **Arnoldi process** we have

$$H_k = V_k^{\mathsf{T}} A V_k, \quad k = 1, 2, \ldots.$$

As the matrix A is symmetric and the matrix H_k is upper Hessenberg, it is easily seen that H_k is a symmetric tridiagonal matrix.

Lemma 6.20. *Let $A \in \mathbb{R}^{n \times n}$ be a symmetric matrix. Then the coefficients h_{ij} generated by the Arnoldi process satisfy*

$$h_{ij} = 0, \quad for \quad |i - j| > 1,$$

and

$$h_{j,j+1} = h_{j+1,j}, \quad for \, j = 1, 2, \ldots,$$

that is to say, the Hessenberg matrix H_k obtained by the Arnoldi process is symmetric and tridiagonal.

For simplicity, we set $\alpha_j = h_{j,j}$ and $\beta_j = h_{j,j+1}$, and rewrite H_k as T_k, where

$$T_k = \begin{bmatrix} \alpha_1 & \beta_1 & & & \\ \beta_1 & \ddots & \ddots & & \\ & \ddots & \ddots & \beta_{k-1} \\ & & \beta_{k-1} & \alpha_k \end{bmatrix}.$$

Then, it holds that

$$AV_k = V_k T_k + \beta_k v_{k+1} e_k^{\mathsf{T}} \quad \text{and} \quad V_k^{\mathsf{T}} AV_k = T_k, \quad k = 1, 2, \ldots. \tag{6.18}$$

Also, the following **three-term recurrence** relationship holds true:

$$\beta_j v_{j+1} = Av_j - \alpha_j v_j - \beta_{j-1} v_{j-1}, \quad j = 1, 2, \ldots,$$

where $\beta_0 = 0$ and $v_0 = 0$. Correspondingly, the Arnoldi process is reduced to the following so-called **Lanczos process**.

Algorithm 6.8: Lanczos Process

1: Let r_0 be a nonzero vector, and set $v_1 = r_0 / \|r_0\|_2$
2: set $\beta_0 = 0$ and $v_0 = 0$
3: **for** $j = 1, 2, \ldots,$ **do**
4:     $w_j = Av_j - \beta_{j-1} v_{j-1}$
5:     $\alpha_j = \langle w_j, v_j \rangle$
6:     $\tilde{w}_j = w_j - \alpha_j v_j$
7:     $\beta_j = \|\tilde{w}_j\|_2$
8:     **if** $\beta_j = 0$, **then**
9:         stop
10:    **end if**
11:    $v_{j+1} = \tilde{w}_j / \beta_j$
12: **end for**

In **exact arithmetic**, the vectors generated by the Lanczos process form an **orthonormal set**.

Lemma 6.21. *Let the vectors $v_1, v_2, \ldots, v_k, \ldots$, be generated by Algorithm 6.8. Then, it holds that*

$$\langle v_i, v_j \rangle = \delta_{ij} \triangleq \begin{cases} 1, & i = j, \\ 0, & i \neq j, \end{cases} \quad \text{for } i, j = 1, 2, \ldots.$$

Proof. It is clear that

$$\langle v_k, v_k \rangle = \|v_k\|_2^2 = 1$$

holds for $k = 1, 2, \ldots$. We only need to show that for any integer $k \geq 2$, it holds that $\langle v_k, v_j \rangle = 0$ for $1 \leq j < k$. This statement is demonstrated by induction.

For $k = 2$, we have

$$\langle v_2, v_1 \rangle = \langle \tilde{w}_1 / \beta_1, v_1 \rangle = \frac{1}{\beta_1} \langle w_1 - \alpha_1 v_1, v_1 \rangle = \frac{1}{\beta_1} \left(\langle w_1, v_1 \rangle - \alpha_1 \right) = 0.$$

Assume that the statement holds true for $i \leq k$, i.e., $\langle v_i, v_j \rangle = 0$ for all i, j such that $1 \leq j < i \leq k$. Since the matrix $A \in \mathbb{R}^{n \times n}$ is symmetric, it follows from Algorithm 6.8 that

$$
\begin{aligned}
\langle Av_k, v_{k-1} \rangle = \langle v_k, Av_{k-1} \rangle &= \langle v_k, w_{k-1} + \beta_{k-2} v_{k-2} \rangle \\
&= \langle v_k, \tilde{w}_{k-1} + \alpha_{k-1} v_{k-1} + \beta_{k-2} v_{k-2} \rangle \\
&= \langle v_k, \beta_{k-1} v_k + \alpha_{k-1} v_{k-1} + \beta_{k-2} v_{k-2} \rangle \\
&= \beta_{k-1}.
\end{aligned}
$$

Therefore, we have

$$
\begin{aligned}
\langle v_{k+1}, v_k \rangle &= \frac{1}{\beta_k} \langle w_k - \alpha_k v_k, v_k \rangle \\
&= \frac{1}{\beta_k} (\langle w_k, v_k \rangle - \alpha_k) \\
&= \frac{1}{\beta_k} (\alpha_k - \alpha_k) = 0,
\end{aligned}
$$

$$
\begin{aligned}
\langle v_{k+1}, v_{k-1} \rangle &= \frac{1}{\beta_k} \langle w_k - \alpha_k v_k, v_{k-1} \rangle \\
&= \frac{1}{\beta_k} \langle Av_k - \beta_{k-1} v_{k-1} - \alpha_k v_k, v_{k-1} \rangle \\
&= \frac{1}{\beta_k} (\langle Av_k, v_{k-1} \rangle - \beta_{k-1} \langle v_{k-1}, v_{k-1} \rangle - \alpha_k \langle v_k, v_{k-1} \rangle) \\
&= \frac{1}{\beta_k} (\beta_{k-1} - \beta_{k-1} - 0) = 0,
\end{aligned}
$$

and, for $j \leq k - 2$,

$$
\begin{aligned}
\langle v_{k+1}, v_j \rangle &= \frac{1}{\beta_k} \langle Av_k - \beta_{k-1} v_{k-1} - \alpha_k v_k, v_j \rangle \\
&= \frac{1}{\beta_k} (\langle Av_k, v_j \rangle - \beta_{k-1} \langle v_{k-1}, v_j \rangle - \alpha_k \langle v_k, v_j \rangle) \\
&= \frac{1}{\beta_k} (\langle v_k, Av_j \rangle - 0 - 0) \\
&= \frac{1}{\beta_k} \langle v_k, \tilde{w}_j + \alpha_j v_j + \beta_{j-1} v_{j-1} \rangle \\
&= \frac{1}{\beta_k} \langle v_k, \beta_j v_{j+1} + \alpha_j v_j + \beta_{j-1} v_{j-1} \rangle = 0.
\end{aligned}
$$

As a result, we see that $\langle v_{k+1}, v_j \rangle = 0$ for $j = 1, 2, \ldots, k$. By induction, the conclusion follows. $\square$

The Lanczos process can be regarded as the Arnoldi process particularly applied to a symmetric matrix; the major difference between them is that the matrix H_m in the Lanczos process is tridiagonal, while in the Arnoldi process it is upper Hessenberg. In the Lanczos process, we only need to orthogonalize the three adjacent vectors and save three vectors, which implies that the Lanczos process needs much less memory storage and computational costs than the Arnoldi process; see also [221, 302].

In practical computations, because of **round-off error**, the orthogonality of these vectors may be easily lost after some steps of iteration. If this situation happens, we can recover the global orthogonality by partial or selective orthogonalization. For more details, we refer to Parlett [271].

In the following, we introduce two famous Krylov subspace methods for solving symmetric linear systems, which are based on taking $\mathcal{L} = \mathcal{K}$ and $\mathcal{L} = A\mathcal{K}$, respectively.

6.4.2 ▪ Conjugate Gradient Method

In this subsection, we suppose that the coefficient matrix $A \in \mathbb{R}^{n \times n}$ of the linear system (6.1) is symmetric and positive definite.

The ***conjugate gradient*** (CG) [195] method is one of the best known iteration techniques for solving symmetric positive definite linear systems. The CG method can be viewed as an orthogonal projection technique onto the Krylov subspace $\mathcal{L} = \mathcal{K}$. Therefore, it is mathematically equivalent to the FOM. However, because the coefficient matrix A is symmetric and positive definite, some simplifications resulting from the three-term Lanczos process will lead to a more elegant scheme.

Unlike FOM and GMRES, the CG method computes the approximate solution and residual vector at each step. Let $x^{(0)} \in \mathbb{R}^n$ be a given initial guess, and $x^{(k)} \in \mathbb{R}^n$ ($k \geq 1$) be the approximate solution in $x^{(0)} + \mathcal{K}_k$ obtained by CG after k steps of iteration, that is,

$$x^{(k)} \in x^{(0)} + \mathcal{K}_k \quad \text{and} \quad b - Ax^{(k)} \perp \mathcal{K}_k,$$

where

$$\mathcal{K}_k = \text{span}\{r_0, Ar_0, \ldots, A^{k-1}r_0\}.$$

Analogously to FOM, we know that the vector $x^{(k)}$ is given by

$$x^{(k)} = x^{(0)} + V_k y_k \quad \text{with} \quad y_k = T_k^{-1}(\beta e_1^{(k)}),$$

where

$$V_k = [v_1, v_2, \ldots, v_k], \quad \beta = \|r_0\|_2$$

and

$$e_1^{(k)} = [1, 0, \ldots, 0]^\mathsf{T} \in \mathbb{R}^k.$$

Here, we need to solve the linear system with the coefficient matrix T_k for the vector y_k. As the matrix A is symmetric and positive definite, so is the tridiagonal matrix T_k. Hence, we can solve the tridiagonal linear system with respect to the matrix T_k by making use of the **LU decomposition**.

Let $x^{(k+1)}$ be the approximate solution in $x^{(0)} + \mathcal{K}_{k+1}$ obtained by CG after $k+1$ steps of iteration, that is,

$$x^{(k+1)} = x^{(0)} + V_{k+1} T_{k+1}^{-1}(\beta e_1^{(k+1)}),$$

where

$$e_1^{(k+1)} = [1, 0, \ldots, 0]^\mathsf{T} \in \mathbb{R}^{k+1}.$$

We now investigate the updating scheme from $x^{(k)}$ to $x^{(k+1)}$.

Lemma 6.22. *Let $A \in \mathbb{R}^{n \times n}$ be symmetric and positive definite, and T_k and T_{k+1} be the tridiagonal matrices obtained by applying the Lanczos process on the subspaces $\mathcal{K}_k$ and $\mathcal{K}_{k+1}$, respectively. Then the LU decompositions of the matrices T_k and T_{k+1} are given by*

$$T_k = L_k U_k \quad \text{and} \quad T_{k+1} = L_{k+1} U_{k+1},$$

where

$$L_\ell = \begin{bmatrix} 1 & & & \\ \gamma_1 & 1 & & \\ & \ddots & \ddots & \\ & & \gamma_{\ell-1} & 1 \end{bmatrix}, \quad U_\ell = \begin{bmatrix} \eta_1 & \beta_1 & & \\ & \eta_2 & \ddots & \\ & & \ddots & \beta_{\ell-1} \\ & & & \eta_\ell \end{bmatrix}, \quad \ell = k, k+1,$$

and

$$\begin{cases} \eta_1 = \alpha_1, \\ \gamma_i = \beta_i/\eta_i, & i = 1, 2, \ldots, \\ \eta_{i+1} = \alpha_{i+1} - \gamma_i\beta_i, & i = 1, 2, \ldots, \end{cases}$$

that is to say, L_k and U_k are the k-th leading principal submatrices of the triangular matrices L_{k+1} and U_{k+1}, respectively.

Proof. This statement can be proved by straightforward computations; see Exercise 6.3. $\square$

Note that

$$x^{(k)} = x^{(0)} + V_k T_k^{-1}(\beta e_1^{(k)}) = x^{(0)} + \beta V_k U_k^{-1} L_k^{-1} e_1^{(k)} = x^{(0)} + P_k z^{(k)}, \qquad (6.19)$$

where

$$P_k \triangleq V_k U_k^{-1} \in \mathbb{R}^{n \times k} \quad \text{and} \quad z^{(k)} \triangleq \beta L_k^{-1} e_1^{(k)} \in \mathbb{R}^k.$$

Denote by

$$P_k = [p_1, p_2, \ldots, p_k].$$

Then

$$P_{k+1} \triangleq V_{k+1} U_{k+1}^{-1} = \begin{bmatrix} V_k, v_{k+1} \end{bmatrix} \begin{bmatrix} U_k^{-1} & * \\ 0 & \frac{1}{\eta_{k+1}} \end{bmatrix} = \begin{bmatrix} V_k U_k^{-1}, p_{k+1} \end{bmatrix},$$

where "$*$" denotes some nonzero vector and p_{k+1} denotes the last column of the matrix P_{k+1}. Evidently, the matrices P_k and P_{k+1} have the following relationship:

$$P_{k+1} = [P_k, \ p_{k+1}].$$

As

$$P_{k+1} U_{k+1} = V_{k+1},$$

it holds that

$$v_{k+1} = \beta_k p_k + \eta_{k+1} p_{k+1}.$$

So,

$$p_{k+1} = \frac{1}{\eta_{k+1}}(v_{k+1} - \beta_k p_k), \quad k = 1, 2, \ldots. \qquad (6.20)$$

Note that

$$p_1 = P_1 = V_1 U_1^{-1} = \frac{1}{\eta_1} v_1 \qquad (6.21)$$

Denote

$$z^{(k)} = [z_1, z_2, \ldots, z_k]^\mathsf{T}.$$

Then we have

$$z^{(k+1)} = \beta L_{k+1}^{-1} e_1^{(k+1)} = \beta \begin{bmatrix} L_k^{-1} & 0 \\ * & 1 \end{bmatrix} \begin{bmatrix} e_1^{(k)} \\ 0 \end{bmatrix} = \begin{bmatrix} \beta L_k^{-1} e_1^{(k)} \\ z_{k+1} \end{bmatrix} = \begin{bmatrix} z^{(k)} \\ z_{k+1} \end{bmatrix},$$

where z_{k+1} denotes the last entry of the vector $z^{(k+1)}$. As

$$L_{k+1} z^{(k+1)} = \beta e_1^{(k+1)},$$

it holds that

$$\left[\begin{array}{c|c} L_k & 0 \\ \hline 0 \cdots 0\, \gamma_k & 1 \end{array} \right] \begin{bmatrix} z^{(k)} \\ z_{k+1} \end{bmatrix} = \begin{bmatrix} L_k z^{(k)} \\ \gamma_k z_k + z_{k+1} \end{bmatrix} = \beta e_1^{(k+1)} = \begin{bmatrix} \beta e_1^{(k)} \\ 0 \end{bmatrix},$$

which further yields

$$z_{k+1} = -\gamma_k z_k, \quad k = 1, 2, \ldots. \tag{6.22}$$

Also, note that

$$z_1 = \beta L_1^{-1} e_1^{(1)} = \beta. \tag{6.23}$$

Therefore, we have

$$\begin{aligned} x^{(k+1)} &= x^{(0)} + P_{k+1} z^{(k+1)} \\ &= x^{(0)} + \begin{bmatrix} P_k, & p_{k+1} \end{bmatrix} \begin{bmatrix} z^{(k)} \\ z_{k+1} \end{bmatrix} \\ &= x^{(0)} + P_k z^{(k)} + z_{k+1} p_{k+1} \\ &= x^{(k)} + z_{k+1} p_{k+1}, \quad\quad\quad\quad k = 1, 2, \ldots, \end{aligned} \tag{6.24}$$

and

$$x^{(1)} = x^{(0)} + P_1 z^{(1)} = x^{(0)} + z_1 p_1. \tag{6.25}$$

Combining (6.19)-(6.25), we then obtain the following elegant update scheme:

$$x^{(k+1)} = x^{(k)} + z_{k+1} p_{k+1}, \quad\quad k = 0, 1, 2, \ldots, \tag{6.26}$$

where, for $k = 1, 2, \ldots,$

$$\begin{cases} z_1 = \beta, \quad z_{k+1} = -\gamma_k z_k, \\ p_1 = v_1/\eta_1, \quad p_{k+1} = (v_{k+1} - \beta_k p_k)/\eta_{k+1}, \\ \eta_1 = \alpha_1, \quad \gamma_k = \beta_k/\eta_k, \quad \eta_{k+1} = \alpha_{k+1} - \gamma_k \beta_k. \end{cases}$$

The following theorem is a very important result about the vectors p_k's.

Theorem 6.23. *Let $A \in \mathbb{R}^{n \times n}$ be symmetric positive definite. Then it holds that*

$$\langle Ap_i, p_j \rangle = 0 \quad for \quad i \neq j,$$

*that is to say, the vectors p_i, $i = 1, 2, \ldots,$ are orthogonal to each other with respect to the matrix A, which are called **A-orthogonal** or **A-conjugate vectors**.*

Proof. It is equivalent to show that the matrix $P_k^{\mathsf{T}} A P_k$ is diagonal for $k \geq 1$. As

$$P_k = V_k U_k^{-1} \quad \text{and} \quad V_k^{\mathsf{T}} A V_k = T_k = L_k U_k,$$

it holds that

$$P_k^{\mathsf{T}} A P_k = (U_k^{-1})^{\mathsf{T}} V_k^{\mathsf{T}} A V_k U_k^{-1} = (U_k^{-1})^{\mathsf{T}} L_k.$$

Hence, the matrix $(U_k^{-1})^{\mathsf{T}} L_k$ is symmetric. Since the matrix U_k^{-1} is upper triangular, the matrix $(U_k^{-1})^{\mathsf{T}} L_k$ is lower triangular. Thus, the matrix $(U_k^{-1})^{\mathsf{T}} L_k$ must be diagonal. In fact, as $\gamma_i = \beta_i / \eta_i$, by straightforward computations we can obtain

$$(U_k^{-1})^{\mathsf{T}} L_k = \mathrm{diag}\left(\frac{1}{\eta_1}, \frac{1}{\eta_2}, \ldots, \frac{1}{\eta_k}\right),$$

i.e.,

$$\langle A p_i, p_j \rangle = \begin{cases} \dfrac{1}{\eta_i} & \text{if } i = j, \\[2mm] 0 & \text{if } i \neq j. \end{cases} \qquad \Box$$

The problem remained is when to stop the iteration. Let $r_k = b - A x^{(k)}$ be the residual vector after k steps of the CG iteration. It follows from the Lanczos process that $r_0 = \beta v_1$ with $\beta = \|r_0\|_2$. For $k \geq 1$, by (6.18) we have

$$\begin{aligned}
r_k = b - A x^{(k)} &= b - A(x^{(0)} + V_k y_k) \\
&= r_0 - A V_k y_k \\
&= \beta v_1 - V_k T_k y_k - \beta_k v_{k+1} e_k^{\mathsf{T}} y_k \\
&= -\beta_k (e_k^{\mathsf{T}} y_k) v_{k+1},
\end{aligned}$$

where

$$y_k = \beta T_k^{-1} e_1^{(k)}, \quad \text{and} \quad e_1^{(k)} = [1, 0, \ldots, 0]^{\mathsf{T}} \in \mathbb{R}^k, \ e_k = [0, \ldots, 0, 1]^{\mathsf{T}} \in \mathbb{R}^k.$$

Therefore, r_k is parallel to v_{k+1} for $k = 0, 1, 2, \ldots$. Denote $\varrho_0 = \beta$ and $\varrho_k = -\beta_k e_k^{\mathsf{T}} y_k$ for $k \geq 1$. Then $r_k = \varrho_k v_{k+1}$ and

$$\langle r_i, r_j \rangle = \langle \varrho_i v_{i+1}, \varrho_j v_{j+1} \rangle = \varrho_i \varrho_j \langle v_{i+1}, v_{j+1} \rangle = 0, \quad \text{for} \quad i \neq j.$$

The above argument is summarized in the following theorem.

Theorem 6.24. *Let $r_k = b - A x^{(k)}$ ($k = 0, 1, 2, \ldots$) be the residual vector after k steps of the CG iteration. Then*

$$r_k = \varrho_k v_{k+1},$$

which implies that the residual vectors are orthogonal to each other.

We now derive the CG method by imposing the conjugate property on the vectors p_k, $k = 0, 1, 2, \ldots$, and the orthogonal property on the vectors r_k, $k = 0, 1, 2, \ldots$.

It follows from (6.20) and Theorem 6.24 that

$$\eta_{k+1} p_{k+1} = v_{k+1} - \beta_k p_k = r_k / \varrho_k - \beta_k p_k.$$

Let

$$\tilde{p}_k = \varrho_{k-1} \eta_k p_k.$$

Then

$$\tilde{p}_{k+1} = r_k - \varrho_k \beta_k p_k = r_k + \tau_k \tilde{p}_k, \quad k = 1, 2, \ldots, \tag{6.27}$$

where

$$\tau_k = -\frac{\varrho_k \beta_k}{\varrho_{k-1} \eta_k}.$$

As $\varrho_0 = \beta$ and $p_1 = v_1/\eta_1$, we have

$$\tilde{p}_1 = \varrho_0 \eta_1 p_1 = \beta v_1 = r_0. \tag{6.28}$$

It follows from (6.26) that

$$x^{(k)} = x^{(k-1)} + \xi_k \tilde{p}_k, \quad k = 1, 2, \ldots, \tag{6.29}$$

where

$$\xi_k = \frac{z_k}{\eta_k \varrho_{k-1}}.$$

Thus, the residual vectors satisfy

$$r_k = b - Ax^{(k)} = b - Ax^{(k-1)} - \xi_k A\tilde{p}_k = r_{k-1} - \xi_k A\tilde{p}_k, \quad k = 1, 2, \ldots. \tag{6.30}$$

By Theorem 6.24, we know that the vectors r_k's are orthogonal to each other. Hence,

$$0 = \langle r_k, r_{k-1} \rangle = \langle r_{k-1} - \xi_k A\tilde{p}_k, r_{k-1} \rangle = \langle r_{k-1}, r_{k-1} \rangle - \xi_k \langle A\tilde{p}_k, r_{k-1} \rangle,$$

which yields

$$\xi_k = \frac{\langle r_{k-1}, r_{k-1} \rangle}{\langle A\tilde{p}_k, r_{k-1} \rangle}.$$

As $\langle Ap_k, p_{k-1} \rangle = 0$, it holds that $\langle A\tilde{p}_k, \tilde{p}_{k-1} \rangle = 0$, which, together with (6.27), indicates that

$$\langle A\tilde{p}_k, r_{k-1} \rangle = \langle A\tilde{p}_k, \tilde{p}_k - \tau_{k-1}\tilde{p}_{k-1} \rangle = \langle A\tilde{p}_k, \tilde{p}_k \rangle.$$

Therefore,

$$\xi_k = \frac{\langle r_{k-1}, r_{k-1} \rangle}{\langle A\tilde{p}_k, \tilde{p}_k \rangle}, \quad k = 1, 2, \ldots. \tag{6.31}$$

In addition, it follows from $\langle A\tilde{p}_k, \tilde{p}_{k+1} \rangle = 0$ that

$$0 = \langle A\tilde{p}_k, \tilde{p}_{k+1} \rangle = \langle A\tilde{p}_k, r_k + \tau_k \tilde{p}_k \rangle = \langle A\tilde{p}_k, r_k \rangle + \tau_k \langle A\tilde{p}_k, \tilde{p}_k \rangle,$$

which yields

$$\tau_k = -\frac{\langle A\tilde{p}_k, r_k \rangle}{\langle A\tilde{p}_k, \tilde{p}_k \rangle};$$

and it follows from (6.30) that

$$A\tilde{p}_k = -\frac{r_k - r_{k-1}}{\xi_k}.$$

Hence,

$$\begin{aligned}
\tau_k &= \frac{1}{\xi_k} \frac{\langle r_k - r_{k-1}, r_k \rangle}{\langle A\tilde{p}_k, \tilde{p}_k \rangle} \\
&= \frac{\langle A\tilde{p}_k, \tilde{p}_k \rangle}{\langle r_{k-1}, r_{k-1} \rangle} \cdot \frac{\langle r_k, r_k \rangle - \langle r_{k-1}, r_k \rangle}{\langle A\tilde{p}_k, \tilde{p}_k \rangle} \\
&= \frac{\langle r_k, r_k \rangle}{\langle r_{k-1}, r_{k-1} \rangle}, \quad k = 1, 2, \ldots.
\end{aligned} \tag{6.32}$$

Combining (6.27)–(6.32), we obtain the following update scheme:

$$\tilde{p}_1 = r_0,$$

$$\begin{cases} x^{(k)} = x^{(k-1)} + \xi_k \tilde{p}_k, & \text{with } \xi_k = \dfrac{\langle r_{k-1}, r_{k-1} \rangle}{\langle A\tilde{p}_k, \tilde{p}_k \rangle}, \\ r_k = r_{k-1} - \xi_k A\tilde{p}_k, & k = 1, 2, \ldots. \\ \tilde{p}_{k+1} = r_k + \tau_k \tilde{p}_k, & \text{with } \tau_k = \dfrac{\langle r_k, r_k \rangle}{\langle r_{k-1}, r_{k-1} \rangle}, \end{cases}$$

This scheme is the so-called **CG** method [195]. In the optimization literature, the vector $\tilde{p}_k$ is called the **search direction** and the scalar ξ_k is called the **stepsize**. The name of this method is given as the search directions are A-orthogonal.

In order to confirm with standard notation used in other literature for description of the **CG** method, we replace $\tilde{p}_k$, ξ_k and τ_k with p_k, α_k and β_k, respectively.

Algorithm 6.9: Conjugate Gradient (CG) Method

1: Given an initial guess $x^{(0)}$ and a stopping tolerance $\varepsilon > 0$
2: compute $r_0 = b - Ax^{(0)}$
3: $p_1 = r_0$
4: **for** $k = 1, 2, \ldots$, **do**
5:     $\alpha_k = \langle r_{k-1}, r_{k-1} \rangle / \langle Ap_k, p_k \rangle$
6:     $x^{(k)} = x^{(k-1)} + \alpha_k p_k$
7:     $r_k = r_{k-1} - \alpha_k Ap_k$
8:     **if** $\|r_k\|_2 < \varepsilon$, **then**   % check convergence
9:         stop
10:    **end if**
11:    $\beta_k = \langle r_k, r_k \rangle / \langle r_{k-1}, r_{k-1} \rangle$
12:    $p_{k+1} = r_k + \beta_k p_k$
13: **end for**

We remark that, in practical implementations, besides the matrix A we only need to save the four vectors x, p, Ap, and r, and, in each step we only need to compute one matrix-vector product Ap and two vector inner products.

In the CG method, it is in fact the A-norm of the absolute error that is minimized over the affine subspace $x^{(0)} + \mathcal{K}$.

Theorem 6.25. *Let $A \in \mathbb{R}^{n \times n}$ be symmetric positive definite, and $x_* = A^{-1}b$ be the exact solution of the linear system $Ax = b$ in (6.1). If $x^{(k)} \in \mathbb{R}^n$ is the approximate solution to the exact solution x_* in the affine subspace $x^{(0)} + \mathcal{K}_k(A, r_0)$ obtained by Algorithm 6.9 after k steps of iteration, then*

$$x^{(k)} = \underset{x \in x^{(0)} + \mathcal{K}_k(A, r_0)}{\operatorname{argmin}} \|x_* - x\|_A,$$

where

$$\|x - x_*\|_A = \sqrt{(x - x_*)^{\mathsf{T}} A (x - x_*)}.$$

Proof. Let $\tilde{x} = x^{(k)} - x^{(0)}$. As the vector $x^{(k)}$ is the approximate solution in $x^{(0)} + \mathcal{K}_k(A, r_0)$ obtained by the CG method, we have

$$x^{(k)} \in x^{(0)} + \mathcal{K}_k(A, r_0) \quad \text{and} \quad b - Ax^{(k)} \perp \mathcal{K}_k(A, r_0).$$

Hence, $\tilde{x} \in \mathcal{K}_k(A, r_0)$ and

$$r_0 - A\tilde{x} \perp \mathcal{K}_k(A, r_0).$$

By Corollary 6.10, it holds that

$$
\begin{aligned}
\tilde{x} &= \operatorname*{argmin}_{x \in \mathcal{K}_k(A, r_0)} \|A^{-1} r_0 - x\|_A \\
&= \operatorname*{argmin}_{x \in \mathcal{K}_k(A, r_0)} \|A^{-1}(b - Ax^{(0)}) - x\|_A \\
&= \operatorname*{argmin}_{x \in \mathcal{K}_k(A, r_0)} \|x_* - (x^{(0)} + x)\|_A,
\end{aligned}
$$

which implies that $x^{(k)} = x^{(0)} + \tilde{x}$ is the solution of the minimization problem

$$\min_{x \in x^{(0)} + \mathcal{K}_k(A, r_0)} \|x_* - x\|_A. \qquad \square$$

The CG method computes the approximate solution for the symmetric positive definite linear system (6.1) by minimizing the **A-norm** of the absolute error at each iteration step. If the matrix A is symmetric but indefinite, then $\|\cdot\|_A$ is no longer a norm. Note that the positive definiteness of the matrix A is exploited only to guarantee the existence of the LU decomposition of the tridiagonal matrix T_k for $k = 1, 2, \ldots, n$. If the matrix A is symmetric and indefinite, we can still try the CG method. However, a breakdown may occur; see [261].

6.4.3 ▪ Minimal Residual Method

If the matrix $A \in \mathbb{R}^{n \times n}$ is symmetric but indefinite, so is the matrix H_m or, T_m. In this case, the CG method is no longer well-defined.

The **minimal residual** (MINRES) [263] method is an orthogonal projection method for symmetric linear systems based on taking $\mathcal{L} = A\mathcal{K}$. It can be viewed as a special variant of GMRES for symmetric linear systems. As the coefficient matrix A is symmetric, we can construct the orthogonal vectors $v_1, v_2, \ldots, v_k, \ldots$, by the Lanczos process (i.e., Algorithm 6.8), where we can take advantage of the three-term recurrence. Analogous to GMRES, the approximate solution obtained by MINRES after k steps of iteration is given by

$$x^{(k)} = x^{(0)} + V_k y_k,$$

with

$$y_k = \operatorname*{argmin}_{y \in \mathbb{R}^k} \|\beta e_1 - T_{k+1,k} y\|_2, \tag{6.33}$$

where $T_{k+1,k}$ is the $(k+1) \times k$ upper Hessenberg matrix

$$
T_{k+1,k} = \begin{bmatrix}
\alpha_1 & \beta_1 & & & \\
\beta_1 & \ddots & \ddots & & \\
& \ddots & \ddots & \beta_{k-1} & \\
& & \beta_{k-1} & \alpha_k & \\
& & & \beta_k &
\end{bmatrix},
$$

which is generated by the Lanczos process.

Analogous to CG, we do not need to save all the orthogonal vectors v_i's in developing an update scheme from $x^{(k)}$ to $x^{(k+1)}$.

We use **QR decomposition** to solve the **linear least-squares problem** (6.33). Let

$$T_{k+1,k} = Q_{k+1}R_{k+1,k}$$

be the QR decomposition of the matrix $T_{k+1,k}$, where $Q_{k+1} \in \mathbb{R}^{(k+1)\times(k+1)}$ is an orthogonal matrix and $R_{k+1,k} \in \mathbb{R}^{(k+1)\times k}$ is an upper-triangular matrix. As the matrix $T_{k+1,k}$ is tridiagonal, the matrix $R_{k+1,k}$ is of bandwidth 3, i.e.,

$$R_{k+1,k} = \begin{bmatrix} \tau_1^{(1)} & \tau_1^{(2)} & \tau_1^{(3)} & & & & \\ 0 & \tau_2^{(1)} & \tau_2^{(2)} & \tau_2^{(3)} & & & \\ \vdots & \ddots & \ddots & \ddots & \ddots & & \\ \vdots & & \ddots & \tau_{k-2}^{(1)} & \tau_{k-2}^{(2)} & \tau_{k-2}^{(3)} & \\ \vdots & & & \ddots & \tau_{k-1}^{(1)} & \tau_{k-1}^{(2)} & \\ \vdots & & & & \ddots & \tau_k^{(1)} & \\ 0 & \cdots & \cdots & \cdots & \cdots & 0 & \end{bmatrix}_{(k+1)\times k} \triangleq \begin{bmatrix} R_k \\ 0 \end{bmatrix},$$

where R_k is the k-th leading principal submatrix of the matrix $R_{k+1,k}$. It follows that

$$\|\beta e_1 - T_{k+1,k}y\|_2 = \|\beta e_1 - Q_{k+1}R_{k+1,k}\,y\|_2$$
$$= \left\| Q_{k+1}\left(Q_{k+1}^{\mathsf{T}}(\beta e_1) - \begin{bmatrix} R_k \\ 0 \end{bmatrix}y\right)\right\|_2$$
$$= \left\| [Q_{k+1,k},\ q_{k+1}]^{\mathsf{T}}(\beta e_1) - \begin{bmatrix} R_k y \\ 0 \end{bmatrix}\right\|_2,$$

where the matrix $Q_{k+1,k}$ consists of the first k columns and the vector q_{k+1} denotes the last column of the matrix Q_{k+1}. If the matrix R_k is nonsingular, then the solution of the least-squares problem (6.33) is given by

$$y_k = \beta R_k^{-1}Q_{k+1,k}^{\mathsf{T}}e_1,$$

so that

$$x^{(k)} = x^{(0)} + \beta V_k R_k^{-1}Q_{k+1,k}^{\mathsf{T}}e_1. \tag{6.34}$$

Since $T_{k+1,k}$ is an upper Hessenberg matrix, its QR decomposition can be accomplished by employing a series of Givens rotations to annihilate its subdiagonal entries $\beta_1, \beta_2, \ldots, \beta_k$ successively. In fact, analogous to CG, the QR decomposition of the matrix $T_{k+1,k}$ can be easily obtained by an update from that of the matrix $T_{k,k-1}$. Assume that the QR decomposition of the matrix $T_{k,k-1}$ is achieved by

$$T_{k,k-1} = (G_{k-1}G_{k-2}\cdots G_1)^{\mathsf{T}}R_{k,k-1} = Q_k R_{k,k-1},$$

where G_i denotes the i-th Givens rotation,

$$Q_k = (G_{k-1}G_{k-2}\cdots G_1)^{\mathsf{T}},$$

and $R_{k,k-1}$ is of the form

$$
R_{k,k-1} =
\begin{bmatrix}
\tau_1^{(1)} & \tau_1^{(2)} & \tau_1^{(3)} & & & \\
0 & \tau_2^{(1)} & \tau_2^{(2)} & \tau_2^{(3)} & & \\
\vdots & & \ddots & \ddots & \ddots & \ddots \\
\vdots & & & \ddots & \ddots & \ddots & \tau_{k-3}^{(3)} \\
\vdots & & & & \ddots & \ddots & \tau_{k-2}^{(2)} \\
\vdots & & & & & \ddots & \tau_{k-1}^{(1)} \\
0 & \cdots & \cdots & \cdots & \cdots & & 0
\end{bmatrix}.
$$

Here, in order to make the matrix products consistent, we assume that the dimensions of the Givens rotations G_i ($i = 1, 2, \ldots, k-1$) are all expanded to k. More precisely,

$$
G_i =
\begin{bmatrix}
I_{i-1} & & & \\
& c_i & s_i & \\
& -s_i & c_i & \\
& & & I_{k-i-1}
\end{bmatrix} \in \mathbb{R}^{k \times k}, \quad i = 1, 2, \ldots, k-1.
$$

It is clear that, for a given matrix B, the transformation $B \to G_i B$ only changes its i-th and $(i+1)$-th rows. Hence,

$$
T_{k+1,k} =
\begin{bmatrix}
T_{k,k-1} & \begin{matrix} 0 \\ \vdots \\ 0 \\ \beta_{k-1} \\ \alpha_k \end{matrix} \\
0 & \beta_k
\end{bmatrix}
=
\begin{bmatrix} Q_k & 0 \\ 0 & 1 \end{bmatrix}
\begin{bmatrix}
R_{k,k-1} & Q_k^{-1} \begin{matrix} 0 \\ \vdots \\ 0 \\ \beta_{k-1} \\ \alpha_k \end{matrix} \\
0 & \beta_k
\end{bmatrix}
\triangleq
\begin{bmatrix} Q_k & 0 \\ 0 & 1 \end{bmatrix}
\tilde{T}_{k+1,k}
$$

and

$$
Q_k^{-1}
\begin{bmatrix} 0 \\ \vdots \\ 0 \\ 0 \\ \beta_{k-1} \\ \alpha_k \end{bmatrix}
= G_{k-1} G_{k-2} \cdots G_1
\begin{bmatrix} 0 \\ \vdots \\ 0 \\ \beta_{k-1} \\ \alpha_k \end{bmatrix}
= G_{k-1} G_{k-2}
\begin{bmatrix} 0 \\ \vdots \\ 0 \\ 0 \\ \beta_{k-1} \\ \alpha_k \end{bmatrix}
=
\begin{bmatrix} 0 \\ \vdots \\ 0 \\ \tau_{k-2}^{(3)} \\ \tau_{k-1}^{(2)} \\ \tilde{\alpha}_k \end{bmatrix}.
$$

Let

$$
G_k =
\begin{bmatrix}
I_{k-1} & & \\
& c_k & s_k \\
& -s_k & c_k
\end{bmatrix} \in \mathbb{R}^{(k+1) \times (k+1)}
$$

be the Givens rotation that annihilates β_k in the last column of the matrix $\tilde{T}_{k+1,k}$. As the matrix $R_{k,k-1}$ is upper triangular and the Givens rotation G_k only affects the last two rows of the matrix

$\tilde{T}_{k+1,k}$, it holds that

$$
G_k \tilde{T}_{k+1,k} =
\left[
\begin{array}{c|c}
R_{k,k-1} & \begin{matrix} 0 \\ \vdots \\ 0 \\ \tau_{k-2}^{(3)} \\ \tau_{k-1}^{(2)} \\ \tau_k^{(1)} \end{matrix} \\
\hline
0 & 0
\end{array}
\right]
=
\begin{bmatrix}
\tau_1^{(1)} & \tau_1^{(2)} & \tau_1^{(3)} \\
0 & \ddots & \ddots & \ddots \\
\vdots & & \ddots & \ddots & \ddots & \tau_{k-3}^{(3)} \\
\vdots & & & \ddots & \ddots & \tau_{k-2}^{(2)} & \tau_{k-2}^{(3)} \\
\vdots & & & & \ddots & \tau_{k-1}^{(1)} & \tau_{k-1}^{(2)} \\
\vdots & & & & & \ddots & \tau_k^{(1)} \\
0 & \cdots & \cdots & \cdots & \cdots & 0
\end{bmatrix}
\triangleq R_{k+1,k},
$$

which is a $(k+1)$-by-k upper-triangular matrix. We expand the dimension of the Givens rotation G_i by setting

$$
\tilde{G}_i =
\begin{bmatrix} G_i & 0 \\ 0 & 1 \end{bmatrix}
=
\begin{bmatrix}
I_{i-1} & & \\
& c_i & s_i \\
& -s_i & c_i \\
& & & I_{k-i}
\end{bmatrix}
\in \mathbb{R}^{(k+1)\times(k+1)}, \quad i = 1, 2, \ldots, k-1.
$$

Then

$$
\tilde{G}_{k-1}\tilde{G}_{k-2}\cdots\tilde{G}_1 =
\begin{bmatrix} Q_k^{\mathsf{T}} & 0 \\ 0 & 1 \end{bmatrix}
=
\begin{bmatrix} Q_k & 0 \\ 0 & 1 \end{bmatrix}^{\mathsf{T}}.
$$

Let

$$
Q_{k+1} = (G_k \tilde{G}_{k-1}\cdots\tilde{G}_1)^{\mathsf{T}}.
$$

It follows that

$$
Q_{k+1}^{\mathsf{T}} T_{k+1,k} = G_k
\begin{bmatrix} Q_k^{\mathsf{T}} & 0 \\ 0 & 1 \end{bmatrix}
\begin{bmatrix} Q_k & 0 \\ 0 & 1 \end{bmatrix}
\tilde{T}_{k+1,k} = G_k \tilde{T}_{k+1,k} = R_{k+1,k},
$$

or equivalently,

$$
T_{k+1,k} = Q_{k+1} R_{k+1,k},
$$

which is the QR decomposition of the matrix $T_{k+1,k}$. We remark that $R_{k,k-1}$ is the k-by-$(k-1)$ upper submatrix of the matrix $R_{k+1,k}$ and, hence, R_{k-1} is the $(k-1)$-th leading principal submatrix of the matrix R_k.

In the following, we develop the update scheme of $x^{(k+1)}$ from $x^{(k)}$. Let

$$
P_k = [p_1, p_2, \ldots, p_k] \triangleq V_k R_k^{-1}.
$$

By straightforward computations, it follows from $P_k R_k = V_k$ that

$$
\begin{aligned}
p_1 &= v_1 / \tau_1^{(1)}, \\
p_2 &= \left(v_2 - \tau_1^{(2)} p_1\right) \Big/ \tau_2^{(1)}, \\
p_i &= \left(v_i - \tau_{i-1}^{(2)} p_{i-1} - \tau_{i-2}^{(3)} p_{i-2}\right) \Big/ \tau_i^{(1)}, \quad i = 3, 4, \ldots.
\end{aligned}
\tag{6.35}
$$

As $V_k = [V_{k-1},\, v_k]$ and R_{k-1} is the $(k-1)$-th leading principal submatrix of the matrix R_k, it is easily seen that

$$P_k = [P_{k-1},\, p_k].$$

Now, we investigate the relationship between the matrices Q_k and Q_{k+1}. Let $\xi^{(k)}$ consist of the first k entries of the vector $\beta Q_{k+1}^{\mathsf{T}} e_1$, that is,

$$\beta Q_{k+1}^{\mathsf{T}} e_1 = \begin{bmatrix} \xi^{(k)} \\ \tilde{\xi}_{k+1} \end{bmatrix}.$$

We remark that the tilde is used to indicate that the entry $\tilde{\xi}_{k+1}$ differs from the $(k+1)$-th entry of $\xi^{(k+1)}$. Note also that the first k entries of the vectors $Q_{k+1}^{\mathsf{T}} e_1$ and $Q_{k+1,k}^{\mathsf{T}} e_1$ are the same, i.e.,

$$\xi^{(k)} = \beta Q_{k+1,k}^{\mathsf{T}} e_1.$$

Hence

$$y^{(k)} = \beta R_k^{-1} Q_{k+1,k}^{\mathsf{T}} e_1 = R_k^{-1} \xi^{(k)}. \tag{6.36}$$

It follows from

$$Q_{k+1} = \begin{bmatrix} Q_k & 0 \\ 0 & 1 \end{bmatrix} G_k^{\mathsf{T}}$$

that

$$Q_{k+1}(1, 1:k-1) = Q_k(1, 1:k-1),$$

i.e., the first $k-1$ entries of the vector $Q_{k+1}^{\mathsf{T}} e_1$ is the same as those of the vector $Q_k^{\mathsf{T}} e_1$. This leads to the following relationship between the vectors $\xi^{(k)}$ and $\xi^{(k-1)}$:

$$\xi^{(k)} = \begin{bmatrix} \xi^{(k-1)} \\ \xi_k \end{bmatrix}, \quad k = 2, 3, \ldots,$$

where ξ_k denotes the last entry of the vector $\xi^{(k)}$. Therefore, the vector $\xi^{(k)}$ can be expressed in the following form:

$$\xi^{(k)} = [\xi_1, \xi_2, \ldots, \xi_k]^{\mathsf{T}}, \quad k = 1, 2, \ldots.$$

By (6.34) we have

$$\begin{aligned}
x^{(k)} &= x^{(0)} + V_k R_k^{-1} Q_{k+1,k}^{\mathsf{T}} (\beta e_1) \\
&= x^{(0)} + P_k \xi^{(k)} \\
&= x^{(0)} + [P_{k-1},\, p_k] \begin{bmatrix} \xi^{(k-1)} \\ \xi_k \end{bmatrix} \\
&= x^{(0)} + P_{k-1} \xi^{(k-1)} + \xi_k p_k \\
&= x^{(k-1)} + \xi_k p_k,
\end{aligned}$$

where the vector p_k can be computed by the recurrence formula (6.35) and the scalar ξ_k is the

k-th entry of the vector $\beta Q_{k+1}^{\mathsf{T}} e_1$. It holds that

$$\beta Q_{k+1}^{\mathsf{T}} e_1 = Q_{k+1}^{\mathsf{T}} (\beta e_1) = G_k \tilde{G}_{k-1} \cdots \tilde{G}_1 (\beta e_1),$$

which can be obtained by applying the Givens rotations on the vector βe_1 successively.

From (6.36) we see that the residual norm can be given by

$$\begin{aligned}
\|r_k\|_2 = \|b - Ax^{(k)}\|_2 &= \|r_0 - AV_k y_k\|_2 \\
&= \|\beta v_1 - V_{k+1} T_{k+1,k}\, y_k\|_2 \\
&= \|V_{k+1}(\beta e_1 - Q_{k+1} R_{k+1,k}\, y_k)\|_2 \\
&= \left\| Q_{k+1} \left(Q_{k+1}^{\mathsf{T}}(\beta e_1) - \begin{bmatrix} R_k \\ 0 \end{bmatrix} y_k \right) \right\|_2 \\
&= \left\| \begin{bmatrix} \xi^{(k)} \\ \tilde{\xi}_{k+1} \end{bmatrix} - \begin{bmatrix} R_k y_k \\ 0 \end{bmatrix} \right\|_2 \\
&= |\tilde{\xi}_{k+1}|,
\end{aligned}$$

where $\tilde{\xi}_{k+1}$ is the last entry of the vector

$$Q_{k+1}^{\mathsf{T}}(\beta e_1) = G_k \tilde{G}_{k-1} \cdots \tilde{G}_1 (\beta e_1).$$

Based on the recurrence relations of the matrices P_k and the vectors $x^{(k)}$, $k = 0, 1, 2, \ldots$, we can obtain the following **MINRES** method [263].

Algorithm 6.10: Minimal Residual (MINRES) Method

1: Given an initial guess $x^{(0)}$ and a stopping tolerance $\varepsilon > 0$
2: compute $r_0 = b - Ax^{(0)}$ and $\beta = \|r_0\|_2$
3: set $v_1 = r_0/\beta$ and $\xi = \beta e_1$
4: **for** $k = 1, 2, \ldots,$ **do**
5: $\quad w_k = Av_k - \beta_{k-1} v_{k-1}$, where $\beta_0 = 0$ and $v_0 = 0$
6: $\quad \alpha_k = \langle w_k, v_k \rangle$
7: $\quad \tilde{w}_k = w_k - \alpha_k v_k$
8: $\quad \beta_k = \|\tilde{w}_k\|_2$
9: $\quad$ % apply $G_{k-1} G_{k-2}$ to the last column of $T_{k+1,k}$

10: $\quad \begin{bmatrix} \tau_{k-2}^{(3)} \\ \tilde{\beta}_{k-1} \end{bmatrix} = \begin{bmatrix} c_{k-2} & s_{k-2} \\ -s_{k-2} & c_{k-2} \end{bmatrix} \begin{bmatrix} 0 \\ \beta_{k-1} \end{bmatrix}$ if $k > 2$

11: $\quad \begin{bmatrix} \tau_{k-1}^{(2)} \\ \tilde{\alpha}_k \end{bmatrix} = \begin{bmatrix} c_{k-1} & s_{k-1} \\ -s_{k-1} & c_{k-1} \end{bmatrix} \begin{bmatrix} \tilde{\beta}_{k-1} \\ \alpha_k \end{bmatrix}$ if $k > 1$

12: $\quad$ **if** $|\tilde{\alpha}_k| > |\beta_k|$, **then** $\quad$ % form the Givens rotation G_k
13: $\quad\quad$ set $c_k = \frac{1}{\sqrt{1+\gamma^2}}$, $s_k = c_k \gamma$, where $\gamma = \beta_k / \tilde{\alpha}_k$
14: $\quad$ **else**
15: $\quad\quad$ set $s_k = \frac{1}{\sqrt{1+\gamma^2}}$, $c_k = s_k \gamma$, where $\gamma = \tilde{\alpha}_k / \beta_k$
16: $\quad$ **end if**
17: $\quad \tau_k^{(1)} = c_k \tilde{\alpha}_k + s_k \beta_k$ $\quad$ % apply G_k to the last column of $\tilde{T}_{k+1,k}$

18: $\quad \begin{bmatrix} \xi_k \\ \xi_{k+1} \end{bmatrix} := \begin{bmatrix} c_k & s_k \\ -s_k & c_k \end{bmatrix} \begin{bmatrix} \xi_k \\ 0 \end{bmatrix}$ $\quad$ % apply G_k to ξ

19:     $p_k = \left(v_k - \tau_{k-1}^{(2)} p_{k-1} - \tau_{k-2}^{(3)} p_{k-2} \right) \Big/ \tau_k^{(1)}$, where $p_0 = p_{-1} = 0$

20:     $x^{(k)} = x^{(k-1)} + \xi_k p_k$

21:     **if** $|\xi_{k+1}| < \varepsilon$, **then**   % check convergence : $\|r_k\|_2 \triangleq |\tilde{\xi}_{k+1}| = |\xi_{k+1}|$

22:         stop

23:     **end if**

24:     $v_{k+1} = \tilde{w}_k / \beta_k$

25: **end for**

MINRES is attractive when the coefficient matrix A of the linear system (6.1) is symmetric and indefinite. Note that we do not need to save all the vectors v_i's and p_i's, etc. Most of the variables in the MINRES method may overwrite old ones that are obsolete.

Analogous to GMRES, MINRES minimizes the residual in the 2-norm.

Theorem 6.26. *Let $A \in \mathbb{R}^{n \times n}$ be symmetric and $x^{(k)} \in \mathbb{R}^n$ be the approximate solution for the linear system (6.1) in the affine subspace $x^{(0)} + \mathcal{K}_k$ obtained by the MINRES method after k steps of iteration. Then*

$$x^{(k)} = \operatorname*{argmin}_{x \in x^{(0)} + \mathcal{K}_k} \|b - Ax\|_2,$$

that is, the vector $x^{(k)}$ minimizes the residual norm over the affine subspace $x^{(0)} + \mathcal{K}_k$.

The convergence behavior of CG and MINRES for indefinite linear systems was analyzed by Paige, Parlett, and van der Vorst [261].

However, the use of the three-term recurrence relation makes MINRES very vulnerable to **rounding errors**. As has been shown in [297], the rounding errors are propagated to the approximate solution with a factor proportional to the square of the condition number of the coefficient matrix A, whereas in GMRES these errors depend only on the condition number itself. Therefore, we should be careful with MINRES for ill-conditioned linear systems. In this case, we can consider the usage of SYMMLQ [263], which might converge slower than MINRES but in a more stable manner for ill-conditioned linear systems.

6.4.4 ▪ SYMMLQ Method

SYMMLQ [263] is a projection method for solving symmetric linear systems by taking $\mathcal{L} = \mathcal{K}$. Therefore, it is equivalent to CG when the coefficient matrix A is symmetric positive definite. Let $x^{(k)} \in \mathbb{R}^n$ be an approximate solution of the linear system (6.1) in the affine subspace $x^{(0)} + \mathcal{K}_k$ obtained by SYMMLQ after k steps of iteration. Then

$$x^{(k)} = x^{(0)} + V_k y_k,$$

where $y_k \in \mathbb{R}^k$ is the solution of the tridiagonal linear system

$$T_k y = \beta e_1. \tag{6.37}$$

If the coefficient matrix A is symmetric but indefinite, so is the tridiagonal matrix T_k, and the **LU decomposition** of the matrix T_k is no longer guaranteed. Hence, we cannot solve the linear system (6.37) by the LU decomposition. In this case, we can utilize the **LQ decomposition**, that is,

$$T_k = \tilde{L}_k Q_k,$$

where the matrix $\tilde{L}_k \in \mathbb{R}^{k \times k}$ is lower triangular and the matrix $Q_k \in \mathbb{R}^{k \times k}$ is orthogonal. Therefore, it holds that

$$x^{(k)} = x^{(0)} + V_k T_k^{-1}(\beta e_1) = x^{(0)} + V_k Q_k^{\mathsf{T}} \tilde{L}_k^{-1}(\beta e_1) = x^{(0)} + \tilde{P}_k \tilde{z}^{(k)},$$

where

$$\tilde{P}_k \triangleq V_k Q_k^{\mathsf{T}} \in \mathbb{R}^{n \times k} \quad \text{and} \quad \tilde{z}^{(k)} \triangleq \tilde{L}_k^{-1}(\beta e_1) \in \mathbb{R}^k.$$

The resulting method is known as **SYMMLQ** [263].

Since the matrix T_k is tridiagonal, its LQ decomposition can be accomplished by employing a series of **Givens rotations** on its right to annihilate its superdiagonal entries $\beta_1, \beta_2, \ldots, \beta_{k-1}$ successively. In fact, we can obtain the LQ decomposition of the matrix T_{k+1} by an update from the LQ decomposition of the matrix T_k.

Assume that the LQ decomposition of the matrix T_k is given by

$$T_k = \tilde{L}_k (G_1 G_2 \cdots G_{k-1})^{\mathsf{T}} = \tilde{L}_k Q_k,$$

where

$$Q_k = (G_1 G_2 \cdots G_{k-1})^{\mathsf{T}}$$

and G_i is the Givens rotation

$$G_i = \begin{bmatrix} I_{i-1} & & & \\ & c_i & s_i & \\ & -s_i & c_i & \\ & & & I_{k-i-1} \end{bmatrix} \in \mathbb{R}^{k \times k}, \quad i = 1, 2, \ldots, k-1.$$

As the matrix T_k is tridiagonal, the lower-triangular matrix $\tilde{L}_k = T_k Q_k^{\mathsf{T}}$ is banded and is of bandwidth 3, i.e.,

$$\tilde{L}_k = \begin{bmatrix} l_1^{(1)} & & & & & \\ l_2^{(2)} & l_2^{(1)} & & & & \\ l_3^{(3)} & l_3^{(2)} & l_3^{(1)} & & & \\ & \ddots & \ddots & \ddots & & \\ & & l_{k-1}^{(3)} & l_{k-1}^{(2)} & l_{k-1}^{(1)} & \\ & & & l_k^{(3)} & l_k^{(2)} & \tilde{l}_k^{(1)} \end{bmatrix}.$$

Here the tilde symbol is used to indicate that the matrix $\tilde{L}_k$ differs from the matrix L_k in the (k, k) entry only, where L_k is the k-by-k leading principal submatrix of the matrix $\tilde{L}_{k+1}$. Define

$$\tilde{Q}_{k+1} = \begin{bmatrix} Q_k & 0 \\ 0 & 1 \end{bmatrix} \in \mathbb{R}^{(k+1) \times (k+1)}.$$

Then

$$T_{k+1} \tilde{Q}_{k+1}^{\mathsf{T}} = \left[\begin{array}{c|c} T_k & \begin{matrix} 0 \\ \vdots \\ 0 \\ \beta_k \end{matrix} \\ \hline 0 \cdots 0\, \beta_k & \alpha_{k+1} \end{array} \right] \begin{bmatrix} Q_k^{\mathsf{T}} & 0 \\ 0 & 1 \end{bmatrix} = \left[\begin{array}{c|c} \tilde{L}_k & \begin{matrix} 0 \\ \vdots \\ 0 \\ \beta_k \end{matrix} \\ \hline 0 \cdots 0\, l_{k+1}^{(3)} \, \tilde{\beta}_k & \alpha_{k+1} \end{array} \right],$$

where

$$l_{k+1}^{(3)} = s_{k-1}\beta_k \quad \text{and} \quad \tilde{\beta}_k = c_{k-1}\beta_k.$$

are obtained from the equality

$$\begin{bmatrix} 0 & \cdots & 0 & l^{(3)}_{k+1} & \tilde{\beta}_k \end{bmatrix} = \begin{bmatrix} 0 & \cdots & 0 & \beta_k \end{bmatrix} \cdot Q^{\mathsf{T}}_k = \begin{bmatrix} 0 & \cdots & 0 & \beta_k \end{bmatrix} \cdot G_{k-1}.$$

Let

$$G_k = \begin{bmatrix} I_{k-1} & & \\ & c_k & s_k \\ & -s_k & c_k \end{bmatrix} \in \mathbb{R}^{(k+1)\times(k+1)}$$

be the Givens rotation that annihilates the entry β_k in the last column of the matrix $T_{k+1}\tilde{Q}^{\mathsf{T}}_{k+1}$. Define

$$Q_{k+1} = G^{\mathsf{T}}_k \tilde{Q}_{k+1}.$$

Note that the Givens rotation G_k only changes the values of the last two columns of the matrix $T_{k+1}\tilde{Q}^{\mathsf{T}}_{k+1}$. Hence, we have

$$T_{k+1}Q^{\mathsf{T}}_{k+1} = \begin{bmatrix} \tilde{L}_k & \begin{matrix} 0 \\ \vdots \\ 0 \\ \beta_k \end{matrix} \\ \hline 0 \cdots 0\, l^{(3)}_{k+1}\, \tilde{\beta}_k & \alpha_{k+1} \end{bmatrix} G_k$$

$$= \begin{bmatrix} l^{(1)}_1 & & & & & 0 \\ l^{(2)}_2 & l^{(1)}_2 & & & & \vdots \\ l^{(3)}_3 & l^{(2)}_3 & l^{(1)}_3 & & & \vdots \\ & \ddots & \ddots & \ddots & & 0 \\ & & l^{(3)}_k & l^{(2)}_k & l^{(1)}_k & 0 \\ \hline 0 & \cdots & 0 & l^{(3)}_{k+1} & l^{(2)}_{k+1} & \tilde{l}^{(1)}_{k+1} \end{bmatrix} \triangleq \tilde{L}_{k+1},$$

or

$$T_{k+1} = \tilde{L}_{k+1}Q_{k+1},$$

which is the LQ decomposition of the matrix T_{k+1}.

Let $L_{k-1} \in \mathbb{R}^{(k-1)\times(k-1)}$ be the $(k-1)$-by-$(k-1)$ leading principal submatrix of the matrix $\tilde{L}_k$. As L_k differs from $\tilde{L}_k$ in the (k,k) entry only, L_{k-1} is the $(k-1)$-by-$(k-1)$ leading principal submatrix of the matrix L_k, which forms the recurrence relation of the matrix L_k for $k = 1, 2, \ldots$.

Define

$$z^{(k)} = L^{-1}_k(\beta e_1) \in \mathbb{R}^k.$$

As

$$\tilde{z}^{(k)} = \tilde{L}^{-1}_k(\beta e_1),$$

it is easily seen that

$$z^{(k)} = \begin{bmatrix} z^{(k-1)} \\ z_k \end{bmatrix} \quad \text{and} \quad \tilde{z}^{(k)} = \begin{bmatrix} z^{(k-1)} \\ \tilde{z}_k \end{bmatrix}, \quad \text{with} \quad z^{(k-1)} = L^{-1}_{k-1}(\beta e_1),$$

where z_k and $\tilde{z}_k$ denote the last entries of the vectors $z^{(k)}$ and $\tilde{z}^{(k)}$, respectively. We can write these two vectors as

$$z^{(k)} = [z_1, \ldots, z_{k-1}, z_k]^\mathsf{T} \quad \text{and} \quad \tilde{z}^{(k)} = [z_1, \ldots, z_{k-1}, \tilde{z}_k]^\mathsf{T}, \quad k = 1, 2, \ldots,$$

where

$$\tilde{z}_k = \frac{l_k^{(1)}}{\tilde{l}_k^{(1)}} z_k.$$

It follows from

$$L_k z^{(k)} = \beta e_1$$

that

$$\begin{cases} z_1 = \beta/l_1^{(1)}, \\ z_2 = -l_2^{(2)} z_1 / l_2^{(1)}, \\ z_i = -\left(l_i^{(3)} z_{i-2} + l_i^{(2)} z_{i-1} \right) \Big/ l_i^{(1)}, \quad i = 3, 4, \ldots, k. \end{cases}$$

Let the matrices P_{k-1} and P_k consist of the first $k-1$ and k columns of the matrices

$$\tilde{P}_k = V_k Q_k^\mathsf{T} \quad \text{and} \quad \tilde{P}_{k+1} = V_{k+1} Q_{k+1}^\mathsf{T},$$

respectively. Then

$$\begin{aligned} \tilde{P}_{k+1} = V_{k+1} Q_{k+1}^\mathsf{T} &= [V_k, v_{k+1}] \begin{bmatrix} Q_k^\mathsf{T} & 0 \\ 0 & 1 \end{bmatrix} G_k \\ &= \left[\tilde{P}_k, v_{k+1} \right] G_k \\ &= [P_{k-1}, \tilde{p}_k, v_{k+1}] \begin{bmatrix} I_{k-1} & & \\ & c_k & s_k \\ & -s_k & c_k \end{bmatrix} \\ &= [P_{k-1}, p_k, \tilde{p}_{k+1}] \\ &= [P_k, \tilde{p}_{k+1}], \end{aligned} \tag{6.38}$$

where $\tilde{p}_k$ and $\tilde{p}_{k+1}$ denote the last columns of the matrices $\tilde{P}_k$ and $\tilde{P}_{k+1}$, respectively. Therefore, the matrices P_k and P_{k-1} possess the following recurrence relationship:

$$P_k = [P_{k-1}, p_k],$$

where p_k denotes the last column of the matrix P_k. We write

$$P_k = [p_1, p_2, \ldots, p_k], \quad k = 1, 2, \ldots.$$

Then it follows from (6.38) and

$$\tilde{p}_1 = \tilde{P}_1 = v_1 \quad .$$

that

$$\begin{cases} \tilde{p}_1 = v_1, \\ p_k = c_k \tilde{p}_k - s_k v_{k+1}, \\ \tilde{p}_{k+1} = s_k \tilde{p}_k + c_k v_{k+1}, \quad k = 1, 2, \ldots. \end{cases}$$

Let

$$\tilde{x}^{(k)} = x^{(0)} + P_k z^{(k)}, \quad k = 1, 2, \ldots.$$

Then

$$\tilde{x}^{(k)} = x^{(0)} + P_k z^{(k)} = x^{(0)} + [P_{k-1}, \, p_k] \begin{bmatrix} z^{(k-1)} \\ z_k \end{bmatrix} = \tilde{x}^{(k-1)} + z_k p_k, \quad k = 1, 2, \ldots.$$

It holds that

$$\begin{aligned}
x^{(k+1)} &= x^{(0)} + \tilde{P}_{k+1} \tilde{z}^{(k+1)} = x^{(0)} + [P_k, \, \tilde{p}_{k+1}] \begin{bmatrix} z^{(k)} \\ \tilde{z}_{k+1} \end{bmatrix} \\
&= x^{(0)} + P_k z^{(k)} + \tilde{z}_{k+1} \tilde{p}_{k+1} \\
&= \tilde{x}^{(k)} + \tilde{z}_{k+1} \tilde{p}_{k+1}.
\end{aligned} \tag{6.39}$$

Rather than updating the vector $x^{(k)}$ at each step, we update the vector $\tilde{x}^{(k)}$ since we are always able to obtain the vector $x^{(k+1)}$ by (6.39) if it is needed.

It follows from Theorem 6.16 that

$$r_k = b - A x^{(k)} = -\beta_k (e_k^{\mathsf{T}} y_k) v_{k+1}.$$

Note that the vector y_k is not directly available in the computation. Since the matrix T_k is symmetric, it follows from

$$T_k^{\mathsf{T}} y_k = T_k y_k = \beta e_1$$

that

$$\tilde{L}_k^{\mathsf{T}} y_k = Q_k(\beta e_1).$$

By comparing the last entries on both sides of this equality, we have

$$\begin{aligned}
\tilde{l}_k^{(1)} e_k^{\mathsf{T}} y_k = e_k^{\mathsf{T}} \tilde{L}_k^{\mathsf{T}} y_k &= e_k^{\mathsf{T}} Q_k(\beta e_1) \\
&= \beta e_k^{\mathsf{T}} (G_1 G_2 \cdots G_{k-1})^{\mathsf{T}} e_1 \\
&= \beta (G_1 G_2 \cdots G_{k-1} e_k)^{\mathsf{T}} e_1 \\
&= \beta s_1 s_2 \cdots s_{k-1}.
\end{aligned}$$

In addition, from the construction of the Givens rotation G_k, we see that

$$s_k \tilde{l}_k^{(1)} + c_k \beta_k = 0.$$

Therefore,

$$\begin{aligned}
r_k = -\beta_k (e_k^{\mathsf{T}} y_k) v_{k+1} &= -\left(\beta s_1 s_2 \cdots s_{k-1} \beta_k / \tilde{l}_k^{(1)} \right) v_{k+1} \\
&= (\beta s_1 s_2 \cdots s_{k-1} s_k / c_k) v_{k+1}
\end{aligned}$$

and

$$\|r_k\|_2 = |\beta s_1 s_2 \cdots s_{k-1} s_k / c_k| = \left| \frac{c_{k-1} s_k}{c_k} \right| \cdot \|r_{k-1}\|_2,$$

which can be used to decide when to terminate the iteration.

Algorithm 6.11: SYMMLQ Method

1: Given an initial guess $x^{(0)}$ and a stopping tolerance $\varepsilon > 0$
2: compute $r_0 = b - Ax^{(0)}$ and $\beta = \|r_0\|_2$
3: set $v_1 = r_0/\beta$, $\xi_0 = \beta$ and $\tilde{x}^{(0)} = x^{(0)}$
4: **for** $k = 1, 2, \ldots,$ **do**
5: $\quad w_k = Av_k - \beta_{k-1}v_{k-1}$, where $\beta_0 = 0$ and $v_0 = 0$
6: $\quad \alpha_k = \langle w_k, v_k \rangle$
7: $\quad \tilde{w}_k = w_k - \alpha_k v_k$
8: $\quad \beta_k = \|\tilde{w}_k\|_2$
9: $\quad$ **if** $k = 1,$ **then**
10: $\quad\quad \tilde{l}_k^{(1)} = \alpha_k$
11: $\quad$ **end if**
12: $\quad$ **if** $k = 2,$ **then**
13: $\quad\quad \tilde{\beta}_{k-1} = \beta_{k-1}$
14: $\quad$ **end if**
15: $\quad$ **if** $k > 2,$ **then** $\quad$ % apply G_{k-2} to the last row of T_k
16: $\quad\quad \begin{bmatrix} l_k^{(3)} & \tilde{\beta}_{k-1} \end{bmatrix} = \begin{bmatrix} 0 & \beta_{k-1} \end{bmatrix} \begin{bmatrix} c_{k-2} & s_{k-2} \\ -s_{k-2} & c_{k-2} \end{bmatrix}$
17: $\quad$ **end if**
18: $\quad$ **if** $k > 1,$ **then** $\quad$ % form the Givens rotation G_{k-1}
19: $\quad\quad$ **if** $|\tilde{l}_{k-1}^{(1)}| > |\beta_{k-1}|,$ **then**
20: $\quad\quad\quad$ set $c_{k-1} = \dfrac{1}{\sqrt{1+\gamma^2}}$, $s_{k-1} = -c_{k-1}\gamma$, where $\gamma = \beta_{k-1}/\tilde{l}_{k-1}^{(1)}$
21: $\quad\quad$ **else**
22: $\quad\quad\quad$ set $s_{k-1} = \dfrac{1}{\sqrt{1+\gamma^2}}$, $c_{k-1} = -s_{k-1}\gamma$, where $\gamma = \tilde{l}_{k-1}^{(1)}/\beta_{k-1}$
23: $\quad\quad$ **end if**
24: $\quad$ **end if**
25: $\quad$ **if** $k > 1,$ **then** $\quad$ % apply G_{k-1} to the last two columns of $T_k \tilde{Q}_k^{\mathsf{T}}$
26: $\quad\quad l_{k-1}^{(1)} = \sqrt{\left(\tilde{l}_{k-1}^{(1)}\right)^2 + \beta_{k-1}^2}$
27: $\quad\quad \begin{bmatrix} l_k^{(2)} & \tilde{l}_k^{(1)} \end{bmatrix} = \begin{bmatrix} \tilde{\beta}_{k-1} & \alpha_k \end{bmatrix} \begin{bmatrix} c_{k-1} & s_{k-1} \\ -s_{k-1} & c_{k-1} \end{bmatrix}$
28: $\quad$ **end if**
29: $\quad$ **if** $k = 2,$ **then** $\quad$ % compute z_k
30: $\quad\quad z_1 = \beta/l_1^{(1)}$
31: $\quad$ **end if**
32: $\quad$ **if** $k = 3,$ **then**
33: $\quad\quad z_2 = -l_2^{(2)} z_1 / l_2^{(1)}$
34: $\quad$ **end if**
35: $\quad$ **if** $k > 3,$ **then**
36: $\quad\quad z_{k-1} = -\left(l_{k-1}^{(3)} z_{k-3} + l_{k-1}^{(2)} z_{k-2} \right) \Big/ l_{k-1}^{(1)}$
37: $\quad$ **end if**
38: $\quad$ **if** $k = 1,$ **then** $\quad$ % compute p_k
39: $\quad\quad \tilde{p}_1 = v_1$
40: $\quad$ **end if**
41: $\quad$ **if** $k > 1,$ **then**
42: $\quad\quad p_{k-1} = c_{k-1}\tilde{p}_{k-1} - s_{k-1}v_k$
43: $\quad\quad \tilde{p}_k = s_{k-1}\tilde{p}_{k-1} + c_{k-1}v_k$

```
44:    end if
45:    if k > 1, then    % update x̃^(k)
46:       x̃^(k-1) = x̃^(k-2) + z_{k-1} p_{k-1}
47:    end if
48:    if k > 1, then    % check convergence
49:       ξ_{k-1} = (c_{k-2} s_{k-1}/c_{k-1}) ξ_{k-2}, where c_0 = 1
50:       if |ξ_{k-1}| < ε then
51:          x^(k-1) = x̃^(k-2) + (l^{(1)}_{k-1} z_{k-1}/l̃^{(1)}_{k-1}) p̃_{k-1}
52:          stop
53:       end if
54:    end if
55:    v_{k+1} = w̃_k/β_k
56: end for
```

SYMMLQ keeps the residual orthogonal to all previous ones. If the matrix A is symmetric positive definite, then SYMMLQ is equivalent to CG, so it minimizes the **A-norm** of the residual. When the matrix A is symmetric but indefinite, the A-norm is no longer well-defined. However, it can be shown that SYMMLQ minimizes the 2-norm of the error $\|x^{(k)} - x_*\|_2$ over the affine subspace $x^{(0)} + A\mathcal{K}_k(A, r_0)$; see [141, 149].

6.5 ▪ Convergence Analysis

In **exact arithmetic**, Krylov subspace methods will terminate at most in n steps. However, in practical implementations, it is always desired that an acceptable approximate solution can be found in $m \ll n$ steps.

Convergence analysis of the Krylov subspace methods not only is of great theoretical importance, but also can help to improve the performance of these methods.

In this section, we concentrate on the convergence results of the CG and GMRES methods. A survey on the convergence analysis of Krylov subspace methods can be found in [228].

If the matrix A is normal, i.e., it is unitarily diagonalizable, then the convergence behavior of CG and GMRES is completely determined by its spectrum. However, in the general nonnormal case, the convergence analysis of GMRES method is very difficult and, indeed, it is still an open problem; see [20].

6.5.1 ▪ Convergence of CG for SPD Matrices

Assume that $A \in \mathbb{R}^{n \times n}$ is symmetric positive definite, and let $x^{(k)} \in \mathbb{R}^n$ be an approximate solution for the symmetric positive definite linear system (6.1) in the affine subspace $x^{(0)} + \mathcal{K}_k(A, r_0)$ obtained by the **CG** method. It follows from Theorem 6.25 that

$$\|x^{(k)} - x_*\|_A = \min_{x \in x^{(0)} + \mathcal{K}_k(A, r_0)} \|x - x_*\|_A, \qquad (6.40)$$

where $x_* = A^{-1}b$ is the exact solution of the linear system (6.1), and $r_0 = b - Ax^{(0)}$ is the initial residual.

Let $\mathcal{P}_k$ be the set of all real polynomials whose degree is at most k. Since $\mathcal{K}_k(A, r_0)$ is the subspace of all vectors that can be written as

$$x = p(A) r_0 \quad \text{with} \quad p(t) \in \mathcal{P}_{k-1},$$

for any vector

$$x \in x^{(0)} + \mathcal{K}_k(A, r_0),$$

there exists a polynomial $p(t) \in \mathcal{P}_{k-1}$ such that

$$x = x^{(0)} + p(A)\, r_0.$$

Denote

$$\epsilon_0 \triangleq x^{(0)} - x_*.$$

Then

$$x - x_* = \epsilon_0 + p(A)\, (b - Ax^{(0)}) = \epsilon_0 + p(A)\, (Ax_* - Ax^{(0)}) = (I - A\, p(A))\epsilon_0$$

and

$$\begin{aligned}
\|x - x_*\|_A^2 &= \|(I - A\, p(A))\epsilon_0\|_A^2 = \epsilon_0^\mathsf{T}(I - A\, p(A))A(I - A\, p(A))\epsilon_0 \\
&\triangleq \epsilon_0^\mathsf{T} q(A)^\mathsf{T} A\, q(A)\, \epsilon_0,
\end{aligned} \tag{6.41}$$

where

$$q(t) = 1 - t\, p(t) \in \mathcal{P}_k$$

satisfies

$$q(0) = 1.$$

Let $A = Q\Lambda Q^\mathsf{T}$ be the eigendecomposition of the matrix $A \in \mathbb{R}^{n \times n}$, where the matrix $Q \in \mathbb{R}^{n \times n}$ is orthogonal and $\Lambda = \mathrm{diag}(\lambda_1, \lambda_2, \dots, \lambda_n)$, with $\lambda_i > 0$, $i = 1, 2, \dots, n$, being the eigenvalues of the matrix A. Denote

$$y = [y_1, y_2, \dots, y_n]^\mathsf{T} \triangleq Q^\mathsf{T}\epsilon_0.$$

Then, it follows from (6.40) and (6.41) that

$$\begin{aligned}
\|x^{(k)} - x_*\|_A^2 &= \min_{x \in x^{(0)} + \mathcal{K}_k(A, r_0)} \|x - x_*\|_A^2 \\
&= \min_{q \in \mathcal{P}_k,\ q(0)=1} \epsilon_0^\mathsf{T} q(A)^\mathsf{T} A\, q(A)\, \epsilon_0 \\
&= \min_{q \in \mathcal{P}_k,\ q(0)=1} \epsilon_0^\mathsf{T} Q\, q(\Lambda)^\mathsf{T} \Lambda\, q(\Lambda)\, Q^\mathsf{T}\epsilon_0 \\
&= \min_{q \in \mathcal{P}_k,\ q(0)=1} y^\mathsf{T} q(\Lambda)^\mathsf{T} \Lambda\, q(\Lambda)\, y \\
&= \min_{q \in \mathcal{P}_k,\ q(0)=1} \sum_{i=1}^{n} y_i^2 \lambda_i\, q(\lambda_i)^2 \\
&\leq \min_{q \in \mathcal{P}_k,\ q(0)=1} \max_{1 \leq i \leq n} \{q(\lambda_i)^2\} \sum_{i=1}^{n} y_i^2 \lambda_i \\
&= \min_{q \in \mathcal{P}_k,\ q(0)=1} \max_{1 \leq i \leq n} \{q(\lambda_i)^2\}\, y^\mathsf{T} \Lambda y \\
&= \min_{q \in \mathcal{P}_k,\ q(0)=1} \max_{1 \leq i \leq n} \{q(\lambda_i)^2\}\, \epsilon_0^\mathsf{T} A\epsilon_0 \\
&= \min_{q \in \mathcal{P}_k,\ q(0)=1} \max_{1 \leq i \leq n} \{q(\lambda_i)^2\}\, \|\epsilon_0\|_A^2,
\end{aligned}$$

which implies

$$\frac{\|x^{(k)} - x_*\|_A^2}{\|x^{(0)} - x_*\|_A^2} \leq \min_{q \in \mathcal{P}_k,\, q(0)=1} \max_{1 \leq i \leq n} \{q(\lambda_i)^2\}.$$

Therefore, we have the following result.

Theorem 6.27. *Let $A \in \mathbb{R}^{n \times n}$ be symmetric positive definite and $x^{(k)} \in \mathbb{R}^n$ be an approximate solution for the linear system (6.1) obtained by the CG method after k steps of iteration. Then*

$$\frac{\|x^{(k)} - x_*\|_A}{\|x^{(0)} - x_*\|_A} \leq \min_{q \in \mathcal{P}_k,\, q(0)=1} \max_{1 \leq i \leq n} |q(\lambda_i)|. \tag{6.42}$$

It is worth pointing out that the upper bound in (6.42) is sharp, i.e., for each iteration step k there exists a right-hand side vector $b \in \mathbb{R}^n$ or an initial guess $x^{(0)} \in \mathbb{R}^n$ (depending on the iteration index k and the coefficient matrix A) such that the equality holds in (6.42); see [172]. In this sense, the upper bound in (6.42) completely describes the ***worst-case*** behavior of the CG method.

It is clear that the upper bound in (6.42) depends only on the eigenvalues of the matrix A. However, not all eigenvalues of the matrix A are available, so the analysis based on (6.42) cannot be applied. Fortunately, in many cases, the largest and smallest eigenvalues $\lambda_{\max}$ and $\lambda_{\min}$ (or at least estimates for them) of the matrix A are known. Then we can replace the discrete set of the eigenvalues by an interval which contains all of these eigenvalues, obtaining the estimate

$$\frac{\|x^{(k)} - x_*\|_A}{\|x^{(0)} - x_*\|_A} \leq \min_{q \in \mathcal{P}_k,\, q(0)=1} \max_{1 \leq i \leq n} |q(\lambda_i)| \leq \min_{q \in \mathcal{P}_k,\, q(0)=1} \max_{\lambda_{\min} \leq \lambda \leq \lambda_{\max}} |q(\lambda)|.$$

By utilizing the approximation property of Chebyshev polynomials, we can obtain the following well-known upper bound for the convergence factor of the CG method.

Theorem 6.28. *Let $A \in \mathbb{R}^{n \times n}$ be symmetric positive definite, and $\lambda_{\max}$ and $\lambda_{\min}$ be its largest and smallest eigenvalues, respectively. Then it holds that*

$$\frac{\|x^{(k)} - x_*\|_A}{\|x^{(0)} - x_*\|_A} \leq 2 \left(\frac{\sqrt{\kappa(A)} - 1}{\sqrt{\kappa(A)} + 1} \right)^k, \quad k = 0, 1, 2, \ldots, \tag{6.43}$$

*where $\kappa(A) = \frac{\lambda_{\max}}{\lambda_{\min}}$ is the **spectral condition number** of the matrix A.*

Proof. As $\lambda_{\min} > 0$, by Theorem 5.78 we know that the unique solution of the **min-max problem**

$$\min_{q \in \mathcal{P}_k,\, q(0)=1} \max_{\lambda_{\min} \leq \lambda \leq \lambda_{\max}} |q(\lambda)|$$

is given by

$$\tilde{T}_k(\lambda) = \frac{T_k \left(\frac{2\lambda - (\lambda_{\max} + \lambda_{\min})}{\lambda_{\max} - \lambda_{\min}} \right)}{T_k \left(-\frac{\lambda_{\max} + \lambda_{\min}}{\lambda_{\max} - \lambda_{\min}} \right)}, \quad \lambda \in [\lambda_{\min}, \lambda_{\max}],$$

where T_k is the **Chebyshev polynomial** of degree k defined in (5.61). As $|T_k(t)| \leq 1$ holds for $-1 \leq t \leq 1$ and

$$T_k(-t) = (-1)^k\, T_k(t),$$

we have

$$\frac{\|x^{(k)} - x_*\|_A}{\|x^{(0)} - x_*\|_A} \leq \frac{1}{T_k\left(\frac{\lambda_{\max} + \lambda_{\min}}{\lambda_{\max} - \lambda_{\min}}\right)}.$$

Since

$$T_k(t) = \frac{1}{2}\left[\left(t + \sqrt{t^2 - 1}\right)^k + \left(t + \sqrt{t^2 - 1}\right)^{-k}\right] \geq \frac{1}{2}\left(t + \sqrt{t^2 - 1}\right)^k$$

holds for $t > 1$, we can obtain

$$\begin{aligned}
T_k\left(\frac{\lambda_{\max} + \lambda_{\min}}{\lambda_{\max} - \lambda_{\min}}\right) &\geq \frac{1}{2}\left(\frac{\lambda_{\max} + \lambda_{\min}}{\lambda_{\max} - \lambda_{\min}} + \sqrt{\frac{(\lambda_{\max} + \lambda_{\min})^2}{(\lambda_{\max} - \lambda_{\min})^2} - 1}\right)^k \\
&= \frac{1}{2}\left(\frac{\lambda_{\max} + \lambda_{\min}}{\lambda_{\max} - \lambda_{\min}} + \frac{2\sqrt{\lambda_{\max}\lambda_{\min}}}{\lambda_{\max} - \lambda_{\min}}\right)^k \\
&= \frac{1}{2}\left(\frac{\sqrt{\lambda_{\max}} + \sqrt{\lambda_{\min}}}{\sqrt{\lambda_{\max}} - \sqrt{\lambda_{\min}}}\right)^k \\
&= \frac{1}{2}\left(\frac{\sqrt{\kappa(A)} + 1}{\sqrt{\kappa(A)} - 1}\right)^k.
\end{aligned}$$

Therefore, it follows that

$$\frac{\|x^{(k)} - x_*\|_A}{\|x^{(0)} - x_*\|_A} \leq 2\left(\frac{\sqrt{\kappa(A)} - 1}{\sqrt{\kappa(A)} + 1}\right)^k. \qquad \square$$

By Theorem 6.25, we know that small condition number usually implies fast convergence of the CG method. On the other hand, it does not show that a large condition number results in slow convergence.

We remark that there is a principal difference between the upper bounds in (6.42) and (6.43). In fact, their values can differ significantly [290]. In addition, the bound in (6.43) describes the worst-case behavior for all possible eigenvalue distributions in the interval $[\lambda_{\min}, \lambda_{\max}]$, therefore, it cannot be identified with the CG convergence, and it represents an overestimate for even the worst-case behavior except for very special eigenvalue distributions in the given interval [229].

Theorem 6.25 implies the global linear convergence of the CG method. However, in many applications, it has been observed that the CG method may converge superlinearly, which means that the average speed of convergence seems to increase during the iteration. Some efforts have been made to explain this behavior; see [61, 62, 97, 296, 321, 349].

6.5.2 ▪ Convergence of GMRES for Normal Matrices

Assume that the matrix $A \in \mathbb{R}^{n \times n}$ is normal, that is, there exists a unitary matrix $U \in \mathbb{C}^{n \times n}$ such that

$$A = U\Lambda U^*,$$

where $\Lambda = \mathrm{diag}(\lambda_1, \lambda_2, \ldots, \lambda_n)$, with $\lambda_i \in \mathbb{C}$, $i = 1, 2, \ldots, n$, being the eigenvalues of the matrix A. Let

$$x \subset x^{(0)} + \mathcal{K}_k(A, r_0).$$

Then, it can be written as

$$x = x^{(0)} + p(A)\, r_0$$

for certain $p(t) \in \mathcal{P}_{k-1}$. Hence, we have

$$b - Ax = b - Ax^{(0)} - A\, p(A)\, r_0 = (I - A\, p(A)) r_0 \triangleq q(A)\, r_0,$$

where

$$q(t) = 1 - t\, p(t) \in \mathcal{P}_k \quad \text{and} \quad q(0) = 1.$$

It follows that

$$\|b - Ax\|_2 = \|q(A)\, r_0\|_2 = \|U q(\Lambda)\, U^* r_0\|_2$$
$$\leq \|U\|_2 \|U^*\|_2 \|q(\Lambda)\|_2 \|r_0\|_2 = \|q(\Lambda)\|_2 \|r_0\|_2.$$

Since Λ is a diagonal matrix, we have

$$\|q(\Lambda)\|_2 = \max_{1 \leq i \leq n} |q(\lambda_i)|.$$

Let $x^{(k)} \in \mathbb{R}^n$ be the approximate solution of the linear system (6.1) in the affine subspace $x^{(0)} + \mathcal{K}_k(A, r_0)$ obtained by GMRES. Then, from Theorem 6.17, we know that the vector $x^{(k)}$ minimizes the 2-norm of the residual over the subspace $x^{(0)} + \mathcal{K}_k(A, r_0)$. Hence, it holds that

$$\|b - Ax^{(k)}\|_2 = \min_{x \in x^{(0)} + \mathcal{K}_k(A, r_0)} \|b - Ax\|_2$$
$$= \min_{q \in \mathcal{P}_k,\, q(0)=1} \|q(A)\, r_0\|_2$$
$$\leq \min_{q \in \mathcal{P}_k,\, q(0)=1} \|q(\Lambda)\|_2 \|r_0\|_2$$
$$= \|r_0\|_2 \min_{q \in \mathcal{P}_k,\, q(0)=1} \max_{1 \leq i \leq n} |q(\lambda_i)|.$$

Theorem 6.29. *Let $A \in \mathbb{R}^{n \times n}$ be normal and $x^{(k)} \in \mathbb{R}^n$ be the approximate solution for the linear system (6.1) obtained by GMRES after k steps of iteration. Then it holds that*

$$\frac{\|b - Ax^{(k)}\|_2}{\|r_0\|_2} \leq \min_{q \in \mathcal{P}_k,\, q(0)=1} \max_{1 \leq i \leq n} |q(\lambda_i)|. \tag{6.44}$$

Again, the upper bound in (6.44) is sharp [174, 212]. Similar to the case of the CG method, we can replace the discrete set of the eigenvalues by some domain $\Omega \subset \mathbb{C}$ on which (nearly) optimal polynomials are explicitly known. Usually, the domain Ω should be connected since polynomial approximation on disconnected sets is not well understood (even in the case of two disjoint intervals, see, e.g., [136]). In addition, the domain Ω should not include the origin.

The simplest result is obtained when we use a disc in the complex plane which excludes the origin, say, with radius $\varrho > 0$ and center at $(c, 0)$. Here we assume that the center of the disc locates at the real axis as the complex eigenvalues of a real matrix must appear in conjugate pairs. Define the complex polynomial

$$q_k(z) = \left(\frac{c - z}{c}\right)^k.$$

Then $q_k(z) \in \mathcal{P}_k$ and $q_k(0) = 1$. Moreover, we have

$$\min_{q \in \mathcal{P}_k,\, q(0)=1} \max_{1 \leq i \leq n} |q(\lambda_i)| \leq \max_{1 \leq i \leq n} |q_k(\lambda_i)| = \max_{1 \leq i \leq n} \left| \frac{(c - \lambda_i)^k}{c^k} \right| \leq \frac{\varrho^k}{|c|^k}.$$

Therefore, a disc that is far from the origin and of small radius guarantees fast convergence of the GMRES method.

More refined bounds can be obtained by replacing the disc by an ellipse. Assume that the spectrum of the matrix A is contained in an ellipse $\mathcal{E}(c, d, a)$ with center at $(c, 0)$, focal distance $d > 0$, and major semi-axis $a > 0$. As the origin is outside the ellipse, the two possible cases are listed in the following figure, where we assume that the real parts of the eigenvalues are positive.

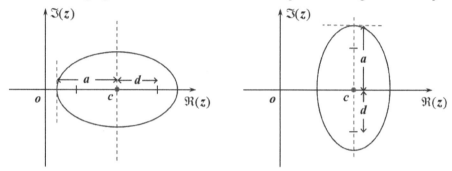

Let $T_k(z)$ be the complex **Chebyshev polynomial** of degree k defined in (5.65). Define the complex polynomial

$$\tilde{T}_k(z) = \frac{T_k\left(\frac{c-z}{d}\right)}{T_k\left(\frac{c}{d}\right)},$$

which is the asymptotically optimal solution of the **min-max problem**

$$\min_{q \in \mathcal{P}_k,\, q(0)=1} \max_{\lambda \in \mathcal{E}(c,d,a)} |q(\lambda)|. \tag{6.45}$$

Then it holds that

$$\min_{q \in \mathcal{P}_k,\, q(0)=1} \max_{1 \leq i \leq n} |q(\lambda_i)| \leq \min_{q \in \mathcal{P}_k,\, q(0)=1} \max_{\lambda \in \mathcal{E}(c,d,a)} |q(\lambda)| \leq \max_{\lambda \in \mathcal{E}(c,d,a)} |\tilde{T}_k(\lambda)|.$$

The validity of the first inequality is due to the fact that the maximum modulus of a complex analytical function is achieved on the boundary of a bounded domain. It follows from (5.71) that

$$\max_{\lambda \in \mathcal{E}(c,d,a)} |\tilde{T}_k(\lambda)| = \frac{T_k\left(\frac{a}{d}\right)}{|T_k\left(\frac{c}{d}\right)|}$$

and, hence,

$$\min_{q \in \mathcal{P}_k,\, q(0)=1} \max_{1 \leq i \leq n} |q(\lambda_i)| \leq \frac{T_k\left(\frac{a}{d}\right)}{|T_k\left(\frac{c}{d}\right)|}.$$

Corollary 6.30. *Let $A \in \mathbb{R}^{n \times n}$ be normal and its spectrum be contained in the ellipse $\mathcal{E}(c, d, a)$. If $x^{(k)} \in \mathbb{R}^n$ is the approximate solution for the linear system (6.1) obtained by the GMRES method after k steps of iteration, then it holds that*

$$\frac{\|b - Ax^{(k)}\|_2}{\|r_0\|_2} \leq \frac{T_k\left(\frac{a}{d}\right)}{|T_k\left(\frac{c}{d}\right)|}. \tag{6.46}$$

We remark that, although the normalized Chebyshev polynomial $\tilde{T}_k(z)$ is, in general, not the solution of the min-max problem (6.45), the upper bound in (6.46) can predict the correct rate of convergence of the GMRES method [228].

From the approximate property (5.72), the upper bound in (6.46) is approximately equal to

$$\left(\frac{a + \sqrt{a^2 - d^2}}{c + \sqrt{c^2 - d^2}} \right)^k,$$

which is much easier to be calculated.

6.5.3 ▪ Convergence of GMRES for Nonnormal Matrices

For general nonnormal matrices, it is very difficult to analyze the convergence behavior of the **GMRES method**.

We first consider the case when the matrix $A \in \mathbb{R}^{n \times n}$ is diagonalizable, that is, there exists a nonsingular matrix $X \in \mathbb{C}^{n \times n}$ such that

$$A = X \Lambda X^{-1},$$

where $\Lambda = \text{diag}(\lambda_1, \lambda_2, \ldots, \lambda_n)$, with $\lambda_i \in \mathbb{C}$, $i = 1, 2, \ldots, n$, being the eigenvalues of the matrix A. Let $x^{(k)} \in \mathbb{R}^n$ be an approximate solution for the linear system (6.1) obtained by the GMRES method after k steps of iteration. Then we have

$$\|b - Ax^{(k)}\|_2 = \min_{x \in x^{(0)} + \mathcal{K}_k(A, r_0)} \|b - Ax\|_2 = \min_{q \in \mathcal{P}_k,\, q(0)=1} \|q(A)\, r_0\|_2. \tag{6.47}$$

Analogously, we can obtain the following result [289].

Theorem 6.31. *Let $A \in \mathbb{R}^{n \times n}$ be a diagonalizable matrix, and $x^{(k)} \in \mathbb{R}^n$ be the approximate solution for the linear system (6.1) obtained by GMRES after k steps of iteration. Then, it holds that*

$$\frac{\|b - Ax^{(k)}\|_2}{\|r_0\|_2} \leq \|X\|_2 \|X^{-1}\|_2 \min_{q \in \mathcal{P}_k,\, q(0)=1} \max_{1 \leq i \leq n} |q(\lambda_i)|$$
$$\triangleq \kappa(X) \min_{q \in \mathcal{P}_k,\, q(0)=1} \max_{1 \leq i \leq n} |q(\lambda_i)|, \tag{6.48}$$

*where $\kappa(X) = \|X\|_2 \|X^{-1}\|_2$ denotes the **spectral condition number** of the matrix X.*

When the matrix A is nearly normal, it follows that $\kappa(X) \approx 1$ and, hence, the upper bound in (6.48) typically represents a good bound for the convergence rate of the GMRES method. However, when the matrix X is far from unitary, $\kappa(X)$ can be very large and the upper bound may lose its practical interest.

It is stressed in [228] that, from an analytic point of view, the principal difficulty of nonnormality is not the belief that the convergence speed is slower for nonnormal than for normal matrices. This belief is incorrect because for each nonnormal matrix A there exists a normal matrix B for which the same convergence behavior can be observed (for the same initial residual r_0); see [3, 175, 176, 227]. Unfortunately, the mapping from the nonnormal matrix A to the normal matrix B is highly nonlinear, and it depends strongly on the initial residual r_0.

For general nonnormal matrices, a typical approach to understand the worst-case convergence behavior of the GMRES method is to replace the minimization problem (6.47) by another one that is easier to analyze and that, in some sense, approximates well the original problem (6.47). In fact, we have

$$\frac{\|b - Ax^{(k)}\|_2}{\|r_0\|_2} = \frac{\min\limits_{q \in \mathcal{P}_k,\, q(0)=1} \|q(A)\, r_0\|_2}{\|r_0\|_2}$$

$$\leq \max_{\|v\|_2=1} \min_{q \in \mathcal{P}_k,\, q(0)=1} \|q(A)\, v\|_2 \qquad (6.49)$$

$$\leq \min_{q \in \mathcal{P}_k,\, q(0)=1} \|q(A)\|_2. \qquad (6.50)$$

The upper bound in (6.49) corresponds to the worst-case GMRES behavior and represents a sharp upper bound. In this sense, it is the best bound that is independent of the initial residual r_0. However, it is not clear in general which properties of the matrix A influence this bound [129]. The quantity in (6.49) can be further bounded by the **ideal GMRES** approximation problem (6.50), which was introduced by Greenbaum and Trefethen [177]. It was shown in [174, 212] that the upper bounds in (6.49) and (6.50) are equal whenever the matrix A is normal. However, it is still an open question whether the upper bound in (6.49) is equal or close to that in (6.50) for larger classes of nonnormal matrices [228].

Finally, it is important to note that the convergence property can depend strongly on the right-hand side vector or the initial guess, so that the upper bounds in Theorems 6.28, 6.29, and 6.31 may overestimate the actual convergence behavior of the CG and the GMRES method.

In addition, we mention that a general and sharp bound for the convergence rate of the GMRES method, when the coefficient matrix $A \in \mathbb{R}^{n \times n}$ of the linear system (6.1) is not assumed to be diagonalizable, was derived in [20].

6.6 ▪ More Methods for Nonsymmetric Linear Systems

Besides the FOM and GMRES methods, there is another class of Krylov subspace methods which is based on the **bi-orthogonalization** or **(two-sided) Lanczos process** for nonsymmetric matrices [219]. The main disadvantage of the GMRES method is that as the iteration step increases the memory storage and the computational cost grow rapidly. For symmetric linear systems, we can impose the three-term recurrence which makes the method much more efficient and desirable. But for nonsymmetric ones, the residual vectors cannot be made orthogonal with short recurrences; see [130, 333].

The bi-orthogonalization process is a process that constructs a pair of bi-orthogonal bases of the Krylov subspaces $\mathcal{K}(A, r_0)$ and $\mathcal{K}(A^\mathsf{T}, \tilde{r}_0)$, respectively. The linear subspace $\mathcal{K}(A^\mathsf{T}, \tilde{r}_0)$ is usually called the **left Krylov subspace**. The advantage of this process is that these two bases can be constructed by two coupled three-term recurrences.

6.6.1 ▪ Bi-Orthogonalization Process

The bi-orthogonalization process can be viewed as an extension of the Lanczos orthogonalization process to the nonsymmetric matrices. In such an algorithm we generate a pair of bi-orthogonal bases $\{v_k\}_{k=1}^m$ and $\{w_k\}_{k=1}^m$ for the Krylov subspaces $\mathcal{K}_m(A, r_0)$ and $\mathcal{K}_m(A^\mathsf{T}, \tilde{r}_0)$, respectively. Here $\tilde{r}_0$ is an **auxiliary vector** satisfying $\langle \tilde{r}_0, r_0 \rangle \neq 0$. One common choice is $\tilde{r}_0 = r_0$. During the bi-orthogonalization process, instead of orthogonalizing with the vectors v_k and v_{k-1}, the vector Av_k is orthogonalized against the vectors w_k and w_{k-1} to obtain the vector v_{k+1}. Simultaneously, the vector w_{k+1} is obtained by orthogonalizing the vector $A^\mathsf{T} w_k$ against the vectors v_k and v_{k-1}. This process can be described as follows.

Algorithm 6.12: Bi-Orthogonalization or Two-Sided Lanczos Process

1: Let m be a given positive integer, and r_0, $\tilde{r}_0$ be two nonzero vectors such that $\langle \tilde{r}_0, r_0 \rangle \neq 0$
2: compute $\beta = \|r_0\|_2$
3: set $v_1 = r_0/\beta$ and $w_1 = \beta \tilde{r}_0/\langle \tilde{r}_0, r_0 \rangle$ % make sure that $w_1^{\mathsf{T}} v_1 = 1$
4: set $\beta_0 = 0$ and $\gamma_0 = 0$
5: **for** $k = 1, 2, \ldots, m$ **do**
6:    $\hat{v}_{k+1} = Av_k - \beta_{k-1}v_{k-1}$
7:    $\hat{w}_{k+1} = A^{\mathsf{T}}w_k - \gamma_{k-1}w_{k-1}$
8:    $\alpha_k = \langle v_k, \hat{w}_{k+1} \rangle$ % $\alpha_k = w_k^{\mathsf{T}} Av_k$
9:    $\tilde{v}_{k+1} = \hat{v}_{k+1} - \alpha_k v_k$
10:    $\tilde{w}_{k+1} = \hat{w}_{k+1} - \alpha_k w_k$
11:    $\gamma_k = \sqrt{|\langle \tilde{v}_{k+1}, \tilde{w}_{k+1} \rangle|}$
12:    **if** $\gamma_k = 0$, **then**   % ghost breakdown
13:        stop
14:    **end if**
15:    $\beta_k = \langle \tilde{v}_{k+1}, \tilde{w}_{k+1} \rangle / \gamma_k$ % so that $\beta_k \gamma_k = \langle \tilde{v}_{k+1}, \tilde{w}_{k+1} \rangle$
16:    $v_{k+1} = \tilde{v}_{k+1}/\gamma_k$
17:    $w_{k+1} = \tilde{w}_{k+1}/\beta_k$
18: **end for**

From Algorithm 6.12, we can obtain the following **three-term recurrences**:

$$\gamma_k v_{k+1} = Av_k - \alpha_k v_k - \beta_{k-1}v_{k-1}, \tag{6.51}$$

$$\beta_k w_{k+1} = A^{\mathsf{T}}w_k - \alpha_k w_k - \gamma_{k-1}w_{k-1}, \quad k = 1, 2, \ldots, m. \tag{6.52}$$

Analogous to the Lanczos process, we have the following result.

Lemma 6.32. *Assume that Algorithm 6.12 does not terminate before the first $m-1$ steps. Then, the two bases $\{v_k\}_{k=1}^m$ and $\{w_k\}_{k=1}^m$ are bi-orthogonal, that is,*

$$W_m^{\mathsf{T}} V_m = I, \tag{6.53}$$

where

$$V_m = [v_1, v_2, \ldots, v_m] \quad and \quad W_m = [w_1, w_2, \ldots, w_m].$$

Proof. Obviously, we have $w_1^{\mathsf{T}} v_1 = 1$. It is easily seen from lines 15-17 of Algorithm 6.12 that

$$w_{k+1}^{\mathsf{T}} v_{k+1} = \langle \tilde{v}_{k+1}, \tilde{w}_{k+1} \rangle / (\beta_k \gamma_k) = 1, \quad k = 1, 2, \ldots, m-1.$$

Hence, it remains to show that for an integer k with $2 \leq k \leq m$, it holds that

$$w_k^{\mathsf{T}} v_i = 0 \quad and \quad w_i^{\mathsf{T}} v_k = 0, \quad i = 1, 2, \ldots, k-1. \tag{6.54}$$

We prove this result by induction. For $k = 2$, we have

$$v_2 = (Av_1 - \alpha_1 v_1)/\gamma_1 \quad and \quad w_2 = (A^{\mathsf{T}}w_1 - \alpha_1 w_1)/\beta_1,$$

where $\alpha_1 = w_1^{\mathsf{T}} Av_1$. Therefore,

$$w_2^{\mathsf{T}} v_1 = (A^{\mathsf{T}}w_1 - \alpha_1 w_1)^{\mathsf{T}} v_1 / \beta_1$$
$$= (w_1^{\mathsf{T}} Av_1 - \alpha_1)/\beta_1 = 0,$$
$$w_1^{\mathsf{T}} v_2 = w_1^{\mathsf{T}}(Av_1 - \alpha_1 v_1)/\gamma_1$$
$$= (w_1^{\mathsf{T}} Av_1 - \alpha_1)/\gamma_1 = 0.$$

Suppose that (6.54) holds for k. Then

$$\alpha_k = \langle v_k, \hat{w}_{k+1} \rangle = (w_k^\mathsf{T} A - \gamma_{k-1} w_{k-1}^\mathsf{T}) v_k = w_k^\mathsf{T} A v_k.$$

It follows that

$$
\begin{aligned}
w_{k+1}^\mathsf{T} v_k &= (A^\mathsf{T} w_k - \alpha_k w_k - \gamma_{k-1} w_{k-1})^\mathsf{T} v_k / \beta_k \\
&= (w_k^\mathsf{T} A v_k - \alpha_k) / \beta_k = 0, \\
w_{k+1}^\mathsf{T} v_{k-1} &= (A^\mathsf{T} w_k - \alpha_k w_k - \gamma_{k-1} w_{k-1})^\mathsf{T} v_{k-1} / \beta_k \\
&= (w_k^\mathsf{T} A v_{k-1} - \gamma_{k-1}) / \beta_k \\
&= \left[w_k^\mathsf{T} (\gamma_{k-1} v_k + \alpha_{k-1} v_{k-1} + \beta_{k-2} v_{k-2}) - \gamma_{k-1} \right] / \beta_k \\
&= (\gamma_{k-1} w_k^\mathsf{T} v_k - \gamma_{k-1}) / \beta_k = 0,
\end{aligned}
$$

and, for $i \le k - 2$,

$$
\begin{aligned}
w_{k+1}^\mathsf{T} v_i &= (A^\mathsf{T} w_k - \alpha_k w_k - \gamma_{k-1} w_{k-1})^\mathsf{T} v_i / \beta_k \\
&= w_k^\mathsf{T} A v_i / \beta_k \\
&= w_k^\mathsf{T} (\gamma_i v_{i+1} + \alpha_i v_i + \beta_{i-1} v_{i-1}) / \beta_k = 0.
\end{aligned}
$$

Analogously, we can show that $w_i^\mathsf{T} v_{k+1} = 0$ holds for all $i \le k$. By induction, we have then demonstrated that the bi-orthogonal relationship in (6.54) holds true.   □

We remark that there are many different ways to define the values of the parameters β_k and γ_k. The only requirement is that

$$\beta_k \gamma_k = \langle \tilde{v}_{k+1}, \tilde{w}_{k+1} \rangle,$$

so that we have

$$\langle v_{k+1}, w_{k+1} \rangle = \frac{\langle \tilde{v}_{k+1}, \tilde{w}_{k+1} \rangle}{\beta_k \gamma_k} = 1.$$

The two coupled three-term recurrences (6.51) and (6.52) can be written in the matrix form as

$$
\begin{aligned}
A V_k &= V_{k+1} T_{k+1,k} = V_k T_k + \gamma_k v_{k+1} e_k^\mathsf{T}, \\
A^\mathsf{T} W_k &= W_{k+1} \tilde{T}_{k+1,k}^\mathsf{T} = W_k T_k^\mathsf{T} + \beta_k w_{k+1} e_k^\mathsf{T},
\end{aligned}
\qquad k = 1, 2, \ldots, m, \qquad (6.55)
$$

where $e_k = [0, \ldots, 0, 1]^\mathsf{T} \in \mathbb{R}^k$,

$$
T_{k+1,k} =
\begin{bmatrix}
\alpha_1 & \beta_1 & & \\
\gamma_1 & \ddots & \ddots & \\
& \ddots & \ddots & \beta_{k-1} \\
& & \gamma_{k-1} & \alpha_k \\
& & & \gamma_k
\end{bmatrix}_{(k+1) \times k}
$$

and

$$
\tilde{T}_{k+1,k}^\mathsf{T} =
\begin{bmatrix}
\alpha_1 & \gamma_1 & & \\
\beta_1 & \ddots & \ddots & \\
& \ddots & \ddots & \gamma_{k-1} \\
& & \beta_{k-1} & \alpha_k \\
& & & \beta_k
\end{bmatrix}_{(k+1) \times k},
$$

and $T_k \in \mathbb{R}^{k \times k}$ consists of the first k-rows of either the matrix $T_{k+1,k}$ or the matrix $\tilde{T}_{k+1,k}$. It follows from (6.53) and (6.55) that

$$W_k^\mathsf{T} A V_k = W_k^\mathsf{T} V_k T_k + \gamma_k (W_k^\mathsf{T} v_{k+1}) e_k^\mathsf{T} = T_k, \quad k = 1, 2, \ldots, m.$$

Note that the matrix T_k is tridiagonal but not symmetric. Analogously to the Lanczos process, we have the following result.

Theorem 6.33. *If Algorithm 6.12 does not terminate before the first m steps, then*

(1) $\{v_k\}_{k=1}^m$ *and* $\{w_k\}_{k=1}^m$ *form the bases of the Krylov subspaces* $\mathcal{K}_m(A, r_0)$ *and* $\mathcal{K}_m(A^\mathsf{T}, \tilde{r}_0)$, *respectively;*

(2) *the following relations hold true:*

$$\begin{aligned} A V_m &= V_m T_m + \gamma_m v_{m+1} e_m^\mathsf{T}, \\ A^\mathsf{T} W_m &= W_m T_m^\mathsf{T} + \beta_m w_{m+1} e_m^\mathsf{T}, \\ W_m^\mathsf{T} A V_m &= T_m, \end{aligned}$$

where $e_m = [0, \ldots, 0, 1]^\mathsf{T} \in \mathbb{R}^m$.

It should be pointed out that, in general, $\{v_k\}_{k=1}^m$ or $\{w_k\}_{k=1}^m$ is not orthogonal by itself.

It is clear that the bi-orthogonalization process is another way to construct a basis of the Krylov subspace. It differs from the Arnoldi process in that the basis constructed by the bi-orthogonalization process is nonorthogonal. The significant advantage of the bi-orthogonalization process over the Arnoldi process is that it can utilize short-term recurrence; see [221, 302]. Hence, besides the matrix A, it only needs to save six vectors. But the disadvantage is that it is more likely to break down [81, 184]. Strategies that try to overcome breakdowns have been proposed in the literature. A typical remedy, called **look-ahead Lanczos**, is to relax the constraint $W_m^\mathsf{T} V_m = I$ by only requiring that $W_m^\mathsf{T} V_m$ is a block-diagonal matrix. Intuitively, the look-ahead Lanczos looks ahead for the next basis vectors that will keep the matrix $W_m^\mathsf{T} V_m$ to be nonsingular. The look-ahead idea was first suggested by Parlett, Taylor, and Liu [272], but they only considered the case of 2×2 diagonal blocks, while in Freund, Gutknecht, and Nachtigal [145], an implementation was presented with diagonal blocks of arbitrary sizes; see also [80, 82, 182, 183, 314] for further analyses about breakdown. **Incurable breakdown** occurs if the diagonal block cannot be "closed." In this case, the process needs to be restarted with the current approximate solution as initial guess, and with a new auxiliary starting vector.

Based on the nonorthogonal basis generated by the bi-orthogonalization process, some efficient Krylov subspace iteration methods for nonsymmetric linear systems have been proposed.

6.6.2 ▪ Bi-Conjugate Gradient Method

Assume that the Lanczos bi-orthogonalization algorithm (i.e., Algorithm 6.12) does not break down. We can define a projection method onto the affine subspace $x^{(0)} + \mathcal{K}(A, r_0)$ and orthogonal to the left Krylov subspace $\mathcal{L} = \mathcal{K}(A^\mathsf{T}, \tilde{r}_0)$, that is, a method for finding a vector x such that

$$x \in x^{(0)} + \mathcal{K}(A, r_0) \quad \text{and} \quad r \triangleq b - Ax \perp \mathcal{K}(A^\mathsf{T}, \tilde{r}_0).$$

This leads to the *bi-conjugate gradient* (BiCG) method. Let $x^{(k)} \in \mathbb{R}^n$ be the approximate solution for the linear system (6.1) in the affine subspace $x^{(0)} + \mathcal{K}_k(A, r_0)$ obtained by the BiCG method. As the columns of the matrix V_k form a basis of the Krylov subspace $\mathcal{K}_k(A, r_0)$, we have

$$x^{(k)} = x^{(0)} + V_k y_k$$

for some vector $y_k \in \mathbb{R}^k$. By the facts that the columns of the matrix W_k form a basis of the left Krylov subspace $\mathcal{K}_k(A^\mathsf{T}, \tilde{r}_0)$ and that

$$b - Ax^{(k)} \perp \mathcal{K}_k(A^\mathsf{T}, \tilde{r}_0),$$

we have

$$0 = W_k^\mathsf{T}(b - Ax^{(k)}) = W_k^\mathsf{T}(r_0 - AV_k y_k) = W_k^\mathsf{T} r_0 - W_k^\mathsf{T} AV_k y_k = \beta W_k^\mathsf{T} v_1 - T_k y_k.$$

Thus, the vector y_k is the solution of the following tridiagonal linear system:

$$T_k y = \beta W_k^\mathsf{T} v_1 = \beta e_1. \qquad (6.56)$$

Analogously to the CG method, we use the LU decomposition to solve the tridiagonal linear system (6.56). Therefore, in the same way as the derivation of the CG method, we can obtain the following BiCG method for solving general nonsymmetric linear systems of the form (6.1).

Algorithm 6.13: Bi-Conjugate Gradient (BiCG) Method

1: Given an initial guess $x^{(0)}$ and a stopping tolerance $\varepsilon > 0$
2: compute $r_0 = b - Ax^{(0)}$
3: choose $\tilde{r}_0$ such that $\langle r_0, \tilde{r}_0 \rangle \neq 0$ % one common choice is $\tilde{r}_0 = r_0$
4: set $p_1 = r_0$ and $\tilde{p}_1 = \tilde{r}_0$
5: **for** $k = 1, 2, \ldots,$ **do**
6:     $\alpha_k = \langle r_{k-1}, \tilde{r}_{k-1} \rangle / \langle Ap_k, \tilde{p}_k \rangle$
7:     $x^{(k)} = x^{(k-1)} + \alpha_k p_k$
8:     $r_k = r_{k-1} - \alpha_k Ap_k$
9:     **if** $\|r_k\|_2 < \varepsilon$, **then**   % check convergence
10:       stop
11:     **end if**
12:     $\tilde{r}_k = \tilde{r}_{k-1} - \alpha_k A^\mathsf{T} \tilde{p}_k$
13:     $\beta_k = \langle r_k, \tilde{r}_k \rangle / \langle r_{k-1}, \tilde{r}_{k-1} \rangle$
14:     $p_{k+1} = r_k + \beta_k p_k$
15:     $\tilde{p}_{k+1} = \tilde{r}_k + \beta_k \tilde{p}_k$
16: **end for**

The BiCG method was first proposed by Lanczos [219] and, then in a different form (i.e., in its conjugate gradient-like version) by Fletcher [141]. If the matrix A is symmetric and positive definite and if $\tilde{r}_0 = r_0$, then BiCG reduces to CG.

In fact, we can simultaneously solve the two linear systems $Ax = b$ and $A^\mathsf{T} \tilde{x} = \tilde{b}$ with the BiCG method by choosing $\tilde{r}_0 = \tilde{b} - A^\mathsf{T} \tilde{x}^{(0)}$, where $\tilde{x}^{(0)}$ is some initial guess for the second linear system. Note that the updating scheme for the second linear system is

$$\tilde{x}^{(k)} = \tilde{x}^{(k-1)} + \alpha_k \tilde{p}_k.$$

We remark that the BiCG method may break down if the LU decomposition of the tridiagonal matrix T_k without pivoting does not exist. In addition, if the matrix T_k is singular at some step k, then the tridiagonal linear system (6.56) may have no solution, and the BiCG method may fail.

The following result is one property about the vectors produced by Algorithm 6.13.

Proposition 6.34. *Let the vectors r_k, $\tilde{r}_k$, p_k, and $\tilde{p}_k$ be generated by Algorithm 6.13. Then, it holds that*

$$\langle r_i, \tilde{r}_j \rangle = 0 \quad and \quad \langle Ap_i, \tilde{p}_j \rangle = 0, \quad for \; i \neq j.$$

Proof. The proof is left as Exercise 6.5. □

6.6.3 ▪ Quasi-Minimal Residual Method

The BiCG method is not very stable (see, e.g. [185]), and it often displays rather irregular (or erratic) convergence behavior. In fact, unlike the GMRES method, the norm of the residual with respect to the BiCG method is not necessarily non-increasing. The **quasi-minimal residual** method is proposed to overcome these shortcomings by solving a least-squares problem instead of solving the linear system with the coefficient matrix T_k, which may be singular or does not host an LU decomposition.

The quasi-minimal residual method can be viewed as an extension of the GMRES method. Let

$$x^{(k)} \in x^{(0)} + \mathcal{K}_k(A, r_0)$$

be the approximate solution of the form

$$x^{(k)} = x^{(0)} + V_k y_k$$

for the linear system (6.1). Then, by (6.55) we see that the corresponding residual is given by

$$r_k \triangleq b - Ax^{(k)} = r_0 - AV_k y_k = \beta v_1 - V_{k+1} T_{k+1,k} y_k = V_{k+1}(\beta e_1 - T_{k+1,k} y_k).$$

Hence, it holds that

$$\|r_k\|_2 = \|V_{k+1}(\beta e_1 - T_{k+1,k} y_k)\|_2.$$

In GMRES, the matrix V_{k+1} is columnwise orthonormal and the vector $x^{(k)}$ is obtained by minimizing the 2-norm of the residual, i.e.,

$$\|r_k\|_2 = \|\beta e_1 - T_{k+1,k} y_k\|_2.$$

However, in the bi-orthogonalization process, the matrix V_{k+1} is no longer columnwise orthogonal. Hence, it is difficult to find the vector y_k that minimizes the residual norm $\|r_k\|_2$ or

$$\|V_{k+1}(\beta e_1 - T_{k+1,k} y_k)\|_2.$$

As

$$\|r_k\|_2 \leq \|V_{k+1}\|_2 \cdot \|\beta e_1 - T_{k+1,k} y_k\|_2,$$

it is, however, still reasonable to minimize the quantity

$$\|\beta e_1 - T_{k+1,k} y_k\|_2. \tag{6.57}$$

This leads to the *quasi-minimal residual* (QMR) method [146]; the norm in (6.57) is called the **quasi-residual norm**.

The approximate solution $x^{(k)} \in \mathbb{R}^n$ for the linear system (6.1) obtained by the QMR method after k steps of iteration can be written as

$$x^{(k)} = x^{(0)} + V_k y_k, \quad \text{with} \quad y_k = \underset{y \in \mathbb{R}^k}{\operatorname{argmin}} \|\beta e_1 - T_{k+1,k} y\|_2. \tag{6.58}$$

It is clear that the QMR method is much similar to the GMRES method, except that the Arnoldi process is replaced by the bi-orthogonalization process. However, because of the tridiagonal structure of the matrix $T_{k+1,k}$, it is easier to solve the corresponding least-squares problem in (6.58). Analogously to GMRES, we can obtain an update scheme from the current iterate $x^{(k)}$ to the next iterate $x^{(k+1)}$.

For details of the implementation of the QMR method, we refer to [323, page 101].

It should be pointed out that in the QMR method, we minimize the quasi-residual norm instead of the real residual norm.

It was observed in [146] that the convergence behavior of QMR is much smoother than that of BiCG. From a relation between the residuals in BiCG and QMR (Freund and Nachtigal [101, relation (5.10)]) one may deduce that when BiCG makes significant progress in terms of iteration process, QMR has arrived at about the same approximation. On the other hand, when BiCG makes no progress at all, QMR may still show slow convergence. In addition, QMR uses the look-ahead technique to avoid any breakdown in the underlying bi-orthogonalization process, which makes it more robust than BiCG [147].

6.7 ▪ Transpose-Free Methods

In both BiCG and QMR methods, the matrix-vector product with the matrix A^T is needed at each step, whereas the transpose matrix A^T may not be available or it is much inconvenient to do the matrix-vector product with the matrix A^T. A typical situation occurs, for instance, when the matrix A is given only as an operator subroutine. Hence, it is desirable to develop some other methods that can avoid using the transpose of the matrix A but still keep the short-term recurrence property.

6.7.1 ▪ Conjugate Gradient Squared Method

We observe from Algorithm 6.13 (i.e., the BiCG method) that the residual vector after k steps of iteration can be written as

$$r_k = \varphi_k(A) r_0, \tag{6.59}$$

where φ_k, the **residual polynomial**, is a certain polynomial of degree not greater than k satisfying $\varphi_k(0) = 1$. Meanwhile, the **search direction** p_{k+1} can be written as

$$p_{k+1} = \psi_k(A) r_0, \tag{6.60}$$

where ψ_k is a certain polynomial of degree not greater than k. Note that the vectors $\tilde{r}_k$ and $\tilde{p}_{k+1}$ are updated through the same schemes as those of the vectors r_k and p_{k+1}, respectively, except that the matrix A is replaced by its transpose matrix A^T. Therefore, it holds that

$$\tilde{r}_k = \varphi_k(A^\mathsf{T}) \tilde{r}_0 \quad \text{and} \quad \tilde{p}_{k+1} = \psi_k(A^\mathsf{T}) \tilde{r}_0, \quad k = 1, 2, \ldots.$$

The parameters α_k and β_k in BiCG can be rewritten as

$$\alpha_k = \frac{\langle r_{k-1}, \tilde{r}_{k-1} \rangle}{\langle Ap_k, \tilde{p}_k \rangle} = \frac{\langle \varphi_{k-1}(A) r_0, \varphi_{k-1}(A^\mathsf{T}) \tilde{r}_0 \rangle}{\langle A \psi_{k-1}(A) r_0, \psi_{k-1}(A^\mathsf{T}) \tilde{r}_0 \rangle} = \frac{\langle \varphi_{k-1}^2(A) r_0, \tilde{r}_0 \rangle}{\langle A \psi_{k-1}^2(A) r_0, \tilde{r}_0 \rangle},$$

$$\beta_k = \frac{\langle r_k, \tilde{r}_k \rangle}{\langle r_{k-1}, \tilde{r}_{k-1} \rangle} = \frac{\langle \varphi_k(A) r_0, \varphi_k(A^\mathsf{T}) \tilde{r}_0 \rangle}{\langle \varphi_{k-1}(A) r_0, \varphi_{k-1}(A^\mathsf{T}) \tilde{r}_0 \rangle} = \frac{\langle \varphi_k^2(A) r_0, \tilde{r}_0 \rangle}{\langle \varphi_{k-1}^2(A) r_0, \tilde{r}_0 \rangle},$$

which indicate that it is possible to update the vectors $x^{(k+1)}$ and r_{k+1} without computing the matrix-vector product with the matrix A^T. The problem left is whether we can compute the vectors $\varphi_k^2(A) r_0$ and $\psi_k^2(A) r_0$ by some recursions.

It follows from

$$r_k = r_{k-1} - \alpha_k A p_k \quad \text{and} \quad p_{k+1} = r_k + \beta_k p_k$$

that

$$\varphi_k(A) = \varphi_{k-1}(A) - \alpha_k A \, \psi_{k-1}(A), \tag{6.61}$$
$$\psi_k(A) = \varphi_k(A) + \beta_k \, \psi_{k-1}(A), \quad k = 1, 2, \ldots, \tag{6.62}$$

where

$$\varphi_0(A) = I \quad \text{and} \quad \psi_0(A) = I.$$

By squaring the two equations in (6.61) and (6.62), we obtain

$$\varphi_k^2(A) = \varphi_{k-1}^2(A) + \alpha_k^2 A^2 \psi_{k-1}^2(A) - 2\alpha_k A \, \varphi_{k-1}(A) \, \psi_{k-1}(A),$$
$$\psi_k^2(A) = \varphi_k^2(A) + \beta_k^2 \psi_{k-1}^2(A) + 2\beta_k \, \varphi_k(A) \, \psi_{k-1}(A).$$

For the cross terms $\varphi_{k-1}(A) \, \psi_{k-1}(A)$ and $\varphi_k(A) \, \psi_{k-1}(A)$, we have

$$\varphi_{k-1}(A) \, \psi_{k-1}(A) = \varphi_{k-1}(A)(\varphi_{k-1}(A) + \beta_{k-1} \, \psi_{k-2}(A))$$
$$= \varphi_{k-1}^2(A) + \beta_{k-1} \, \varphi_{k-1}(A) \, \psi_{k-2}(A), \quad k = 2, 3, \ldots,$$

and

$$\varphi_k(A) \, \psi_{k-1}(A) = (\varphi_{k-1}(A) - \alpha_k A \, \psi_{k-1}(A)) \, \psi_{k-1}(A)$$
$$= \varphi_{k-1}(A) \, \psi_{k-1}(A) - \alpha_k A \, \psi_{k-1}^2(A)$$
$$= \varphi_{k-1}^2(A) + \beta_{k-1} \, \varphi_{k-1}(A) \, \psi_{k-2}(A) - \alpha_k A \, \psi_{k-1}^2(A), \quad k = 2, 3, \ldots.$$

Therefore, we obtain the recursive relationships (hereafter in this subsection, we omit the variable A in the matrix polynomials $\varphi_k(A)$ and $\psi_k(A)$, $k = 0, 1, 2, \ldots$, only for simplification) as follows:

$$\begin{aligned} \varphi_1^2 &= (\varphi_0 - \alpha_1 A \psi_0)^2 = (I - \alpha_1 A)^2, \\ \varphi_1 \psi_0 &= \varphi_1 = I - \alpha_1 A, \\ \psi_1^2 &= (\varphi_1 + \beta_1 \psi_0)^2 = (\varphi_1 + \beta_1 I)^2 \end{aligned} \tag{6.63}$$

and

$$\begin{aligned} \varphi_k^2 &= \varphi_{k-1}^2 + \alpha_k^2 A^2 \psi_{k-1}^2 - 2\alpha_k A(\varphi_{k-1}^2 + \beta_{k-1}\varphi_{k-1}\psi_{k-2}), \\ \varphi_k \psi_{k-1} &= \varphi_{k-1}^2 + \beta_{k-1}\varphi_{k-1}\psi_{k-2} - \alpha_k A \psi_{k-1}^2, \qquad k = 2, 3, \ldots. \\ \psi_k^2 &= \varphi_k^2 + \beta_k^2 \psi_{k-1}^2 + 2\beta_k \varphi_k \psi_{k-1}, \end{aligned} \tag{6.64}$$

Define

$$\hat{r}_k = \varphi_k^2(A) \, r_0, \quad \hat{p}_{k+1} = \psi_k^2(A) \, r_0, \quad \hat{q}_k = \varphi_k(A) \, \psi_{k-1}(A) \, r_0.$$

Then (6.63) and (6.64) lead to the following recursive formulas:

$$\begin{cases} \hat{r}_k = \hat{r}_{k-1} + \alpha_k^2 A^2 \hat{p}_k - 2\alpha_k A(\hat{r}_{k-1} + \beta_{k-1}\hat{q}_{k-1}) \\ \quad = \hat{r}_{k-1} + \alpha_k A(\alpha_k A \hat{p}_k - 2\hat{r}_{k-1} - 2\beta_{k-1}\hat{q}_{k-1}), \\ \hat{q}_k = \hat{r}_{k-1} + \beta_{k-1}\hat{q}_{k-1} - \alpha_k A \hat{p}_k, \\ \hat{p}_{k+1} = \hat{r}_k + \beta_k^2 \hat{p}_k + 2\beta_k \hat{q}_k, \end{cases} \quad k = 1, 2, \ldots,$$

where

$$\hat{r}_0 = r_0, \quad \hat{p}_1 = r_0, \quad \hat{q}_0 = 0, \quad \beta_0 = 0$$

and

$$
\begin{cases}
\alpha_k = \dfrac{\langle \varphi_{k-1}^2(A)\, r_0, \tilde{r}_0 \rangle}{\langle A\psi_{k-1}^2(A)\, r_0, \tilde{r}_0 \rangle} = \dfrac{\langle \hat{r}_{k-1}, \tilde{r}_0 \rangle}{\langle A\hat{p}_k, \tilde{r}_0 \rangle}, \\[3mm]
\beta_k = \dfrac{\langle \varphi_k^2(A)\, r_0, \tilde{r}_0 \rangle}{\langle \varphi_{k-1}^2(A)\, r_0, \tilde{r}_0 \rangle} = \dfrac{\langle \hat{r}_k, \tilde{r}_0 \rangle}{\langle \hat{r}_{k-1}, \tilde{r}_0 \rangle},
\end{cases}
\qquad k = 1, 2, \ldots .
$$

For brevity, we further define an auxiliary vector

$$
u_k = \hat{r}_k + \beta_k \hat{q}_k .
$$

Then, it follows that

$$
\begin{cases}
\hat{q}_k = u_{k-1} - \alpha_k A\hat{p}_k, \\[1mm]
\hat{r}_k = \hat{r}_{k-1} + \alpha_k A(\alpha_k A\hat{p}_k - 2u_{k-1}) \\[1mm]
\qquad = \hat{r}_{k-1} - \alpha_k A(\hat{q}_k + u_{k-1}), \\[1mm]
\hat{p}_{k+1} = u_k + \beta_k^2 \hat{p}_k + \beta_k \hat{q}_k,
\end{cases}
\qquad k = 1, 2, \ldots . \qquad (6.65)
$$

If the BiCG method converges, then $\|r_k\| = \|\varphi_k(A)\, r_0\|$ tends to zero and one might expect that $\|\hat{r}_k\| = \|\varphi_k^2(A)\, r_0\|$ would tend to zero much faster. Hence, we choose the approximate solution $x^{(k)}$ of the linear system (6.1) such that the corresponding residual vector is equal to $\hat{r}_k$, i.e.,

$$
\hat{r}_k \triangleq b - Ax^{(k)} .
$$

It follows from (6.65) that the update scheme for the approximate solutions becomes

$$
x^{(k)} = x^{(k-1)} + \alpha_k(\hat{q}_k + u_{k-1}), \quad k = 0, 1, 2, \ldots .
$$

The above relations lead to the following ***conjugate gradient squared*** (CGS) method, which was proposed by Sonneveld [301].

Algorithm 6.14: Conjugate Gradient Squared (CGS) Method

1: Given an initial guess $x^{(0)}$ and a stopping tolerance $\varepsilon > 0$
2: compute $r_0 = b - Ax^{(0)}$
3: choose $\tilde{r}_0$ such that $\langle r_0, \tilde{r}_0 \rangle \neq 0$ % one common choice is $\tilde{r}_0 = r_0$
4: set $\hat{p}_1 = r_0$, $\hat{r}_0 = r_0$ and $u_0 = r_0$
5: **for** $k = 1, 2, \ldots,$ **do**
6:     $\alpha_k = \langle \hat{r}_{k-1}, \tilde{r}_0 \rangle / \langle A\hat{p}_k, \tilde{r}_0 \rangle$
7:     $\hat{q}_k = u_{k-1} - \alpha_k A\hat{p}_k$
8:     $x^{(k)} = x^{(k-1)} + \alpha_k(\hat{q}_k + u_{k-1})$
9:     $\hat{r}_k = \hat{r}_{k-1} - \alpha_k A(\hat{q}_k + u_{k-1})$
10:     **if** $\|\hat{r}_k\|_2 < \varepsilon,$ **then**   % check convergence
11:         stop
12:     **end if**
13:     $\beta_k = \langle \hat{r}_k, \tilde{r}_0 \rangle / \langle \hat{r}_{k-1}, \tilde{r}_0 \rangle$
14:     $u_k = \hat{r}_k + \beta_k \hat{q}_k$
15:     $\hat{p}_{k+1} = u_k + \beta_k^2 \hat{p}_k + \beta_k \hat{q}_k$
16: **end for**

In the CGS method, there are two matrix-vector products at each iteration step. Hence, the amount of work at each of its iteration steps is almost the same as that of BiCG. But there is no product with the matrix A^T in CGS. Usually, CGS works very well for solving many nonsymmetric linear systems [301] and, in general, it often converges twice as fast as BiCG. However, as the residual polynomial is squared, if the residual norm of BiCG increases at one step, then the residual norm of CGS would increase much more. Hence, the convergence curve of CGS may have wild oscillations, which usually leads to numerical instability.

6.7.2 ▪ Bi-Conjugate Gradient Stabilized Method

We do not require the transpose of the matrix A in the CGS method, but the oscillatory behavior of the convergence is amplified. In [322], van der Vorst proposed the so-called **bi-conjugate gradient stabilized** (BiCGSTAB) method, whose residual vectors are of the form

$$r_k = \phi_k(A)\,\varphi_k(A)\,r_0, \quad k = 1, 2, \ldots,$$

where φ_k is the residual polynomial of the BiCG method and ϕ_k is a new k-th degree polynomial introduced to remedy the oscillation. In BiCGSTAB, the polynomials ϕ_k's are defined by the following recurrence:

$$\phi_0(A) = I, \quad \phi_k(A) = (I - \omega_k A)\,\phi_{k-1}(A), \quad k = 1, 2, \ldots, \tag{6.66}$$

where ω_k's are the parameters chosen to minimize the residual norm. Then, the residual and direction vectors can be written as

$$r_k = \phi_k(A)\,\varphi_k(A)\,r_0 \quad \text{and} \quad p_{k+1} = \phi_k(A)\,\psi_k(A)\,r_0, \quad k = 1, 2, \ldots,$$

where φ_k and ψ_k are defined by (6.59) and (6.60), respectively. Now we need to derive the recursive update schemes for the vectors r_k and p_k. It follows from (6.61), (6.62), and (6.66) that

$$\phi_k(A)\,\varphi_k(A) = (I - \omega_k A)\,\phi_{k-1}(A)\,(\varphi_{k-1}(A) - \alpha_k A\,\psi_{k-1}(A))$$
$$= (I - \omega_k A)\,(\phi_{k-1}(A)\,\varphi_{k-1}(A) - \alpha_k A\,\phi_{k-1}(A)\,\psi_{k-1}(A))$$

and

$$\phi_k(A)\,\psi_k(A) = \phi_k(A)\,(\varphi_k(A) + \beta_k \psi_{k-1}(A))$$
$$= \phi_k(A)\,\varphi_k(A) + \beta_k(I - \omega_k A)\,\phi_{k-1}(A)\,\psi_{k-1}(A).$$

Therefore, we have

$$\begin{aligned} r_k &= \phi_k(A)\,\varphi_k(A)\,r_0 \\ &= (I - \omega_k A)(\phi_{k-1}(A)\,\varphi_{k-1}(A)\,r_0 - \alpha_k A\,\phi_{k-1}(A)\,\psi_{k-1}(A)\,r_0) \\ &= (I - \omega_k A)(r_{k-1} - \alpha_k A p_k) \end{aligned} \tag{6.67}$$

and

$$\begin{aligned} p_{k+1} &= \phi_k(A)\,\psi_k(A)\,r_0 \\ &= \phi_k(A)\,\varphi_k(A)\,r_0 + \beta_k(I - \omega_k A)\,\phi_{k-1}(A)\,\psi_{k-1}(A)\,r_0 \\ &= r_k + \beta_k(I - \omega_k A)p_k. \end{aligned} \tag{6.68}$$

The scalars α_k, β_k are still defined by

$$\alpha_k = \frac{\langle \varphi_{k-1}(A)\, r_0, \varphi_{k-1}(A^\mathsf{T})\, \tilde{r}_0 \rangle}{\langle A\psi_{k-1}(A)\, r_0, \psi_{k-1}(A^\mathsf{T})\, \tilde{r}_0 \rangle}, \quad \beta_k = \frac{\langle \varphi_k(A)\, r_0, \varphi_k(A^\mathsf{T})\, \tilde{r}_0 \rangle}{\langle \varphi_{k-1}(A)\, r_0, \varphi_{k-1}(A^\mathsf{T})\, \tilde{r}_0 \rangle}.$$

Since we do not compute the vector $\varphi_k^2(A)\, r_0$ or the vector $\psi_k^2(A)\, r_0$ in BiCGSTAB, we need to find other ways to compute the scalars α_{k+1} and β_{k+1}.

From (6.61) and (6.62), we see that

$$\begin{aligned}
\varphi_k(A^\mathsf{T}) &= \varphi_{k-1}(A^\mathsf{T}) - \alpha_k A^\mathsf{T}\, \psi_{k-1}(A^\mathsf{T}) \\
&= \varphi_{k-1}(A^\mathsf{T}) - \alpha_k A^\mathsf{T}(\varphi_{k-1}(A^\mathsf{T}) + \beta_k\, \psi_{k-2}(A^\mathsf{T})) \\
&= -\alpha_k A^\mathsf{T}\varphi_{k-1}(A^\mathsf{T}) + \varphi_{k-1}(A^\mathsf{T}) - \alpha_k\beta_k A^\mathsf{T}\, \psi_{k-2}(A^\mathsf{T}).
\end{aligned}$$

Thus, the coefficient of the highest-order term of the matrix polynomial $\varphi_k(A^\mathsf{T})$ is the same as that of the matrix polynomial

$$-\alpha_k A^\mathsf{T}\, \varphi_{k-1}(A^\mathsf{T}),$$

which, by induction, is given by

$$(-1)^k \alpha_k \alpha_{k-1} \cdots \alpha_1.$$

As $\varphi_i(A)\, r_0$ and $\varphi_i(A^\mathsf{T})\, \tilde{r}_0$ ($i = 0, 1, 2, \ldots$) are the residual vectors of the BiCG method, it follows from Proposition 6.34 that

$$\langle \varphi_i(A)\, r_0, \varphi_j(A^\mathsf{T})\, \tilde{r}_0 \rangle = 0, \quad \text{for } i \neq j,$$

which implies

$$\langle \varphi_i(A)\, r_0, (A^\mathsf{T})^j\, \tilde{r}_0 \rangle = 0, \quad \text{for } i \neq j.$$

So, we only need to consider the highest-order term of the matrix polynomial $\varphi_{k-1}(A^\mathsf{T})$ when computing the inner product

$$\langle \varphi_{k-1}(A)\, r_0, \varphi_{k-1}(A^\mathsf{T})\, \tilde{r}_0 \rangle,$$

which is implied in

$$\langle \varphi_{k-1}(A)\, r_0, \varphi_{k-1}(A^\mathsf{T})\, \tilde{r}_0 \rangle = (-1)^{k-1}\alpha_{k-1}\alpha_{k-2} \cdots \alpha_1 \langle \varphi_{k-1}(A)\, r_0, (A^\mathsf{T})^{k-1}\, \tilde{r}_0 \rangle.$$

On the other hand, it follows from (6.66) that the highest-order term of the matrix polynomial $\phi_{k-1}(A^\mathsf{T})$ is given by

$$(-1)^{k-1}\omega_{k-1}\omega_{k-2} \cdots \omega_1 (A^\mathsf{T})^{k-1}$$

and, hence,

$$\langle \varphi_{k-1}(A)\, r_0, \phi_{k-1}(A^\mathsf{T})\, \tilde{r}_0 \rangle = (-1)^{k-1}\omega_{k-1}\omega_{k-2} \cdots \omega_1 \langle \varphi_{k-1}(A)\, r_0, (A^\mathsf{T})^{k-1}\, \tilde{r}_0 \rangle.$$

As a result, we have the following relationships:

$$\frac{\langle \varphi_{k-1}(A)\, r_0, \varphi_{k-1}(A^\mathsf{T})\, \tilde{r}_0 \rangle}{\langle \varphi_{k-1}(A)\, r_0, \phi_{k-1}(A^\mathsf{T})\, \tilde{r}_0 \rangle} = \frac{\alpha_{k-1}\alpha_{k-2} \cdots \alpha_1}{\omega_{k-1}\omega_{k-2} \cdots \omega_1}, \quad k = 1, 2, \ldots,$$

which indicates that we can compute the inner product $\langle \varphi_k(A)\, r_0, \varphi_k(A^\mathsf{T})\, \tilde{r}_0 \rangle$ through the inner product $\langle \varphi_k(A)\, r_0, \phi_k(A^\mathsf{T})\, \tilde{r}_0 \rangle$.

Now, we consider the computation of the inner product $\langle A\psi_{k-1}(A)\, r_0, \psi_{k-1}(A^\mathsf{T})\, \tilde{r}_0 \rangle$. It follows from (6.62) that the highest-order term of the matrix polynomial $\psi_k(A^\mathsf{T})$ is the same as that of the matrix polynomial $\varphi_k(A^\mathsf{T})$. By Proposition 6.34 again, we have

$$\langle A\, \psi_i(A)\, p_1, \psi_j(A^\mathsf{T})\, \tilde{p}_1 \rangle = 0, \quad \text{for } i \neq j,$$

which implies
$$\langle A\,\psi_i(A)\,p_1, (A^{\mathsf{T}})^j\,\tilde{p}_1 \rangle = 0, \quad \text{for } i \neq j.$$

Note that $p_1 = r_0$ and $\tilde{p}_1 = \tilde{r}_0$, it follows that
$$\langle A\,\psi_i(A)\,r_0, (A^{\mathsf{T}})^j\,\tilde{r}_0 \rangle = 0, \quad \text{for } i \neq j.$$

Hence, we only need to consider the highest-order term of the matrix polynomial $\psi_{k-1}(A^{\mathsf{T}})$ when computing the inner product $\langle A\,\psi_{k-1}(A)\,r_0, \psi_{k-1}(A^{\mathsf{T}})\,\tilde{r}_0 \rangle$. In fact, it holds that
$$\langle A\,\psi_{k-1}(A)\,r_0, \psi_{k-1}(A^{\mathsf{T}})\,\tilde{r}_0 \rangle = (-1)^{k-1}\alpha_{k-1}\alpha_{k-2}\cdots\alpha_1\langle A\,\psi_{k-1}(A)\,r_0, (A^{\mathsf{T}})^{k-1}\,\tilde{r}_0 \rangle,$$

and, analogously,
$$\langle A\,\psi_{k-1}(A)\,r_0, \phi_{k-1}(A^{\mathsf{T}})\,\tilde{r}_0 \rangle = (-1)^{k-1}\omega_{k-1}\omega_{k-2}\cdots\omega_1\langle A\,\psi_{k-1}(A)\,r_0, (A^{\mathsf{T}})^{k-1}\,\tilde{r}_0 \rangle.$$

So,
$$\frac{\langle A\,\psi_{k-1}(A)\,r_0, \psi_{k-1}(A^{\mathsf{T}})\,\tilde{r}_0 \rangle}{\langle A\,\psi_{k-1}(A)\,r_0, \phi_{k-1}(A^{\mathsf{T}})\,\tilde{r}_0 \rangle} = \frac{\alpha_{k-1}\alpha_{k-2}\cdots\alpha_1}{\omega_{k-1}\omega_{k-2}\cdots\omega_1}, \quad k = 1, 2, \ldots.$$

It then follows that
$$\begin{aligned}
\alpha_k &= \frac{\langle\varphi_{k-1}(A)\,r_0, \varphi_{k-1}(A^{\mathsf{T}})\,\tilde{r}_0 \rangle}{\langle A\,\psi_{k-1}(A)\,r_0, \psi_{k-1}(A^{\mathsf{T}})\,\tilde{r}_0 \rangle} = \frac{\langle\varphi_{k-1}(A)\,r_0, \phi_{k-1}(A^{\mathsf{T}})\,\tilde{r}_0 \rangle}{\langle A\,\psi_{k-1}(A)\,r_0, \phi_{k-1}(A^{\mathsf{T}})\,\tilde{r}_0 \rangle} \\
&= \frac{\langle\phi_{k-1}(A)\,\varphi_{k-1}(A)\,r_0, \tilde{r}_0 \rangle}{\langle A\,\phi_{k-1}(A)\,\psi_{k-1}(A)\,r_0, \tilde{r}_0 \rangle} \\
&= \frac{\langle r_{k-1}, \tilde{r}_0 \rangle}{\langle Ap_k, \tilde{r}_0 \rangle},
\end{aligned}$$

$$\begin{aligned}
\beta_k &= \frac{\langle\varphi_k(A)\,r_0, \varphi_k(A^{\mathsf{T}})\,\tilde{r}_0 \rangle}{\langle\varphi_{k-1}(A)\,r_0, \varphi_{k-1}(A^{\mathsf{T}})\,\tilde{r}_0 \rangle} = \frac{\alpha_k}{\omega_k} \cdot \frac{\langle\varphi_k(A)\,r_0, \phi_k(A^{\mathsf{T}})\,\tilde{r}_0 \rangle}{\langle\varphi_{k-1}(A)\,r_0, \phi_{k-1}(A^{\mathsf{T}})\,\tilde{r}_0 \rangle} \\
&= \frac{\alpha_k}{\omega_k} \cdot \frac{\langle\phi_k(A)\,\varphi_k(A)\,r_0, \tilde{r}_0 \rangle}{\langle\phi_{k-1}(A)\,\varphi_{k-1}(A)\,r_0, \tilde{r}_0 \rangle} \\
&= \frac{\alpha_k}{\omega_k} \cdot \frac{\langle r_k, \tilde{r}_0 \rangle}{\langle r_{k-1}, \tilde{r}_0 \rangle}.
\end{aligned}$$

In summary, we have obtained the following updating scheme for the BiCGSTAB method:
$$\begin{cases}
r_k = (I - \omega_k A)(r_{k-1} - \alpha_k Ap_k), & \text{with } \alpha_k = \dfrac{\langle r_{k-1}, \tilde{r}_0 \rangle}{\langle Ap_k, \tilde{r}_0 \rangle}, \\
p_{k+1} = r_k + \beta_k(I - \omega_k A)p_k, & \text{with } \beta_k = \dfrac{\alpha_k}{\omega_k} \cdot \dfrac{\langle r_k, \tilde{r}_0 \rangle}{\langle r_{k-1}, \tilde{r}_0 \rangle},
\end{cases} \quad k = 1, 2, \ldots,$$

where $p_1 = r_0$.

Note that our goal is to find the approximate solution $x^{(k)}$ for the linear system (6.1). So, we need to determine the update formula for the vector $x^{(k)}$. It follows from (6.67) and (6.68) that
$$\begin{aligned}
b - Ax^{(k)} = r_k &= (I - \omega_k A)(r_{k-1} - \alpha_k Ap_k) \\
&= r_{k-1} - \alpha_k Ap_k - \omega_k A(r_{k-1} - \alpha_k Ap_k) \\
&= b - Ax^{(k-1)} - \alpha_k Ap_k - \omega_k A(r_{k-1} - \alpha_k Ap_k),
\end{aligned}$$

which yields

$$x^{(k)} = x^{(k-1)} + \alpha_k p_k + \omega_k(r_{k-1} - \alpha_k A p_k).$$

The only problem left is how to choose the parameter ω_k at the current iteration step. As we mentioned before, it is determined by minimizing the residual norm $\|r_k\|_2$, i.e.,

$$\omega_k = \operatorname*{argmin}_{\omega} \|(I - \omega A)(r_{k-1} - \alpha_k A p_k)\|_2.$$

Define

$$q_k = r_{k-1} - \alpha_k A p_k.$$

Then the solution of the above minimization problem is given by

$$\omega_k = \frac{\langle q_k, A q_k \rangle}{\langle A q_k, A q_k \rangle}.$$

Now, by summarizing the above argument and derivation, we can give a precise description of the BiCGSTAB method.

Algorithm 6.15: Bi-Conjugate Gradient Stabilized (BiCGSTAB) Method

---

1: Given an initial guess $x^{(0)}$ and a stopping tolerance $\varepsilon > 0$
2: compute $r_0 = b - A x^{(0)}$
3: choose $\tilde{r}_0$ such that $\langle r_0, \tilde{r}_0 \rangle \neq 0$ % one common choice is $\tilde{r}_0 = r_0$
4: set $p_1 = r_0$
5: **for** $k = 1, 2, \ldots,$ **do**
6:     $\alpha_k = \langle r_{k-1}, \tilde{r}_0 \rangle / \langle A p_k, \tilde{r}_0 \rangle$
7:     $q_k = r_{k-1} - \alpha_k A p_k$
8:     $\omega_k = \langle q_k, A q_k \rangle / \langle A q_k, A q_k \rangle$
9:     $x^{(k)} = x^{(k-1)} + \alpha_k p_k + \omega_k q_k$
10:     $r_k = q_k - \omega_k A q_k$
11:     **if** $\|r_k\|_2 < \varepsilon$, **then**   % check convergence
12:         stop
13:     **end if**
14:     $\beta_k = (\alpha_k / \omega_k) \langle r_k, \tilde{r}_0 \rangle / \langle r_{k-1}, \tilde{r}_0 \rangle$
15:     $p_{k+1} = r_k + \beta_k(p_k - \omega_k A p_k)$
16: **end for**

6.8 ▪ Methods for Normal Equations

Another type of approach for solving the nonsymmetric linear system (6.1) is first transforming it into an equivalent linear system

$$A^\mathsf{T} A x = A^\mathsf{T} b, \tag{6.69}$$

which is symmetric and positive definite, and then solving this **transformed linear system** by the CG method. The transformed linear system (6.69) is also known as the **normal equation** associated with the **linear least-squares problem**

$$\min_{x \in \mathbb{R}^n} \|A x - b\|_2.$$

This kind of approach has a disadvantage that, roughly speaking, it squares the condition number of the original linear system. Hence, the resulting iteration methods may converge slower, especially for the ill-conditioned linear systems. In particular, the amount of work for each CG iteration step is approximately doubled. However, this kind of method may be attractive in some situations, for example, when the singular values of the matrix A are tightly clustered.

6.8.1 · CGLS and CGNE Methods

It was pointed out by Paige and Saunders [265] that applying the CG method, i.e., Algorithm 6.9, naively to the normal equation (6.69) is not advisable, largely because the CG method would generate vectors of the form $A^\mathsf{T} A p_k$, which does not lead to sufficient accuracy for the coefficient α_k. An algorithm with better numerical properties is obtained after a slight algebraic rearrangement, where we make use of the intermediate vector $A p_k$. This leads to the following **CGLS** method [265], that is, the conjugate gradient method for the least-squares problem.

Algorithm 6.16: CGLS Method

1: Given an initial guess $x^{(0)}$ and a stopping tolerance $\varepsilon > 0$
2: compute $r_0 = b - Ax^{(0)}$ and set $p_1 = A^\mathsf{T} r_0$
3: **for** $k = 1, 2, \ldots,$ **do**
4:      $\alpha_k = \langle A^\mathsf{T} r_{k-1}, A^\mathsf{T} r_{k-1} \rangle / \langle A p_k, A p_k \rangle$
5:      $x^{(k)} = x^{(k-1)} + \alpha_k p_k$
6:      $r_k = r_{k-1} - \alpha_k A p_k$
7:      **if** $\|r_k\|_2 < \varepsilon$, **then**
8:          stop
9:      **end if**
10:     $\beta_k = \langle A^\mathsf{T} r_k, A^\mathsf{T} r_k \rangle / \langle A^\mathsf{T} r_{k-1}, A^\mathsf{T} r_{k-1} \rangle$
11:     $p_{k+1} = A^\mathsf{T} r_k + \beta_k p_k$
12: **end for**

The CGLS method is also termed as the CGNR method, i.e., the conjugate gradient method for the normal residual.

We remark that in CGLS the vector r_k is the k-th residual vector of the original linear system $Ax = b$, which makes it convenient to check the convergence of the method based on the relative residual norm of the original linear system. The approximate solution $x^{(k)}$ obtained by the CGLS method has the property that it minimizes the residual norm $\|b - Ax\|_2$ over the affine subspace $x^{(0)} + \mathcal{K}_k(A^\mathsf{T} A, A^\mathsf{T} r_0)$.

Proposition 6.35. *Let $x^{(k)} \in \mathbb{R}^n$ be the approximate solution for the linear system* (6.1) *obtained by Algorithm 6.16 after k steps of iteration. Then, it holds that*

$$\|b - Ax^{(k)}\|_2 = \min_{x \in x^{(0)} + \mathcal{K}_k(A^\mathsf{T} A, A^\mathsf{T} r_0)} \|b - Ax\|_2.$$

Proof. The proof is left as Exercise 6.8.   □

A similar alternative is to set $x = A^\mathsf{T} y$. Then we obtain another equivalent linear system

$$AA^\mathsf{T} y = b. \tag{6.70}$$

By applying CG to the normal equation (6.70), we can obtain a similar method to CGLS, which is known as the CGNE [288] method or the Craig method [131, 259]. Here CGNE is the abbreviation of the conjugate gradient method for the normal equation.

Algorithm 6.17: CGNE Method

1: Given an initial guess $x^{(0)}$ and a stopping tolerance $\varepsilon > 0$
2: compute $r_0 = b - Ax^{(0)}$ and set $p_1 = A^\mathsf{T} r_0$
3: **for** $k = 1, 2, \ldots,$ **do**
4:     $\alpha_k = \langle r_{k-1}, r_{k-1} \rangle / \langle p_k, p_k \rangle$
5:     $x^{(k)} = x^{(k-1)} + \alpha_k p_k$
6:     $r_k = r_{k-1} - \alpha_k A p_k$
7:     **if** $\|r_k\|_2 < \varepsilon$ **then**
8:         stop
9:     **end if**
10:     $\beta_k = \langle r_k, r_k \rangle / \langle r_{k-1}, r_{k-1} \rangle$
11:     $p_{k+1} = A^\mathsf{T} r_k + \beta_k p_k$
12: **end for**

Proposition 6.36. *Let $x^{(k)} \in \mathbb{R}^n$ be the approximate solution for the linear system* (6.1) *obtained by Algorithm 6.17 after k steps of iteration. Then, it holds that*

$$\|x^{(k)} - x_*\|_2 = \min_{x \in x^{(0)} + \mathcal{K}_k(A^\mathsf{T} A, A^\mathsf{T} r_0)} \|x - x_*\|_2,$$

where $x_* = A^{-1}b$ denotes the exact solution of the linear system (6.1).

Proof. The proof is left as Exercise 6.9.   ☐

It follows from Propositions 6.35 and 6.36 that both CGLS and CGNE seek the approximate solution for the linear system (6.1) in the same affine subspace, but they achieve different **optimality properties**.

We remark that the CGLS and CGNE methods can also be used to solve the linear systems when the coefficient matrices are not square, i.e., to solve the so-called overdetermined or the underdetermined linear systems.

As we have pointed out before, when the linear system is ill-conditioned, it may be numerically unattractive to solve the normal equation directly. Paige and Saunders proposed a method that behaves numerically better, which is called **LSQR** [265]. In fact, LSQR is equivalent to CGLS but exhibits better computational results for ill-conditioned linear systems, in particular when the singular vectors associated with the small singular values carry important information about the solution.

6.8.2 ▪ LSQR Method

Note that the original linear system $Ax = b$ in (6.1) is also equivalent to the following **saddle-point problem**

$$\begin{bmatrix} I & A \\ A^\mathsf{T} & 0 \end{bmatrix} \begin{bmatrix} r \\ x \end{bmatrix} = \begin{bmatrix} b \\ 0 \end{bmatrix} \iff \mathbf{A}z = f, \tag{6.71}$$

where $r \triangleq b - Ax$. We set the initial guess to be $[0, 0]^\mathsf{T}$, and apply the Lanczos process to construct the orthonormal basis of the Krylov subspace $\mathcal{K}(\mathbf{A}, f_0)$ as the matrix $\mathbf{A}$ is symmetric, where $f_0 = [b^\mathsf{T}, 0]^\mathsf{T}$. To this end, we choose the starting vector as

$$v_0 = \frac{1}{\|b\|_2} \begin{bmatrix} b \\ 0 \end{bmatrix}, \tag{6.72}$$

It follows from direct computations that

$$v_1 = \frac{1}{\|A^\mathsf{T}b\|_2} \begin{bmatrix} 0 \\ A^\mathsf{T}b \end{bmatrix}.$$

By induction, the basis vectors v_{2k} and v_{2k+1} are of the forms

$$\begin{bmatrix} * \\ 0 \end{bmatrix} \quad \text{and} \quad \begin{bmatrix} 0 \\ * \end{bmatrix},$$

respectively; see Exercise 6.10. Hence, they can be written as

$$v_{2k} = \begin{bmatrix} u_k \\ 0 \end{bmatrix} \quad \text{and} \quad v_{2k+1} = \begin{bmatrix} 0 \\ w_k \end{bmatrix}, \quad k = 0, 1, 2, \dots,$$

where

$$\|u_k\|_2 = \|w_k\|_2 = 1.$$

The Lanczos process for the symmetric **saddle-point linear system** (6.71) can be reformulated into the following one:

$$\beta_0 u_0 = b, \quad \alpha_0 w_0 = A^\mathsf{T} u_0,$$

$$\begin{cases} \beta_{k+1} u_{k+1} = A w_k - \alpha_k u_k, \\ \alpha_{k+1} w_{k+1} = A^\mathsf{T} u_{k+1} - \beta_{k+1} w_k, \end{cases} \quad k = 0, 1, 2, \dots,$$

where the positive scalars α_k and β_k are chosen so that

$$\|u_k\|_2 = \|w_k\|_2 = 1.$$

We remark that these α_k and β_k are different from those in the Lanczos process, i.e., in Algorithm 6.8.

The above procedure is known as the **bidiagonalization procedure** due to Golub and Kahan [164].

Denote by

$$\begin{aligned} U_m = [u_0, u_1, \dots, u_{m-1}], \\ W_m = [w_0, w_1, \dots, w_{m-1}], \end{aligned} \quad \tilde{B}_m = \begin{bmatrix} \alpha_0 & & & \\ \beta_1 & \alpha_1 & & \\ & \beta_2 & \ddots & \\ & & \ddots & \alpha_{m-1} \\ & & & \beta_m \end{bmatrix} \in \mathbb{R}^{(m+1)\times m}. \quad (6.73)$$

Then we have

$$\begin{aligned} U_{m+1}(\beta_0 e_1) &= b, \\ A W_m &= U_{m+1} \tilde{B}_m, \\ A^\mathsf{T} U_{m+1} &= W_m \tilde{B}_m^\mathsf{T} + \alpha_m w_m e_{m+1}^\mathsf{T}, \end{aligned} \quad (6.74)$$

with

$$e_{m+1} = [0, \dots, 0, 1]^\mathsf{T} \in \mathbb{R}^{m+1}.$$

As $\{v_0, v_1, v_2, \ldots\}$ is an orthonormal basis of the Krylov subspace $\mathcal{K}(\mathbf{A}, f_0)$, it holds that

$$U_{m+1}^{\mathsf{T}} U_{m+1} = I_{m+1} \quad \text{and} \quad W_m^{\mathsf{T}} W_m = I_m.$$

So, the columns of the matrix

$$\begin{bmatrix} u_0 & 0 & u_1 & 0 & \cdots & 0 & u_m \\ 0 & w_0 & 0 & w_1 & \cdots & w_{m-1} & 0 \end{bmatrix},$$

or equivalently,

$$\begin{bmatrix} U_{m+1} & 0 \\ 0 & W_m \end{bmatrix},$$

form an orthonormal basis of the Krylov subspace $\mathcal{K}_{2m+1}(\mathbf{A}, f_0)$.

We now seek for the approximate solution $[\tilde{r}^{\mathsf{T}}, \tilde{x}^{\mathsf{T}}]^{\mathsf{T}}$ of the saddle-point problem (6.71) in the Krylov subspace $\mathcal{K}_{2m+1}(\mathbf{A}, f_0)$ such that the residual norm of the original linear system $Ax = b$ is minimized. To this end, we write the approximate solution $[\tilde{r}^{\mathsf{T}}, \tilde{x}^{\mathsf{T}}]^{\mathsf{T}}$ as

$$\begin{bmatrix} \tilde{r} \\ \tilde{x} \end{bmatrix} = \begin{bmatrix} U_{m+1} & 0 \\ 0 & W_m \end{bmatrix} \begin{bmatrix} t_{m+1} \\ y_m \end{bmatrix},$$

or

$$\begin{cases} \tilde{r} = U_{m+1} t_{m+1}, \\ \tilde{x} = W_m y_m. \end{cases}$$

Then, it follows from (6.74) that

$$\begin{aligned} b - A\tilde{x} &= U_{m+1}(\beta_0 e_1) - A W_m y_m \\ &= U_{m+1}(\beta_0 e_1) - U_{m+1} \tilde{B}_m y_m \\ &= U_{m+1}(\beta_0 e_1 - \tilde{B}_m y_m). \end{aligned}$$

Note that the matrix $\tilde{B}_m$ is the bidiagonal factor of the tridiagonal matrix T_m obtained from the Lanczos process for the normal equation $A^{\mathsf{T}} A x = A^{\mathsf{T}} b$; see Exercise 6.11.

As

$$U_{m+1}^{\mathsf{T}} U_{m+1} = I_{m+1},$$

we see that

$$\|b - A\tilde{x}\|_2 = \|U_{m+1}(\beta_0 e_1 - \tilde{B}_m y_m)\|_2 = \|\beta_0 e_1 - \tilde{B}_m y_m\|_2.$$

Hence, the problem of minimizing the residual norm is equivalent to the **linear least-squares problem**:

$$\min_{y \in \mathbb{R}^m} \|\beta_0 e_1 - \tilde{B}_m y\|_2, \quad \text{with} \quad \beta_0 = \|b\|_2,$$

which can be solved through using the QR factorization of the bidiagonal matrix $\tilde{B}_m$. This is the basic principle for constructing the LSQR method.

The LSQR method may have better numerical property than the CG method for the normal equations, because the bidiagonal factor is formed for the Lanczos tridiagonal matrix and the QR factorization is used to solve the reduced least-squares problem, which can avoid additional difficulties if the reduced tridiagonal linear system is ill conditioned.

6.9 ▪ Exercises

6.1. Let the matrix $A \in \mathbb{C}^{n \times n}$ be nonsingular, and the vector $x_* \in \mathbb{C}^n$ be the unique solution of the linear system $Ax = b$, with $b \in \mathbb{C}^n$ being a given right-hand side vector. Prove that there exists a positive integer ℓ such that

$$x_* \in \mathcal{K}_\ell(A, b) \triangleq \mathrm{span}\{b, Ab, \ldots, A^{\ell-1}b\}.$$

(Hint: use the minimal polynomial of the matrix A; see [26].)

6.2. Prove Corollary 6.10.

6.3. Prove Lemma 6.22.

6.4. Let $x^{(k)} \in \mathbb{R}^n$ be the k-th iterate generated by the CG method, i.e., Algorithm 6.9. Show that the vector $x^{(k)}$ minimizes the norm $\|b - Ax\|_{A^{-1}}$ over the affine subspace $x^{(0)} + \mathcal{K}_k(A, r_0)$, i.e.,

$$\|b - Ax^{(k)}\|_{A^{-1}} \le \|b - Ax\|_{A^{-1}}, \quad \forall x \in x^{(0)} + \mathcal{K}_k(A, r_0).$$

6.5. Prove Proposition 6.34.

6.6. Derive the BiCG method through the LU decomposition.

6.7. Show that Algorithm 6.16 (CGLS) is equivalent to Algorithm 6.9 (CG) applied to the normal-residual equation (6.69).

6.8. Show that the m-th iterate $x^{(m)} \in \mathbb{R}^n$ generated by the CGLS method minimizes the residual norm $\|b - Ax\|_2$ over the affine subspace $x^{(0)} + \mathcal{K}_m(A^\mathsf{T}A, A^\mathsf{T}r_0)$, i.e.,

$$x^{(m)} = \underset{x \in x^{(0)} + \mathcal{K}_m(A^\mathsf{T}A, A^\mathsf{T}r_0)}{\mathrm{argmin}} \|b - Ax\|_2.$$

6.9. For a nonsingular matrix $A \in \mathbb{R}^{n \times n}$ and a given vector $b \in \mathbb{R}^n$, let $x = A^\mathsf{T}y$ and $x_* \in \mathbb{R}^n$ be the exact solution of the linear system $Ax = b$. Show that the m-th iterate $x^{(m)} \in \mathbb{R}^n$ generated by applying the CG method to the normal equation $AA^\mathsf{T}y = b$ minimizes the error norm $\|x - x_*\|_2$ over the affine subspace $x^{(0)} + \mathcal{K}_m(A^\mathsf{T}A, A^\mathsf{T}r_0)$, i.e.,

$$x^{(m)} = \underset{x \in x^{(0)} + \mathcal{K}_m(A^\mathsf{T}A, A^\mathsf{T}r_0)}{\mathrm{argmin}} \|x - x_*\|_2.$$

6.10. Show that the basis vectors v_k's, obtained by the Lanczos process applied to the saddle-point linear system (6.71) with the starting vector given by (6.72), satisfy

$$v_{2k} = \begin{bmatrix} u_k \\ 0 \end{bmatrix} \quad \text{and} \quad v_{2k+1} = \begin{bmatrix} 0 \\ w_k \end{bmatrix},$$

where $\|u_k\|_2 = \|w_k\|_2 = 1$.

6.11. For $A \in \mathbb{R}^{n \times n}$ and $b \in \mathbb{R}^n$, let $T_m \in \mathbb{R}^{m \times m}$ be the tridiagonal matrix obtained by the Lanczos process applied to the normal-residual equation $A^\mathsf{T}Ax = A^\mathsf{T}b$, and let the bidiagonal matrix $\tilde{B}_m \in \mathbb{R}^{(m+1) \times m}$ be defined in (6.73). Show that

$$T_m = \tilde{B}_m^\mathsf{T} \tilde{B}_m$$

and

$$A^\mathsf{T}AW_m = W_m T_m + \beta_m \alpha_m w_m e_{m+1}^\mathsf{T},$$

where $W_m, \beta_m, \alpha_m,$ and w_m are defined in (6.73) and (6.74), with $e_{m+1} = [0, \ldots, 0, 1]^\mathsf{T} \in \mathbb{R}^{m+1}$.

Chapter 7

Preconditioning

We consider the large sparse system of linear equations

$$Ax = b, \quad \text{with} \quad A \in \mathbb{R}^{n \times n} \quad \text{nonsingular and} \quad b \in \mathbb{R}^n. \tag{7.1}$$

Iterative methods, especially the **Krylov subspace methods**, have become the most popular and efficient methods for solving this kind of problem. However, it is known that the rates of convergence of Krylov subspace methods are strongly influenced by the spectral property of the coefficient matrix and, if the coefficient matrix is nonsymmetric, by the eigenvectors as well [8,20,26,288]. If the coefficient matrix A is ill-conditioned and/or has bad spectral property, Krylov subspace methods usually converge very slowly. Moreover, lack of robustness is a widely recognized weakness of these iterative methods. Therefore, preconditioning techniques are proposed to improve the efficiency and robustness of the **Krylov subspace iteration methods**. In fact, **preconditioning** is the most critical ingredient in the development of efficient solvers for challenging problems in scientific computing, and its importance is destined to increase even further [8,63,86,167,288,338].

In general, the term "preconditioning" refers to "the art of transforming a problem that appears intractable into another whose solution can be approximated rapidly" [317]. For Krylov subspace methods, the **preconditioner** is a matrix, an operator, or even an iteration process, that is responsible for such a transformation. For the linear system (7.1), a typical way of preconditioning is to find a **nonsingular matrix** $P \in \mathbb{R}^{n \times n}$ and rewrite this linear system into the equivalent form

$$P^{-1}Ax = P^{-1}b, \tag{7.2}$$

which is usually called the **preconditioned linear system**. The matrix P is called a **preconditioning matrix** or simply a **preconditioner** [125].

The preconditioned linear system (7.2) has the same solution as the original linear system (7.1). Therefore, instead of solving the original linear system (7.1), we turn to solve the preconditioned linear system (7.2).

The critical point in preconditioning is how to find a good or high-quality preconditioner. Usually, the preconditioning matrix P should be close to the matrix A in some sense in order to make the preconditioned linear system (7.2) easier to solve. At each step we need to compute the product of the (preconditioned) coefficient matrix with a given vector. In practical implementations, one does not actually compute the matrix P^{-1} or the matrix $P^{-1}A$ explicitly. Instead, some direct or iterative approach is employed to solve a linear system with the coefficient matrix P, in order to compute the product of the matrix P^{-1} with an arbitrary vector. Therefore, another basic requirement about the preconditioning matrix P is that it should be inexpensive to solve the linear system with respect to the matrix P. In a word, a good preconditioner P should be nonsingular, and, in addition, should possess the following characteristics:

- $P \approx A$, the **condition number** of the preconditioned matrix $P^{-1}A$ should be better than that of the matrix A;
- the **preconditioned linear system** (7.2) should be easier to solve;
- the **preconditioner** P should be inexpensive to construct and apply;
- the **preconditioned matrix** $P^{-1}A$ should be as **normal** as possible.

Roughly speaking, the closer the preconditioning matrix P is to the matrix A, the higher the rates of convergence of the corresponding preconditioned iteration methods will be. In the extreme case, if we choose $P = A$, then the preconditioned linear system becomes trivial and gives the exact solution directly. But constructing and applying such a preconditioner are equivalent to solving the original linear system. On the other hand, if we choose $P = I$, the identity matrix, then there is no cost associated with the preconditioner P, but nothing is changed. Hence, an appropriate trade-off must be found for a specific problem.

In practice, a good preconditioner P will ensure fast convergence of the corresponding preconditioned iteration method, that is, the total time for solving the preconditioned linear system (7.2) is much less than that for solving the unpreconditioned linear system (7.1). Essentially, at each step of iteration, the cost of applying the preconditioner P should be no more than the order of the cost of the unpreconditioned iteration.

There are many excellent survey papers and books for preconditioning techniques; see, for example, [63,92,338] and [86,288]. In this chapter, we will discuss some popular preconditioners for the **Krylov subspace methods**.

7.1 ▪ Preconditioned Krylov Subspace Methods

In general, there are three ways to apply a preconditioner, say, the matrix P, to the linear system (7.1).

- **Left preconditioning**: applying the preconditioner P from the left, that is,

$$P^{-1}Ax = P^{-1}b.$$

- **Right preconditioning**: applying the preconditioner P from the right, that is,

$$AP^{-1}u = b, \quad \text{with} \quad x = P^{-1}u.$$

- **Split preconditioning**: if a factorization of the preconditioner $P = P_L P_R$ is available, then we can apply the preconditioner from both sides, that is,

$$P_L^{-1}AP_R^{-1}u = P_L^{-1}b, \quad \text{with} \quad x = P_R^{-1}u.$$

The split preconditioning can be used to preserve the symmetric property when the original linear system (7.1) is symmetric.

Note that the matrices $P^{-1}A$, AP^{-1}, and $P_L^{-1}AP_R^{-1}$ are **similar** and, hence, they have the same eigenvalues but distinct eigenvector sets. If both matrices A and P are symmetric positive definite, the convergence behavior of the CG method will be the same in all three of these cases. However, in the nonnormal case, the Krylov subspace solvers, e.g., GMRES, may behave very differently as the above three preconditioned matrices have different sets of eigenvectors.

In fact, the convergence property of a **Krylov subspace iteration method** is determined not only by clustering of the eigenvalues, but also by conditioning of the eigenvectors, of the preconditioned matrix; see [20, 26, 288, 289], for instance. This is why we require that a preconditioning matrix should possess the characteristic that the corresponding preconditioned matrix should be as normal as possible. Note that the normalized eigenvectors of a normal matrix can form a unitary matrix that is, thus, of the condition number 1.

7.1.1 ▪ Preconditioned CG Method

Let the coefficient matrix $A \in \mathbb{R}^{n \times n}$ of the linear system (7.1) be **symmetric positive definite**, and assume that the preconditioner $P \in \mathbb{R}^{n \times n}$ is also symmetric positive definite.

In order to preserve the symmetry, we use **split preconditioning**. Assume

$$P = LL^{\mathsf{T}}$$

to be the **Cholesky factorization** of the preconditioning matrix P. Then we obtain the following **preconditioned linear system**

$$L^{-1}AL^{-\mathsf{T}}u = L^{-1}b, \quad \text{with} \quad x = L^{-\mathsf{T}}u. \tag{7.3}$$

Let $u^{(k)} \in \mathbb{R}^n$ be the approximate solution of the CG method for the preconditioned linear system (7.3) after k steps of iteration, and denote

$$\tilde{r}_k = L^{-1}b - L^{-1}AL^{-\mathsf{T}}u^{(k)}$$

as the **preconditioned residual vector**. Then, the CG method for the linear system in (7.3) can be described as follows:

1: Given an initial guess $x^{(0)}$
2: compute $r_0 = b - Ax^{(0)}$ and $u^{(0)} = L^{\mathsf{T}}x^{(0)}$
3: set $\tilde{r}_0 = L^{-1}r_0$ and $\tilde{p}_1 = \tilde{r}_0$
4: **for** $k = 1, 2, \ldots$, until convergence, **do**

5: $\quad \alpha_k = \dfrac{\langle \tilde{r}_{k-1}, \tilde{r}_{k-1} \rangle}{\langle L^{-1}AL^{-\mathsf{T}}\tilde{p}_k, \tilde{p}_k \rangle}$

6: $\quad u^{(k)} = u^{(k-1)} + \alpha_k \tilde{p}_k$
7: $\quad \tilde{r}_k = \tilde{r}_{k-1} - \alpha_k L^{-1}AL^{-\mathsf{T}}\tilde{p}_k$

8: $\quad \beta_k = \dfrac{\langle \tilde{r}_k, \tilde{r}_k \rangle}{\langle \tilde{r}_{k-1}, \tilde{r}_{k-1} \rangle}$

9: $\quad \tilde{p}_{k+1} = \tilde{r}_k + \beta_k \tilde{p}_k$
10: **end for**

In order to obtain the approximate solution $x^{(k)}$ and the residual $r_k = b - Ax^{(k)}$ of the original linear system (7.1), we need to reformulate this method. Let p_k be an auxiliary vector defined by

$$p_k = L^{-\mathsf{T}}\tilde{p}_k, \quad k = 1, 2, \ldots.$$

Then we have

$$p_{k+1} = L^{-\mathsf{T}}\tilde{p}_{k+1} = L^{-\mathsf{T}}(\tilde{r}_k + \beta_k \tilde{p}_k) = L^{-\mathsf{T}}\tilde{r}_k + \beta_k p_k.$$

It follows from $\tilde{r}_k = L^{-1}r_k$ that

$$r_k = L\tilde{r}_k = L(\tilde{r}_{k-1} - \alpha_k L^{-1}AL^{-\mathsf{T}}\tilde{p}_k) = r_{k-1} - \alpha_k Ap_k,$$
$$p_{k+1} = L^{-\mathsf{T}}\tilde{r}_k + \beta_k p_k = L^{-\mathsf{T}}L^{-1}r_k + \beta_k p_k = P^{-1}r_k + \beta_k p_k,$$
$$x^{(k)} = L^{-\mathsf{T}}u^{(k)} = L^{-\mathsf{T}}(u^{(k-1)} + \alpha_k\tilde{p}_k) = x^{(k-1)} + \alpha_k p_k,$$
$$\alpha_k = \frac{\langle L^{-1}r_{k-1}, L^{-1}r_{k-1}\rangle}{\langle L^{-1}AL^{-\mathsf{T}}\tilde{p}_k, \tilde{p}_k\rangle} = \frac{\langle r_{k-1}, L^{-\mathsf{T}}L^{-1}r_{k-1}\rangle}{\langle AL^{-\mathsf{T}}\tilde{p}_k, L^{-\mathsf{T}}\tilde{p}_k\rangle} = \frac{\langle r_{k-1}, P^{-1}r_{k-1}\rangle}{\langle Ap_k, p_k\rangle},$$
$$\beta_k = \frac{\langle L^{-1}r_k, L^{-1}r_k\rangle}{\langle L^{-1}r_{k-1}, L^{-1}r_{k-1}\rangle} = \frac{\langle r_k, L^{-\mathsf{T}}L^{-1}r_k\rangle}{\langle r_{k-1}, L^{-\mathsf{T}}L^{-1}r_{k-1}\rangle} = \frac{\langle r_k, P^{-1}r_k\rangle}{\langle r_{k-1}, P^{-1}r_{k-1}\rangle}.$$

Define $z_k = P^{-1}r_k$. Then we obtain the preconditioned CG method described algorithmically in the following.

Algorithm 7.1: Preconditioned Conjugate Gradient (PCG) Method

1: Given an initial guess $x^{(0)}$ and a stopping tolerance $\varepsilon > 0$
2: compute $r_0 = b - Ax^{(0)}$
3: set $z_0 = P^{-1}r_0$ and $p_1 = z_0$
4: **for** $k = 1, 2, \ldots,$ **do**
5:      $\alpha_k = \dfrac{\langle r_{k-1}, z_{k-1}\rangle}{\langle Ap_k, p_k\rangle}$
6:      $x^{(k)} = x^{(k-1)} + \alpha_k p_k$
7:      $r_k = r_{k-1} - \alpha_k Ap_k$
8:      **if** $\|r_k\|_2 < \varepsilon$, **then**
9:          stop
10:      **end if**
11:      $z_k = P^{-1}r_k$
12:      $\beta_k = \dfrac{\langle r_k, z_k\rangle}{\langle r_{k-1}, z_{k-1}\rangle}$
13:      $p_{k+1} = z_k + \beta_k p_k$
14: **end for**

Note that the matrix L does not appear in the PCG method, i.e., Algorithm 7.1. Hence, we do not need to compute explicitly the Cholesky factorization of the preconditioning matrix P.

In fact, Algorithm 7.1 can also be deduced from the **left preconditioning**. Consider the **left-preconditioned linear system**

$$P^{-1}Ax = P^{-1}b. \tag{7.4}$$

As the preconditioned matrix $P^{-1}A$ is usually not symmetric, we cannot apply the CG method directly to solve the **preconditioned linear system** (7.4). However, as the matrix P is symmetric and positive definite, we can define the P-inner product as

$$\langle x, y\rangle_P \triangleq \langle Px, y\rangle = \langle x, Py\rangle, \tag{7.5}$$

so that

$$\langle P^{-1}Ax, y\rangle_P = \langle Ax, y\rangle = \langle x, Ay\rangle = \langle x, P(P^{-1}Ay)\rangle = \langle x, P^{-1}Ay\rangle_P,$$

which indicates that the matrix $P^{-1}A$ is self-adjoint with respect to the P-inner product. Hence, we can reformulate the CG method by replacing the usual **Euclidean inner product** with the P-inner product. Denote the **preconditioned residual vector** by z_k, that is, $z_k = P^{-1}r_k$. Then, we can describe the new CG method for the left-preconditioned linear system (7.4) as follows.

Algorithm 7.2: CG Method with P-inner Product

1: Given an initial guess $x^{(0)}$ and a stopping tolerance $\varepsilon > 0$
2: compute $r_0 = b - Ax^{(0)}$
3: set $z_0 = P^{-1}r_0$ and $p_1 = z_0$
4: **for** $k = 1, 2, \ldots,$ **do**
5: $\qquad \alpha_k = \dfrac{\langle z_{k-1}, z_{k-1} \rangle_P}{\langle P^{-1}Ap_k, p_k \rangle_P} \qquad \% \; \alpha_k = \dfrac{\langle r_{k-1}, z_{k-1} \rangle}{\langle Ap_k, p_k \rangle}$
6: $\qquad x^{(k)} = x^{(k-1)} + \alpha_k p_k$
7: $\qquad r_k = r_{k-1} - \alpha_k Ap_k$
8: $\qquad$ **if** $\|r_k\|_2 < \varepsilon,$ **then**
9: $\qquad\qquad$ stop
10: $\qquad$ **end if**
11: $\qquad z_k = z_{k-1} - \alpha_k P^{-1}Ap_k \qquad \% \; z_k = P^{-1}r_k$
12: $\qquad \beta_k = \dfrac{\langle z_k, z_k \rangle_P}{\langle z_{k-1}, z_{k-1} \rangle_P} \qquad \% \; \beta_k = \dfrac{\langle r_k, z_k \rangle}{\langle r_{k-1}, z_{k-1} \rangle}$
13: $\qquad p_{k+1} = z_k + \beta_k p_k$
14: **end for**

It is clear that Algorithm 7.2 is mathematically equivalent to Algorithm 7.1, but computationally, these two algorithms may have different properties.

Analogously, we can deduce the PCG method with respect to the **right preconditioning**. Consider the **preconditioned linear system**

$$AP^{-1}y = b, \quad \text{with} \quad x = P^{-1}y. \tag{7.6}$$

Note that the preconditioned matrix AP^{-1} is not symmetric with respect to either the Euclidean inner product or the P-inner product. However, it is symmetric with respect to the P^{-1}-inner product. Hence, by replacing the Euclidean inner product by the P^{-1}-inner product, we can obtain the CG method for the **right-preconditioned linear system** (7.6). It can be shown that the CG method with respect to the P^{-1}-inner product for the right-preconditioned linear system (7.6) is mathematically equivalent to the CG method with respect to the P-inner product for the left-preconditioned linear system (7.4).

7.1.2 ▪ Preconditioned GMRES Method

For the nonsymmetric Krylov subspace methods, there are also three ways to implement a preconditioner. However, unlike the PCG method, there may be fundamental differences among these three different implementations.

Let $P \in \mathbb{R}^{n \times n}$ be a nonsingular matrix. We consider the **GMRES method** for solving the linear system (7.1) with the preconditioner P.

We first consider the **left-preconditioned linear system**

$$P^{-1}Ax = P^{-1}b. \tag{7.7}$$

By applying the GMRES method to the linear system (7.7), we obtain the **left-preconditioned GMRES method** as follows.

Algorithm 7.3: GMRES Method with Left Preconditioning

1: Given an initial guess $x^{(0)}$ and a stopping tolerance $\varepsilon > 0$
2: compute $r_0 = b - Ax^{(0)}$ and solve $P\tilde{r}_0 = r_0$ for $\tilde{r}_0$
3: set $\beta = \|\tilde{r}_0\|_2$, $\xi = \beta e_1$ and $v_1 = \tilde{r}_0/\beta$
4: **for** $j = 1, 2, \ldots,$ **do**
5:      $w = Av_j$
6:      solve $Pw_j = w$ for w_j % apply the preconditioner
7:      **for** $i = 1, 2, \ldots, j$ **do**   % Arnoldi process
8:          $h_{ij} = \langle w_j, v_i \rangle$
9:          $w_j := w_j - h_{ij}v_i$
10:      **end for**
11:      $h_{j+1,j} = \|w_j\|_2$
12:      **if** $h_{j+1,j} = 0$, **then**
13:          set $m = j$ and break
14:      **end if**
15:      $v_{j+1} = w_j/h_{j+1,j}$
16:      **for** $i = 1, 2, \ldots, j - 1$ **do**   % apply $G_{j-1}, \ldots, G_1$ to the last column of $H_{j+1,j}$
17:          $\begin{bmatrix} h_{i,j} \\ h_{i+1,j} \end{bmatrix} := \begin{bmatrix} c_i & s_i \\ -s_i & c_i \end{bmatrix} \begin{bmatrix} h_{i,j} \\ h_{i+1,j} \end{bmatrix}$
18:      **end for**
19:      **if** $|h_{j,j}| > |h_{j+1,j}|$, **then**   % form the Givens rotation G_j
20:          set $c_j = \frac{1}{\sqrt{1+\tau^2}}$, $s_j = c_j\tau$, where $\tau = \frac{h_{j+1,j}}{h_{j,j}}$
21:      **else**
22:          set $s_j = \frac{1}{\sqrt{1+\tau^2}}$, $c_j = s_j\tau$, where $\tau = \frac{h_{j,j}}{h_{j+1,j}}$
23:      **end if**
24:      $h_{j,j} := c_j h_{j,j} + s_j h_{j+1,j}$, $h_{j+1,j} := 0$ % apply G_j to the last column of $H_{j+1,j}$
25:      $\begin{bmatrix} \xi_j \\ \xi_{j+1} \end{bmatrix} := \begin{bmatrix} c_j & s_j \\ -s_j & c_j \end{bmatrix} \begin{bmatrix} \xi_j \\ 0 \end{bmatrix}$ % apply G_j to the right-hand side
26:      **if** $|\xi_{j+1}| < \varepsilon$, **then**   % check the convergence: $\|\tilde{r}\|_2 = |\xi_{j+1}|$
27:          set $m = j$ and break
28:      **end if**
29: **end for**
30: compute $\tilde{y} = R_m^{-1}\xi_m$ with $R_m = H(1 : m, 1 : m)$ being upper triangular and $\xi_m = \xi(1 : m)$
31: compute the approximate solution $x^{(m)} = x^{(0)} + V_m\tilde{y}$ with $V_m = [v_1, v_2, \ldots, v_m]$

We remark that, in the left-preconditioned GMRES method, the residual vectors obtained are the **preconditioned residuals**, i.e.,

$$\tilde{r}_k = P^{-1}(b - Ax^{(k)}),$$

instead of the original residuals $r_k = b - Ax^{(k)}$. In addition, there is no easy way to obtain the original residuals unless they are computed explicitly. Hence, it may cause difficulty if the stopping criterion is based on the norm of the original residual.

Fortunately, the **right-preconditioned GMRES method** does not have such a problem. By applying the preconditioner P from the right, we have

$$AP^{-1}u = b, \quad \text{with} \quad x = P^{-1}u. \tag{7.8}$$

Given an initial guess $x^{(0)} \in \mathbb{R}^n$, we have $u^{(0)} = Px^{(0)}$. Hence, the preconditioned initial residual vector is given by

$$\tilde{r}_0 = b - AP^{-1}u^{(0)} = b - Ax^{(0)} = r_0.$$

It is obvious that there is no need to compute the vector $u^{(0)}$. Let

$$u^{(k)} = u^{(0)} + V_k y_k$$

be the approximate solution of the preconditioned linear system (7.8) after k steps of the GMRES iteration. Then, the approximate solution $x^{(k)}$ of the original linear system (7.1) is given by

$$x^{(k)} = P^{-1}u^{(k)} = P^{-1}(u^{(0)} + V_k y_k) = x^{(0)} + P^{-1}V_k y_k.$$

As a consequence, the **right-preconditioned GMRES method** can be described as follows.

Algorithm 7.4: GMRES Method with Right Preconditioning

1: Given an initial guess $x^{(0)}$ and a stopping tolerance $\varepsilon > 0$
2: compute $r_0 = b - Ax^{(0)}$
3: set $\beta = \|r_0\|_2, \xi = \beta e_1$ and $v_1 = r_0/\beta$
4: **for** $j = 1, 2, \ldots,$ **do**
5:     solve $Pw = v_j$ for w, that is, $w = P^{-1}v_j$ % apply the preconditioner
6:     $w_j = Aw$
7:     **for** $i = 1, 2, \ldots, j$ **do**   % Arnoldi process
8:         $h_{ij} = \langle w_j, v_i \rangle$
9:         $w_j := w_j - h_{ij}v_i$
10:     **end for**
11:     $h_{j+1,j} = \|w_j\|_2$
12:     **if** $h_{j+1,j} = 0,$ **then**
13:         set $m = j$ and break
14:     **end if**
15:     $v_{j+1} = w_j/h_{j+1,j}$
16:     **for** $i = 1, 2, \ldots, j-1$ **do**   % apply $G_{j-1}, \ldots, G_1$ to the last column of $H_{j+1,j}$

17:         $\begin{bmatrix} h_{i,j} \\ h_{i+1,j} \end{bmatrix} := \begin{bmatrix} c_i & s_i \\ -s_i & c_i \end{bmatrix} \begin{bmatrix} h_{i,j} \\ h_{i+1,j} \end{bmatrix}$

18:     **end for**
19:     **if** $|h_{j,j}| > |h_{j+1,j}|,$ **then**   % form the Givens rotation G_j
20:         set $c_j = \frac{1}{\sqrt{1+\tau^2}}, s_j = c_j\tau,$ where $\tau = \frac{h_{j+1,j}}{h_{j,j}}$
21:     **else**
22:         set $s_j = \frac{1}{\sqrt{1+\tau^2}}, c_j = s_j\tau,$ where $\tau = \frac{h_{j,j}}{h_{j+1,j}}$
23:     **end if**
24:     $h_{j,j} := c_j h_{j,j} + s_j h_{j+1,j}, h_{j+1,j} := 0$ % apply G_j to the last column of $H_{j+1,j}$

25:     $\begin{bmatrix} \xi_j \\ \xi_{j+1} \end{bmatrix} := \begin{bmatrix} c_j & s_j \\ -s_j & c_j \end{bmatrix} \begin{bmatrix} \xi_j \\ 0 \end{bmatrix}$ % apply G_j to the right-hand side

26:     **if** $|\xi_{j+1}| < \varepsilon$ **then**   % check the convergence: $\|\tilde{r}\|_2 = |\xi_{j+1}|$
27:         set $m = j$ and break
28:     **end if**
29: **end for**
30: compute $\tilde{y} = R_m^{-1}\xi_m$ with $R_m = H(1:m, 1:m)$ being upper triangular and $\xi_m = \xi(1:m)$
31: compute the approximate solution $x^{(m)} = x^{(0)} + P^{-1}V_m\tilde{y}$ with $V_m = [v_1, v_2, \ldots, v_m]$

It can be shown that, in the right-preconditioned GMRES method, the **preconditioned residual vectors** are the same as the original ones, i.e.,

$$\tilde{r}_k = b - AP^{-1}u^{(k)} = b - Ax^{(k)} = r_k.$$

This is an essential difference of the right-preconditioned GMRES method from the left-preconditioned GMRES method.

If the preconditioning matrix P is in the factorized form

$$P = P_L P_R,$$

then we can apply the GMRES method to solve the **split-preconditioned linear system**

$$P_L^{-1}AP_R^{-1}u = P_L^{-1}b, \quad \text{with} \quad x = P_R^{-1}u.$$

This results in the **split-preconditioned GMRES method**, in which the preconditioned residual vectors are

$$\tilde{r}_k = P_L^{-1}(b - Ax^{(k)}).$$

We remark that the preconditioned residual vectors in the left- and in the split-preconditioned GMRES methods may cause the method to stop either prematurely or with delay, especially when the preconditioner P is very ill-conditioned. Therefore, it may be more reliable to use the right-preconditioned GMRES method.

There is an interesting relationship between the approximate solutions obtained by the left- and the right-preconditioned GMRES methods. Let $x^{(0)}$ be the initial guess, and $x_L^{(k)}$ and $x_R^{(k)}$ be the approximate solutions obtained by applying the GMRES method to the left-preconditioned linear system (7.7) and to the right-preconditioned linear system (7.8), respectively. Then, according to the **optimality property** of GMRES, we have

$$x_L^{(k)} = \operatorname*{argmin}_{x \in x^{(0)} + \mathcal{K}_k(P^{-1}A, P^{-1}r_0)} \|P^{-1}(b - Ax)\|_2 \tag{7.9}$$

and $x_R^{(k)} = P^{-1}u^{(k)}$, where

$$u^{(k)} = \operatorname*{argmin}_{u \in u^{(0)} + \mathcal{K}_k(AP^{-1}, r_0)} \|b - AP^{-1}u\|_2.$$

By making use of the transformation $x = P^{-1}u$, we have

$$x_R^{(k)} = \operatorname*{argmin}_{x \in x^{(0)} + P^{-1}\mathcal{K}_k(AP^{-1}, r_0)} \|b - Ax\|_2. \tag{7.10}$$

Note that

$$
\begin{aligned}
P^{-1}\mathcal{K}_k(AP^{-1}, r_0) &= P^{-1}\operatorname{span}\{r_0, AP^{-1}r_0, (AP^{-1})^2 r_0, \ldots, (AP^{-1})^{k-1}r_0\} \\
&= \operatorname{span}\{P^{-1}r_0, P^{-1}AP^{-1}r_0, P^{-1}(AP^{-1})^2 r_0, \ldots, P^{-1}(AP^{-1})^{k-1}r_0\} \\
&= \operatorname{span}\{P^{-1}r_0, (P^{-1}A)P^{-1}r_0, (P^{-1}A)^2 P^{-1}r_0, \ldots, (P^{-1}A)^{k-1}P^{-1}r_0\} \\
&= \mathcal{K}_k(P^{-1}A, P^{-1}r_0).
\end{aligned}
$$

It then follows from (7.9) and (7.10) that both $x_L^{(k)}$ and $x_R^{(k)}$ are in the same shifted **Krylov subspace**. The only difference is that $x_L^{(k)}$ minimizes the norm of the preconditioned residual, while $x_R^{(k)}$ minimizes the norm of the original residual, both over the same affine subspace.

Theorem 7.1. *Let $x_L^{(k)}$ and $x_R^{(k)}$ be the approximate solutions for the linear system (7.1) obtained by the left- and the right-preconditioned GMRES methods, respectively, with the same initial guess $x^{(0)}$. Then $x_L^{(k)}$ minimizes $\|P^{-1}(b - Ax)\|_2$ over the affine subspace $x^{(0)} + \mathcal{K}_k(P^{-1}A, P^{-1}r_0)$ and $x_R^{(k)}$ minimizes $\|b - Ax\|_2$ over the same affine subspace.*

7.1.3 ▪ Flexible GMRES Method

In the previous discussion, we assumed that the preconditioner P is fixed in the whole iteration procedure. However, in some cases, we can allow the preconditioner to vary from step to step, which may result in a better performance of the corresponding preconditioned Krylov subspace iteration method. These cases may happen when, for example, the preconditioner is defined through another iteration process.

In the following, we introduce the flexible right-preconditioned GMRES method, which is proposed by Saad [286].

We observe that in the right-preconditioned GMRES method (i.e., Algorithm 7.4), the approximate solution is of the form

$$
x^{(m)} = x^{(0)} + P^{-1}V_m \tilde{y} = x^{(0)} + \sum_{j=1}^{m}(P^{-1}v_j)\tilde{y}_j, \tag{7.11}
$$

which indicates that the vector $x^{(m)} - x^{(0)}$ is a **linear combination** of the vectors $P^{-1}v_j$, $j = 1, 2, \ldots, m$. These vectors are computed in line 5 in Algorithm 7.4, and are not necessary to be saved, because they are obtained by applying the same preconditioner P to the vectors v_j's. As a result, we only need to apply the matrix P^{-1} to the linear combination $\sum_{j=1}^{m} \tilde{y}_j v_j$ of the vectors v_j's, that is, the vector $V_m \tilde{y}$, to obtain the approximate solution $x^{(m)}$. Suppose now that the preconditioner varies at each step. Then, in Algorithm 7.4, line 5 can be replaced by

---

5': solve $P_j w = v_j$ for w, that is, $w = P_j^{-1} v_j$

Therefore, it is natural to compute the approximate solution in the following form:

$$
x^{(m)} = x^{(0)} + \sum_{j=1}^{m}(P_j^{-1}v_j)\tilde{y}_j = x^{(0)} + Z_m \tilde{y},
$$

where

$$Z_m = [z_1, z_2, \ldots, z_m], \quad \text{with} \quad z_j = P_j^{-1} v_j,$$

and the vector $\tilde{y}$ is computed as before. Note that now we need to save all the vectors

$$z_j = P_j^{-1} v_j, \quad j = 1, 2, \ldots, m.$$

This is the main difference between the **flexible GMRES** (FGMRES) method and the right-preconditioned GMRES method.

The flexible GMRES method can be described algorithmically as follows.

Algorithm 7.5: Flexible GMRES (FGMRES) Method

1: Given an initial guess $x^{(0)}$ and a stopping tolerance $\varepsilon > 0$
2: compute $r_0 = b - Ax^{(0)}$
3: set $\beta = \|r_0\|_2$, $\xi = \beta e_1$ and $v_1 = r_0/\beta$
4: **for** $j = 1, 2, \ldots,$ **do**
5:      solve $P_j z_j = v_j$ for z_j, that is, $z_j = P_j^{-1} v_j$ % apply the preconditioner
6:      $w_j = Az_j$
7:      **for** $i = 1, 2, \ldots, j$ **do**   % Arnoldi process
8:          $h_{ij} = \langle w_j, v_i \rangle$
9:          $w_j := w_j - h_{ij} v_i$
10:      **end for**
11:      $h_{j+1,j} = \|w_j\|_2$
12:      **if** $h_{j+1,j} = 0$, **then**
13:          set $m = j$ and break
14:      **end if**
15:      $v_{j+1} = w_j/h_{j+1,j}$
16:      **for** $i = 1, 2, \ldots, j-1$ **do**   % apply $G_{j-1}, \ldots, G_1$ to the last column of $H_{j+1,j}$
17:          $\begin{bmatrix} h_{i,j} \\ h_{i+1,j} \end{bmatrix} := \begin{bmatrix} c_i & s_i \\ -s_i & c_i \end{bmatrix} \begin{bmatrix} h_{i,j} \\ h_{i+1,j} \end{bmatrix}$
18:      **end for**
19:      **if** $|h_{j,j}| > |h_{j+1,j}|$, **then**   % form the Givens rotation G_j
20:          set $c_j = \frac{1}{\sqrt{1+\tau^2}}$, $s_j = c_j \tau$, where $\tau = \frac{h_{j+1,j}}{h_{j,j}}$
21:      **else**
22:          set $s_j = \frac{1}{\sqrt{1+\tau^2}}$, $c_j = s_j \tau$, where $\tau = \frac{h_{j,j}}{h_{j+1,j}}$
23:      **end if**
24:      $h_{j,j} := c_j h_{j,j} + s_j h_{j+1,j}$, $h_{j+1,j} := 0$ % apply G_j to the last column of $H_{j+1,j}$
25:      $\begin{bmatrix} \xi_j \\ \xi_{j+1} \end{bmatrix} := \begin{bmatrix} c_j & s_j \\ -s_j & c_j \end{bmatrix} \begin{bmatrix} \xi_j \\ 0 \end{bmatrix}$ % apply G_j to the right-hand side
26:      **if** $|\xi_{j+1}| < \varepsilon$, **then**   % check the convergence: $\|\tilde{r}\|_2 = |\xi_{j+1}|$
27:          set $m = j$ and break
28:      **end if**
29: **end for**
30: compute $\tilde{y} = R_m^{-1} \xi_m$ with $R_m = H(1:m, 1:m)$ being upper triangular and $\xi_m = \xi(1:m)$
31: compute the approximate solution $x^{(m)} = x^{(0)} + Z_m \tilde{y}$

As can be seen, the **FGMRES** method differs from the right-preconditioned GMRES method (Algorithm 7.4) only in lines 5, 6, and 31. We remark that the vectors z_j's in line 5 are used to form the solution subspace. These vectors can be defined quite freely, even without reference to any preconditioner, provided they are linearly independent. This makes the FGMRES method much more flexible. For example, any iterative procedure terminated within any numbers of iteration steps can be employed as preconditioners to compute these vectors. However, this added flexibility may cause the method some problems. Indeed, if the vector z_j is poorly selected, a **breakdown** may occur in the iteration process of the FGMRES method.

It is expected that the FGMRES method may have some **optimality property** as that possessed by the standard right-preconditioned GMRES method, that is, the approximate solution obtained by FGMRES may minimize the norm of the residual over some affine subspace.

In the right-preconditioned GMRES method, we have the following relationship:

$$AP^{-1}V_m = V_{m+1}H_{m+1,m}.$$

But it does not hold for the FGMRES method, as in which the preconditioner is not fixed. However, the following relationship holds for the FGMRES method:

$$AZ_m = V_{m+1}H_{m+1,m} = V_m H_m + h_{m+1,m}v_{m+1}\, e_m^\mathsf{T}, \tag{7.12}$$

where $e_m = [0, \ldots, 0, 1]^\mathsf{T} \in \mathbb{R}^m$. It follows from (7.11) that the approximate solution $x^{(m)}$ is in the affine subspace $x^{(0)} + \mathrm{span}(Z_m)$, where

$$\mathrm{span}(Z_m) := \mathrm{span}\{z_1, z_2, \ldots, z_m\}.$$

Let

$$x = x^{(0)} + Z_m y$$

be an arbitrary vector in $x^{(0)} + \mathrm{span}(Z_m)$. Then, the **residual vector** can be written as

$$\begin{aligned}
b - Ax &= b - Ax^{(0)} - AZ_m y \\
&= r_0 - AZ_m y \\
&= \beta v_1 - V_{m+1}H_{m+1,m}\, y \\
&= V_{m+1}(\beta e_1 - H_{m+1,m}\, y),
\end{aligned}$$

where $e_1 = [1, 0, \ldots, 0]^\mathsf{T} \in \mathbb{R}^{m+1}$. Since the matrix V_{m+1} is column orthonormal, it holds that

$$\|b - Ax\|_2 = \|V_{m+1}(\beta e_1 - H_{m+1,m}\, y)\|_2 = \|\beta e_1 - H_{m+1,m}\, y\|_2.$$

As the vector $\tilde{y} \in \mathbb{R}^m$ is the solution of the **least-squares problem**

$$\min_{y \in \mathbb{R}^m} \|\beta e_1 - H_{m+1,m}\, y\|_2,$$

the approximate solution $x^{(m)} = x^{(0)} + Z_m \tilde{y}$ minimizes the residual norm. Hence, we have the following **optimality property** for the FGMRES method.

Theorem 7.2. *Let $x^{(m)} \in \mathbb{R}^n$ be the approximate solution for the linear system (7.1) obtained by the FGMRES method (i.e., Algorithm 7.5). Then*

$$x^{(m)} = \underset{x \in x^{(0)} + \mathrm{span}(Z_m)}{\mathrm{argmin}} \|b - Ax\|_2.$$

The FGMRES method may break down if $h_{j+1,j} = 0$; see line 12 in Algorithm 7.5. This is a **lucky breakdown** for the standard GMRES method, as when this happens the approximate solution is actually the exact one. For the FGMRES method, this still holds true, provided that the matrix H_j is nonsingular.

Theorem 7.3. *Suppose that $r_0 \neq 0$, and $h_{i+1,i} \neq 0$ for $i < j$. If the matrix H_j is nonsingular, then the vector $x^{(j)}$ is the exact solution of the linear system (7.1) if and only if $h_{j+1,j} = 0$.*

Proof. Suppose that $h_{j+1,j} = 0$ and $h_{i+1,i} \neq 0$ for $i < j$. Then, it follows from (7.12) that $AZ_j = V_j H_j$. For any vector

$$x = x^{(0)} + Z_j y \in x^{(0)} + \mathrm{span}(Z_j),$$

we have

$$\|b - Ax\|_2 = \|r_0 - AZ_j y\|_2 = \|\beta v_1 - V_j H_j y\|_2 = \|\beta e_1 - H_j y\|_2,$$

where $e_1 = [1, 0, \ldots, 0]^{\mathsf{T}} \in \mathbb{R}^j$. If the matrix H_j is invertible, then the solution of the least-squares problem

$$\min_{y \in \mathbb{R}^j} \|b - A(x^{(0)} + Z_j y)\|_2 = \min_{y \in \mathbb{R}^j} \|\beta e_1 - H_j y\|_2$$

is given by

$$\tilde{y} = \beta H_j^{-1} e_1.$$

Thus, the approximate solution is

$$x^{(j)} = x^{(0)} + Z_j \tilde{y},$$

and the norm of the residual is

$$\|b - Ax^{(j)}\|_2 = \|\beta e_1 - H_j \tilde{y}\|_2 = 0,$$

which indicates that the vector $x^{(j)}$ is the exact solution of the linear system (7.1).

Conversely, let

$$x^{(j)} = x^{(0)} + Z_m \tilde{y}$$

be the exact solution of the linear system (7.1). Then

$$0 = b - Ax^{(j)} = V_{j+1}(\beta e_1 - H_{j+1,j}\, \tilde{y}). \tag{7.13}$$

Assume that $h_{j+1,j} \neq 0$. Then $v_{j+1} \neq 0$ and the matrix V_{j+1} is column orthonormal, which, together with (7.13), implies

$$\beta e_1 - H_{j+1,j}\, \tilde{y} = 0.$$

Note that $H_{j+1,j} \in \mathbb{R}^{(j+1) \times j}$ is an upper Hessenberg matrix, and $h_{i+1,i} \neq 0$ for $i \leq j$. By a simple backward substitution we can easily obtain $\tilde{y} = 0$ and, hence, $\beta = 0$, which contradicts with the condition $\beta = \|r_0\|_2 \neq 0$. Therefore, $h_{j+1,j} = 0$. $\qquad\square$

We remark that if the matrix Z_j is of full rank, then by (7.12) the matrix H_j is nonsingular. For the right-preconditioned GMRES method with a fixed preconditioner P, we have $Z_j = P^{-1} V_j$, which implies that the matrix Z_j is of full rank and, hence, the nonsingularity of the matrix H_j is guaranteed automatically.

As the preconditioner varies step by step, the subspace in FGMRES is no longer a standard Krylov subspace. Thus, the general convergence results are not easily obtainable. In some specific situations, FGMRES is guaranteed to converge independently of the dimension m of the subspace; see [288].

7.1.4 · Restrictively Preconditioned CG Method

When the coefficient matrix is nonsymmetric or indefinite, in a different approach, by first transforming the original linear system (7.1) into a symmetric positive definite form, and then solving the obtained linear system by the classical preconditioned **conjugate gradient method**, Bai and Li in [42] presented a *restrictively preconditioned conjugate gradient* (RPCG) method for the linear system that is of intrinsic symmetric positive definiteness in certain sense. This method has wide generality, because it covers many known Krylov subspace iteration methods such as the conjugate gradient method, the conjugate residual method, CGNR (or CGLS), CGNE, and their preconditioned variants.

Let $A = PHQ$, where $H \in \mathbb{R}^{n \times n}$ is a symmetric positive definite matrix, and $P \in \mathbb{R}^{n \times n}$ and $Q \in \mathbb{R}^{n \times n}$ are nonsingular matrices. Denote by $W = Q^{-1}P^{\mathsf{T}}$. Assume that $M = PGQ$ is a preconditioner to the matrix $A \in \mathbb{R}^{n \times n}$, with the matrix $G \in \mathbb{R}^{n \times n}$ being symmetric positive definite. Because $G \in \mathbb{R}^{n \times n}$ is a symmetric positive definite matrix, there exists a nonsingular matrix $S \in \mathbb{R}^{n \times n}$ such that $G = S^{\mathsf{T}}S$. In addition, if we let

$$\mathbf{x} = (SQ)x \quad \text{and} \quad \mathbf{b} = (PS^{\mathsf{T}})^{-1}b,$$

then the linear system (7.1) can be equivalently written as

$$\mathbf{R}\mathbf{x} = \mathbf{b}, \quad \text{where} \quad \mathbf{R} = (PS^{\mathsf{T}})^{-1}A(SQ)^{-1}. \tag{7.14}$$

Evidently, the matrix

$$\mathbf{R} = (PS^{\mathsf{T}})^{-1}A(SQ)^{-1} = S^{-\mathsf{T}}HS^{-1}$$

is symmetric positive definite. We can solve the linear system (7.1) iteratively through solving the transformed linear system (7.14) by the CG method. The resulted method is called the **restrictively preconditioned conjugate gradient method**, because its preconditioner sufficiently employs the structure of the original matrix by keeping the same restrictive matrices P and Q but only approximating the kernel matrix H by the matrix G. We give the precise description of the **RPCG** method as follows.

Algorithm 7.6: CG Method for the Linear System $\mathbf{R}\mathbf{x} = \mathbf{b}$

1: Choose an initial guess $\mathbf{x}^{(0)} \in \mathbb{R}^n$
2: compute $\mathbf{r}_0 = \mathbf{b} - \mathbf{R}\mathbf{x}^{(0)}$ and set $\mathbf{p}_0 = \mathbf{r}_0$
3: **for** $k = 0, 1, 2, \ldots$, until convergence **do**

4: $\qquad \alpha_k = -\dfrac{\mathbf{r}_k^{\mathsf{T}}\mathbf{r}_k}{\mathbf{p}_k^{\mathsf{T}}\mathbf{R}\mathbf{p}_k}$

5: $\qquad \mathbf{x}^{(k+1)} = \mathbf{x}^{(k)} - \alpha_k \mathbf{p}_k$
6: $\qquad \mathbf{r}_{k+1} = \mathbf{r}_k + \alpha_k \mathbf{R}\mathbf{p}_k$

7: $\qquad \beta_k = \dfrac{\mathbf{r}_{k+1}^{\mathsf{T}}\mathbf{r}_{k+1}}{\mathbf{r}_k^{\mathsf{T}}\mathbf{r}_k}$

8: $\qquad \mathbf{p}_{k+1} = \mathbf{r}_{k+1} + \beta_k \mathbf{p}_k$
9: **end for**

Algorithm 7.6 can be reformulated by information with respect to the original linear system (7.1).

For a given starting vector $x^{(0)} \in \mathbb{R}^n$, let

$$r_0 = b - Ax^{(0)}, \quad z_0 = M^{-1}r_0, \quad p_0 = z_0, \quad v_0 = W^{-1}z_0, \quad \text{and} \quad q_0 = v_0,$$

and define

$$\begin{cases} x^{(k)} = (SQ)^{-1}\mathbf{x}^{(k)}, & r_k = (PS^\mathsf{T})\mathbf{r}_k, & z_k = (SQ)^{-1}\mathbf{r}_k, \\ p_k = (SQ)^{-1}\mathbf{p}_k, & v_k = W^{-1}z_k, & q_k = W^{-1}p_k. \end{cases} \tag{7.15}$$

Then it holds that

$$\mathbf{r}_0 = \mathbf{b} - \mathbf{R}\mathbf{x}^{(0)} = (PS^\mathsf{T})^{-1}(b - Ax^{(0)}) = (PS^\mathsf{T})^{-1}r_0 \tag{7.16}$$

and

$$r_k = (PS^\mathsf{T})\mathbf{r}_k = (PS^\mathsf{T})(SQ)z_k = Mz_k. \tag{7.17}$$

Moreover, because

$$\mathbf{r}_k^\mathsf{T}\mathbf{r}_k = (SQz_k)^\mathsf{T}(SQz_k) = z_k^\mathsf{T}Q^\mathsf{T}P^{-1}Mz_k = v_k^\mathsf{T}r_k$$

and

$$\mathbf{p}_k^\mathsf{T}\mathbf{R}\mathbf{p}_k = (SQp_k)^\mathsf{T}(PS^\mathsf{T})^{-1}A(SQ)^{-1}(SQp_k) = p_k^\mathsf{T}Q^\mathsf{T}P^{-1}Ap_k = q_k^\mathsf{T}Ap_k,$$

we obtain

$$\alpha_k = -\frac{\mathbf{r}_k^\mathsf{T}\mathbf{r}_k}{\mathbf{p}_k^\mathsf{T}\mathbf{R}\mathbf{p}_k} = -\frac{v_k^\mathsf{T}r_k}{q_k^\mathsf{T}Ap_k} \tag{7.18}$$

and

$$\beta_k = \frac{\mathbf{r}_{k+1}^\mathsf{T}\mathbf{r}_{k+1}}{\mathbf{r}_k^\mathsf{T}\mathbf{r}_k} = \frac{v_{k+1}^\mathsf{T}r_{k+1}}{v_k^\mathsf{T}r_k}. \tag{7.19}$$

In addition, it straightforwardly follows from (7.15) and (7.17) that the relations

$$\begin{cases} x^{(k+1)} = x^{(k)} - \alpha_k p_k, \\ r_{k+1} = r_k + \alpha_k Ap_k, \\ p_{k+1} = z_{k+1} + \beta_k p_k, \\ q_{k+1} = v_{k+1} + \beta_k q_k \end{cases} \tag{7.20}$$

hold true. By rearranging (7.15)–(7.16) and (7.18)–(7.20), we then obtain the following algorithmic description of the **RPCG** method.

Algorithm 7.7: RPCG Method for the Linear System $Ax = b$

1: Choose $x^{(0)} \in \mathbb{R}^n$, compute $r_0 = b - Ax^{(0)}$
2: solve $Mz_0 = r_0$, and set $p_0 = z_0$
3: solve $Wv_0 = z_0$, and set $q_0 = v_0$
4: **for** $k = 0, 1, 2, \ldots,$ **do**
5: $\quad \alpha_k = -\dfrac{v_k^\mathsf{T}r_k}{q_k^\mathsf{T}Ap_k}$
6: $\quad x^{(k+1)} = x^{(k)} - \alpha_k p_k$
7: $\quad r_{k+1} = r_k + \alpha_k Ap_k$
8: $\quad$ solve $Mz_{k+1} = r_{k+1}$

9:     solve $Wv_{k+1} = z_{k+1}$

10:    $\beta_k = \dfrac{v_{k+1}^\mathsf{T} r_{k+1}}{v_k^\mathsf{T} r_k}$

11:    $p_{k+1} = z_{k+1} + \beta_k p_k$
12:    $q_{k+1} = v_{k+1} + \beta_k q_k$
13: **end for**

In Algorithm 7.7, $W = Q^{-1}P^\mathsf{T}$ is an auxiliary matrix, $P, Q \in \mathbb{R}^{n \times n}$ are two nonsingular matrices such that $A = PHQ$ with $H \in \mathbb{R}^{n \times n}$ being symmetric positive definite, and $M = PGQ$ is the preconditioner to the matrix A with the matrix G being a symmetric positive definite approximation to the matrix H.

We remark that when $M = I$, the identity matrix, the RPCG method naturally leads to its no-preconditioned version, called as the ***restrictive conjugate gradient*** (RCG) method. Moreover, both RCG and RPCG methods are applicable to linear systems which may have a nonsymmetric and nonsingular coefficient matrix, provided this matrix is isomorphic to a symmetric positive definite matrix.

In actual applications, we should suitably choose the transformation matrices P and Q, and the preconditioning matrix M, such that both linear systems $Mz = r$ and $Wv = z$ are cheaply solvable. Of course, the preconditioner M must have a remarkable effect on improving the spectral property of the coefficient matrix A in the sense that the condition number of the preconditioned matrix $M^{-1}A$, say $\kappa(M^{-1}A)$, is much less than that of the original matrix A. Moreover, the RPCG method covers many known Krylov subspace methods for solving the linear system (7.1). For example,

(a) when $A \in \mathbb{R}^{n \times n}$ is a symmetric positive definite matrix, $W = I$, and $M \in \mathbb{R}^{n \times n}$ is a symmetric positive definite preconditioner to the matrix A, the RPCG method reduces to the *preconditioned conjugate gradient* (PCG) method [167, 195, 240];

(b) when $A \in \mathbb{R}^{n \times n}$ is a symmetric and nonsingular matrix, $W = A^{-1}$, and $M \in \mathbb{R}^{n \times n}$ is a symmetric and nonsingular preconditioner to the matrix A, the RPCG method reduces to the *preconditioned conjugate residual* (PCR) method [167, 288];

(c) when $A \in \mathbb{R}^{n \times n}$ is a nonsingular matrix, $P = A^{-\mathsf{T}}$, $Q = I$, and $G \in \mathbb{R}^{n \times n}$ is a symmetric positive definite preconditioner to the matrix $A^\mathsf{T}A$, the RPCG method reduces to the left-preconditioned CGNR (or CGLS) method [167, 288];

(d) when $A \in \mathbb{R}^{n \times n}$ is a nonsingular matrix, $P = I$, $Q = A^{-\mathsf{T}}$, and $G \in \mathbb{R}^{n \times n}$ is a symmetric positive definite preconditioner to the matrix AA^T, the RPCG method reduces to the left-preconditioned CGNE method [167, 288].

According to the convergence of the RPCG method, by making use of the standard convergence theorem about the CG method [167, 288] we can obtain the following result.

Theorem 7.4. *Let $A \in \mathbb{R}^{n \times n}$ be a nonsingular matrix, and there exist two nonsingular matrices $P \in \mathbb{R}^{n \times n}$ and $Q \in \mathbb{R}^{n \times n}$ such that $A = PHQ$, with $H \in \mathbb{R}^{n \times n}$ a symmetric positive definite matrix. Let $M = PGQ$, where $G \in \mathbb{R}^{n \times n}$ is a symmetric positive definite matrix. If the RPCG method is started from an initial vector $x^{(0)} \in \mathbb{R}^n$, then after k steps of iteration, it generates an approximation $x^{(k)} \in \mathbb{R}^n$ to the solution x_* of the linear system (7.1), which satisfies*

$$\|x^{(k)} - x_*\|_{W^{-\mathsf{T}}A} \leq 2\left(\frac{\sqrt{\kappa(M^{-1}A)} - 1}{\sqrt{\kappa(M^{-1}A)} + 1}\right)^k \|x^{(0)} - x_*\|_{W^{-\mathsf{T}}A},$$

where $\kappa(M^{-1}A) = \frac{\lambda_{\max}(M^{-1}A)}{\lambda_{\min}(M^{-1}A)}$ with $\lambda_{\min}(M^{-1}A)$ and $\lambda_{\max}(M^{-1}A)$ representing the smallest and largest eigenvalues of the matrix $M^{-1}A$, and for any $x \in \mathbb{R}^n$ and any symmetric positive definite matrix $X \in \mathbb{R}^{n \times n}$, the weighted norm $\| \cdot \|_X$ is defined as

$$\|x\|_X = \sqrt{\langle x, Xx \rangle} = \sqrt{x^{\mathsf{T}} X x}.$$

Proof. Because

$$W^{-\mathsf{T}}A = (Q^{\mathsf{T}}P^{-1})(PHQ) = Q^{\mathsf{T}}HQ,$$

$Q \in \mathbb{R}^{n \times n}$ is nonsingular, and $H \in \mathbb{R}^{n \times n}$ is symmetric positive definite, we know that $W^{-\mathsf{T}}A$ is a symmetric positive definite matrix. From $G = S^{\mathsf{T}}S$, with $S \in \mathbb{R}^{n \times n}$ a nonsingular matrix, it follows that

$$\begin{aligned} M^{-1}A &= (PGQ)^{-1}(PHQ) = Q^{-1}G^{-1}HQ \\ &= (SQ)^{-1}(S^{-\mathsf{T}}HS^{-1})(SQ) = (SQ)^{-1}\mathbf{R}(SQ). \end{aligned}$$

Therefore, $\kappa(M^{-1}A) = \kappa(\mathbf{R})$. In addition, for $x, \mathbf{x} \in \mathbb{R}^n$ satisfying $\mathbf{x} = (SQ)x$, we have

$$\begin{aligned} \|\mathbf{x}\|_{\mathbf{R}}^2 &= \langle \mathbf{x}, \mathbf{R}\mathbf{x} \rangle = \langle (SQ)x, ((PS^{\mathsf{T}})^{-1}A(SQ)^{-1})(SQ)x \rangle \\ &= \langle (SQ)x, (PS^{\mathsf{T}})^{-1}Ax \rangle = x^{\mathsf{T}}W^{-\mathsf{T}}Ax = \|x\|_{W^{-\mathsf{T}}A}^2. \end{aligned}$$

Now, the conclusion of this theorem follows straightforwardly from the standard convergence theorem of the classical CG method applied to the linear system (7.14), that is, the linear system $\mathbf{R}\mathbf{x} = \mathbf{b}$; see [167, 288]. $\quad \square$

Alternatively, we note that for $W = Q^{-1}P^{\mathsf{T}}$, $A = PHQ$, and $M = PGQ$, both matrices

$$\tilde{A} := AW = (PHQ)(Q^{-1}P^{\mathsf{T}}) = PHP^{\mathsf{T}}$$

and

$$\tilde{M} := MW = (PGQ)(Q^{-1}P^{\mathsf{T}}) = PGP^{\mathsf{T}}$$

are symmetric positive definite, and the linear system (7.1) is equivalent to the linear system

$$\tilde{A}y = b, \quad \text{where} \quad x = Wy. \tag{7.21}$$

By straightforwardly applying PCG with the preconditioner $\tilde{M}$ to the linear system (7.21), we can also obtain Algorithm 7.7. It then follows that, basically, we have two ways to compute the final approximation $\hat{x}$ to the solution x_* of the linear system $Ax = b$ in (7.1): one is computing an approximation to the solution vector x_* by successively computing the iteration sequence $\{x^{(k)}\}_{k=0}^{\infty}$ by using RPCG, without explicitly forming the iterates with respect to the variable y; another is first computing a final approximation $\hat{y}$ to the solution y_* of the linear system (7.21) by directly applying PCG with the preconditioner $\tilde{M}$, and then recovering an approximation $\hat{x}$ to the solution vector x_* from $\hat{x} = W\hat{y}$. These two implementation ways are mathematically equivalent, but, numerically, may be quite different, due to **round-off errors**.

However, in general, we realize that for two given n-by-n matrices A and M, to find a nonsingular matrix $W \in \mathbb{R}^{n \times n}$ such that both matrices AW and MW are symmetric positive definite is much more difficult in practical implementations than to find two nonsingular matrices $P \in \mathbb{R}^{n \times n}$ and $Q \in \mathbb{R}^{n \times n}$ such that $A = PHQ$ with the matrix $H \in \mathbb{R}^{n \times n}$ being symmetric positive definite, and then construct $M = PGQ$ with the matrix $G \in \mathbb{R}^{n \times n}$ being an approximation to the matrix $H \in \mathbb{R}^{n \times n}$.

7.2 ▪ Preconditioners Based on Matrix Splittings

The critical point in preconditioning is, of course, how to find a good preconditioner. However, it is widely recognized that preconditioners are strongly problem-dependent, and an optimal general-purpose preconditioner is unlikely to exist. Theoretical results are rare, and many somewhat "empirical" preconditioners work surprisingly well despite the lack of a rigorous theoretical foundation. This is why Saad emphasized in his book [288] that "*finding a good preconditioner to solve a given sparse linear system is often viewed as a combination of art and science.*"

In general, there are two major classes of preconditioners:

(a) general-purpose preconditioners (or algebraic preconditioners), which only use the information of the coefficient matrix, and

(b) problem-specific preconditioners, which can be derived from the knowledge of the original physical problems from which the linear system arises.

The problem-specific preconditioners usually have significant good performance, but they require a complete knowledge of the original physical problem, and they are generally very sensitive to the information in hand. Thus, they may not always be feasible. Among the widely used problem-specific preconditioners, the multigrid and the domain decomposition techniques have received extensive investigations and achieved great success in some application areas; see [77, 78, 238, 277, 292, 311, 316, 318, 332].

In this chapter, we will focus on the algebraic preconditioners, that is, the preconditioning techniques that are based on the coefficient matrix and can be applied to general large sparse linear systems.

Consider the linear system (7.1) again. As discussed in Chapter 5, if the coefficient matrix $A \in \mathbb{R}^{n \times n}$ is split into

$$A = P - N, \tag{7.22}$$

where $P \in \mathbb{R}^{n \times n}$ is nonsingular, then we can define an iterative scheme as

$$\begin{aligned} x^{(k+1)} &= P^{-1} N x^{(k)} + P^{-1} b \\ &= (I - P^{-1} A) x^{(k)} + P^{-1} b \\ &= x^{(k)} + P^{-1}(b - A x^{(k)}), \quad k = 0, 1, 2, \dots. \end{aligned}$$

This is equivalent to solve the linear system

$$P^{-1} A x = P^{-1} b, \tag{7.23}$$

which is the **preconditioned linear system** associated with the **matrix splitting** (7.22). If the Krylov subspace methods are employed to solve the preconditioned linear system (7.23), then we can obtain the preconditioned versions of the Krylov subspace methods.

In theory, any matrix splitting can lead to a preconditioner. However, to be a good preconditioner, the matrix P should be close to the matrix A in some sense, at least the corresponding matrix splitting in (7.22) should be a convergent splitting.

In Chapter 5, we introduced the classical iterative methods including Jacobi, Gauss–Seidel, SOR, SSOR, and HSS-type iterations.

The preconditioner corresponding to the **Jacobi iteration** is

$$P_{\text{J}} = D,$$

which is simply the diagonal part of the matrix A. Applying the Jacobi preconditioner P_{J} to the original linear system from the left is equivalent to scaling all rows of the matrix A to make its diagonal entries equal to 1. This is also known as the **diagonal scaling**.

The preconditioner corresponding to the **Gauss–Seidel iteration** is

$$P_{\mathrm{GS}} = D - L,$$

which is the lower-triangular part of the matrix A.

For the **SOR iteration**, the corresponding preconditioner

$$P_{\mathrm{SOR}} = D - \omega L$$

is also a lower-triangular matrix. Clearly, both preconditioners P_{GS} and P_{SOR}, called the Gauss–Seidel and SOR preconditioners, respectively, are easily applicable.

If the matrix A is symmetric, we may expect that the preconditioner is also symmetric. Note that the **SSOR preconditioner** is defined as

$$P_{\mathrm{SSOR}} = (D - \omega L)D^{-1}(D - \omega U),$$

which is symmetric if the matrix A is, as when it holds that $U = L^{\mathsf{T}}$. In practice, it is not necessary to choose the parameter ω carefully. By taking $\omega = 1$, we obtain the **SGS preconditioner**

$$P_{\mathrm{SGS}} = (D - L)D^{-1}(D - U) = \tilde{L}\tilde{U}, \tag{7.24}$$

where

$$\tilde{L} \triangleq (D - L)D^{-1} = I - LD^{-1}$$

is a unit lower-triangular matrix and

$$\tilde{U} \triangleq D - U$$

is an upper-triangular matrix. This indicates that (7.24) is an **LU factorization** of the SGS preconditioning matrix P_{SGS}. Furthermore, the triangular matrices $\tilde{L}$ and $\tilde{U}$ have the same **sparsity pattern** as the lower- and upper-triangular parts of the matrix A, respectively. That is to say, $\tilde{L}(i,j) \neq 0$ if and only if $A(i,j) \neq 0$ for $i \geq j$, and $\tilde{U}(i,j) \neq 0$ if and only if $A(i,j) \neq 0$ for $i \leq j$.

In order to measure the **approximate degree** of the preconditioning matrix P to the original coefficient matrix A, we define the **error matrix**

$$E \triangleq P - A.$$

For SGS preconditioner, it holds that

$$E = P_{\mathrm{SGS}} - A = (D - L)D^{-1}(D - U) - (D - L - U) = LD^{-1}U.$$

To achieve a better performance, we may expect that the error matrix E is small in certain sense such as it is small in quantity with respect to a specified measure, or it is small by satisfying a specified **sparsity pattern**. Consequently, the problem becomes to whether we can find a unit lower-triangular matrix $\tilde{L}$ and an upper-triangular matrix $\tilde{U}$ satisfying certain constrains, so that the error is as small as possible in some sense. This leads to the *incomplete LU* (ILU) factorization preconditioner.

If the matrix A is non-Hermitian but positive definite, we can turn to consider the HSS-type iterations such as HSS, NSS, and PSS.

The preconditioner corresponding to the **HSS iteration** is

$$P_{\mathrm{HSS}} = \frac{1}{2\alpha}(\alpha I + H)(\alpha I + S),$$

which is a product of the shifted Hermitian and shifted skew-Hermitian parts of the matrix A, where α is a prescribed positive parameter.

The preconditioner corresponding to the **NSS iteration** is

$$P_{\text{NSS}} = \frac{1}{2\alpha}(\alpha I + N)(\alpha I + S),$$

which is a product of the shifted normal and shifted skew-Hermitian parts of the matrix A, where α is a prescribed positive parameter.

The preconditioner corresponding to the **PSS iteration** is

$$P_{\text{PSS}} = \frac{1}{2\alpha}(\alpha I + P)(\alpha I + S),$$

which is a product of the shifted positive-definite and shifted skew-Hermitian parts of the matrix A, where α is a prescribed positive parameter.

7.3 ▪ Preconditioners Based on Incomplete LU Factorizations

One class of the most popular preconditioners is based on the incomplete factorizations, which is usually effective for large and sparse matrices. The **incomplete factorization** was first introduced by Buleev [87,88] in the late 1950's, and also independently by Varga [328]; see also [205]. However, a major breakthrough took place in 1977, by Meijerink and van der Vorst [240], where the *incomplete Cholesky conjugate gradient* (ICCG) method was proposed and analyzed. Since then, a number of improvements and extensions have been made, including incomplete factorizations based on **level-of-fill** and on **drop tolerance**, and so on.

7.3.1 ▪ Incomplete LU Factorization

Let $\mathbb{Z}_n$ be the index set $\{1, 2, \ldots, n\}$. A **sparsity pattern** $\mathbb{S}$ is a subset of $\mathbb{Z}_n \times \mathbb{Z}_n$, that is,

$$\mathbb{S} \subseteq \{(i, j) \; : \; i, j \in \mathbb{Z}_n\}.$$

If a sparse matrix $A = [a_{ij}] \in \mathbb{R}^{n \times n}$ satisfies $a_{ij} \neq 0$ for $(i, j) \in \mathbb{S}$ and $a_{ij} = 0$ elsewhere, then we say that the matrix A has the sparsity pattern $\mathbb{S}$.

When the **LU factorization** of a sparse matrix A is carried out through **Gaussian elimination, fill-in** is usually unavoidable [116]. This means that the triangular factors L and U are usually much less sparse than the matrix A. However, if we pre-select a sparsity pattern of the matrices L and U and drop the fill-ins outside this pattern during the process of the factorization, then we can obtain an *incomplete LU* (ILU) factorization of the matrix A, that is,

$$A = LU - E,$$

where the matrix $E \in \mathbb{R}^{n \times n}$ represents the error due to the dropped fill-ins. The matrices L and U are called the **incomplete LU factors**. Then $P = LU$ can be taken as a simple but useful preconditioner.

It is clear that different sparsity patterns lead to different incomplete factorizations. Moreover, fill-ins can be dropped based on several different criteria, such as position, value, or a combination of them.

For a given sparsity pattern $\mathbb{S}$ for the matrices L and U, the **ILU factorization** can be described as follows.

Algorithm 7.8: General ILU Factorization

1: Given a sparse matrix $A = [a_{ij}] \in \mathbb{R}^{n \times n}$ and a sparsity pattern $\mathbb{S}$
2: set L to be the identity matrix and U the zero matrix
3: **for** $k = 1, 2, \ldots, n - 1$ **do**
4:     **for** $i = k + 1, k + 2, \ldots, n$ and $(i, k) \in \mathbb{S}$ **do**
5:         $a_{ik} := a_{ik}/a_{kk}$
6:         **for** $j = k + 1, k + 2, \ldots, n$ and $(i, j) \in \mathbb{S}$ **do**
7:             $a_{ij} := a_{ij} - a_{ik}a_{kj}$
8:         **end for**
9:     **end for**
10: **end for**

Theoretically speaking, we can choose the sparsity pattern $\mathbb{S}$ arbitrarily. However, it is always suggested to include the diagonal entries and the nonzero entries of the matrix A. One simple choice is taking $\mathbb{S}$ to be exactly the sparsity pattern of the matrix A, i.e.,

$$\mathbb{S} = \{(i, j) : i = j \text{ or } a_{ij} \neq 0, \quad i, j = 1, 2, \ldots, n\}. \tag{7.25}$$

Then we obtain the no fill-in ILU factorization, which is denoted as **ILU(0)**.

In practice, Algorithm 7.8 is not recommended because, at the k-th step, all rows from $k + 1$ to n are being modified, which will make the algorithm less efficient. For a row-contiguous data structure, the following IKJ version is the most popular variant.

Algorithm 7.9: ILU Factorization of IKJ Version

1: For $(i, j) \notin \mathbb{S}$, set $a_{ij} := 0$
2: **for** $i = 2, 3, \ldots, n$ **do**
3:     **for** $k = 1, 2, \ldots, i - 1$ and $(i, k) \in \mathbb{S}$ **do**
4:         $a_{ik} := a_{ik}/a_{kk}$
5:         **for** $j = k + 1, k + 2, \ldots, n$ and $(i, j) \in \mathbb{S}$ **do**
6:             $a_{ij} := a_{ij} - a_{ik}a_{kj}$
7:         **end for**
8:     **end for**
9: **end for**

It is easy to check that Algorithm 7.9 is mathematically equivalent to Algorithm 7.8. If the sparsity pattern $\mathbb{S}$ includes the sparsity pattern of the matrix A, then Step 1 in Algorithm 7.9 can be skipped.

Let $L = [l_{ij}] \in \mathbb{R}^{n \times n}$ and $U = [u_{ij}] \in \mathbb{R}^{n \times n}$ be the unit lower-triangular and the upper-triangular matrix obtained by Algorithm 7.9. Then we have

$$A = LU - E,$$

where $E = [e_{ij}] \in \mathbb{R}^{n \times n}$ is the **error matrix**. From Algorithm 7.9 we know that

$$a_{ij} = \sum_{k=1}^{i} l_{ik}u_{kj} - e_{ij},$$

where

$$u_{kj} = \begin{cases} a_{kj} - \sum_{i=1}^{k-1} l_{ki} u_{ij}, & k \le j \le n \text{ and } (k,j) \in \mathbb{S}, \\ 0, & k \le j \le n \text{ and } (k,j) \notin \mathbb{S}, \end{cases} \tag{7.26}$$

$$l_{ik} = \begin{cases} \left(a_{ik} - \sum_{j=1}^{k-1} l_{ij} u_{jk} \right) \Big/ u_{kk}, & k < i \le n \text{ and } (i,k) \in \mathbb{S}, \\ 0, & k < i \le n \text{ and } (i,k) \notin \mathbb{S}, \end{cases} \tag{7.27}$$

for $k = 1, 2, \ldots, n$, so that

$$e_{ij} = \begin{cases} 0, & (i,j) \in \mathbb{S}, \\ \sum_{k=1}^{i} l_{ik} u_{kj}, & (i,j) \notin \mathbb{S}. \end{cases}$$

Therefore, the ILU(0) factorization can be defined in general terms as any pair of the matrices L (unit lower triangular) and U (upper triangular) so that the entries of the error matrix $E = LU - A$ are zero in the locations $(i,j) \in \mathbb{S}$. Clearly, this does not define the ILU(0) uniquely. However, the standard ILU(0) is defined constructively by using Algorithm 7.9 with the sparsity pattern given in (7.25).

If the matrix A is symmetric positive definite, then the same technique can be applied to the Cholesky factorization, which leads to the no fill-in *incomplete Cholesky* (IC) factorization, denoted as **IC(0)**.

Both ILU(0) and IC(0) are simple to construct and cheap to implement as well. Also, they are quite effective for some problems, especially for the low-order discretizations of constant-coefficient elliptic partial differential equations which often lead to ***M*-matrices** or **diagonally dominant matrices**. Indeed, these are the typical types of problems for which ILU(0) and IC(0) are originally proposed [240]. For certain matrices with a special structure (e.g., five-point finite-difference matrices), CG with IC(0) preconditioning can be implemented at nearly the same computational cost as CG with no preconditioning [43, 119].

7.3.2 · Level-of-Fill and ILU(p)

ILU(0) may be incapable of yielding a satisfactory approximation for a more difficult and realistic problem. Therefore, more sophisticated preconditioners are demanded. This can be realized by utilizing more accurate incomplete LU factorizations, which allow some fill-ins in the incomplete factors L and U. This approach leads to the incomplete factorization based on level-of-fill [180, 288, 340].

A **level-of-fill** is a nonnegative integer that is attributed to each entry of the matrix $A = [a_{ij}] \in \mathbb{R}^{n \times n}$ during the procedure of the incomplete factorization. We denote the level of a_{ij} by lev_{ij}. The initial value of lev_{ij} is defined as

$$lev_{ij} = \begin{cases} 0 & \text{if } i = j \text{ or } a_{ij} \neq 0, \\ \infty & \text{otherwise.} \end{cases} \tag{7.28}$$

The update of lev_{ij} can be illustrated with a simple model [288]: A size of $\varepsilon^{lev_{ij}}$ is attributed to the entry a_{ij}, where $0 < \varepsilon < 1$. The idea behind this definition is that the level-of-fill should be indicative of the size: the higher the level-of-fill of an entry is, the smaller the entry tends to be in magnitude.

When a_{ij} is updated in the **Gaussian elimination** by the formula

$$a_{ij} := a_{ij} - a_{ik}a_{kj},$$

the size of the updated entry a_{ij} should become

$$\varepsilon^{lev_{ij}} - \varepsilon^{lev_{ik}}\varepsilon^{lev_{kj}} = \varepsilon^{lev_{ij}} - \varepsilon^{lev_{ik}+lev_{kj}}.$$

Therefore, the new value of lev_{ij} can be updated by

$$lev_{ij} := \min\{lev_{ij},\ lev_{ik} + lev_{kj}\}. \tag{7.29}$$

It is clear that lev_{ij} will never increase. Thus, if $a_{ij} \neq 0$ in the original matrix A, then lev_{ij} is equal to zero throughout the factorization. However, it follows from the formula (7.29) that the value of lev_{ij} will be either zero or infinity throughout the process of the factorization. Therefore, we can only define two dropping rules: dropping the entries whose level-of-fill are infinity or keeping all fill-ins. This is obviously not our desired result. Fortunately, we can improve the updating principle (7.29) by

$$lev_{ij} := \min\{lev_{ij},\ lev_{ik} + lev_{kj} + 1\}, \tag{7.30}$$

which is a common updating formula used in actual applications. This formula seems to be more reasonable: when the value of a_{ij} is changed from zero to nonzero, its level-of-fill is changed from infinity to a finite integer correspondingly, but it should be larger than those whose current values are nonzero.

Different types of ILU preconditioners can be defined based on different dropping strategies which are, in turn, based on the value of lev_{ij}. Let p be a nonnegative integer. We define the ILU of level p, denoted by **ILU(p)**, in which the entries with level-of-fill larger than p are dropped. Thus, the **sparsity pattern** adopted in ILU(p) is

$$\mathbb{S}_p = \{(i,j)\ :\ lev_{ij} \leq p,\quad i,j = 1,2,\ldots,n\},$$

where lev_{ij} is the final value of the **level-of-fill** after all updates (7.30) are fulfilled.

Note that the case $p = 0$ coincides with the ILU(0) preconditioner defined in Subsection 7.3.1 corresponding to the sparsity pattern (7.25).

We remark that (7.30) is not the unique updating principle used in practice. An alternative formula may be [288]

$$lev_{ij} := \min\{lev_{ij},\ \max\{lev_{ik}, lev_{kj}\} + 1\}.$$

Algorithm 7.10: ILU(p) Factorization

1: Set the initial value of lev_{ij} according to (7.28)
2: **for** $i = 2, 3, \ldots, n$ **do**
3:     **for** $k = 1, 2, \ldots, i - 1$ and $lev_{ik} \leq p$ **do**
4:         $a_{ik} := a_{ik}/a_{kk}$
5:         **for** $j = k + 1, k + 2, \ldots, n$ **do**
6:             $a_{ij} := a_{ij} - a_{ik}a_{kj}$
7:             $lev_{ij} := \min\{lev_{ij},\ lev_{ik} + lev_{kj} + 1\}$
8:         **end for**
9:     **end for**
10:     **for** $j = 1, 2, \ldots, n$ and $lev_{ij} > p$ **do**
11:         $a_{ij} := 0$
12:     **end for**
13. **end for**

In many realistic problems, ILU(1) is already a considerable improvement over ILU(0). The cost of construction and application of ILU(1) is still acceptable. Higher level ILU(p) are rarely used in practice due to the rapid increases of memory requirement and computational cost, except perhaps for very difficult problems.

There are several drawbacks in Algorithm 7.10:

(1) The amount of fill-ins and computational costs are not predictable for $p > 0$;

(2) The cost of updating the levels can be expensive;

(3) The level-of-fill for an indefinite matrix may not be a good indicator of the size of the entry that is dropped and, thus, the algorithm may lead to an inaccurate incomplete factorization, in which the error matrix $E = LU - A$ is not small in quantity. As a result, the corresponding preconditioned Krylov subspace method may require a larger number of iteration steps to achieve the convergence.

Therefore, more feasible techniques should be developed to overcome these difficulties.

7.3.3 ▪ Existence of ILU

It is well known that a matrix A admits an **LU factorization** if and only if all of its **leading principal submatrices** are nonsingular. However, we should be aware that ILU may fail due to a division by zero, even if the matrix A admits an LU factorization without pivoting. This is usually referred to as a **breakdown**. By far, we can only prove that ILU exists for certain matrices of special structures or properties.

The following lemma is due to Ky Fan [133].

Lemma 7.5. *Let* $A \in \mathbb{R}^{n \times n}$ *be an* **M-matrix** *and let* A_1 *be the matrix obtained from the first step of the Gaussian elimination. Then the matrix* $A_1 \in \mathbb{R}^{n \times n}$ *is an M-matrix.*

Proof. Let $A = [a_{ij}] \in \mathbb{R}^{n \times n}$. Denote the entries of the matrix A_1 by $a_{ij}^{(1)}$, i.e., $A_1 = [a_{ij}^{(1)}]$. It follows from the **Gaussian elimination** that

$$A_1 = L_1 A,$$

where L_1 is a unit lower-triangular matrix of the form

$$L_1 = \begin{bmatrix} 1 & & & & \\ -l_{21} & 1 & & & \\ -l_{31} & 0 & 1 & & \\ \vdots & \vdots & \ddots & \ddots & \\ -l_{n1} & 0 & \cdots & 0 & 1 \end{bmatrix}, \quad \text{with} \quad l_{i1} = \frac{a_{i1}}{a_{11}}, \ i = 2, 3, \ldots, n.$$

Hence,

$$a_{1j}^{(1)} = a_{1j}, \quad j = 1, 2, \ldots, n,$$
$$a_{ij}^{(1)} = a_{ij} - \frac{a_{i1} a_{1j}}{a_{11}}, \quad i, j = 2, 3, \ldots, n.$$

As the matrix A is an **M-matrix**, we have $A^{-1} \geq 0$, $a_{ii} > 0$, and $a_{ij} \leq 0$ for $i \neq j$, $i, j = 1, 2, \ldots, n$. Thus $a_{ij}^{(1)} \leq 0$ for $i \neq j$, $i, j = 1, 2, \ldots, n$, which indicates that the matrix A_1 is a **Z-matrix**.

In the following, we need to show that $A_1^{-1} \geq 0$. It is easy to verify that

$$
L_1^{-1} = \begin{bmatrix}
1 & & & & \\
l_{21} & 1 & & & \\
l_{31} & 0 & 1 & & \\
\vdots & \vdots & \ddots & \ddots & \\
l_{n1} & 0 & \cdots & 0 & 1
\end{bmatrix}.
$$

Let e_i be the i-th column of the identity matrix. Then for $i \geq 2$ we have

$$
A_1^{-1} e_i = A^{-1} L_1^{-1} e_i = A^{-1} e_i \geq 0.
$$

For the first column of the matrix A_1^{-1}, it is clear that

$$
A_1^{-1} e_1 = \frac{1}{a_{11}^{(1)}} e_1 = \frac{1}{a_{11}} e_1 \geq 0.
$$

Hence, $A_1^{-1} \geq 0$. It follows from Theorem 4.80 that the matrix A_1 is an M-matrix. □

During the **ILU factorization**, by applying the **sparsity pattern** $\mathbb{S}$ on the matrix A_1, some off-diagonal entries are dropped, that is,

$$
\tilde{A}_1 = A_1 + E_1.
$$

As the dropped fill-ins are nonpositive, it holds that $E_1 \geq 0$ and, from Corollary 4.86, the resulting matrix $\tilde{A}_1$ is still an M-matrix. By Corollary 4.87, we know that $\tilde{A}_1(2 : n, 2 : n)$, the submatrix obtained from the matrix $\tilde{A}_1$ by removing its first row and first column, is also an M-matrix.

This process can be repeated on the matrix $\tilde{A}_1(2 : n, 2 : n)$, and then continued until the incomplete factorization is fulfilled. This means that the ILU factorization does not break down.

Theorem 7.6. [240] *Let $A \in \mathbb{R}^{n \times n}$ be an M-matrix. Then for any sparsity pattern $\mathbb{S}$ including the main diagonal entries of the matrix A, Algorithm 7.9 does not break down. Furthermore, the factors L and U satisfy*

$$
A = LU - E,
$$

*which is a **regular splitting** and is, thus, convergent.*

Proof. Without loss of generality, we assume that the sparsity pattern $\mathbb{S}$ includes all nonzero entries of the matrix A. Then Step 1 in Algorithm 7.9 is skipped.

We denote by $A_k = [a_{ij}^{(k)}] \in \mathbb{R}^{n \times n}$ the resulting matrix obtained after k steps of the Gaussian elimination and by $\tilde{A}_k = [\tilde{a}_{ij}^{(k)}] \in \mathbb{R}^{n \times n}$ the matrix obtained by applying the sparsity pattern $\mathbb{S}$ on the matrix A_k. Here we stipulate that $\tilde{A}_0 = A$. Then both matrices A_k and $\tilde{A}_k$ are M-matrices, and

$$
\begin{aligned}
A_k &= L_k \tilde{A}_{k-1}, \\
\tilde{A}_k &= A_k + E_k, \quad k = 1, 2, \ldots, n-1,
\end{aligned}
$$

where $E_k \geq 0$ and

$$
L_k = \begin{bmatrix} 1 & & & & & \\ & \ddots & & & & \\ & & 1 & & & \\ & & -l_{k+1,k} & \ddots & & \\ & & \vdots & & \ddots & \\ & & -l_{n,k} & & & 1 \end{bmatrix}, \quad \text{with} \quad l_{ik} = \frac{\tilde{a}_{ik}^{(k-1)}}{\tilde{a}_{kk}^{(k-1)}} \leq 0, \ i > k.
$$

It holds that $L_k \geq 0$ and

$$
\begin{aligned}
U \triangleq \tilde{A}_{n-1} &= A_{n-1} + E_{n-1} \\
&= L_{n-1}\tilde{A}_{n-2} + E_{n-1} \\
&= L_{n-1}(L_{n-2}\tilde{A}_{n-3} + E_{n-2}) + E_{n-1} \\
&= \cdots \\
&= L_{n-1}\cdots L_1\tilde{A}_0 + L_{n-1}\cdots L_2 E_1 + \cdots + L_{n-1}E_{n-2} + E_{n-1}.
\end{aligned}
$$

As the matrix $\tilde{A}_k$ is obtained by applying the sparsity pattern $\mathbb{S}$ on the submatrix $A_k(k+1 : n, k+1 : n)$, the first k rows and columns of the error matrix E_k are zero. Thus we have

$$
L_{n-1}\cdots L_{k+1}E_k = L_{n-1}\cdots L_1 E_k
$$

and

$$
U = L_{n-1}\cdots L_1(A + E_1 + E_2 + \cdots + E_{n-1}).
$$

Here we have used the fact that $\tilde{A}_0 = A$. Denote by

$$
L \triangleq (L_{n-1}L_{n-2}\cdots L_1)^{-1}
$$

and

$$
E \triangleq E_1 + E_2 + \cdots + E_{n-1} \geq 0.
$$

Then

$$
L^{-1} = L_{n-1}L_{n-2}\cdots L_1 \geq 0
$$

and

$$
A = LU - E. \tag{7.31}
$$

As $U = \tilde{A}_{n-1}$ is an M-matrix, it holds that

$$
(LU)^{-1} = U^{-1}L^{-1} \geq 0.
$$

So the matrix splitting in (7.31) is a regular splitting. $\quad\square$

Remark 7.1. *As $E_k \geq 0$, we have*

$$0 < a_{ii}^{(k)} \leq \tilde{a}_{ii}^{(k)}, \quad i = k+1, k+2, \ldots, n,$$
$$a_{ij}^{(k)} \leq \tilde{a}_{ij}^{(k)} \leq 0, \quad i, j = k+1, k+2, \ldots, n, \ i \neq j.$$

If the matrix A is a symmetric M-matrix, then it must be positive definite. As the Cholesky factorization is equivalent to the LU factorization except for a positive diagonal matrix, and this extra diagonal matrix does not affect places that contain zeros, we can easily obtain the following existence result for the **incomplete Cholesky factorization**.

Theorem 7.7. [240] *Let $A \in \mathbb{R}^{n \times n}$ be a symmetric M-matrix. Then for any sparsity pattern $\mathbb{S}$ including the main diagonal entries of the matrix A and having the property that $(i, j) \in \mathbb{S}$ implies $(j, i) \in \mathbb{S}$, there exist a lower-triangular matrix $L = [l_{ij}] \in \mathbb{R}^{n \times n}$ and a symmetric nonnegative matrix $E = [e_{ij}] \in \mathbb{R}^{n \times n}$, with $l_{ij} = 0$ for $(i, j) \notin \mathbb{S}$ and $e_{ij} = 0$ for $(i, j) \in \mathbb{S}$, such that*

$$A = LL^{\mathsf{T}} - E$$

*is a **regular splitting** and is, thus, convergent.*

The above results can be straightforwardly extended to **H-matrices**; see, e.g., [234, 282, 331] for more details.

Theorem 7.8. [234] *Let $A \in \mathbb{R}^{n \times n}$ be an **H-matrix** with positive diagonal entries (i.e., the matrix A is an H_+-matrix; see [19]), with $\langle A \rangle$ being its **comparison matrix**. Then, for any given sparsity pattern $\mathbb{S}$ including the main diagonal entries of the matrix A, the ILU factorizations of the matrices A and $\langle A \rangle$ are given, respectively, by*

$$A = LU - E \quad \text{and} \quad \langle A \rangle = \hat{L}\hat{U} - \hat{E},$$

with

$$L = [l_{ij}], \ U = [u_{ij}] \quad \text{and} \quad \hat{L} = [\hat{l}_{ij}], \ \hat{U} = [\hat{u}_{ij}],$$

such that

$$0 < \hat{u}_{ii} \leq |u_{ii}|, \quad \hat{l}_{ji} \leq -|l_{ji}| \leq 0, \quad \hat{u}_{ij} \leq -|u_{ij}| \leq 0, \qquad 1 \leq i < j \leq n.$$

Proof. The proof follows from induction based on the equations (7.26) and (7.27). □

Remark 7.2. *Note that a **strictly diagonally dominant matrix** or an **irreducibly weakly diagonally dominant matrix** is an H-matrix. Hence, the result in Theorem 7.8 holds true also for these two classes of matrices.*

The following result shows that, for M-matrices, the improvement in condition is essentially monotone with respect to the sparsity pattern $\mathbb{S}$.

Theorem 7.9. [234] *Let $A \in \mathbb{R}^{n \times n}$ be an M-matrix, and let $\mathbb{S}_1$ and $\mathbb{S}_2$, with $\mathbb{S}_1 \subseteq \mathbb{S}_2$, be two sparsity patterns including the main diagonal entries of the matrix A. Assume that*

$$A = L_1 U_1 - E_1 \quad \text{and} \quad A = L_2 U_2 - E_2$$

are the ILU factorizations of the matrix A corresponding to the sparsity patterns $\mathbb{S}_1$ and $\mathbb{S}_2$, *respectively, with*

$$L_k = [l_{ij}^{(k)}], \ U_k = [u_{ij}^{(k)}], \quad k = 1, 2.$$

Then we have

$$0 < u_{ii}^{(2)} \le u_{ii}^{(1)}, \quad l_{ji}^{(2)} \le l_{ji}^{(1)} \le 0, \quad u_{ij}^{(2)} \le u_{ij}^{(1)} \le 0,$$

for $1 \le i < j \le n$.

Proof. The proof is analogous to the proof of Theorem 7.6. □

7.3.4 ▪ ILU with Threshold

In many applications such as those of matrices which are indefinite or far from being diagonally dominant, the level-of-fill may not be a good indicator for the size of the entry. This means that the entries with higher level-of-fill may have larger magnitude. Thus, the ILU factorization which depends only on the level-of-fill may lead to a poor approximation where the error $E = LU - A$ is not small in quantity.

An alternative strategy is available where the fill-ins are dropped according to their absolute values rather than their positions. In this way, a **drop tolerance** τ is used in the **dropping rule**: only fill-ins that are greater than τ in absolute value are stored and used, which indicates that the sparsity pattern $\mathbb{S}$ is determined dynamically.

However, this dropping rule may work poorly if the matrix is badly scaled. Hence, it is suggested to use a **relative drop tolerance**. That is to say, a fill-in is dropped if it is less than the product of τ with the norm of either the row or the column in which the fill-in is located.

A drawback of this approach is that it is difficult to predict the amount of storage needed to store the ILU factors. An efficient, predictable algorithm can be obtained by additionally limiting the number of nonzeros allowed in each row or each column of the matrices L and U. Saad [287] proposed the ***dual threshold ILU factorization***, denoted by **ILUT(p, τ)**, in which the following two dropping strategies are employed:

DS1 The fill-in is dropped if it is less than the relative tolerance obtained by multiplying τ with the norm of the original row or column.

DS2 Keep at most the p largest entries in the L part of the row or the column and the p largest entries in the U part of the row or the column, in addition to the diagonal entry, which is always kept.

Roughly speaking, τ can be viewed as a parameter that helps to reduce the computational cost, while p helps control the memory requirement.

The ILUT(p, τ) algorithm can be derived from the Gaussian elimination by employing the threshold strategies **DS1** and **DS2**. In the following algorithm, w is a full-length working row vector with w_k being its k-th entry, and $\| \cdot \|$ is a suitably chosen norm.

Algorithm 7.11: ILUT(p, τ): ILU with Dual Threshold

1: **for** $i = 1, 2, \ldots, n$ **do**
2:     **for** $k = 1, 2, \ldots, n$ **do**   % copy the i-th row of A to w
3:         $w_k := a_{ik}$
4:     **end for**
5:     $\tau_i := \tau \|w\|$ % relative drop tolerance
6:     **for** $k = 1, 2, \ldots, i - 1$ and $w_k \ne 0$ **do**
7:         $w_k := w_k / a_{kk}$

8:   **if** $|w_k| < \tau_i$, **then** % apply **DS1** on w_k

9:    $w_k := 0$

10:   **else**

11:    **for** $j = k+1, k+2, \ldots, n$ **do**

12:     $w_j := w_j - w_k u_{kj}$

13:    **end for**

14:   **end if**

15: **end for**

16: **for** $k = i+1, i+2, \ldots, n$ and $|w_k| < \tau_i$ **do** % apply **DS1** on w

17:   $w_k := 0$

18: **end for**

   % apply **DS2** on w

19: find the largest p entries of $w(1 : i-1)$ and drop the others

20: find the largest p entries of $w(i+1 : n)$ and drop the others

21: **for** $k = 1, 2, \ldots, i-1$ **do**

22:   $l_{ik} := w_k$

23: **end for**

24: **for** $k = i, i+1, \ldots, n$ **do**

25:   $u_{ik} := w_k$

26: **end for**

27: set $w := 0$

28: **end for**

A practical variant of this approach is that, in addition to the nonzero entries in the original matrix A, p fill-ins are allowed in each row in the incomplete factors. This makes sense for irregular problems in which the nonzeros in the coefficient matrix A are not distributed uniformly.

The ILUT(p, τ) preconditioner is quite powerful. If it fails for a given parameter pair (p, τ), it will often succeed by taking a larger value of p and/or a smaller value of τ.

One difficulty of ILUT(p, τ) is the problem of how to choose the parameters p and τ. Clearly, the optimal values are strongly problem-dependent, which may cause difficulty to implement the ILUT(p, τ) preconditioner in a black-box fashion.

For a symmetric positive definite matrix $A \in \mathbb{R}^{n \times n}$, Jones and Plassmann [210, 211] proposed a variant of the incomplete Cholesky factorization preconditioner, which does not require the drop tolerance and has predictable storage requirement. In their approach, a fixed number n_k of nonzeros is allowed in the k-th row of the incomplete Cholesky factor L, where n_k is simply the number of nonzeros in the k-th row of the lower-triangular part of the original matrix A. This means that the original sparsity pattern is ignored and only the nonzeros with the largest magnitude are kept. The resulting preconditioner has the same storage requirement as the no fill-in incomplete Cholesky factorization preconditioner, but has better performance in many cases. This strategy has the advantage of being a black-box algorithm, but convergence speed can be slow on difficult problems.

Lin and Moré [230] extended the approach by allowing additional p fill-ins in each row of the Cholesky factor L, that is, the number of nonzeros retained in the k-th row of the matrix L is $n_k + p$, where p is a given nonnegative integer. If $p = 0$, then it is reduced to the approach of Jones and Plassmann. For $p > 0$, it may improve the convergence behavior dramatically at the expense of somewhat higher storage requirement. This preconditioner is no longer entirely a black-box one, but only one parameter is necessary. The optimal value of p is problem-dependent, but a value around 5 is suggested in many situations [230]. Note that exactly the same preconditioner can be obtained from ILUT(p, τ) by setting the drop tolerance to 0.

7.3.5 ▪ Modified ILU

In some applications such as the discretizations of the second-order self-adjoint elliptic partial differential equations with constant coefficients, when no fill-in is allowed in the incomplete factors, the preconditioner will be of less help. This situation can be improved by means of a technique called **modified ILU** (MILU) factorization, where a **diagonal compensation** strategy is used: adding the dropped fill-ins to the diagonal entries of the matrix U after the completion of the k-loop of Algorithm 7.9. This strategy guarantees that the **row sums** of the coefficient matrix A are equal to those of the matrix LU, i.e.,

$$Ae = LUe,$$

where $e = [1, 1, \ldots, 1]^\mathsf{T} \in \mathbb{R}^n$.

This kind of preconditioner often works well for the partial differential equations with constant coefficients; see [43]. For other problems, the MILU preconditioners are usually not better than their ILU counterparts.

This modification strategy can be applied to any form of the ILU preconditioners. In addition, there are variants of **diagonal compensation** in which only part of the sum of the dropped fill-ins is added to the diagonal entry, that is, the sum is multiplied by a relaxation factor typically between 0 and 1 prior to being added to the diagonal entry of the matrix U [242]. Other strategies are also available in which the sum of dropped fill-ins is added to certain position rather than the diagonal.

7.4 ▪ Preconditioners Based on Incomplete QR Factorizations

Again, we consider the solution of the large sparse linear system (7.1). For a general nonsymmetric matrix $A \in \mathbb{R}^{n \times n}$, although a number of efficient incomplete LU factorization techniques have been presented (see [8] and [288]), it is more difficult to give theoretical assurances about the feasibility and efficiency for these incomplete triangular factorization preconditioners. There can be breakdowns in the factorization process due to zero pivots, inaccuracies of the incomplete triangular factors due to small pivots and inefficient dropping rules, as well as instability of the triangular solves due to the poorly conditioned incomplete triangular factors.

In this section, we introduce another class of incomplete factorization preconditioners known as incomplete QR factorizations, which compute a sparse and generally nonorthogonal matrix Q, and a sparse upper-triangular matrix R.

7.4.1 ▪ Incomplete QR Factorization

The incomplete factorization technique based on the modified Gram–Schmidt process incorporating some dropping rule was initially developed for general sparse matrices in [284]. Thereafter, much attention was paid to practical applications rather than theoretical properties, since its theoretical properties such as existence, stability, and accuracy are too complicated to be analyzed. For details, we refer to [284, 288]. For a special strategy that only drops entries of the upper-triangular matrix R, the existence and stability of the associated **incomplete QR** (IQR) factorization preconditioner were proved in [337]. For particular sparsity patterns, this special strategy produces an R factor identical to that produced by the incomplete Cholesky factorization applied to the normal equation.

In addition to the drawbacks of breakdowns, inaccuracies, and instabilities as in the incomplete LU factorization methods, one major problem about the above-mentioned incomplete QR factorization methods is that the matrix Q is not in general orthogonal, and nothing guarantees that it is even nonsingular unless we adopt a strategy that does not drop many entries. However, this makes the resulting incomplete factors Q and R likely to be too dense to be useful in practice (see [284]).

In fact, the main motivation for developing incomplete orthogonal factorization preconditioners derives from the power of the *complete* orthogonal factorization process. Some advantages of complete QR factorizations over complete LU factorizations are [29]:

(a) they will never break down and will always produce an orthogonal matrix Q and an upper-triangular matrix R such that $A = QR$;

(b) orthogonal factorization is strongly robust and numerically stable; and

(c) the orthogonality of the matrix Q makes the solution of the original linear system (7.1) easily obtainable through solving the upper-triangular linear system with respect to the upper-triangular factor R.

Another useful feature is that the upper-triangular factor R is the Cholesky factor of the coefficient matrix of the normal equation. Here, the orthogonality of the factor Q is the key point for ensuring the success of these orthogonal factorization methods. For a good incomplete QR factorization preconditioner, we naturally expect that it will roughly inherit the above three advantages of the complete QR factorization, or at least, it should possess some of the following properties [29]:

(I) $Q \in \mathbb{R}^{n \times n}$ is an orthogonal matrix and $R \in \mathbb{R}^{n \times n}$ is a sparse upper-triangular matrix such that the **error matrix** $E = QR - A$ is "small";

(II) $Q \in \mathbb{R}^{n \times n}$ is a sparse nonsingular matrix and $R \in \mathbb{R}^{n \times n}$ is a sparse upper-triangular matrix such that the error matrices $E = QR - A$ and $E_0 = Q^\mathsf{T} Q - I$ are small, where I is the identity matrix; and

(III) if the original matrix A is nonsingular, then the matrix R must also be nonsingular.

The meaning of "small" can be understood in the sense that either the entries dropped during the factorization process are small enough, or the error matrices satisfy certain constraints such as having zero entries in some positions. We will show, in the analyses in the next section, that incomplete QR factorization preconditioners based on the modified Gram–Schmidt orthogonalization process do not satisfy either Property (I) or (II). However, we will show that incomplete QR factorization preconditioners based on Givens rotations, which we will introduce and study in this chapter, do satisfy Property (III) and at least one of Properties (I) and (II). That such incomplete Givens strategies can always compute an orthogonal factor Q (orthogonal to the limits of **finite precision arithmetic**) is a particular feature: one consequence is that the R factor is always an incomplete Cholesky factor of the normal equation. For this situation, the matrix Q is not generally required and, therefore, needs not be stored.

Throughout the remainder of this chapter, we use the term "incomplete orthogonal factor" for the factor Q of an incomplete orthogonalization method even though such incomplete factors are not necessarily orthogonal matrices.

7.4.2 ▪ Incomplete Modified Gram–Schmidt Method

The *classical Gram–Schmidt* (CGS) method is one of the oldest methods for computing a QR factorization

$$A = QR$$

of a given matrix

$$A = [a_{ij}]_{n \times n} = [a_1, a_2, \ldots, a_n],$$

where

$$Q = [q_{ij}]_{n \times n} = [q_1, q_2, \ldots, q_n]$$

is an orthogonal matrix and $R = [r_{ij}]_{n \times n}$ is an upper-triangular matrix. This method does not break down if and only if the matrix A is of full rank and, in this case, the QR factorization is well defined. A numerically stable alternative of the standard or classical Gram–Schmidt process is known as the ***modified Gram–Schmidt*** (MGS) method.

Algorithm 7.12: MGS Method

1: Define $r_{11} := \|a_1\|_2$. If $r_{11} = 0$ then stop, else $q_1 := a_1/r_{11}$
2: **for** $j = 2, 3, \ldots, n$ **do**
3:     define $\hat{q} := a_j$
4:     **for** $i = 1, 2, \ldots, j - 1$ **do**
5:         compute $r_{ij} := \langle \hat{q}, q_i \rangle$
6:         compute $\hat{q} := \hat{q} - r_{ij} q_i$
7:     **end for**
8:     compute $r_{jj} := \|\hat{q}\|_2$
9:     **if** $r_{jj} = 0$ **then**
10:         stop
11:     **else**
12:         $q_j := \hat{q}/r_{jj}$
13:     **end if**
14: **end for**

The MGS is quite efficient for solving sparse nonsymmetric linear systems because:

(a) it is numerically stable and the inverse of the matrix Q is given explicitly by the matrix Q^T; and

(b) it can be simply implemented in a similar way to the **left-looking LU factorization** where, at each step, a given column is combined with previous columns and then normalized.

To define the corresponding ***incomplete modified Gram–Schmidt*** (IMGS) method, dropping strategies or **nonzero patterns** for the incomplete factorization matrices Q and R must be defined. This can be done in a very general way as follows. Introduce two sets of integer pairs

$$P_n = \{(i,j) : 1 \leq i, j \leq n\} \quad \text{and} \quad P_U = \{(i,j) : i \leq j, \quad 1 \leq i, j \leq n\},$$

and let P_Q and P_R be the chosen nonzero patterns for the matrices Q and R, respectively. The only restriction on P_R is that $P_R \subseteq P_U$. As for P_Q, we require that $P_Q \subseteq P_n$ and for each row there must be at least one nonzero entry. The two sets P_Q and P_R can be selected in similar ways to those defined for ILU factorizations. For details, one can refer to [284].

Algorithm 7.13: IMGS Method

1: **for** $j = 1, 2, \ldots, n$ **do**
2:     set $q_j := a_j$
3:     **for** $i = 1, 2, \ldots, j - 1$ **do**
4:         **if** $(i, j) \in P_R$, **then**
5:             compute $r_{ij} := \langle q_i, q_j \rangle$
6:         **else**

```
 7:              set $r_{ij} := 0$
 8:          end if
 9:          compute $q_j := q_j - r_{ij}q_i$
10:      end for
11:      for $i = 1, 2, \ldots, n$ and $(i, j) \notin P_Q$ do
12:          set $q_{ij} := 0$
13:      end for
14:      compute $r_{jj} := \|q_j\|_2$
15:      if $r_{jj} = 0$, then
16:          stop
17:      else
18:          $q_j := q_j / r_{jj}$
19:      end if
20: end for
```

Simple algebraic manipulation shows that this IMGS method produces a sparse matrix Q and a sparse upper-triangular matrix R satisfying $A = QR + E$, where E is the **error matrix** whose j-th column ϵ_j is the column of entries that were dropped from column q_j in lines 11-13. Typically, the error matrix E is small because of the strategy adopted in dropping entries. One major problem with the above decomposition is that the matrix Q is not usually orthogonal. In fact, nothing guarantees that it is even nonsingular unless the set P_Q is of a large **cardinality**. For the purpose of this discussion, we will assume that line 9 of Algorithm 7.13 is replaced by an ideal orthogonalization process (see, for example, [103]), in which the vector q_j is forced to be orthogonal to all of the vectors $q_1, q_2, \ldots, q_{j-1}$.

Theorem 7.10. [284] *Assume that at every step $j \leq i - 1$ of the IMGS method, the vector q_j is orthogonal to all of the vectors $q_1, q_2, \ldots, q_{j-1}$. Let $\prod_{i-1}$ be the orthogonal projector onto the span of the columns $q_1, q_2, \ldots, q_{i-1}$. Then the matrix $Q_i = [q_1, q_2, \ldots, q_i]$ is of full rank if and only if $\| \prod_{i-1} \epsilon_i \|_2 < r_{ii}$. A fortiori, the matrix Q_i is of full rank if $\|\epsilon_i\|_2 < r_{ii}$.*

Although this theorem provides conditions under which the constructed matrix Q_i remains of full rank at every step, it is not likely to be useful in practice because, at every step, the vector q_j must be made orthogonal to the previous vectors $q_1, q_2, \ldots, q_{j-1}$. In addition, even if we were to obtain a reasonably simple criterion for ensuring the nonsingularity of the matrix Q, this criterion might be so severe that the only way in which it could be satisfied is by making ϵ_i very small, which means allowing more fill-ins in the matrices Q and R.

The case where the entries in the matrix Q are not dropped, that is, the case when $P_Q = P_n$, is of particular interest. Indeed, in this situation, the error matrix $E = 0$ and we have the exact relation $A = QR$. Of course, the matrix Q is still not orthogonal and it may be dense. However, in this case, the nonsingularity of the matrices Q and R can be easily guaranteed.

Theorem 7.11. [337] *Let $A \in \mathbb{R}^{n \times n}$ be nonsingular and $P_Q = P_n$. Then the IMGS method computes an incomplete QR factorization $A = QR$, in which the matrix Q is nonsingular and the matrix R is upper triangular with positive diagonal entries.*

In [337], it is claimed that an attraction of this special IMGS method is that it can efficiently produce an incomplete Cholesky factorization preconditioner for the normal equations of linear least-squares problems.

7.5 • Preconditioners Based on Incomplete Givens Orthogonalizations

Another way to compute the QR factorization is to use Givens rotations. A **Givens rotation** (or plane rotation) $G(i, j, \theta) \in \mathbb{R}^{n \times n}$ is equal to the identity matrix except that

$$G([i, j], [i, j]) = \begin{bmatrix} c & s \\ -s & c \end{bmatrix},$$

where $c = \cos \theta$ and $s = \sin \theta$. The operation $y = G(i, j, \theta) x$ rotates $x = [x_1, x_2, \ldots, x_n]^\mathsf{T} \in \mathbb{R}^n$ through θ radians clockwise in the (i, j)-plane. Algebraically, for $y = [y_1, y_2, \ldots, y_n]^\mathsf{T} \in \mathbb{R}^n$,

$$y_k = \begin{cases} x_k, & \text{for } k \neq i, j, \\ cx_i + sx_j, & \text{for } k = i, \qquad 1 \leq k \leq n, \\ -sx_i + cx_j, & \text{for } k = j, \end{cases}$$

and so, $y_j = 0$ if

$$c = \frac{x_i}{\sqrt{x_i^2 + x_j^2}}, \qquad s = \frac{x_j}{\sqrt{x_i^2 + x_j^2}}.$$

Givens rotations are therefore useful for introducing zeros into a vector one at a time. Note that there is no need to compute the angle θ, since c and s in the above are all that are needed to apply the rotation.

To define an incomplete QR factorization of the matrix $A = [a_{ij}]_{n \times n}$ based on Givens rotations, in addition to the **nonzero patterns** P_Q, P_U, and P_R, we need to introduce the following sets of integer pairs:

$$P_{A,L} = \{(i, j) : a_{ij} \neq 0, \quad i \geq j, \quad 1 \leq i, j \leq n\},$$
$$P_{A,U} = \{(i, j) : a_{ij} \neq 0, \quad i \leq j, \quad 1 \leq i, j \leq n\},$$
$$P_A = \{(i, j) : a_{ij} \neq 0, \quad 1 \leq i, j \leq n\},$$
$$P_L = \{(i, j) : i \geq j, \quad 1 \leq i, j \leq n\}, \text{ and}$$
$$P_U = \{(i, j) : i \leq j, \quad 1 \leq i, j \leq n\}.$$

That is to say, $P_{A,L}$ and $P_{A,U}$ are the nonzero patterns of the lower- and upper-triangular parts of the matrix A, respectively, P_A is the nonzero pattern of the matrix A, and P_L and P_U are the nonzero patterns of any lower- and upper-triangular matrices in $\mathbb{R}^{n \times n}$, respectively. Now, for given sets of integer pairs P_l and P_u satisfying $P_{A,L} \subseteq P_l \subseteq P_L$ and $P_{A,U} \subseteq P_u \subseteq P_U$, we can define the *incomplete Givens orthogonalization* (IGO) method.

7.5.1 • IGO

The IGO method consists of the following three elementary processes [29]:
For each column in turn:

(a) Annihilate, using Givens rotations, the nonzero entries located in the strictly lower-triangular part of the matrix $A \in \mathbb{R}^{n \times n}$ from the bottom up to the first sub-diagonal;

(b) Update the incomplete orthogonal matrix $Q \in \mathbb{R}^{n \times n}$ by postmultiplying by the transpose of the Givens rotation using some dropping rule;

(c) After Steps (a) and (b) have been done for all nonzeros in the current column, form the corresponding row of the incomplete upper-triangular matrix $R \in \mathbb{R}^{n \times n}$ using some dropping rule.

More precisely, this method can be described as follows:

Algorithm 7.14: IGO Method

1: Set $Q := I$
2: **for** $j = 1, 2, \ldots, n - 1$ **do**
3:     define $k_r(j) := \max\{i : i \geq j, a_{ij} \neq 0\}$
4:     **if** $k_r(j) = j$ **then**
5:         cycle
6:     **end if**
7:     **for** $i = k_r(j)$ down to $j + 1$ and $a_{ij} \neq 0$ **do**
8:         % all nonzero sub-diagonals in column j are annihilated
9:         compute $\varrho := \sqrt{a_{jj}^2 + a_{ij}^2}$
10:        compute $c := a_{jj}/\varrho$
11:        compute $s := a_{ij}/\varrho$
12:        set $a_{jj} := \varrho$
13:        **for** $k = j + 1, j + 2, \ldots, n$ and $a_{ik} \neq 0$ and $a_{jk} \neq 0$ **do**   % update matrix
14:           compute $temp := -sa_{jk} + ca_{ik}$
15:           compute $a_{jk} := ca_{jk} + sa_{ik}$
16:           set $a_{ik} := temp$
17:        **end for**
18:        **for** $k = 1, 2, \ldots, n$ **do**   % update Q and respect sparsity pattern for Q
19:           compute $temp := -sq_{kj} + cq_{ki}$ if $(k, i) \in P_Q$
20:           compute $q_{kj} := cq_{kj} + sq_{ki}$ if $(k, j) \in P_Q$
21:           set $q_{ki} := temp$ if $(k, i) \in P_Q$
22:        **end for**
23:     **end for**
24:     **for** $k = j, j + 1, \ldots, n$ and $(j, k) \in P_R$ **do**   % respect sparsity pattern for R
25:        set $r_{jk} := a_{jk}$
26:     **end for**
27: **end for**
28: set $r_{nn} := a_{nn}$

In actual computations, there is no need to store the matrix $R = [r_{ij}]$ separately. The matrix $A = [a_{ij}]$ is updated successively and, at the end of the algorithm, its upper-triangular part gives the matrix R.

To analyze the numerical properties of the IGO method, we denote the Givens rotation defined in lines 9–11 by $G(i, j)$, and define matrices

$$\begin{cases} G_j = G(j + 1, j) \cdots G(k_r(j), j) \triangleq \prod_{i=j+1}^{k_r(j)} G(i, j), \\ R_j = G_j R_{j-1} + E_j^{(R)}, \quad R_0 = A, \end{cases} \tag{7.32}$$

where $E_j^{(R)}$ is the **error matrix** determined by lines 24–26. Then, it is clear that $R = R_{n-1}$, and for $j = 1, 2, \ldots, n - 1$, G_j are orthogonal matrices, $E_j^{(R)}$ are strictly upper-triangular matrices with their bottom-right $(n-j) \times (n-j)$ blocks zero, and R_j are upper-triangular matrices except for their bottom-right $(n - j) \times (n - j)$ blocks which are nonsingular submatrices in the case that the matrix A is nonsingular. In addition, if we denote the matrix determined by lines 18-22 by $Q(i, j)$, the corresponding error matrix by $E^{(Q)}(i, j)$, and let $Q_0 = I$, then we easily see that $Q = Q_{n-1}$ and it can be computed by the following procedure:

Algorithm 7.15: Procedure for Generating the Incomplete Orthogonal Matrix

1: **for** $j = 1, 2, \ldots, n - 1$ **do**
2:      set $Q(k_r(j) + 1, j) := Q_{j-1}$
3:      **for** $i = k_r(j)$ down to $j + 1$ **do**
4:          compute $\tilde{Q}(i, j) := Q(i + 1, j)\, G(i, j)^\mathsf{T}$
5:          set $Q(i, j) := \tilde{Q}(i, j) + E^{(Q)}(i, j)$
6:      **end for**
7:      set $Q_j := Q(j + 1, j)$
8: **end for**

We assume that the original matrix $A \in \mathbb{R}^{n \times n}$ is nonsingular and let

$$G = G_{n-1} G_{n-2} \cdots G_1 \equiv \prod_{j=n-1}^{1} G_j. \tag{7.33}$$

Then, from the construction of the IGO method and the structure of the matrices R_j and $E_j^{(R)}$ in (7.32), we immediately know that R_j is a nonsingular matrix and its first j diagonal entries are positive. Therefore, the incomplete upper-triangular matrix R must be nonsingular. Moreover, if all $E^{(Q)}(i, j) = 0$, that is, $P_Q = P_n$ or the entries in the matrix Q are not dropped, then $Q = G^\mathsf{T}$ is an orthogonal matrix, so that it is nonsingular. We state this property in the following theorem.

Theorem 7.12. *Let $A \in \mathbb{R}^{n \times n}$ be a nonsingular matrix, and $Q, R \in \mathbb{R}^{n \times n}$ be the incomplete orthogonal and upper-triangular matrices, respectively, produced by the IGO method. Then*

(i) the matrix R is sparse and nonsingular, and its diagonal entries are positive except possibly for the last one;

(ii) the matrix $Q = G^\mathsf{T}$ is orthogonal, provided $P_Q = P_n$.

Moreover, we have the following result from (7.32) and (7.33).

Theorem 7.13. *Let the conditions of Theorem 7.12 be satisfied. Then $Q, R \in \mathbb{R}^{n \times n}$ are sparse matrices and*

(i) $A = G^\mathsf{T} R - E^{(R)}$ and the matrix R is nonsingular, where $E^{(R)} = \sum_{j=1}^{n-1} \left(\prod_{i=1}^{j} G_i^\mathsf{T} \right) E_j^{(R)}$;

(ii) $Q = G^\mathsf{T} + E^{(Q)}$, where $E^{(Q)} = \sum_{j=1}^{n-1} E_j^{(Q)} \left(\prod_{i=j}^{n-1} G_i^\mathsf{T} \right)$,

$$E_j^{(Q)} = \sum_{i=j+1}^{k_r(j)} E^{(Q)}(i, j) \prod_{k=i}^{k_r(j)} G(k, j);$$

(iii) the matrix Q is nonsingular if $\|E^{(Q)}\|_2 < 1$. Furthermore, $\sum_{j=1}^{n-1} \sum_{i=j+1}^{k_r(j)} \|E^{(Q)}(i, j)\|_2 < 1$

implies $\|E^{(Q)}\|_2 < 1$;

(iv) $A = QR - E$, where $E = E^{(R)} + E^{(Q)} R$.

Proof. We first verify (i). According to Theorem 7.12, the matrix $R \in \mathbb{R}^{n \times n}$ is nonsingular. By using (7.32) recursively, we have

$$
\begin{aligned}
R_j &= G_j R_{j-1} + E_j^{(R)} \\
&= G_j \left(G_{j-1} R_{j-2} + E_{j-1}^{(R)} \right) + E_j^{(R)} \\
&= G_j G_{j-1} R_{j-2} + G_j E_{j-1}^{(R)} + E_j^{(R)} \\
&= \cdots \\
&= G_j G_{j-1} \cdots G_1 R_0 + G_j G_{j-1} \cdots G_2 E_1^{(R)} + \cdots + G_j E_{j-1}^{(R)} + E_j^{(R)}.
\end{aligned}
$$

Letting $j = n - 1$ we get

$$
R = GA + G_{n-1} G_{n-2} \cdots G_2 E_1^{(R)} + \cdots + G_{n-1} E_{n-2}^{(R)} + E_{n-1}^{(R)}. \tag{7.34}
$$

Because of the orthogonality of the matrices G_j, $j = 1, 2, \ldots, n-1$, the equality in (7.34) implies that

$$
\begin{aligned}
A &= G^{\mathsf{T}} R - G_1^{\mathsf{T}} E_1^{(R)} - \cdots - (G_{n-2} G_{n-3} \cdots G_1)^{\mathsf{T}} E_{n-2}^{(R)} - (G_{n-1} G_{n-2} \cdots G_1)^{\mathsf{T}} E_{n-1}^{(R)} \\
&= G^{\mathsf{T}} R - E^{(R)}.
\end{aligned}
$$

To verify (ii), from Algorithm 7.15 we have

$$
\begin{aligned}
Q(i, j) &= Q(i+1, j) G(i, j)^{\mathsf{T}} + E^{(Q)}(i, j) \\
&= \left[Q(i+2, j) G(i+1, j)^{\mathsf{T}} + E^{(Q)}(i+1, j) \right] G(i, j)^{\mathsf{T}} + E^{(Q)}(i, j) \\
&= Q(i+2, j) \left[G(i, j) G(i+1, j) \right]^{\mathsf{T}} + E^{(Q)}(i+1, j) G(i, j)^{\mathsf{T}} + E^{(Q)}(i, j) \\
&= \cdots \\
&= Q(k_r(j)+1, j) \left[G(i, j) G(i+1, j) \cdots G(k_r(j), j) \right]^{\mathsf{T}} \\
&\quad + E^{(Q)}(k_r(j), j) \left[G(i, j) G(i+1, j) \cdots G(k_r(j)-1, j) \right]^{\mathsf{T}} \\
&\quad + \cdots + E^{(Q)}(i+1, j) G(i, j)^{\mathsf{T}} + E^{(Q)}(i, j).
\end{aligned}
$$

Letting $i = j + 1$ we get

$$
\begin{aligned}
Q_j &= Q_{j-1} G_j^{\mathsf{T}} + \sum_{i=j+1}^{k_r(j)} E^{(Q)}(i, j) \left(\prod_{k=j+1}^{i-1} G(k, j) \right)^{\mathsf{T}} \\
&= Q_{j-1} G_j^{\mathsf{T}} + \sum_{i=j+1}^{k_r(j)} E^{(Q)}(i, j) \left(\prod_{k=i}^{k_r(j)} G(k, j) \right) G_j^{\mathsf{T}} \\
&= \left(Q_{j-1} + E_j^{(Q)} \right) G_j^{\mathsf{T}},
\end{aligned}
$$

where we have stipulated that

$$
\prod_{k=k_1}^{k_2} G(k, j) = I
$$

if $k_1 > k_2$. That is to say,

$$
Q_{j-1} = Q_j G_j - E_j^{(Q)}
$$

and, therefore,

$$
\begin{aligned}
Q_{j-1} &= Q_j G_j - E_j^{(Q)} \\
&= \left(Q_{j+1} G_{j+1} - E_{j+1}^{(Q)} \right) G_j - E_j^{(Q)} \\
&= Q_{j+1} G_{j+1} G_j - E_{j+1}^{(Q)} G_j - E_j^{(Q)} \\
&= \cdots \\
&= Q_{n-1} G_{n-1} G_{n-2} \cdots G_j - E_{n-1}^{(Q)} G_{n-2} G_{n-3} \cdots G_j \\
&\quad - \cdots - E_{j+1}^{(Q)} G_j - E_j^{(Q)}.
\end{aligned}
$$

Taking $j = 1$ we have

$$
\begin{aligned}
I &= QG - \sum_{j=1}^{n-1} E_j^{(Q)} G_{j-1} G_{j-2} \cdots G_1 \\
&= QG - \sum_{j=1}^{n-1} E_j^{(Q)} \left(G_{n-1} G_{n-2} \cdots G_j \right)^\mathsf{T} G \\
&= (Q - E^{(Q)}) G.
\end{aligned}
$$

This equality is equivalent to

$$
Q = G^\mathsf{T} + E^{(Q)}.
$$

Finally, (iii) follows directly from (ii) since the matrix G is orthogonal; and (iv) follows directly from (i) and (ii). □

From Theorems 7.12 and 7.13 we see that the matrices Q and R satisfy Property (III) and at least one of Properties (I) and (II). In actual applications, the matrix $M = QR$, given by the IGO method, is used as a preconditioner for Krylov subspace iterations. Moreover, it follows from Theorem 7.13 (i) that if $P_Q = P_n$ the IGO method produces an incomplete Cholesky factorization preconditioner for the normal equation of the linear least-squares problem.

7.5.2 ▪ Generalized IGO

The **generalized IGO method**, designated as the **GIGO** method, consists of the following four elementary processes [29]:

(a) Choose sparse **nonzero patterns** P_Q and P_R of the incomplete orthogonal and upper-triangular matrices Q and R, respectively, and determine sparse nonzero patterns P_l and P_u for which the entries of the matrix $A \in \mathbb{R}^{n \times n}$ need to be annihilated and updated, respectively, during the incomplete orthogonal factorization process;

For each column in turn:

(b) Annihilate all the nonzero entries of the matrix $A \in \mathbb{R}^{n \times n}$ in P_l from the bottom up to the first sub-diagonal by Givens rotations, and update the entries of the matrix $A \in \mathbb{R}^{n \times n}$ in P_l or P_u, correspondingly;

(c) Update the incomplete orthogonal matrix $Q \in \mathbb{R}^{n \times n}$ by postmultiplying by the transpose of the Givens rotation, with the entries not in P_Q being dropped;

(d) After Steps (b) and (c) have been done for all nonzeros in the current column, form the corresponding row of the incomplete upper-triangular matrix $R \in \mathbb{R}^{n \times n}$ using some dropping rule.

More precisely, this method can be described as follows:

Algorithm 7.16: GIGO Method

1: Set $Q := I$
2: **for** $j = 1, 2, \ldots, n-1$ **do**
3:     define $k_r(j) := \max\{i : i \geq j, (i,j) \in P_l\}$
4:     **if** $k_r(j) = j$, **then**
5:         cycle
6:     **end if**
7:     **for** $i = k_r(j)$ down to $j + 1$, $a_{ij} \neq 0$ and $(i,j) \in P_l$ **do**
8:         compute $\varrho := \sqrt{a_{jj}^2 + a_{ij}^2}$
9:         compute $c := a_{jj}/\varrho$
10:         compute $s := a_{ij}/\varrho$
11:         set $a_{jj} := \varrho$
12:         define $k_c(i) := \max\{k : k \geq j+1, (i,k) \in P_l \cup P_u\}$
13:         **for** $k = j, j+1, \ldots, k_c(i)$ and $(i,k) \in P_l \cup P_u$ **do**
14:             compute $temp_k := -sa_{jk} + ca_{ik}$
15:         **end for**
16:         define $k_c'(j) := \max\{k : k \geq j+1, (j,k) \in P_u\}$
17:         **for** $k = j+1, j+2, \ldots, k_c'(j)$ and $(j,k) \in P_u$ **do**
18:             compute $a_{jk} := ca_{jk} + sa_{ik}$
19:         **end for**
20:         **for** $k = j, j+1, \ldots, k_c(i)$ and $(i,k) \in P_l \cup P_u$ **do**
21:             set $a_{ik} := temp_k$
22:         **end for**
23:         **for** $k = 1, 2, \ldots, n$ **do**
24:             compute $temp_k := -sq_{kj} + cq_{ki}$ if $(k,i) \in P_Q$
25:             compute $q_{kj} := cq_{kj} + sq_{ki}$ if $(k,j) \in P_Q$
26:             set $q_{ki} := temp_k$ if $(k,i) \in P_Q$
27:         **end for**
28:     **end for**
29:     **for** $k = j, j+1, \ldots, n$ and $(j,k) \in P_R$ **do**
30:         set $r_{jk} := a_{jk}$
31:     **end for**
32: **end for**
33: set $r_{nn} := a_{nn}$

Similar to the IGO method, in the actual computation in the GIGO method there is no need to store the matrix $R = [r_{ij}] \in \mathbb{R}^{n \times n}$ separately. The matrix $A = [a_{ij}] \in \mathbb{R}^{n \times n}$ is updated successively, and finally, its upper-triangular part gives the matrix R, which may be used as an incomplete Cholesky factorization preconditioner for the normal equation of the linear least-squares problem. More generally, the matrix $M = QR$ given by the GIGO method can be used as a preconditioner for Krylov subspace iterations. Evidently, when $P_l = P_L$ and $P_u = P_U$, the GIGO method naturally reduces to the IGO method.

Denote the Givens rotation determined by lines 8–10 by $G(i,j)$, the incomplete orthogonal matrix determined by lines 23–27 by $Q(i,j)$ with the corresponding **error matrix** $E^{(Q)}(i,j)$, and the error matrix determined by lines 12–22 for the i-loop, together with lines 29–31, by $E_j^{(R)}$.

If we further define

$$G_j = \prod_{\substack{i=j+1 \\ (i,j) \in P_l}}^{k_r(j)} G(i,j) \quad \text{and} \quad G = \prod_{j=n-1}^{1} G_j,$$

then, following a similar analysis as for the IGO method, we find that the GIGO method has the following properties.

Theorem 7.14. *Let $A \in \mathbb{R}^{n \times n}$ be a given matrix, and $Q, R \in \mathbb{R}^{n \times n}$ be the sparse incomplete orthogonal, upper-triangular matrices, respectively, produced by the GIGO method. Then*

(i) $A = G^{\mathsf{T}} R - E^{(R)}$, where $E^{(R)} = \sum_{j=1}^{n-1} \left(\prod_{i=1}^{j} G_i^{\mathsf{T}} \right) E_j^{(R)}$;

(ii) $Q = G^{\mathsf{T}} + E^{(Q)}$, where

$$E^{(Q)} = \sum_{j=1}^{n-1} E_j^{(Q)} \left(\prod_{i=j}^{n-1} G_i^{\mathsf{T}} \right), \quad E_j^{(Q)} = \sum_{\substack{i=j+1 \\ (i,j) \in P_l}}^{k_r(j)} E^{(Q)}(i,j) \prod_{\substack{k=i \\ (k,j) \in P_l}}^{k_r(j)} G(k,j);$$

(iii) $A = QR - E$, where $E = E^{(R)} + E^{(Q)} R$.

Theorem 7.14 shows that even if the matrix $A \in \mathbb{R}^{n \times n}$ is nonsingular, nothing guarantees that the incomplete orthogonal matrix Q generated by the GIGO method is nonsingular unless we make the dropping strategy drop only a few entries. However, from the construction of the GIGO method, we easily see that the nonsingularity of the incomplete upper-triangular matrix R is guaranteed if, for all j, $j = 1, 2, \ldots, n-1$, the integer sets

$$\{(i,j) \in P_l \ : \ j \le i \le k_r(j), \ a_{ij} \ne 0\}$$

determined during the annihilating process are nonempty.

In actual computations, the **nonzero patterns** P_l and P_u in the GIGO method can be determined according to the nonzero structure of the matrix $A \in \mathbb{R}^{n \times n}$. One practical way is to simply take $P_l = P_{A,L}$ and $P_u = P_{A,U}$, another is suggested by the following procedure. Note that this procedure also determines the quantities $k_r(j)$, $k_c(j)$, and $k_c'(j)$ in the GIGO method.

Algorithm 7.17: Procedure for Generating the Nonzero Patterns P_l and P_u

---

1: Compute $k_r(1) := \max\{i \ : \ (i,1) \in P_{A,L}\}$
2: set $k_r := k_r(1)$
3: compute $k_c(1) := \max\{j \ : \ (1,j) \in P_{A,U}\}$
4: set $k_c := k_c(1)$
5: set $j := 1$
6: **while** $j < n$, **do**
7:     set $P_l := \{(i,j) \ : \ j \le i \le k_r\}$
8:     set $P_u := \{(j,i) \ : \ j \le i \le k_c\}$
9:     compute $k_r(j+1) := \max\{k \ : \ (k,j+1) \in P_{A,L}\}$
10:    **if** $k_r(j+1) < k_r(j)$, **then**
11:       set $k_r := k_r(j)$
12:    **else**
13:       compute $k_c(j+1) := \max\{k \ : \ (j+1,k) \in P_{A,U}\}$
14:    **end if**
15:    **if** $k_c(j+1) < k_c(j)$, **then**
16:       set $k_c := k_c(j)$

17:     **else**
18:         set $j := j + 1$
19:     **end if**
20: **end while**
21: **for** $j = 1, 2, \ldots, n$ **do**
22:     set $k'_c(j) := k_c(j)$
23: **end for**

Note that, unlike the IMGS method, the computation of the incomplete orthogonal matrix Q and the incomplete upper-triangular matrix R of the IGO method and the GIGO method are independent. Therefore, if we only need an incomplete Cholesky factorization preconditioner for the normal equation of the linear least-squares problem, there is no need to compute and store the incomplete orthogonal matrix $Q \in \mathbb{R}^{n \times n}$. This not only significantly reduces the operation and storage requirements, but also greatly simplifies the programming of both IGO and GIGO methods.

7.5.3 ▪ Threshold IGO

The incomplete Givens orthogonalization methods discussed in the previous sections are blind to numerical values because entries are dropped only using structural considerations. An alternative is to drop entries in the Givens orthogonalization process according to their magnitudes rather than their positions, as in the threshold ILU methods [287, 288]. In this approach, the **nonzero patterns**, for example, P_l, P_u, P_Q, and P_R, are determined dynamically. This results in a ***threshold incomplete Givens orthogonalization*** method or the **TIGO(τ)** method, which we show below.

Algorithm 7.18: TIGO(τ) Method

1: Input the dropping tolerance $\tau^{(Q)}$ for the factor Q
2: input the dropping tolerance $\tau^{(R)}$ for the factor R
3: set $Q := I$
4: **for** $j = 1, 2, \ldots, n - 1$ **do**
5:     set $P_j := \{i : (i,j) \notin P_{A,L}, |a_{ij}| > \tau^{(R)}, j + 1 \leq i \leq n\}$
6:     define $k_r(j) := \max\{i : (i,j) \in P_{A,L} \cup P_j\}$
7:     **if** $k_r(j) = j$, **then**
8:         cycle
9:     **end if**
10:    **for** $i = k_r(j)$ down to $j + 1$ and $(i,j) \in P_{A,L} \cup P_j$ **do**
11:        compute $\varrho := \sqrt{a_{jj}^2 + a_{ij}^2}$
12:        compute $c := a_{jj}/\varrho$
13:        compute $s := a_{ij}/\varrho$
14:        set $a_{jj} := \varrho$
15:        set $\tilde{P}_i := \{k : (i,k) \notin P_A, |a_{ik}| > \tau^{(R)}, j + 1 \leq k \leq n\}$
16:        define $k_c(i) := \max\{k : (i,k) \in P_A \cup \tilde{P}_i\}$
17:        **for** $k = j + 1, j + 2, \ldots, k_c(i)$ and $(i,k) \in P_A \cup \tilde{P}_i$ **do**
18:            compute $temp_k := -sa_{jk} + ca_{ik}$
19:        **end for**
20:        set $\tilde{P}_j := \{k : (j,k) \notin P_{A,U}, |a_{jk}| > \tau^{(R)}, j \leq k \leq n\}$
21:        define $k_c(j) := \max\{k : (j,k) \in P_{A,U} \cup \tilde{P}_j\}$

22:     **for** $k = j, j + 1, \ldots, k_c(j)$ and $(j, k) \in P_{A,U} \cup \tilde{P}_j$ **do**
23:         compute $a_{jk} := c a_{jk} + s a_{ik}$
24:     **end for**
25:     **for** $k = j + 1, j + 2, \ldots, k_c(i)$ and $(i, k) \in P_A \cup \tilde{P}_i$ **do**
26:         set $a_{ik} := temp_k$
27:     **end for**
28:     **for** $k = 1, 2, \ldots, n$ **do**
29:         compute $temp := -s q_{kj} + c q_{ki}$
30:         compute $q_{kj} := c q_{kj} + s q_{ki}$
31:         **if** $|temp| \leq \tau^{(Q)}$, **then**
32:             set $q_{ki} := 0$
33:         **else**
34:             set $q_{ki} := temp$
35:         **end if**
36:         **if** $|q_{kj}| \leq \tau^{(Q)}$, **then**
37:             set $q_{kj} := 0$
38:         **end if**
39:     **end for**
40:     **end for**
41:     **for** $k = j, j + 1, \ldots, n$ and $|a_{jk}| > \tau^{(R)}$ **do**
42:         set $r_{jk} := a_{jk}$
43:     **end for**
44: **end for**
45: set $r_{nn} := a_{nn}$

We remark that, in the above method, the drop tolerances $\tau^{(Q)}$ and $\tau^{(R)}$ may vary according to the row or the column. For example, **relative drop tolerances** $\tau^{(R)}$ may be obtained by multiplying the initial **drop tolerance** $\tau^{(R)}$ by the current values of $|a_{jj}|$ in line 5, line 20, and lines 41–43, respectively, and by the value of $|a_{ii}|$ in line 15. The relative drop tolerances $\tau^{(Q)}$ may be obtained by multiplying the initial drop tolerance $\tau^{(Q)}$ by $|q_{ii}|$ in line 31 and by $|q_{jj}|$ in line 36.

To further control the memory use, we need to limit the number of nonzero entries in each row (or column) of the incomplete orthogonal and upper-triangular matrices Q and R in the TIGO(τ) method. This can be achieved by introducing another parameter p, the largest number of nonzero entries permitted at each row or column of the matrices Q and R. The resulting method, called the *generalized threshold incomplete Givens orthogonalization* method or the **GTIGO(τ, p)** method, is described in the following.

Algorithm 7.19: GTIGO(τ, p) Method

1: Input the dropping tolerance $\tau^{(Q)}$ for the factor Q
2: input the dropping tolerance $\tau^{(R)}$ for the factor R
3: input the memory-control tolerance $p^{(Q)}$ for the factor Q
4: input the memory-control tolerance $p^{(R)}$ for the factor R
5: set $Q := I$
6: **for** $j = 1, 2, \ldots, n - 1$ **do**
7:     set $P_j := \{i : (i, j) \notin P_{A,L}, |a_{ij}| > \tau^{(R)}, j + 1 \leq i \leq n\}$
8:     define $k_r(j) := \max\{i : (i, j) \in P_{A,L} \cup P_j\}$
9:     **if** $k_r(j) = j$, **then**
10:         cycle

11:     **end if**

12:     **for** $i = k_r(j)$ down to $j + 1$ and $(i, j) \in P_{A,L} \cup P_j$ **do**

13:        compute $\varrho := \sqrt{a_{jj}^2 + a_{ij}^2}$

14:        compute $c := a_{jj}/\varrho$

15:        compute $s := a_{ij}/\varrho$

16:        set $a_{jj} := \varrho$

17:        set $\tilde{P}_i := \{k \,:\, (i, k) \notin P_A, |a_{ik}| > \tau^{(R)}, j + 1 \leq k \leq n\}$

18:        define $k_c(i) := \max\{k \,:\, (i, k) \in P_A \cup \tilde{P}_i\}$

19:        **for** $k = j + 1, j + 2, \ldots, k_c(i)$ and $(i, k) \in P_A \cup \tilde{P}_i$ **do**

20:           compute $temp_k := -sa_{jk} + ca_{ik}$

21:        **end for**

22:        set $\tilde{P}_j := \{k \,:\, (j, k) \notin P_{A,U}, |a_{jk}| > \tau^{(R)}, j \leq k \leq n\}$

23:        define $k_c(j) := \max\{k \,:\, (j, k) \in P_{A,U} \cup \tilde{P}_j\}$

24:        **for** $k = j, j + 1, \ldots, k_c(j)$ and $(j, k) \in P_{A,U} \cup \tilde{P}_j$ **do**

25:           compute $a_{jk} := ca_{jk} + sa_{ik}$

26:        **end for**

27:        keep only the $p^{(R)}$ largest entries in the j-th row a_{j*}

28:        **for** $k = j + 1, j + 2, \ldots, k_c(i)$ and $(i, k) \in P_A \cup \tilde{P}_i$ **do**

29:           set $a_{ik} := temp_k$

30:        **end for**

31:        keep only the $2p^{(R)}$ largest entries in the i-th row a_{i*}

32:        **for** $k = 1, 2, \ldots, n$ **do**

33:           compute $temp := -sq_{kj} + cq_{ki}$

34:           compute $q_{kj} := cq_{kj} + sq_{ki}$

35:           **if** $|temp| \leq \tau^{(Q)}$, **then**

36:              set $q_{ki} := 0$

37:           **else**

38:              set $q_{ki} := temp$

39:           **end if**

40:           **if** $|q_{kj}| \leq \tau^{(Q)}$, **then**

41:              set $q_{kj} := 0$

42:           **end if**

43:        **end for**

44:        keep only the $p^{(Q)}$ largest entries in the i-th column q_{*i}

45:        keep only the $p^{(Q)}$ largest entries in the j-th column q_{*j}

46:     **end for**

47:     **for** $k = j, j + 1, \ldots, n$ and $|a_{jk}| > \tau^{(R)}$ **do**

48:        set $r_{jk} := a_{jk}$

49:     **end for**

50:     keep only the $p^{(R)}$ largest entries in the j-th row r_{j*}

51: **end for**

52: set $r_{nn} := a_{nn}$

The drop tolerances $\tau^{(Q)}$ and $\tau^{(R)}$ in the GTIGO(τ, p) method can be determined according to each row or column of the incomplete orthogonal and upper-triangular matrices Q and R, respectively, in a similar way to the TIGO(τ) method. Moreover, it is possible to dynamically adjust the parameters $p^{(Q)}$ and $p^{(R)}$ during the incomplete Givens orthogonalization process.

Following exactly the analysis for the IGO method, analogous properties to the GIGO method can be established for both TIGO(τ) and GTIGO(τ, p) methods.

7.6 · Modified IQR

Assume that we have known beforehand that the coefficient matrix $A \in \mathbb{R}^{n \times n}$ of the linear system (7.1) possesses the intrinsic property

$$A\phi = \psi, \qquad \phi, \psi \in \mathbb{R}^n, \tag{7.35}$$

with

$$\phi = [\phi_1, \phi_2, \ldots, \phi_n]^\mathsf{T} \quad \text{and} \quad \psi = [\psi_1, \psi_2, \ldots, \psi_n]^\mathsf{T}$$

being given vectors. Let the matrix $A \in \mathbb{R}^{n \times n}$ have the IQR factorization

$$A = Q\tilde{R} + \tilde{E},$$

with Q and $\tilde{R}$ being the incomplete orthogonal and the incomplete upper-triangular factors, and $\tilde{E}$ the factorization error; see [29, 269, 284, 337]. Then $\tilde{M} = Q\tilde{R}$ may be served as the IQR preconditioning matrix of the **target matrix** A. The obtained IQR preconditioner $\tilde{M} \in \mathbb{R}^{n \times n}$ is naturally required to satisfy the constraint (7.35), i.e., $\tilde{M}\phi = \psi$, too, so that it may inherit certain properties possessed by the matrix A. This may be achieved by technically modifying the raw preconditioning matrix $\tilde{M}$ through compensating the diagonal entries of the upper-triangular factor $\tilde{R}$ by the entries of the factorization **error matrix** $\tilde{E} \in \mathbb{R}^{n \times n}$; see [30, 59].

7.6.1 · Modified IQR

More specifically, we define

$$M = QR, \quad \text{with} \quad R = \tilde{R} + D \quad \text{and} \quad \widehat{E} = Q^\mathsf{T}\tilde{E},$$

such that the constraint

$$M\phi = \psi \tag{7.36}$$

is satisfied, where $D = \mathrm{diag}(d_1, d_2, \ldots, d_n) \in \mathbb{R}^{n \times n}$ is a diagonal matrix to be determined according to the equality constraint (7.36).

From (7.35) and (7.36) we know that the diagonal matrix D satisfies

$$(\tilde{R} + D)\phi = Q^\mathsf{T}\psi = Q^\mathsf{T}A\phi = (\tilde{R} + Q^\mathsf{T}\tilde{E})\phi = (\tilde{R} + \widehat{E})\phi,$$

or

$$D\phi = \widehat{E}\phi.$$

It then follows immediately that

$$d_\ell = \frac{1}{\phi_\ell} \sum_{k=1}^n \widehat{e}_{\ell k}\phi_k, \qquad \ell = 1, 2, \ldots, n, \tag{7.37}$$

hold for all $\ell \in \{1, 2, \ldots, n\}$ such that $\phi_\ell \neq 0$, where we have used the tacit notation that $\widehat{e}_{\ell k}$ denotes the (ℓ, k)-th entry of the matrix $\widehat{E}$. In addition, define $d_\ell = 0$ for all $\ell \in \{1, 2, \ldots, n\}$ such that $\phi_\ell = 0$, and let

$$\Phi = \mathrm{diag}(\phi_1, \phi_2, \ldots, \phi_n).$$

Then we can rewrite the equalities in (7.37) in matrix form as

$$D = \Phi^\dagger \mathrm{diag}(\widehat{E}\phi),$$

where $\Phi^\dagger$ denotes the **Moore–Penrose generalized inverse** of the matrix Φ, and

$$\mathrm{diag}(\widehat{E}\phi) = \mathrm{diag}([\widehat{E}\phi]_1, [\widehat{E}\phi]_2, \ldots, [\widehat{E}\phi]_n),$$

with

$$[\widehat{E}\phi]_\ell = \sum_{k=1}^{n} \widehat{e}_{\ell k} \phi_k, \qquad \ell = 1, 2, \ldots, n.$$

To be more specific, here we remark that the Moore–Penrose generalized inverse $\Phi^\dagger$ is explicitly given by

$$\Phi^\dagger = \mathrm{diag}(\phi_1^\dagger, \phi_2^\dagger, \ldots, \phi_n^\dagger),$$

with

$$\phi_\ell^\dagger = \begin{cases} \frac{1}{\phi_\ell}, & \text{for } \phi_\ell \neq 0, \\ 0, & \text{for } \phi_\ell = 0, \end{cases} \quad \ell = 1, 2, \ldots, n.$$

Therefore, the *modified IQR* (MIQR) preconditioning matrix has the ultimate expression

$$M = Q(\tilde{R} + \Phi^\dagger \mathrm{diag}(Q^\mathsf{T} \tilde{E}\phi)). \tag{7.38}$$

In particular, when

$$\phi = e := [1, 1, \ldots, 1]^\mathsf{T} \in \mathbb{R}^n,$$

the MIQR preconditioning matrix $M \in \mathbb{R}^{n \times n}$ in (7.38) is of the form

$$M = Q(\tilde{R} + \mathrm{diag}(Q^\mathsf{T} \tilde{E}e)).$$

This formula can be interpreted as adding the row-sums of the **error matrix** $\widehat{E} := Q^\mathsf{T} \tilde{E}$ to the diagonal entries of the incomplete upper-triangular factor $\tilde{R}$, correspondingly, during the IQR factorization process.

Moreover, we can verify that the MIQR factorization

$$A = M + E, \tag{7.39}$$

with M being defined in (7.38) and $E = \tilde{E} - QD$, has the following properties.

Theorem 7.15. [59] *Let $A \in \mathbb{R}^{n \times n}$ be the coefficient matrix of the linear system (7.1) satisfying the condition (7.35) and having the IQR factorization $A = Q\tilde{R} + \tilde{E}$. Let $M \in \mathbb{R}^{n \times n}$ be the MIQR preconditioning matrix given in (7.38) satisfying (7.39). Then*

(i) *$M\phi = \psi$ and $E\phi = 0$;*

(ii) *$\|E\|_2 \leq \left(1 + \dfrac{\|\phi\|_2}{\min\limits_{\substack{1 \leq \ell \leq n \\ \phi_\ell \neq 0}} |\phi_\ell|}\right) \|\tilde{E}\|_2$ and $\|E\|_\infty \leq \left(1 + \dfrac{n\|\phi\|_\infty}{\min\limits_{\substack{1 \leq \ell \leq n \\ \phi_\ell \neq 0}} |\phi_\ell|}\right) \|\tilde{E}\|_\infty$;*

(iii) *for $\phi = e$, with $e = [1, 1, \ldots, 1]^\mathsf{T} \in \mathbb{R}^n$, it holds that*

$$Ee = 0, \quad \|E\|_2 \leq (1 + \sqrt{n})\|\tilde{E}\|_2, \quad \text{and} \quad \|E\|_\infty \leq (1 + n)\|\tilde{E}\|_\infty.$$

Proof. (i) is clearly true from the construction of the MIQR preconditioning matrix M.
Because

$$E = \tilde{E} - QD = \tilde{E} - Q\Phi^\dagger \operatorname{diag}(Q^\mathsf{T} \tilde{E}\phi),$$

we easily have

$$\begin{aligned}
\|E\|_2 &\leq \|\tilde{E}\|_2 + \|Q\Phi^\dagger \operatorname{diag}(Q^\mathsf{T} \tilde{E}\phi)\|_2 \\
&\leq \|\tilde{E}\|_2 + \|\Phi^\dagger\|_2 \|\operatorname{diag}(Q^\mathsf{T} \tilde{E}\phi)\|_2 \\
&= \|\tilde{E}\|_2 + \|\Phi^\dagger\|_2 \|Q^\mathsf{T} \tilde{E}\phi\|_\infty \\
&\leq \|\tilde{E}\|_2 + \|\Phi^\dagger\|_2 \|Q^\mathsf{T} \tilde{E}\phi\|_2 \\
&\leq \|\tilde{E}\|_2 + \|\Phi^\dagger\|_2 \|\tilde{E}\|_2 \|\phi\|_2 \\
&= \left(1 + \|\Phi^\dagger\|_2 \|\phi\|_2\right) \|\tilde{E}\|_2,
\end{aligned}$$

and analogously,

$$\begin{aligned}
\|E\|_\infty &\leq \|\tilde{E}\|_\infty + \|Q\Phi^\dagger \operatorname{diag}(Q^\mathsf{T} \tilde{E}\phi)\|_\infty \\
&\leq \|\tilde{E}\|_\infty + \sqrt{n}\, \|Q\Phi^\dagger \operatorname{diag}(Q^\mathsf{T} \tilde{E}\phi)\|_2 \\
&\leq \|\tilde{E}\|_\infty + \sqrt{n}\, \|\Phi^\dagger\|_2 \|\operatorname{diag}(Q^\mathsf{T} \tilde{E}\phi)\|_2 \\
&= \|\tilde{E}\|_\infty + \sqrt{n}\, \|\Phi^\dagger\|_2 \|Q^\mathsf{T} \tilde{E}\phi\|_\infty \\
&\leq \|\tilde{E}\|_\infty + \sqrt{n}\, \|\Phi^\dagger\|_2 \|Q^\mathsf{T} \tilde{E}\phi\|_2 \\
&= \|\tilde{E}\|_\infty + \sqrt{n}\, \|\Phi^\dagger\|_2 \|\tilde{E}\phi\|_2 \\
&\leq \|\tilde{E}\|_\infty + n\, \|\Phi^\dagger\|_2 \|\tilde{E}\phi\|_\infty \\
&\leq \|\tilde{E}\|_\infty + n\, \|\Phi^\dagger\|_2 \|\tilde{E}\|_\infty \|\phi\|_\infty \\
&= \left(1 + n\, \|\Phi^\dagger\|_\infty \|\phi\|_\infty\right) \|\tilde{E}\|_\infty,
\end{aligned}$$

which shows that (ii) holds true.

By noticing that

$$E = \tilde{E} - Q \operatorname{diag}(Q^\mathsf{T} \tilde{E}e)$$

when $\phi = e$, we immediately see that $Ee = 0$ and, as special cases of (ii),

$$\|E\|_2 \leq (1 + \sqrt{n})\|\tilde{E}\|_2 \quad \text{and} \quad \|E\|_\infty \leq (1 + n)\|\tilde{E}\|_\infty,$$

which are exactly the results in (iii).   □

We remark that it is possible to add only fractions of the row-sums of the factorization error
matrix to the corresponding diagonal entries of the incomplete upper-triangular factor. This leads
to the generalized variant of the MIQR preconditioning matrix

$$M(\Omega) = Q \left[\tilde{R} + \operatorname{diag}(((Q^\mathsf{T} \tilde{E}) \circ \Omega)e)\right], \tag{7.40}$$

called the *relaxed IQR* (RIQR) preconditioning matrix, where $\Omega = [\omega_{\ell k}] \in \mathbb{R}^{n \times n}$ is a **relaxation
matrix** and "∘" is the **Hadamard product** symbol. Evidently, when

$$\omega_{\ell k} = \frac{\phi_k}{\phi_\ell}, \quad \ell, k = 1, 2, \ldots, n,$$

the matrix $M(\Omega)$ defined in (7.40) is equal to the matrix M defined in (7.38); and when $\Omega = 0$,
it becomes the raw IQR preconditioning matrix $\tilde{M}$.

In addition, we observe that introducing the diagonal matrix

$$D(\Omega) := \operatorname{diag}(((Q^{\mathsf{T}}\tilde{E}) \circ \Omega)e)$$

to the RIQR preconditioning matrix $M(\Omega)$ in (7.40) does not cause extra storage, and adding the diagonal entries of the matrix $D(\Omega)$ to the incomplete upper-triangular factor $\tilde{R}$ is easily realizable and less costly. However, in actual applications we should choose the relaxation matrix Ω such that all diagonal entries of the correspondingly obtained incomplete upper-triangular factor

$$R(\Omega) := \tilde{R} + D(\Omega)$$

in the RIQR preconditioning matrix $M(\Omega)$ are nonzero, so that the singularity of the matrix $R(\Omega)$ can be avoided when the target matrix A is nonsingular.

7.6.2 ▪ Modified IGO

We now specify and apply the modification strategy to the IGO factorization process to obtain the *modified IGO* (MIGO) methods.

The **dropping rule** $P_{\#}$ is given beforehand through the sparsity patterns P_A and P_R of the matrix $A = [a_{ij}] \in \mathbb{R}^{n \times n}$ and its upper-triangular part, respectively, so that the partially incomplete upper-triangular factors can satisfy the prescribed **sparsity pattern** during the eliminating process and, finally, they give the incomplete upper-triangular factor, say, e.g., $\tilde{R}_{inc}$.

For given positive integers i and j with $1 \leq j < i \leq n$, we let $G(i,j)$ be the **Givens rotation** used to annihilate the entry a_{ij} of the target matrix $A = [a_{ij}] \in \mathbb{R}^{n \times n}$, in which the **Givens pair** (c, s) is defined by

$$c = \frac{a_{jj}}{\sqrt{a_{jj}^2 + a_{ij}^2}} \quad \text{and} \quad s = \frac{a_{ij}}{\sqrt{a_{jj}^2 + a_{ij}^2}}.$$

In addition, let $P_{A,L}$ and $P_{A,U}$ be the nonzero patterns of the lower- and upper-triangular parts of the matrix A, respectively, and P_A be the nonzero pattern of the matrix A itself, so that $P_A = P_{A,L} \cup P_{A,U}$. Define

$$P_I = P_{A,L} \cup (P_R \cap P_{A,U}) \quad \text{and} \quad P_J = P_R \cap P_{A,U}.$$

Then a modified variant of the Givens-updating rule presented and used in [30, 59] can be described as follows.

Algorithm 7.20: The Modified Givens-Updating Rule

1: **for** $k = j + 1, j + 2, \ldots, n$ **do**
2:    **if** $(j, k) \in P_J$ and $(i, k) \in P_I$, **then**
3:       **if** $a_{jk} \neq 0$ and $a_{ik} \neq 0$, **then**
4:          $a_{jk} := ca_{jk} + sa_{ik}$
5:          $a_{ik} := ca_{ik} - sa_{jk}$
6:       **end if**
7:    **else**
8:       set $a_{jk} := a_{jk}$
9:       set $a_{ik} := a_{ik}$
10:   **end if**
11: **end for**

Clearly, according to this updating rule, when the Givens rotation $G(i, j)$ is applied to rows i and j $(j < i)$ of the matrix A, it does not update exactly all entries a_{ik} and a_{jk} for $k = j + 1, j+2, \ldots, n$ like those done for the IGO method, and its generalizations and variants, discussed previously; see [29]. We remark that in actual computations there is no need to separately form and store the incomplete orthogonal factor, say, e.g., Q_{inc}, since it can be economically and implicitly stored as a sequence of the Givens pairs.

Let

$$k_r(j) := \max\{i : i \geq j, (i, j) \subset P_{A,L} \text{ and } a_{ij} \neq 0\}$$

and define matrices

$$\begin{cases} G_j = G(j+1, j)\, G(j+2, j) \cdots G(k_r(j), j) \triangleq \prod_{i=j+1}^{k_r(j)} G(i, j), & j = 1, 2, \ldots, n-1, \\ \tilde{R}_j = G_j \tilde{R}_{j-1} + \tilde{E}_j, \quad \tilde{R}_0 = A, \end{cases}$$

$$(7.41)$$

where $\tilde{E}_j$ is the **error matrix**, and a Givens rotation $G(\#, j)$ is tacitly admitted to be the identity matrix I once it is skipped, or in other words, the entry $a_{\# j}$ is not annihilated but is simply set to be zero. Then, it clearly holds that $\tilde{R}_{inc} = \tilde{R}_{n-1}$ and, for $j = 1, 2, \ldots, n-1$, G_j are orthogonal matrices, $\tilde{E}_j$ are strictly upper-triangular matrices with their bottom-right $(n-j) \times (n-j)$ blocks zero, and $\tilde{R}_j$ are upper-triangular matrices except for their bottom-right $(n-j) \times (n-j)$ blocks which are nonsingular submatrices in the case that the matrix A is nonsingular.

In addition, assume that the original matrix $A \in \mathbb{R}^{n \times n}$ is nonsingular and let

$$G = G_{n-1}G_{n-2} \cdots G_1 \triangleq \prod_{j=n-1}^{1} G_j \quad \text{and} \quad G^\mathsf{T} = G_1^\mathsf{T} G_2^\mathsf{T} \cdots G_{n-1}^\mathsf{T} \triangleq \prod_{j=1}^{n-1} G_j^\mathsf{T}, \quad (7.42)$$

where we have tacitly adopted the notations

$$\prod_{j=k}^{k+k'} G_j = I \quad \text{and} \quad \prod_{j=k+k'}^{k} G_j^\mathsf{T} = I,$$

with k and k' being two positive integers and I the identity matrix. Then, from the construction of the IGO method and the structures of the matrices $\tilde{R}_j$ and $\tilde{E}_j$ in (7.41), we immediately know that $\tilde{R}_j$ is a nonsingular matrix and its first j diagonal entries are positive. Therefore, the incomplete upper-triangular matrix $\tilde{R}_{inc}$ must be nonsingular. We state this property as the following result.

Theorem 7.16. [29] *Let $A \in \mathbb{R}^{n \times n}$ be nonsingular, and $Q_{inc}, \tilde{R}_{inc} \in \mathbb{R}^{n \times n}$ be the incomplete orthogonal and the incomplete upper-triangular factors, respectively, produced by the IGO method. Then*

(i) *the matrix $\tilde{R}_{inc}$ is sparse and nonsingular, and its diagonal entries are positive except possibly for the last one;*

(ii) *the matrix $Q_{inc} = G^\mathsf{T}$ is orthogonal;*

(iii) *$A = \tilde{M}_{inc} - \tilde{E}_{inc}$, where $\tilde{M}_{inc} = G^\mathsf{T} \tilde{R}_{inc}$ and $\tilde{E}_{inc} = \sum_{j=1}^{n-1} \left(\prod_{i=1}^{j} G_i^\mathsf{T} \right) \tilde{E}_j.$*

Of course, an explicit expression of the IGO preconditioning matrix

$$\tilde{M}_{inc} := Q_{inc}R_{inc} = G^{\mathsf{T}}\tilde{R}_{inc}, \quad \text{with} \quad R_{inc} \triangleq \tilde{R}_{inc},$$

can be easily obtained by straightforward applications of (7.41)–(7.42) and Theorem 7.16 (ii)–(iii) to (7.38); this approach is, however, algorithmically too complicated and practically useless. Below we will derive an equivalent formula for the MIGO preconditioning matrix M_{inc}, which can be conveniently implemented in actual computations.

To this end, we see from Theorem 7.16 (iii) that

$$\tilde{E}_j\phi = 0, \quad j = 1, 2, \ldots, n-1, \tag{7.43}$$

readily imply that $\tilde{E}_{inc}\,\phi = 0$ and, hence,

$$\tilde{M}_{inc}\,\phi = G^{\mathsf{T}}\tilde{R}_{inc}\,\phi = (A + \tilde{E}_{inc})\phi = \psi.$$

Therefore, from (7.41) we know that (7.43) is equivalent to

$$G_j\tilde{R}_{j-1}\phi = \tilde{R}_j\phi, \quad j = 1, 2, \ldots, n-1. \tag{7.44}$$

By recalling $\tilde{R}_0 = A$ and $\tilde{R}_{inc} = \tilde{R}_{n-1}$, and applying the constraint condition (7.35), we can obtain from (7.44) that

$$
\begin{aligned}
\tilde{R}_j\phi &= G_jG_{j-1}\cdots G_1\tilde{R}_0\phi \\
&\quad + (G_jG_{j-1}\cdots G_2\tilde{E}_1 + G_jG_{j-1}\cdots G_3\tilde{E}_2 + \cdots + G_j\tilde{E}_{j-1} + \tilde{E}_j)\phi \\
&= G_jG_{j-1}\cdots G_1A\phi \\
&= G_jG_{j-1}\cdots G_1\psi
\end{aligned}
$$

and

$$\tilde{R}_{inc}\,\phi = G_{n-1}G_{n-2}\cdots G_1\psi = G\psi.$$

It follows immediately from the last identity that

$$\tilde{M}_{inc}\,\phi = \psi. \tag{7.45}$$

Hence, in order to modify the diagonal of the incomplete upper-triangular factor $\tilde{R}_{inc}$ such that the constraint condition (7.45) imposed on the IGO preconditioning matrix $\tilde{M}_{inc}$ is satisfied, we add all the dropped entries, possibly after certain weighting treatments, to the corresponding diagonal entries of the upper-triangular matrices $\tilde{R}_j$, $j = 1, 2\ldots, n-1$, such that either of the equality constraints (7.44) and (7.43) is satisfied. More precisely, this **diagonal compensation** strategy can be described as follows.

For $j = 1, 2, \ldots, n-1$, assume

$$D_j = \text{diag}(d_1^{(j)}, d_2^{(j)}, \ldots, d_n^{(j)}) \in \mathbb{R}^{n \times n}.$$

to be diagonal matrices, and define

$$R_j = \tilde{R}_j + D_j \quad \text{and} \quad E_j = \tilde{E}_j + D_j, \tag{7.46}$$

where

$$R_j = [r_{\ell k}^{(j)}], \quad \tilde{R}_j = [\tilde{r}_{\ell k}^{(j)}], \quad E_j = [e_{\ell k}^{(j)}], \quad \tilde{E}_j = [\tilde{e}_{\ell k}^{(j)}]$$

are real n-by-n matrices. We are going to choose the diagonal matrices D_j, $j = 1, 2, \ldots, n-1$, so that

$$R_j\phi = G_j\tilde{R}_{j-1}\phi \quad \text{or} \quad E_j\phi = 0, \quad j = 1, 2, \ldots, n-1. \tag{7.47}$$

Then, the correspondingly obtained MIGO preconditioning matrix is of the form

$$M_{inc} = G^\mathsf{T} R_{inc}, \quad \text{with} \quad R_{inc} = R_{n-1}, \tag{7.48}$$

which automatically satisfies the constraint condition

$$M_{inc}\,\phi = \psi.$$

Through straightforwardly solving (7.47) we can obtain

$$d_\ell^{(j)} = \begin{cases} -\dfrac{1}{\phi_\ell} \displaystyle\sum_{k=1}^n \tilde{e}_{\ell k}^{(j)} \phi_k, & \text{for} \quad \phi_\ell \neq 0, \\ 0, & \text{for} \quad \phi_\ell = 0, \end{cases} \quad \ell = 1,2,\ldots,n, \quad j = 1,2,\ldots,n-1. \tag{7.49}$$

In matrix form, (7.49) can be equivalently rewritten as

$$D_j = -\Phi^\dagger \operatorname{diag}(\tilde{E}_j \phi), \quad j = 1,2,\ldots,n-1,$$

where

$$\operatorname{diag}(\tilde{E}_j \phi) = \operatorname{diag}([\tilde{E}_j \phi]_1, [\tilde{E}_j \phi]_2, \ldots, [\tilde{E}_j \phi]_n),$$

with

$$[\tilde{E}_j \phi]_\ell = \sum_{k=1}^n \tilde{e}_{\ell k}^{(j)} \phi_k.$$

Therefore, we have

$$R_j = \tilde{R}_j - \Phi^\dagger \operatorname{diag}(\tilde{E}_j \phi), \quad j = 1,2,\ldots,n-1. \tag{7.50}$$

In particular, when $\phi = e \triangleq [1,1,\ldots,1]^\mathsf{T} \in \mathbb{R}^n$, the diagonal matrices D_j, $j = 1,2,\ldots,$ $n-1$, have the simplified expressions

$$D_j = -\operatorname{diag}(\tilde{E}_j e), \quad j = 1,2,\ldots,n-1, \tag{7.51}$$

and, thereby, the MIGO preconditioning matrix can be determined by (7.48), (7.46), and (7.51).

Analogously, these formulas can be interpreted as adding the negative row-sums of the error matrix $\tilde{E}_j$ to the diagonal entries of the partially incomplete upper-triangular factor $\tilde{R}_j$, correspondingly, during the IGO factorization process. Of course, this generic idea of lumping together all the entries dropped during the elimination process and then adding the obtained quantities to the diagonals of the partially incomplete upper-triangular factors can be used for any form of the IGO methods.

We remark that it is also possible to add only fractions of the row-sums of the factorization error matrices to the corresponding diagonal entries of the partially incomplete upper-triangular factors. This leads to the generalized variant of the MIGO preconditioning matrix, which is called the ***relaxed IGO*** (RIGO) preconditioning matrix and is defined by (7.48) and

$$R_j = \tilde{R}_j - \operatorname{diag}((\tilde{E}_j \circ \Omega)e), \quad j = 1,2,\ldots,n-1,$$

where $\Omega = [\omega_{\ell k}] \in \mathbb{R}^{n \times n}$ is a **relaxation matrix**. Evidently, when

$$\omega_{\ell k} = \frac{\phi_k}{\phi_\ell}, \quad \ell, k = 1,2,\ldots,n,$$

the RIGO preconditioning matrix is equal to the MIGO preconditioning matrix derived in the above; and when $\Omega = 0$, it becomes the raw IGO preconditioning matrix $\tilde{M}_{inc}$; see (7.50) and Theorem 7.16 (iii).

Based on the above demonstration, we now give an algorithmic description of the RIGO method.

Algorithm 7.21: RIGO Method

1: **for** $j = 1, 2, \ldots, n - 1$ **do**
2:      $k_r(j) := \max\{i : i \geq j, (i, j) \in P_{A,L} \text{ and } a_{ij} \neq 0\}$
3:      **for** $i = k_r(j)$ down to $j + 1$ and $a_{ij} \neq 0$ **do**
4:          compute $\rho := \sqrt{a_{jj}^2 + a_{ij}^2}$, $c := a_{jj}/\rho$ and $s := a_{ij}/\rho$
5:          set $a_{jj} := \rho$ and $a_{ij} := 0$
6:          store c and s
7:          **for** $k = j + 1, j + 2, \ldots, n$ **do**
8:              set $\text{sum}_i := 0$ and $\text{sum}_j := 0$
9:              **if** $(i, k) \in P_I$ and $(j, k) \in P_J$ **then**
10:                  compute $\text{temp} := -sa_{jk} + ca_{ik}$
11:                  compute $a_{jk} := ca_{jk} + sa_{ik}$
12:                  set $a_{ik} := \text{temp}$
13:              **else if** $(i, k) \in P_I$ and $(j, k) \notin P_J$ **then**
14:                  compute $\text{sum}_j := \text{sum}_j - s\omega_{jk}a_{ik}$
15:                  compute $a_{ik} := ca_{ik}$
16:              **else if** $(i, k) \notin P_I$ and $(j, k) \in P_J$ **then**
17:                  compute $\text{sum}_i := \text{sum}_i + s\omega_{ik}a_{jk}$
18:                  compute $a_{jk} := ca_{jk}$
19:              **end if**
20:          **end for**
21:          compute $a_{jj} := a_{jj} + \text{sum}_j$
22:          compute $a_{ii} := a_{ii} + \text{sum}_i$
23:      **end for**
24: **end for**

Before moving on, we make the following remarks about the above RIGO method.

(i) The incomplete orthogonal factor Q_{inc}, being always orthogonal, is stored implicitly through storing a sequence of Givens pairs, and it does not need to be formed explicitly. This may considerably save the computer storage and the computational cost.

(ii) The **generalized residual vector** z, defined by the linear system $Q_{inc}R_{inc}z = r$ with the vector r being the currently available residual, can be effectively computed through solving the upper-triangular linear system $R_{inc}z = Q_{inc}^{\mathsf{T}}r$, for which the **right-hand side** vector $v := Q_{inc}^{\mathsf{T}}r$ can be conveniently computed by acting successively the Givens transforms on the preceding vector.

(iii) The factorization error actually comes from lines 9–19. Here, the **diagonal compensation** and the Givens update are only done for those entries located in the **nonzero pattern** $P_{A,L} \cup (P_{A,U} \cap P_R)$, and no fill-in is introduced outside this **sparsity pattern**.

(iv) The **relaxation matrix** Ω can be chosen by sufficiently making use of the property of the target matrix A. In general, its entries are set to be suitable quantities in the interval $[0, 1]$.

(v) As an extreme case, if the nonzero pattern is large enough so that no fill-in is produced and no entry is dropped during the incomplete factorization process, then the diagonal compensation is unnecessary.

(vi) As every Givens rotation is determined by a diagonal entry of the currently available updated matrix from the target matrix A, we may do the **diagonal compensation** until all entries in each column below its main diagonal are annihilated so that the total computational cost for evaluating the Givens pairs can be further reduced.

Moreover, when $P_R = P_{A,U}$ and $\Omega = \omega I$, by utilizing the *modified Givens-updating rule*, i.e., Algorithm 7.20, we can obtain the following *practical RIGO method*, which can be implemented conveniently with cheap computer storage and low computational cost.

Algorithm 7.22: Practical RIGO Method

1: **for** $j = 1, 2, \ldots, n - 1$ **do**
2: $\quad k_r(j) := \max\{i : i \geq j, (i, j) \in P_{A,L} \text{ and } a_{ij} \neq 0\}$
3: $\quad$ **for** $i = k_r(j)$ down to $j + 1$ and $a_{ij} \neq 0$ **do**
4: $\quad\quad$ compute $\rho := \sqrt{a_{jj}^2 + a_{ij}^2}$, $c := a_{jj}/\rho$ and $s := a_{ij}/\rho$
5: $\quad\quad$ set $a_{jj} := \rho$ and $a_{ij} := 0$
6: $\quad\quad$ store c and s
7: $\quad\quad$ **for** $k = j + 1, j + 2, \ldots, n$ **do**
8: $\quad\quad\quad$ **if** $(i, k) \in P_A$ and $(j, k) \in P_{A,U}$ **then**
9: $\quad\quad\quad\quad$ **if** $a_{ik} \neq 0$ and $a_{jk} \neq 0$ **then**
10: $\quad\quad\quad\quad\quad$ compute temp $:= -sa_{jk} + ca_{ik}$
11: $\quad\quad\quad\quad\quad$ compute $a_{jk} := ca_{jk} + sa_{ik}$
12: $\quad\quad\quad\quad\quad$ set $a_{ik} :=$ temp
13: $\quad\quad\quad\quad$ **end if**
14: $\quad\quad\quad$ **else if** $(i, k) \in P_A$ and $a_{ik} \neq 0$ **then**
15: $\quad\quad\quad\quad$ compute $a_{jj} := a_{jj} - s\omega a_{ik}$
16: $\quad\quad\quad\quad$ compute $a_{ik} := ca_{ik}$
17: $\quad\quad\quad$ **else if** $(j, k) \in P_{A,U}$ and $a_{jk} \neq 0$ **then**
18: $\quad\quad\quad\quad$ compute $a_{ii} := a_{ii} + s\omega a_{jk}$
19: $\quad\quad\quad\quad$ compute $a_{jk} := ca_{jk}$
20: $\quad\quad\quad$ **end if**
21: $\quad\quad$ **end for**
22: $\quad$ **end for**
23: **end for**

Similarly, we remark that the **diagonal compensation** (see lines 15 and 18) may be done until each i-loop is completed so that the total computational cost for evaluating the Givens pairs can be further reduced. It is clear that the practical RIGO method can elaborate well the advantages of both the zero fill-in IGO method and the diagonal compensation strategy and, therefore, it has the potential to show better performance than the IGO methods without using such a modification, when they are used to precondition the Krylov subspace iteration methods [173, 288, 289, 323].

7.7 ▪ Sparse Approximate Inverse Preconditioners

The incomplete LU factorization is sequential and thus not well suited for the massively parallel computing architectures. Block incomplete LU variants have been developed as a remedy, but the price to pay is that more iterations are necessary. In this section, we introduce the *sparse approximate inverse* (SPAI) preconditioners, which show a very high degree of parallelism.

Preconditioning techniques based on sparse approximate inverses have been vigorously developed in recent years. The basic idea underlying this class of methods is that a sparse matrix $M \approx A^{-1}$ is explicitly computed and Krylov subspace iteration methods are applied to solve the **preconditioned linear system**

$$MAx = Mb, \tag{7.52}$$

or

$$AMu = b \quad \text{with} \quad x = Mu. \tag{7.53}$$

If the matrix M is, in certain sense, a good approximation to the inverse of the matrix A, then the iterative methods applied to solve the **left-preconditioned linear system** (7.52) or the **right-preconditioned linear system** (7.53) converge considerably faster.

The main advantages of this approach are as follows:

- SPAI is inherently parallel, because each column (or row, respectively) of the preconditioner M can be processed in parallel.

- SPAI can autonomously identify new entries for the sparsity pattern of the preconditioner M.

- The application of SPAI to the current residual in iterative solvers reduces to a matrix-vector product, which can be well parallelized.

Therefore, both the setup of the preconditioner as well as the application to the residual allow for a massive parallelism. Furthermore, the construction and application of SPAI tend to be immune from numerical difficulties such as pivot breakdowns and instability, and indeed these techniques have been shown to be remarkably robust in practice [71].

SPAI relies on the assumption that, for a given sparse matrix A, it is possible to find a sparse matrix M which is a good approximation, in some sense, to the matrix A^{-1}. However, this is not at all obvious, since the inverse of a sparse matrix is usually not sparse. For example, it can be proved that the inverse of an irreducible sparse matrix is structurally full. Nevertheless, it is often the case that many of the entries in the inverse of a sparse matrix are relatively small in absolute value, thus making the approximation of the matrix A^{-1} with a sparse matrix possible.

There exist several different methods for computing a sparse approximate inverse, with each approach having its own strengths and limitations; see [71] for more details. We can divide the approximate inverses into two basic types depending on whether the preconditioner $M \approx A^{-1}$ is expressed as a single matrix or as a product of two or more matrices.

7.7.1 ▪ Frobenius Norm Minimization

The essence of the SPAI method is to determine a sparse matrix M which minimizes

$$\|AM - I\|_F^2, \tag{7.54}$$

where the matrix M has a prescribed nonzero pattern. The parallel nature of SPAI can be readily seen when rewriting (7.54) as

$$\|AM - I\|_F^2 = \sum_{i=1}^{n} \|Am_i - e_i\|_2^2,$$

where m_i denotes the i-th column of the matrix M and e_i is the i-th column of the identity matrix I. Thus, we need to solve n **linear least-squares problems**

$$\min_{m_i} \|Am_i - e_i\|_2^2, \quad i = 1, 2, \ldots, n,$$

with respect to the columns m_i of the matrix M for $i = 1, 2, \ldots, n$. For the solution of each of the linear least-squares problems, either a direct method such as that through the QR decompositions can be utilized, or an iterative method such as that based on matrix splitting or Krylov subspace can be employed.

Alternatively, the SPAI preconditioning matrix M can be also obtained through solving the **matrix minimization problem**

$$\min_{M} \|AM - I\|_F^2,$$

or through finding the corresponding stationary point that satisfies the **linear matrix equation**

$$A^\mathsf{T} A M = A^\mathsf{T},$$

by adopting an appropriate iteration method.

In general, the SPAI method can be reinterpreted as constructing a sparse matrix M such that the product AM targets the identity, so we need not restrict ourselves to the identity but can instead consider the minimization problem

$$\min_{M} \|AM - T\|_F^2,$$

i.e., find a preconditioning matrix M such that AM targets T (which is termed as the "target" matrix), whereby the corresponding **preconditioned linear system** becomes

$$AMT^{-1}u = b \quad \text{with} \quad x = MT^{-1}u.$$

This approach requires that the action of the matrix T^{-1} be readily available. Easy parallelization is preserved when an appropriate **target matrix**, T, is employed. For more details, we refer the reader to [198].

In addition, as discussed in [198], the **Frobenius norm** may be replaced by other norms such as the **weighted** or the **generalized Frobenius norm**:

$$\|X\|_{F,H} \triangleq \sqrt{\langle X, X \rangle_H} = [\text{tr}(X^\mathsf{T} H X)]^{\frac{1}{2}}, \quad \forall X \in \mathbb{R}^{n \times n},$$

where $H \in \mathbb{R}^{n \times n}$, called the **weighting matrix**, is assumed to be symmetric positive definite. A few typical choices of such norms are the Frobenius A^{-1}-norm, that is, $H = A^{-1}$, if the matrix A is symmetric positive definite, or the Frobenius $\mathscr{H}(A^{-1})$-norm, that is, $H = \mathscr{H}(A^{-1})$, if the matrix A is nonsymmetric but positive definite, where

$$\mathscr{H}(A^{-1}) = \frac{1}{2}\left(A^{-1} + A^{-\mathsf{T}}\right)$$

is the symmetric part of the matrix A^{-1}.

According to the target T, in order not to obtain a trivial result, we may normalize it by setting its diagonal entries to be 1. Moreover, we can choose the target T as a diagonal, tridiagonal, or even a Hessenberg matrix. However, it is obvious that a more dense matrix T involves more computation in applying the preconditioner at every iteration step.

The above approach produces a **right sparse approximate inverse** for the nonsingular matrix A. Analogously, a **left sparse approximate inverse** can be computed by solving the **matrix minimization problem**

$$\|MA - I\|_F^2$$

or the corresponding **matrix-type normal equation**

$$MAA^\mathsf{T} = A^\mathsf{T}$$

by employing an appropriate iteration method.

More generally, with a target T we can find a left sparse approximate inverse for the matrix A by solving either the minimization problem

$$\min_{M} \|MA - T\|_F^2$$

in the Frobenius norm, or the minimization problem

$$\min_{M} \|MA - T\|_{F,H}^2$$

in the weighted Frobenius norm, with the weighting matrix $H = A^{-1}$ if the matrix A is symmetric positive definite, or $H = \mathcal{H}(A^{-1})$ if the matrix A is nonsymmetric but positive definite. As

$$\|MA - I\|_F = \|A^\mathsf{T} M^\mathsf{T} - I\|_F$$

and

$$\|MA - T\|_F = \|A^\mathsf{T} M^\mathsf{T} - T^\mathsf{T}\|_F,$$

computing a left sparse approximate inverse for the matrix A is then essentially equivalent to computing a right sparse approximate inverse for the matrix A^T.

In the case of nonsymmetric matrices, the distinction between left and right approximate inverses can be important. Indeed, there are situations where it is difficult to compute a good right approximate inverse but easy to find a good left approximate inverse, and vice versa. Furthermore, when the matrix A is strongly nonsymmetric and highly ill-conditioned, a matrix $M \approx A^{-1}$ may be a poor right (left) approximate inverse but a good left (right) approximate inverse. See [63] for a comprehensive survey.

7.7.2 ▪ Approximated Direct Factorizations

A sparse approximate inverse of a nonsingular matrix A can be computed by making use of incomplete inverse factorizations, that is, on incomplete factorizations of the matrix A^{-1}. If the matrix A admits the factorization $A = LDU$, where the matrix L is unit lower triangular, the matrix D is diagonal, and the matrix U is unit upper triangular, then

$$A^{-1} = U^{-1} D^{-1} L^{-1} \triangleq Z D^{-1} W^\mathsf{T},$$

with

$$Z = U^{-1} \quad \text{and} \quad W = L^{-\mathsf{T}}$$

being unit upper-triangular matrices. Note that in general the inverse factors Z and W will be rather dense. Factorized SPAI preconditioning matrices can be constructed by computing sparse approximations

$$\tilde{Z} \approx Z \quad \text{and} \quad \tilde{W} \approx W.$$

The factorized approximate inverse is then

$$M = \tilde{Z} \tilde{D}^{-1} \tilde{W}^\mathsf{T} \approx A^{-1},$$

where $\tilde{D}$ is a nonsingular diagonal matrix satisfying $\tilde{D} \approx D$.

Several typical approaches available for computing approximate inverse factors of a nonsingular matrix A include the *factorized sparse approximate inverse* (FSAI) method [216], the **incomplete biconjugation** process or **AINV** [67, 70], the *approximate inverse via bordering* (AIB) scheme [288], and the inverse ILU techniques [71]. For detailed algorithmic descriptions and implementable strategies using these preconditioning techniques, we refer the reader to [63, 71] and the references therein.

7.8 ▪ Exercises

7.1. Prove that (7.5) is an inner product provided that the matrix P is symmetric positive definite.

7.2. Prove the following statements:

(i) A matrix M is a solution of the matrix minimization problem $\min_{M} \|AM - I\|_F^2$ if it satisfies the matrix-type normal-residual equation $A^\mathsf{T} AM = A^\mathsf{T}$; moreover, the condition is also sufficient if the matrix A is of full column rank.

(ii) A matrix M is a solution of the matrix minimization problem $\min_{M} \|MA - I\|_F^2$ if it satisfies the matrix-type normal equation $MAA^\mathsf{T} = A^\mathsf{T}$; moreover, the condition is also sufficient if the matrix A is of full row rank.

7.3. Is it possible to discuss approximated direct factorizations for the matrix A based on the incomplete QR factorizations instead of the incomplete LU factorizations?

Chapter 8

Saddle-Point Problems

In this chapter, we consider systems of linear equations of the following **block two-by-two** form:

$$\begin{bmatrix} B & E \\ E^{\mathsf{T}} & -C \end{bmatrix} \begin{bmatrix} x \\ y \end{bmatrix} = \begin{bmatrix} f \\ g \end{bmatrix}, \qquad \text{or} \quad Az = b, \tag{8.1}$$

where $B \in \mathbb{R}^{n \times n}$, $E \in \mathbb{R}^{n \times m}$, and $C \in \mathbb{R}^{m \times m}$, with $n \geq m$. The special case where the matrix $C = 0$ and the matrix B is symmetric positive semidefinite, that is,

$$\begin{bmatrix} B & E \\ E^{\mathsf{T}} & 0 \end{bmatrix} \begin{bmatrix} x \\ y \end{bmatrix} = \begin{bmatrix} f \\ g \end{bmatrix}, \qquad \text{or} \quad Az = b, \tag{8.2}$$

is called the *standard saddle-point problem* (SSPP) [66]. Here we consider a more general case, which is called the *generalized saddle-point problem* (GSPP) [66], where the matrix C is not zero and is symmetric positive semidefinite. In the vast majority of cases, the matrix B in (8.1) is positive semidefinite and is usually symmetric.

Linear systems of the form (8.1) arise in a wide variety of applications throughout computational science and engineering. For example, the ever-increasing popularity of mixed or hybrid finite element approximations of second-order elliptic problems, elasticity problems or the Stokes equations in numerical partial differential equations [83, 124], and the extraordinary success of equality-constrained quadratic programming problems, interior point methods, or Lagrange multiplier methods [143] in numerical optimization require, at their hearts, the solution of a sequence of linear systems in the saddle-point form (8.1) or (8.2). For more details, see, e.g., [194, 250, 276, 327, 353, 354] and the references therein.

Due to their indefiniteness and poor spectral properties, this class of linear systems represents a significant challenge in modern scientific computing and engineering applications. In recent years, there has been a surge of interest in iteratively solving the standard and generalized saddle-point problems, and numerous solution techniques have been proposed for them, especially in the fields of numerical partial differential equations and numerical optimization.

8.1 ▪ Basic Properties

In this section, we discuss the **nonsingularity** and eigenproperties of the **standard** and **generalized saddle-point matrices**.

8.1.1 ▪ Solvability

For the block two-by-two matrix A in (8.1), suppose that the matrix B is nonsingular. Then we have the **block-triangular factorizations**

$$A = \begin{bmatrix} B & E \\ E^\mathsf{T} & -C \end{bmatrix}$$

$$= \begin{bmatrix} I & 0 \\ E^\mathsf{T} B^{-1} & I \end{bmatrix} \begin{bmatrix} B & E \\ 0 & S \end{bmatrix} = \begin{bmatrix} B & 0 \\ E^\mathsf{T} & S \end{bmatrix} \begin{bmatrix} I & B^{-1}E \\ 0 & I \end{bmatrix}$$

$$= \begin{bmatrix} I & 0 \\ E^\mathsf{T} B^{-1} & I \end{bmatrix} \begin{bmatrix} B & 0 \\ 0 & S \end{bmatrix} \begin{bmatrix} I & B^{-1}E \\ 0 & I \end{bmatrix}, \tag{8.3}$$

where

$$S = -(C + E^\mathsf{T} B^{-1} E) \tag{8.4}$$

is the so-called **Schur complement** of the matrix block B in the matrix A. (Alternatively, $S_{\text{neg}} \triangleq C + E^\mathsf{T} B^{-1} E = -S$ is called the negative Schur complement.) In particular, if the rank of the matrix B is the same as the rank of the matrix A, then it holds that

$$A = \begin{bmatrix} B & E \\ E^\mathsf{T} & -S \end{bmatrix}. \tag{8.5}$$

More important properties of the matrix A and many of the most popular solution methods for the saddle-point problems can be derived based on the block-triangular factorizations in (8.3).

We first consider the **solvability** of the linear system (8.1), i.e., the **nonsingularity** of its coefficient matrix A. The following result follows immediately from (8.3).

Theorem 8.1. *Let the matrix $B \in \mathbb{R}^{n \times n}$ be nonsingular and the matrix S be defined as in (8.4). Then the generalized saddle-point matrix A is nonsingular if and only if its Schur complement S is nonsingular.*

In fact, if both matrices B and S are nonsingular, then, based on the block-triangular factorizations in (8.3), we have

$$A^{-1} = \begin{bmatrix} B & E \\ E^\mathsf{T} & -C \end{bmatrix}^{-1}$$

$$= \begin{bmatrix} B^{-1} + B^{-1}ES^{-1}E^\mathsf{T} B^{-1} & -B^{-1}ES^{-1} \\ -S^{-1}E^\mathsf{T} B^{-1} & S^{-1} \end{bmatrix}.$$

In the following, we consider the nonsingularity of the generalized saddle-point matrix A in some special but common cases.

Case 1. The matrix B is symmetric positive definite and the matrix $C = 0$. In this case, the matrix

$$A = \begin{bmatrix} B & E \\ E^\mathsf{T} & 0 \end{bmatrix}$$

is the **standard saddle-point matrix** in (8.2), and $S = -E^\mathsf{T} B^{-1} E$ is the corresponding **Schur complement**. It follows from Theorem 8.1 that the matrix A is nonsingular if and only if its Schur complement S is nonsingular. This immediately leads to the following result.

Theorem 8.2. *Let $B \in \mathbb{R}^{n \times n}$ be symmetric positive definite and $C = 0$. Then the standard saddle-point matrix A is nonsingular if and only if $E \in \mathbb{R}^{n \times m}$ is of full column rank.*

Case 2. The matrix B is symmetric positive semidefinite and the matrix $C = 0$. In this case, the matrix A is the standard saddle-point matrix in (8.2) again, and $S = -E^\mathsf{T}B^{-1}E$ is the corresponding Schur complement.

Theorem 8.3. [188, 231] *Let $B \in \mathbb{R}^{n\times n}$ be symmetric positive semidefinite and $C = 0$. Assume that $E \in \mathbb{R}^{n\times m}$ is of full column rank. Then the standard saddle-point matrix A is nonsingular if and only if*

$$\mathrm{Ker}(B) \cap \mathrm{Ker}(E^\mathsf{T}) = \{0\}.$$

Proof. Suppose that
$$\mathrm{Ker}(B) \cap \mathrm{Ker}(E^\mathsf{T}) = \{0\},$$

and let $z = [x^\mathsf{T}, y^\mathsf{T}]^\mathsf{T} \in \mathbb{R}^{n+m}$, with $x \in \mathbb{R}^n$ and $y \in \mathbb{R}^m$, be a vector such that $Az = 0$. Then

$$Bx + Ey = 0 \quad \text{and} \quad E^\mathsf{T}x = 0. \tag{8.6}$$

It follows that $x \in \mathrm{Ker}(E^\mathsf{T})$ and

$$x^\mathsf{T}Bx = -x^\mathsf{T}Ey = -(E^\mathsf{T}x)^\mathsf{T}y = 0.$$

As the matrix B is symmetric positive semidefinite, we have $Bx = 0$. Hence,

$$x \in \mathrm{Ker}(B) \cap \mathrm{Ker}(E^\mathsf{T}),$$

which implies $x = 0$. As a result, from (8.6) we see that $Ey = 0$. Since the matrix E is of full column rank, it holds that $y = 0$. Hence, the above argument indicates that $z = 0$. That is to say, the linear system $Az = 0$ only has the zero solution, which is possible if and only if the matrix A is nonsingular.

On the other hand, suppose that the matrix A is nonsingular. If

$$\mathrm{Ker}(B) \cap \mathrm{Ker}(E^\mathsf{T}) \neq \{0\},$$

we may take a vector
$$x \in \mathrm{Ker}(B) \cap \mathrm{Ker}(E^\mathsf{T}), \quad \text{with} \quad x \neq 0.$$

That is to say, the vector $x \in \mathbb{R}^n$ satisfies

$$Bx = 0 \quad \text{and} \quad E^\mathsf{T}x = 0.$$

Let $z = [x^\mathsf{T}, 0]^\mathsf{T} \in \mathbb{R}^{n+m}$. Then it holds that

$$Az = \begin{bmatrix} B & E \\ E^\mathsf{T} & 0 \end{bmatrix} \begin{bmatrix} x \\ 0 \end{bmatrix} = \begin{bmatrix} Bx \\ E^\mathsf{T}x \end{bmatrix} = 0,$$

which implies that the matrix A is singular, a contradiction. Hence,

$$\mathrm{Ker}(B) \cap \mathrm{Ker}(E^\mathsf{T}) = \{0\}$$

must be true. $\square$

We remark that the condition that the matrix B is symmetric positive semidefinite can be further relaxed. For instance, it suffices that $x^\mathsf{T}Bx \neq 0$ for $x \in \mathrm{Ker}(E^\mathsf{T}) \setminus \{0\}$. This can be guaranteed by the condition that the matrix B is either positive definite or negative definite on $\mathrm{Ker}(E^\mathsf{T})$. In any case, the rank of the matrix B should be at least $n - m$.

Case 3. The matrix B is symmetric positive definite and the matrix C is symmetric positive semidefinite. In this case, the matrix A is the **generalized saddle-point matrix** in (8.1), and $S = -(C + E^\mathsf{T}B^{-1}E)$ is the corresponding **Schur complement**; see (8.4).

Theorem 8.4. *Let $B \in \mathbb{R}^{n \times n}$ be symmetric positive definite and $C \in \mathbb{R}^{m \times m}$ be symmetric positive semidefinite. Then the generalized saddle-point matrix A is nonsingular if and only if*

$$\mathrm{Ker}(C) \cap \mathrm{Ker}(E) = \{0\}.$$

Proof. Under the assumptions on the matrices B and C, we know that the Schur complement $S = -(C + E^\mathsf{T}B^{-1}E)$ is symmetric negative semidefinite. Assume

$$\mathrm{Ker}(C) \cap \mathrm{Ker}(E) = \{0\}.$$

If $y \in \mathbb{R}^m$ is a vector such that $Sy = 0$, then $y^\mathsf{T} Sy = 0$, so that

$$y^\mathsf{T} Cy = y^\mathsf{T} E^\mathsf{T} B^{-1} Ey = 0.$$

Since the matrix C is symmetric positive semidefinite and the matrix B^{-1} is symmetric positive definite, we have $Cy = 0$ and $Ey = 0$. Thus, it holds that

$$y \in \mathrm{Ker}(C) \cap \mathrm{Ker}(E),$$

so that $y = 0$. Consequently, the Schur complement S is nonsingular. In accordance with Theorem 8.1, we see that the matrix A is nonsingular.

On the other hand, suppose that the matrix A is nonsingular. Then, in accordance with Theorem 8.1 again, we know that the Schur complement $S = -(C + E^\mathsf{T}B^{-1}E)$ is nonsingular too. If

$$\mathrm{Ker}(C) \cap \mathrm{Ker}(E) \neq \{0\},$$

we may take a vector

$$y \in \mathrm{Ker}(C) \cap \mathrm{Ker}(E), \quad \text{with} \quad y \neq 0,$$

leading to

$$Sy = -(Cy + E^\mathsf{T} B^{-1} Ey) = 0.$$

This implies that the matrix S is singular, which results in a contradiction. Hence,

$$\mathrm{Ker}(C) \cap \mathrm{Ker}(E) = \{0\}. \qquad \square$$

Case 4. The matrix B is nonsymmetric but positive semidefinite. In this case, the matrix A is the generalized saddle-point matrix in (8.1) again, and $S = -(C + E^\mathsf{T}B^{-1}E)$ is the corresponding Schur complement.

Theorem 8.5. *Let $H_B = \frac{1}{2}(B + B^\mathsf{T}) \in \mathbb{R}^{n \times n}$ be symmetric positive semidefinite. Assume that $E \in \mathbb{R}^{n \times m}$ is of full rank and $C \in \mathbb{R}^{m \times m}$ is symmetric positive semidefinite. Then the following two statements hold true:*

  (i) $\mathrm{Ker}(H_B) \cap \mathrm{Ker}(E^\mathsf{T}) = \{0\}$ *implies that the matrix A is invertible.*
  (ii) *The matrix A being invertible implies that* $\mathrm{Ker}(B) \cap \mathrm{Ker}(E^\mathsf{T}) = \{0\}$.

Proof. The proof is similar to that of Theorem 8.3 and is left as Exercise 8.3. $\qquad \square$

We remark that the converses of (i) and (ii) do not hold in general.

Suppose that the matrix E is of full column rank and the matrix $C = 0$. Let $Z \in \mathbb{R}^{n \times (n-m)}$ be any matrix whose columns form a basis of the subspace $\text{Ker}(E^\mathsf{T})$. In addition, suppose that the matrix $H_B = \frac{1}{2}(B + B^\mathsf{T})$ is symmetric positive semidefinite. Then Condition (i) in Theorem 8.5 implies that the matrix $Z^\mathsf{T} H_B Z$ is symmetric positive definite. Let

$$W = Z(Z^\mathsf{T} B Z)^{-1} Z^\mathsf{T}.$$

Then we have the following formula for the inverse of the matrix A [155]:

$$
\begin{aligned}
A^{-1} &= \begin{bmatrix} B & E \\ E^\mathsf{T} & 0 \end{bmatrix}^{-1} \\
&= \begin{bmatrix} W & (I - WB)E(E^\mathsf{T}E)^{-1} \\ (E^\mathsf{T}E)^{-1}E^\mathsf{T}(I - BW) & -(E^\mathsf{T}E)^{-1}E^\mathsf{T}(B - BWB)E(E^\mathsf{T}E)^{-1} \end{bmatrix},
\end{aligned} \tag{8.7}
$$

which does not require that the matrix block B be invertible.

8.1.2 ▪ Eigenvalues

We first consider the case that the matrix B is symmetric positive definite, the matrix E is of full rank, and the matrix C is symmetric positive semidefinite. It follows from (8.3) that

$$
A = \begin{bmatrix} B & E \\ E^\mathsf{T} & -C \end{bmatrix} = \begin{bmatrix} I & B^{-1}E \\ 0 & I \end{bmatrix}^\mathsf{T} \begin{bmatrix} B & 0 \\ 0 & S \end{bmatrix} \begin{bmatrix} I & B^{-1}E \\ 0 & I \end{bmatrix},
$$

where

$$S = -(C + E^\mathsf{T} B^{-1} E)$$

is the Schur complement. Therefore, the matrix A is congruent to the block-diagonal matrix

$$\begin{bmatrix} B & 0 \\ 0 & S \end{bmatrix}.$$

As $B \in \mathbb{R}^{n \times n}$ is symmetric positive definite and $S \in \mathbb{R}^{m \times m}$ is symmetric negative definite, this block-diagonal matrix has n positive eigenvalues and m negative eigenvalues. By **Sylvester's inertia law**, we know that the matrix A is indefinite with n positive and m negative eigenvalues.

If $E \in \mathbb{R}^{n \times m}$ is rank deficient, $S \in \mathbb{R}^{m \times m}$ can be symmetric negative semidefinite. Suppose that the matrix S has r ($0 \le r \le m$) zero eigenvalues, i.e., $\text{rank}(S) = m - r$. Then, $A \in \mathbb{R}^{(n+m) \times (n+m)}$ has n positive, $m - r$ negative, and r zero eigenvalues.

The following result about bounds of the eigenvalues is due to Rusten and Winther [283], which treats the case $C = 0$, that is, the **standard saddle-point matrix** A in (8.2); see also [294].

Theorem 8.6. *Let $B \in \mathbb{R}^{n \times n}$ be symmetric positive definite and $C = 0$. Assume that $E \in \mathbb{R}^{n \times m}$ is of full column rank. Denote the largest and smallest eigenvalues of the matrix B by μ_1 and μ_n, and the largest and smallest singular values of the matrix E by σ_1 and σ_m. Then it holds that*

$$\lambda(A) \in \mathcal{I}_- \cup \mathcal{I}_+,$$

where

$$\mathcal{I}_- = \left[\frac{1}{2}\left(\mu_n - \sqrt{\mu_n^2 + 4\sigma_1^2} \right), \frac{1}{2}\left(\mu_1 - \sqrt{\mu_1^2 + 4\sigma_m^2} \right) \right]$$

and

$$\mathcal{I}_+ = \left[\mu_n, \frac{1}{2}\left(\mu_1 + \sqrt{\mu_1^2 + 4\sigma_1^2}\right)\right].$$

Proof. Let λ be an eigenvalue of the matrix A with the corresponding eigenvector $z = [x^\mathsf{T}, y^\mathsf{T}]^\mathsf{T}$, with $x \in \mathbb{R}^n$ and $y \in \mathbb{R}^m$. That is to say, the eigenpair (λ, z) satisfies

$$\begin{bmatrix} B & E \\ E^\mathsf{T} & 0 \end{bmatrix} \begin{bmatrix} x \\ y \end{bmatrix} = \lambda \begin{bmatrix} x \\ y \end{bmatrix},$$

or equivalently,

$$Bx + Ey = \lambda x, \tag{8.8}$$
$$E^\mathsf{T}x = \lambda y. \tag{8.9}$$

Note that $\lambda \neq 0$ as the matrix A is nonsingular. Also, $x \neq 0$ as, otherwise, $y = 0$ from (8.9), so that $z = 0$, which contradicts with the fact that the vector z is an eigenvector of the matrix A. Then, it follows from (8.9) again that

$$y = \frac{1}{\lambda}E^\mathsf{T}x.$$

Substituting this relationship into (8.8) and then multiplying both sides of the obtained equality from left by the vector x^T, we have

$$\lambda^2 - \lambda \frac{x^\mathsf{T} Bx}{x^\mathsf{T}x} - \frac{x^\mathsf{T} EE^\mathsf{T}x}{x^\mathsf{T}x} = 0.$$

The two real solutions of this **quadratic polynomial equation** are

$$\lambda = \frac{1}{2}\left(\mu \pm \sqrt{\mu^2 + 4\sigma^2}\right),$$

where we have introduced the notation

$$\mu = \frac{x^\mathsf{T} Bx}{x^\mathsf{T}x} \quad \text{and} \quad \sigma = \sqrt{\frac{x^\mathsf{T} EE^\mathsf{T}x}{x^\mathsf{T}x}}.$$

Since the matrix B is symmetric positive definite and the matrix EE^T is symmetric positive semidefinite, it holds that

$$\mu_n \leq \mu \leq \mu_1 \quad \text{and} \quad 0 \leq \sigma \leq \sigma_1.$$

Therefore, by detailed analysis we know that

$$\lambda \in \left[\frac{1}{2}\left(\mu_n - \sqrt{\mu_n^2 + 4\sigma_1^2}\right), 0\right] \cup \mathcal{I}_+. \tag{8.10}$$

Now we further refine the upper bound for the negative eigenvalues of the matrix A. To this end, we suppose $\lambda < 0$. Then the matrix $B - \lambda I$ is symmetric positive definite. It follows that $y \neq 0$ as, otherwise, the equation (8.8) reduces to $(B - \lambda I)x = 0$, so that $x = 0$ and $Ey = 0$. Then $y = 0$ due to the full-rank assumption on the matrix E. This argument shows that $z = 0$, which contradicts the fact that the vector z is an eigenvector of the matrix A too. Hence, for this case, it holds that $y \neq 0$ and $Ey \neq 0$.

From (8.8) we get

$$x = -(B - \lambda I)^{-1} E y.$$

Substituting this relationship into (8.9) and then multiplying both sides of the resulting equality from the left by the vector y^T, we obtain

$$
\begin{aligned}
-\lambda &= \frac{y^\mathsf{T} E^\mathsf{T} (B - \lambda I)^{-1} E y}{y^\mathsf{T} y} \\
&= \frac{y^\mathsf{T} E^\mathsf{T} (B - \lambda I)^{-1} E y}{y^\mathsf{T} E^\mathsf{T} E y} \cdot \frac{y^\mathsf{T} E^\mathsf{T} E y}{y^\mathsf{T} y} \\
&\geq (\mu_1 - \lambda)^{-1} \sigma_m^2,
\end{aligned}
$$

or in other words,

$$\lambda^2 - \mu_1 \lambda - \sigma_m^2 \geq 0.$$

Therefore, for the case $\lambda < 0$ it holds that

$$\lambda \leq \frac{1}{2} \left(\mu_1 - \sqrt{\mu_1^2 + 4\sigma_m^2} \right).$$

This bound, together with the bounds in (8.10), then leads to the conclusion. ☐

This result can be extended to the case where the matrix $C \neq 0$ [294].

Theorem 8.7. *Let $B \in \mathbb{R}^{n \times n}$ be symmetric positive definite and $C \in \mathbb{R}^{m \times m}$ be symmetric positive semidefinite. Assume that $E \in \mathbb{R}^{n \times m}$ is of full rank. Denote the largest and smallest eigenvalues of the matrix B by μ_1 and μ_n, the largest eigenvalue of the matrix C by ν_1, and the largest and smallest singular values of the matrix E by σ_1 and σ_m. Then it holds that*

$$\lambda(A) \in \mathcal{I}_- \cup \mathcal{I}_+,$$

where

$$\mathcal{I}_- = \left[\frac{1}{2} \left(\mu_n - \nu_1 - \sqrt{(\mu_n + \nu_1)^2 + 4\sigma_1^2} \right), \frac{1}{2} \left(\mu_1 - \sqrt{\mu_1^2 + 4\sigma_m^2} \right) \right]$$

and

$$\mathcal{I}_+ = \left[\mu_n, \frac{1}{2} \left(\mu_1 + \sqrt{\mu_1^2 + 4\sigma_1^2} \right) \right].$$

Proof. Let λ be an eigenvalue of the matrix A with the corresponding eigenvector $z = [x^\mathsf{T}, y^\mathsf{T}]^\mathsf{T}$, with $x \in \mathbb{R}^n$ and $y \in \mathbb{R}^m$. Then

$$Bx + Ey = \lambda x, \tag{8.11}$$
$$E^\mathsf{T} x - Cy = \lambda y. \tag{8.12}$$

We first consider the positive eigenvalues, that is, $\lambda > 0$. Note that now $x \neq 0$ as, otherwise, from (8.12) it holds that $(\lambda I + C)y = 0$, so that $y = 0$, which implies $z = 0$ that contradicts with the fact that the vector z is an eigenvector of the matrix A. Then, it follows from (8.12) that

$$y = (\lambda I + C)^{-1} E^\mathsf{T} x = \frac{1}{\lambda} \left(I + \frac{1}{\lambda} C \right)^{-1} E^\mathsf{T} x.$$

Substituting this relationship into (8.11) and then multiplying both sides of the obtained equality from the left by the vector x^T, we have

$$\frac{x^\mathsf{T} B x}{x^\mathsf{T} x} + \frac{1}{\lambda} \frac{x^\mathsf{T} E \left(I + \frac{1}{\lambda} C\right)^{-1} E^\mathsf{T} x}{x^\mathsf{T} x} = \lambda.$$

As

$$\mu_n \le \frac{x^\mathsf{T} B x}{x^\mathsf{T} x} \le \mu_1 \quad \text{and} \quad \frac{x^\mathsf{T} E \left(I + \frac{1}{\lambda} C\right)^{-1} E^\mathsf{T} x}{x^\mathsf{T} x} \le \sigma_1^2,$$

it holds that

$$\lambda \le \mu_1 + \frac{1}{\lambda} \sigma_1^2,$$

that is,

$$\lambda^2 - \mu_1 \lambda - \sigma_1^2 \le 0.$$

Therefore, any positive eigenvalue λ of the matrix A must satisfy

$$\lambda \le \frac{1}{2} \left(\mu_1 + \sqrt{\mu_1^2 + 4\sigma_1^2} \right). \tag{8.13}$$

On the other hand, by first multiplying both sides of the equality (8.11) with the vector x^T and both sides of the equality (8.12) with the vector y^T, and then subtracting the resulting two equalities side by side, respectively, we obtain

$$x^\mathsf{T} B x + y^\mathsf{T} C y = \lambda x^\mathsf{T} x - \lambda y^\mathsf{T} y.$$

Therefore,

$$\lambda = \frac{x^\mathsf{T} B x}{x^\mathsf{T} x} + \frac{y^\mathsf{T} C y}{x^\mathsf{T} x} + \lambda \frac{y^\mathsf{T} y}{x^\mathsf{T} x} \ge \frac{x^\mathsf{T} B x}{x^\mathsf{T} x} \ge \mu_n. \tag{8.14}$$

Now we consider the negative eigenvalues, that is, $\lambda < 0$. Similar to the proof of Theorem 8.6, it holds that

$$\begin{aligned}
-\lambda &= \frac{y^\mathsf{T} E^\mathsf{T} (B - \lambda I)^{-1} E y}{y^\mathsf{T} y} + \frac{y^\mathsf{T} C y}{y^\mathsf{T} y} \\
&\ge \frac{y^\mathsf{T} E^\mathsf{T} (B - \lambda I)^{-1} E y}{y^\mathsf{T} y} \\
&\ge (\mu_1 - \lambda)^{-1} \sigma_m^2
\end{aligned}$$

and

$$\begin{aligned}
-\lambda &= \frac{y^\mathsf{T} E^\mathsf{T} (B - \lambda I)^{-1} E y}{y^\mathsf{T} y} + \frac{y^\mathsf{T} C y}{y^\mathsf{T} y} \\
&\le (\mu_n - \lambda)^{-1} \sigma_1^2 + \nu_1.
\end{aligned}$$

Therefore, for the case $\lambda < 0$ we have

$$\lambda \le \frac{1}{2} \left(\mu_1 - \sqrt{\mu_1^2 + 4\sigma_m^2} \right)$$

and

$$\lambda \geq \frac{1}{2} \left(\mu_n - \nu_1 - \sqrt{(\mu_n + \nu_1)^2 + 4\sigma_1^2} \right).$$

These bounds, together with (8.13) and (8.14), then lead to the conclusion. $\square$

Comparing the bounds in Theorems 8.6 and 8.7, we observe that a nonzero $(2, 2)$-block matrix C only affects the lower bound for the negative eigenvalues of the generalized saddle-point matrix A, but does not affect the other bounds for either the negative or the positive eigenvalues of the matrix A.

In fact, when $C = 0$ that implies $\nu_1 = 0$, the bounds in Theorem 8.7 straightforwardly reduce to the bounds in Theorem 8.6.

For the more general case that the $(1, 1)$-block matrix B is symmetric positive definite and the Schur complement S with respect to the $(2, 2)$-block matrix C is symmetric indefinite, Bai, Ng, and Wang derived in [48] accurate bounds for the negative and positive eigenvalues of the **generalized saddle-point matrix** A in (8.1). Note that, for this case, the $(2, 2)$-block matrix C is only assumed to be symmetric, so it may be indefinite in general. Hence, for simplicity of the statements, in the description of this result we absorb the minus sign in front of the matrix C into C itself, and turn to consider the block two-by-two nonsingular and symmetric indefinite matrix

$$A = \begin{bmatrix} B & E \\ E^\mathsf{T} & C \end{bmatrix}, \tag{8.15}$$

where $B \in \mathbb{R}^{n \times n}$ is symmetric positive definite, $C \in \mathbb{R}^{m \times m}$ is symmetric, and $S = C - E^\mathsf{T} B^{-1} E \in \mathbb{R}^{m \times m}$, the Schur complement of the matrix A, is nonsingular, with $E \in \mathbb{R}^{n \times m}$.

Theorem 8.8. [48] *Let the matrix $A \in \mathbb{R}^{(n+m) \times (n+m)}$ given in (8.15) be nonsingular. Assume that $B \in \mathbb{R}^{n \times n}$ is symmetric positive definite with $\sigma(B) \subseteq [\delta, \Delta]$, and $S = C - E^\mathsf{T} B^{-1} E \in \mathbb{R}^{m \times m}$ is symmetric indefinite with $\sigma(S) \subseteq [-\Theta, -\theta] \cup [\gamma, \Gamma]$, where $\delta, \Delta, \theta, \Theta,$ and γ, Γ are positive reals. In addition, let $\sigma(E^\mathsf{T} B^{-1} E) \subseteq [\omega, \Omega]$. Then it holds that*

$$\sigma(A) \subseteq \mathcal{I}_- \cup \mathcal{I}_+,$$

where

$$\mathcal{I}_- = \left[\frac{1}{2} \left(\omega + \Delta - \Theta - \sqrt{(\omega + \Delta - \Theta)^2 + 4\Theta\Delta} \right), \frac{1}{2} \left(\Omega + \delta - \theta - \sqrt{(\Omega + \delta - \theta)^2 + 4\theta\delta} \right) \right]$$

and

$$\mathcal{I}_+ = \left[\frac{1}{2} \left(\Omega + \delta + \gamma - \sqrt{(\Omega + \delta + \gamma)^2 - 4\delta\gamma} \right), \frac{1}{2} \left(\Omega + \Delta + \Gamma + \sqrt{(\Omega + \Delta + \Gamma)^2 - 4\Delta\Gamma} \right) \right].$$

Proof. Consider the case $\lambda \in \sigma(A)$ with $\lambda > 0$. To prove that such a λ is located in the interval $\mathcal{I}_+$, we only need to verify

$$\lambda_{\max}(A) \leq \frac{1}{2} \left(\Delta + \Gamma + \Omega + \sqrt{(\Delta + \Gamma + \Omega)^2 - 4\Delta\Gamma} \right)$$

and

$$\lambda_{\max}(A^{-1}) \leq \frac{1}{2} \left(\frac{1}{\delta} + \frac{1}{\gamma} + \frac{\Omega}{\delta\gamma} + \sqrt{\left(\frac{1}{\delta} + \frac{1}{\gamma} + \frac{\Omega}{\delta\gamma} \right)^2 - \frac{4}{\delta\gamma}} \right).$$

For the convenience of our statements, we define the matrices

$$D = \begin{pmatrix} B^{\frac{1}{2}} & 0 \\ 0 & I \end{pmatrix}, \quad L = \begin{pmatrix} I & 0 \\ E^{\mathsf{T}} B^{-\frac{1}{2}} & I \end{pmatrix}, \quad \text{and} \quad T = \begin{pmatrix} I & 0 \\ 0 & S \end{pmatrix}.$$

After straightforward computations, we obtain

$$A = DLTL^{\mathsf{T}}D \quad \text{and} \quad A^{-1} = D^{-1}L^{-\mathsf{T}}T^{-1}L^{-1}D^{-1}.$$

Noticing that $S \preceq \Gamma I$ and $S^{-1} \preceq \frac{1}{\gamma} I$, we know $T \preceq T_R$ and $T^{-1} \preceq T_L^{-1}$, where

$$T_R = \begin{pmatrix} I & 0 \\ 0 & \Gamma I \end{pmatrix} \quad \text{and} \quad T_L = \begin{pmatrix} I & 0 \\ 0 & \gamma I \end{pmatrix}.$$

Making use of Proposition 1.54 (2) we obtain

$$A \preceq DLT_R L^{\mathsf{T}} D \quad \text{and} \quad A^{-1} \preceq D^{-1}L^{-\mathsf{T}}T_L^{-1}L^{-1}D^{-1}.$$

Hence, from Proposition 1.54 (3) we get

$$\lambda_{\max}(A) \leq \lambda_{\max}(DLT_R L^{\mathsf{T}} D) = \lambda_{\max}(T_R^{\frac{1}{2}} L^{\mathsf{T}} D^2 L T_R^{\frac{1}{2}}) \tag{8.16}$$

and

$$\lambda_{\max}(A^{-1}) \leq \lambda_{\max}(D^{-1}L^{-\mathsf{T}}T_L^{-1}L^{-1}D^{-1}) = \lambda_{\max}(T_L^{-\frac{1}{2}} L^{-1} D^{-2} L^{-\mathsf{T}} T_L^{-\frac{1}{2}}), \tag{8.17}$$

where $\lambda_{\max}(\cdot)$ indicates the largest eigenvalue of the corresponding matrix. Because of $B \preceq \Delta I$ and $B^{-1} \preceq \frac{1}{\delta} I$, based on Proposition 1.53 (2) we see that $D^2 \preceq D_R^2$ and $D^{-2} \preceq D_L^{-2}$, where

$$D_R = \begin{pmatrix} \sqrt{\Delta} I & 0 \\ 0 & I \end{pmatrix} \quad \text{and} \quad D_L = \begin{pmatrix} \sqrt{\delta} I & 0 \\ 0 & I \end{pmatrix}.$$

Making use of Proposition 1.54 (2) again we obtain

$$T_R^{\frac{1}{2}} L^{\mathsf{T}} D^2 L T_R^{\frac{1}{2}} \preceq T_R^{\frac{1}{2}} L^{\mathsf{T}} D_R^2 L T_R^{\frac{1}{2}}$$

and

$$T_L^{-\frac{1}{2}} L^{-1} D^{-2} L^{-\mathsf{T}} T_L^{-\frac{1}{2}} \preceq T_L^{-\frac{1}{2}} L^{-1} D_L^{-2} L^{-\mathsf{T}} T_L^{-\frac{1}{2}}.$$

It follows from (8.16) and (8.17) that

$$\lambda_{\max}(A) \leq \lambda_{\max}(T_R^{\frac{1}{2}} L^{\mathsf{T}} D_R^2 L T_R^{\frac{1}{2}}) \triangleq \lambda_{\max}(\widetilde{L}^{\mathsf{T}} \widetilde{L}) \tag{8.18}$$

and

$$\lambda_{\max}(A^{-1}) \leq \lambda_{\max}(T_L^{-\frac{1}{2}} L^{-1} D_L^{-2} L^{-\mathsf{T}} T_L^{-\frac{1}{2}}) \triangleq \lambda_{\max}(\widehat{L}\widehat{L}^{\mathsf{T}}) = \lambda_{\max}(\widehat{L}^{\mathsf{T}}\widehat{L}), \tag{8.19}$$

where

$$\widetilde{L} = D_R L T_R^{\frac{1}{2}} = \begin{pmatrix} \sqrt{\Delta} I & 0 \\ E^{\mathsf{T}} B^{-\frac{1}{2}} & \sqrt{\Gamma} I \end{pmatrix}$$

and

$$\widehat{L} = T_L^{-\frac{1}{2}} L^{-1} D_L^{-1} = \begin{pmatrix} \frac{1}{\sqrt{\delta}} I & 0 \\ -\frac{1}{\sqrt{\delta\gamma}} E^{\mathsf{T}} B^{-\frac{1}{2}} & \frac{1}{\sqrt{\gamma}} I \end{pmatrix}.$$

Let

$$B^{-\frac{1}{2}}E = U \begin{pmatrix} \Sigma & 0 \\ 0 & 0 \end{pmatrix} V$$

be the **singular value decomposition** of the matrix $B^{-\frac{1}{2}}E$, where $U \in \mathbb{R}^{n \times n}$ and $V \in \mathbb{R}^{m \times m}$ are orthogonal matrices and $\Sigma = \mathrm{diag}(\sigma_1, \sigma_2, \ldots, \sigma_r) \in \mathbb{R}^{r \times r}$ is a diagonal matrix with $\sigma_1, \sigma_2, \ldots, \sigma_r$, the nonzero singular values of the matrix $B^{-\frac{1}{2}}E$, satisfying $\sigma_1 \geq \sigma_2 \geq \cdots \geq \sigma_r > 0$. It clearly holds that

$$\sigma_1^2 = \lambda_{\max}(E^{\mathsf{T}}B^{-1}E) = \Omega.$$

By direct calculation, we obtain that the eigenvalues of the matrix $\widetilde{L}^{\mathsf{T}}\widetilde{L}$ are Δ, Γ, and

$$\frac{1}{2}\left(\Delta + \Gamma + \sigma_j^2 \pm \sqrt{(\Delta + \Gamma + \sigma_j^2)^2 - 4\Delta\Gamma}\right), \quad j = 1, 2, \ldots, r,$$

and those of the matrix $\widehat{L}^{\mathsf{T}}\widehat{L}$ are $\frac{1}{\delta}$, $\frac{1}{\gamma}$, and

$$\frac{1}{2}\left(\frac{1}{\delta} + \frac{1}{\gamma} + \frac{\sigma_j^2}{\delta\gamma} \pm \sqrt{\left(\frac{1}{\delta} + \frac{1}{\gamma} + \frac{\sigma_j^2}{\delta\gamma}\right)^2 - \frac{4}{\delta\gamma}}\right), \quad j = 1, 2, \ldots, r.$$

Based on (8.18) and (8.19), we immediately obtain

$$\lambda_{\max}(A) \leq \max\left\{\Delta, \Gamma, \frac{1}{2}\left(\Delta + \Gamma + \sigma_1^2 + \sqrt{(\Delta + \Gamma + \sigma_1^2)^2 - 4\Delta\Gamma}\right)\right\}$$

$$\leq \frac{1}{2}\left(\Delta + \Gamma + \Omega + \sqrt{(\Delta + \Gamma + \Omega)^2 - 4\Delta\Gamma}\right)$$

$$\leq \Delta + \Gamma + \Omega$$

and

$$\lambda_{\max}(A^{-1}) \leq \max\left\{\frac{1}{\delta}, \frac{1}{\gamma}, \frac{1}{2}\left(\frac{1}{\delta} + \frac{1}{\gamma} + \frac{\sigma_1^2}{\delta\gamma} + \sqrt{\left(\frac{1}{\delta} + \frac{1}{\gamma} + \frac{\sigma_1^2}{\delta\gamma}\right)^2 - \frac{4}{\delta\gamma}}\right)\right\}$$

$$\leq \frac{1}{2}\left(\frac{1}{\delta} + \frac{1}{\gamma} + \frac{\Omega}{\delta\gamma} + \sqrt{\left(\frac{1}{\delta} + \frac{1}{\gamma} + \frac{\Omega}{\delta\gamma}\right)^2 - \frac{4}{\delta\gamma}}\right)$$

$$\leq \frac{1}{\delta} + \frac{1}{\gamma} + \frac{\Omega}{\delta\gamma}.$$

Now, consider the case $\lambda \in \sigma(A)$ with $\lambda < 0$. To prove that such a λ is located in the interval $\mathcal{I}_-$, we let $z = [x^{\mathsf{T}}, y^{\mathsf{T}}]^{\mathsf{T}} \in \mathbb{R}^{n+m}$, with $x \in \mathbb{R}^n$ and $y \in \mathbb{R}^m$, be the corresponding eigenvector. Obviously, it holds that

$$\begin{cases} Bx + Ey &= \lambda x, \\ E^{\mathsf{T}}x + Cy &= \lambda y. \end{cases}$$

We assert that $y \neq 0$. Otherwise, if $y = 0$, then $Bx = \lambda x$ and $E^{\mathsf{T}}x = 0$. This shows $\lambda \in \sigma(B)$ or $x = 0$, which cannot occur under the assumption as the matrix B is symmetric positive definite and the vector $z = [x^{\mathsf{T}}, y^{\mathsf{T}}]^{\mathsf{T}} \neq 0$. By using the vector and matrix transforms

$$\widetilde{x} = B^{\frac{1}{2}}x \quad \text{and} \quad \widetilde{E} = B^{-\frac{1}{2}}E,$$

we can rewrite the above equation as

$$\begin{cases} \widetilde{x} + \widetilde{E}y &= \lambda B^{-1}\widetilde{x}, \\ \widetilde{E}^{\mathsf{T}}\widetilde{x} + Cy &= \lambda y, \end{cases}$$

or equivalently,

$$\begin{cases} \widetilde{x} + \widetilde{E}y &= \lambda B^{-1}\widetilde{x}, \\ \widetilde{E}^{\mathsf{T}}\widetilde{x} + \widetilde{E}^{\mathsf{T}}\widetilde{E}y &= (\lambda I - S)y. \end{cases} \tag{8.20}$$

Noting that

$$\widetilde{E}^{\mathsf{T}}\widetilde{E} = E^{\mathsf{T}}B^{-1}E,$$

we obtain

$$\sigma(\widetilde{E}^{\mathsf{T}}\widetilde{E}) \subseteq [\omega,\, \Omega]. \tag{8.21}$$

From the first equation in (8.20) we have

$$\widetilde{E}y = \lambda B^{-1}\widetilde{x} - \widetilde{x}.$$

After substituting this relationship into the second equation in (8.20) we get

$$(\lambda I - S)y = \widetilde{E}^{\mathsf{T}}\widetilde{x} + \widetilde{E}^{\mathsf{T}}(\lambda B^{-1} - I)\widetilde{x} = \lambda \widetilde{E}^{\mathsf{T}}B^{-1}\widetilde{x}.$$

As the first equation in (8.20) also implies

$$\widetilde{x} = -(I - \lambda B^{-1})^{-1}\widetilde{E}y,$$

we obtain

$$(\lambda I - S)y = -\lambda \widetilde{E}^{\mathsf{T}}B^{-1}(I - \lambda B^{-1})^{-1}\widetilde{E}y,$$

or

$$-Sy = -\lambda \left[I + \widetilde{E}^{\mathsf{T}}(B - \lambda I)^{-1}\widetilde{E}\right]y.$$

It then follows immediately that

$$-M_\lambda^{-\frac{1}{2}}SM_\lambda^{-\frac{1}{2}}\widetilde{y} = -\lambda\widetilde{y},$$

with

$$M_\lambda = I + \widetilde{E}^{\mathsf{T}}(B - \lambda I)^{-1}\widetilde{E} \quad \text{and} \quad \widetilde{y} = M_\lambda^{\frac{1}{2}}y,$$

or

$$-\lambda \in \sigma(\widetilde{S}_\lambda), \quad \text{with} \quad \widetilde{S}_\lambda = -M_\lambda^{-\frac{1}{2}}SM_\lambda^{-\frac{1}{2}}. \tag{8.22}$$

Here, we have used the fact that $\lambda < 0$ implies that the matrix $B - \lambda I$ is symmetric positive definite, and that $y \neq 0$ implies $\widetilde{y} \neq 0$. Noticing that $-S \preceq \Theta I$ and $-S^{-1} \preceq \frac{1}{\theta}I$, we know

$$\widetilde{S}_\lambda \preceq \Theta M_\lambda^{-1} \quad \text{and} \quad \widetilde{S}_\lambda^{-1} \preceq \frac{1}{\theta}M_\lambda. \tag{8.23}$$

Since $\sigma(B) \subseteq [\delta,\, \Delta]$, we obtain

$$\frac{1}{\Delta - \lambda}I \preceq (B - \lambda I)^{-1} \preceq \frac{1}{\delta - \lambda}I$$

and, therefore,

$$\frac{1}{\Delta - \lambda} \widetilde{E}^{\mathsf{T}} \widetilde{E} \preceq \widetilde{E}^{\mathsf{T}} (B - \lambda I)^{-1} \widetilde{E} \preceq \frac{1}{\delta - \lambda} \widetilde{E}^{\mathsf{T}} \widetilde{E}.$$

Hence, it holds that

$$I + \frac{1}{\Delta - \lambda} \widetilde{E}^{\mathsf{T}} \widetilde{E} \preceq M_\lambda \preceq I + \frac{1}{\delta - \lambda} \widetilde{E}^{\mathsf{T}} \widetilde{E}.$$

By using (8.21), we obtain the estimate

$$\frac{\omega + \Delta - \lambda}{\Delta - \lambda} I \preceq M_\lambda \preceq \frac{\Omega + \delta - \lambda}{\delta - \lambda} I.$$

Hence, it follows from (8.23) that

$$\widetilde{S}_\lambda \preceq \frac{\Theta(\Delta - \lambda)}{\omega + \Delta - \lambda} I \quad \text{and} \quad \widetilde{S}_\lambda^{-1} \preceq \frac{\Omega + \delta - \lambda}{\theta(\delta - \lambda)} I.$$

So, from (8.22) we have

$$\frac{\theta(\delta - \lambda)}{\Omega + \delta - \lambda} \leq -\lambda \leq \frac{\Theta(\Delta - \lambda)}{\omega + \Delta - \lambda}.$$

This evidently shows that

$$\frac{1}{2} \left[\omega + \Delta - \Theta - \sqrt{(\omega + \Delta - \Theta)^2 + 4\Theta\Delta} \right] \leq \lambda \leq \frac{1}{2} \left[\Omega + \delta - \theta - \sqrt{(\Omega + \delta - \theta)^2 + 4\theta\delta} \right].$$

$\square$

Again, it is deserving of emphasis that in Theorem 8.8 we do not assume that the matrix block C is negative semidefinite as is often done in the literature; see, e.g., [10,66,294]. Thereby, Theorem 8.8 substantially generalizes those existing results, especially Theorems 8.6 and 8.7.

Corollary 8.9. [10, 48, 294] *Let the conditions of Theorem 8.8 be satisfied. Then*

(i) *when the Schur complement S is symmetric negative definite with $\sigma(S) \subseteq [-\Theta, -\theta]$, it holds that $\sigma(A) \subseteq \mathcal{I}_- \cup \mathcal{I}_+^{(o)}$, where*

$$\mathcal{I}_+^{(o)} = [\delta, \Delta + \Omega];$$

(ii) *when the Schur complement S is symmetric positive definite with $\sigma(S) \subseteq [\gamma, \Gamma]$, it holds that $\sigma(A) \subseteq \mathcal{I}_+$.*

Note that Case (ii) of Corollary 8.9 corresponds to the requirement that the matrix A is symmetric positive definite.

In addition, we remark that estimates on bounds of the eigenvalues for block two-by-two nonsingular and symmetric indefinite matrices of the form A in (8.1) were derived by Bai in [25], when the $(1, 1)$-block matrix B, the $(2, 2)$-block matrix C, and the Schur complement S are all assumed to be only symmetric and indefinite.

As shown in Theorems 8.6 and 8.7, the eigenvalues of the saddle-point matrices A are located on the real axis, but usually on both sides of the origin, which is generally an unfavorable property for the Krylov subspace iteration methods such as GMRES and BiCGSTAB [26]. However, we observe that the **generalized saddle-point problem** (8.1) is also equivalent to

$$\begin{bmatrix} B & E \\ -E^{\mathsf{T}} & C \end{bmatrix} \begin{bmatrix} x \\ y \end{bmatrix} = \begin{bmatrix} f \\ -g \end{bmatrix}, \quad \text{or} \quad \tilde{A}z = \tilde{b}. \tag{8.24}$$

The special case where $C = 0$, that is,

$$\begin{bmatrix} B & E \\ -E^{\mathsf{T}} & 0 \end{bmatrix} \begin{bmatrix} x \\ y \end{bmatrix} = \begin{bmatrix} f \\ -g \end{bmatrix}, \quad \text{or} \quad \tilde{A}z = \tilde{b}, \tag{8.25}$$

is also termed the **standard saddle-point problem**.

In the literature, for distinction the **block two-by-two linear systems** in (8.1) and (8.2) are also referred to as the **generalized** and **standard saddle-point problems** in **symmetric forms**, while those in (8.24) and (8.25) are referred to as the **generalized** and **standard saddle-point problems** in **nonsymmetric forms**, respectively.

Note that the generalized saddle-point matrix $\tilde{A}$ is nonsingular if and only if the generalized saddle-point matrix A is. Analogous to the block-triangular factorizations in (8.3) for the matrix A, for the matrix $\tilde{A}$ we also have the following **block-triangular factorizations**:

$$\begin{aligned} \tilde{A} &= \begin{bmatrix} B & E \\ -E^{\mathsf{T}} & C \end{bmatrix} \\ &= \begin{bmatrix} I & 0 \\ -E^{\mathsf{T}}B^{-1} & I \end{bmatrix} \begin{bmatrix} B & E \\ 0 & S \end{bmatrix} = \begin{bmatrix} B & 0 \\ -E^{\mathsf{T}} & S \end{bmatrix} \begin{bmatrix} I & B^{-1}E \\ 0 & I \end{bmatrix} \\ &= \begin{bmatrix} I & 0 \\ -E^{\mathsf{T}}B^{-1} & I \end{bmatrix} \begin{bmatrix} B & 0 \\ 0 & S \end{bmatrix} \begin{bmatrix} I & B^{-1}E \\ 0 & I \end{bmatrix}, \end{aligned} \tag{8.26}$$

where

$$S = C + E^{\mathsf{T}}B^{-1}E \tag{8.27}$$

is the **Schur complement** of the matrix block B in the matrix $\tilde{A}$. Note that the Schur complement S in (8.27) is different from that in (8.4) only by a sign. In fact, S is equal to S_{neg}, the negative Schur complement of the generalized saddle-point matrix A in (8.1).

One important property of the matrix $\tilde{A}$ is that all of its eigenvalues are contained in the right-half plane.

Theorem 8.10. *Let $H_B = \frac{1}{2}(B + B^{\mathsf{T}}) \in \mathbb{R}^{n \times n}$ be symmetric positive semidefinite, and $C \in \mathbb{R}^{m \times m}$ be symmetric positive semidefinite too. Assume that $E \in \mathbb{R}^{n \times m}$ is of full rank, and $\text{Ker}(H_B) \cap \text{Ker}(E^{\mathsf{T}}) = \{0\}$. Then*

(1) *the matrix $\tilde{A}$ is real positive semidefinite in the sense that $z^{\mathsf{T}}\tilde{A}z \geq 0$ for all $z \in \mathbb{R}^{n+m}$,*

(2) *the matrix $\tilde{A}$ is positive semi-stable, i.e., all of its eigenvalues have nonnegative real parts.*

Proof. Let $z = [x^{\mathsf{T}}, y^{\mathsf{T}}]^{\mathsf{T}} \in \mathbb{R}^{n+m}$, with $x \in \mathbb{R}^n$ and $y \in \mathbb{R}^m$. Then by straightforward computations we have

$$\begin{aligned} z^{\mathsf{T}}\tilde{A}z &= x^{\mathsf{T}}Bx + x^{\mathsf{T}}Ey - y^{\mathsf{T}}E^{\mathsf{T}}x + y^{\mathsf{T}}Cy \\ &= x^{\mathsf{T}}Bx + y^{\mathsf{T}}Cy \\ &\geq 0. \end{aligned}$$

Here the last inequality is valid as both the matrices H_B and C are symmetric positive semidefinite, and as

$$x^\mathsf{T} B x = x^\mathsf{T} H_B x \geq 0$$

as well. The above argument shows the validity of Statement (1).

In order to demonstrate Statement (2), we let λ be an eigenvalue of the matrix $\tilde{A}$ and $z = [x^\mathsf{T}, y^\mathsf{T}]^\mathsf{T} \in \mathbb{C}^{n+m}$, with $x \in \mathbb{C}^n$ and $y \in \mathbb{C}^m$, be the corresponding eigenvector. Then it must hold that

$$\tilde{A} z = \lambda z.$$

So, we have

$$\lambda = \frac{z^* \tilde{A} z}{z^* z} \quad \text{and} \quad \overline{\lambda} = \frac{z^* \tilde{A}^\mathsf{T} z}{z^* z}.$$

It follows that

$$\Re(\lambda) = \frac{1}{2}(\lambda + \overline{\lambda}) = \frac{z^* \mathscr{H}(\tilde{A}) z}{z^* z},$$

where

$$\mathscr{H}(\tilde{A}) \triangleq \frac{1}{2}(\tilde{A} + \tilde{A}^\mathsf{T}) = \frac{1}{2}\left(\begin{bmatrix} B & E \\ -E^\mathsf{T} & C \end{bmatrix} + \begin{bmatrix} B & E \\ -E^\mathsf{T} & C \end{bmatrix}^\mathsf{T} \right) = \begin{bmatrix} B & 0 \\ 0 & C \end{bmatrix}$$

is the symmetric part of the matrix $\tilde{A}$. As both matrices B and C are symmetric positive semidefinite, the matrix $\mathscr{H}(\tilde{A})$ is symmetric positive semidefinite too. Therefore,

$$z^* \mathscr{H}(\tilde{A}) z \geq 0,$$

which implies that $\Re(\lambda) \geq 0$. That is to say, the matrix $\tilde{A}$ is positive semi-stable. $\quad\square$

We remark that if the symmetric part H_B of the $(1,1)$-block matrix B is symmetric positive definite, then all eigenvalues of the generalized saddle-point matrix $\tilde{A}$ have positive real parts, that is, the matrix $\tilde{A}$ is positive stable.

The following result gives a sufficient condition for the eigenvalues of the matrix $\tilde{A}$ to be real.

Theorem 8.11. [69] *For the standard saddle-point matrix $\tilde{A}$ in (8.25) with $n \geq m$, let its $(1,1)$-block matrix $B \in \mathbb{R}^{n \times n}$ be symmetric positive definite, and its $(1,2)$-block matrix $E \in \mathbb{R}^{n \times m}$ be of full column rank. Denote by μ_n the smallest eigenvalue of the matrix block B. Then, if $\mu_n \geq 4\|S\|_2$ with $S = E^\mathsf{T} B^{-1} E$, all eigenvalues of the matrix $\tilde{A}$ are real and positive.*

Proof. Let λ be an eigenvalue of the matrix $\tilde{A}$ and $z = [x^\mathsf{T}, y^\mathsf{T}]^\mathsf{T}$ be the corresponding eigenvector, with $x \in \mathbb{C}^n$ and $y \in \mathbb{C}^m$. That is to say, the eigenpair (λ, z) satisfies

$$\begin{bmatrix} B & E \\ -E^\mathsf{T} & 0 \end{bmatrix} \begin{bmatrix} x \\ y \end{bmatrix} = \lambda \begin{bmatrix} x \\ y \end{bmatrix},$$

or equivalently,

$$Bx + Ey = \lambda x, \tag{8.28}$$

$$-E^\mathsf{T} x = \lambda y. \tag{8.29}$$

Note that the matrix $\tilde{A}$ is nonsingular. Hence $\lambda \neq 0$, and $x \neq 0$ as, otherwise, the equality (8.29) implies $y = 0$, so that $z = 0$, which contradicts the fact that the vector z is an eigenvector of the matrix $\tilde{A}$. From (8.29) we can get

$$y = -\frac{1}{\lambda} E^\mathsf{T} x.$$

Substituting this relationship into (8.28) and then multiplying both sides of the resulting equality from left by the vector x^*, we obtain

$$\lambda^2 - \lambda \frac{x^* B x}{x^* x} + \frac{x^* E E^\mathsf{T} x}{x^* x} = 0.$$

The two solutions of this **quadratic polynomial equation** are

$$\lambda = \frac{1}{2}\left(\mu \pm \sqrt{\mu^2 - 4\sigma^2}\right), \tag{8.30}$$

where we have used the notation

$$\mu = \frac{x^* B x}{x^* x} \quad \text{and} \quad \sigma = \sqrt{\frac{x^* E E^\mathsf{T} x}{x^* x}}.$$

Note that $\mu \geq \mu_n$.

If $\mu_n \geq 4 \|S\|_2$, then it follows from Theorem 1.19 that

$$\mu_n \geq 4\lambda_{\max}(E^\mathsf{T} B^{-1} E) = 4\lambda_{\max}(B^{-1} E E^\mathsf{T}) = 4\lambda_{\max}(B^{-\frac{1}{2}} E E^\mathsf{T} B^{-\frac{1}{2}}),$$

where $\lambda_{\max}(\cdot)$ denotes the largest eigenvalue of the corresponding matrix. Let $\tilde{x} = B^{\frac{1}{2}} x$. Then it holds that

$$\begin{aligned}
\mu \geq \mu_n &\geq 4\lambda_{\max}(B^{-\frac{1}{2}} E E^\mathsf{T} B^{-\frac{1}{2}}) \\
&\geq \frac{4\tilde{x}^* B^{-\frac{1}{2}} E E^\mathsf{T} B^{-\frac{1}{2}} \tilde{x}}{\tilde{x}^* \tilde{x}} \\
&= \frac{4 x^* E E^\mathsf{T} x}{x^* x} \cdot \frac{x^* x}{x^* B x} \\
&= 4\sigma^2 \cdot \frac{1}{\mu},
\end{aligned}$$

that is, $\mu^2 \geq 4\sigma^2$. Therefore, it follows from (8.30) that λ is real. $\square$

A more special situation is that $B = \eta I$ with $\eta > 0$ a positive scalar, and $C = 0$. We denote the resulting matrices by

$$A_\eta = \begin{bmatrix} \eta I & E \\ E^\mathsf{T} & 0 \end{bmatrix} \quad \text{and} \quad \tilde{A}_\eta = \begin{bmatrix} \eta I & E \\ -E^\mathsf{T} & 0 \end{bmatrix}.$$

Theorem 8.12. [140] *Assume that $E \in \mathbb{R}^{n \times m}$ is of rank $m - r$. Denote the nonzero singular values of the matrix E by $\sigma_1, \sigma_2, \ldots, \sigma_{m-r}$ and assume $\sigma_1 \geq \sigma_2 \geq \cdots \geq \sigma_{m-r} > 0$. Then, the eigenvalues of the matrix A_η are given by*

(1) $\lambda = 0$ *with multiplicity r,*

(2) $\lambda = \eta$ *with multiplicity $n - m + r$,*

(3) $\lambda = \frac{1}{2}\left(\eta \pm \sqrt{\eta^2 + 4\sigma_k^2}\right)$, $k = 1, 2, \ldots, m - r$

Proof. Left as Exercise 8.5.   □

Theorem 8.13. [140] *Assume that* $E \in \mathbb{R}^{n \times m}$ *is of rank* $m - r$. *Denote the nonzero singular values of the matrix* E *by* $\sigma_1, \sigma_2, \ldots, \sigma_{m-r}$ *and assume* $\sigma_1 \geq \sigma_2 \geq \cdots \geq \sigma_{m-r} > 0$. *Then, the eigenvalues of the matrix* $\tilde{A}_\eta$ *are given by*

(1) $\lambda = 0$ *with multiplicity* r,
(2) $\lambda = \eta$ *with multiplicity* $n - m + r$,
(3) $\lambda = \frac{1}{2}\left(\eta \pm \sqrt{\eta^2 - 4\sigma_k^2}\right)$, $k = 1, 2, \ldots, m - r$.

Proof. Left as Exercise 8.5.   □

Remark 8.1. *From Theorem 8.13 we see that if* $\eta \geq 2\sigma_1$, *then all eigenvalues of the matrix* $\tilde{A}_\eta$ *are real; if* $\eta < 2\sigma_{m-r}$, *then all eigenvalues (except zero and* η*) of the matrix* $\tilde{A}_\eta$ *are complex; and if* $2\sigma_{m-r} \leq \eta < 2\sigma_1$, *then the matrix* $\tilde{A}_\eta$ *has both real and complex eigenvalues.*

8.2 ▪ Schur Complement Reduction and Null Space Methods

Solution methods for the **generalized saddle-point problem** (8.1) can be divided into two broad categories: *segregated* and *coupled* methods. Segregated methods compute the solution sub-vectors x and y separately, while coupled methods, on the other hand, compute the solution sub-vectors x and y simultaneously by dealing with the generalized saddle-point problem (8.1) as a whole.

Segregated methods can be either direct, iterative, or a combination of these two. It usually involves solving two **reduced linear systems** of smaller sizes. Two main representatives are the **Schur complement reduction** and the **null space method**, which include both direct solvers based on block-triangular factorizations of the matrix A (see, e.g., (8.3)) and iterative solvers like Krylov subspace methods such as MINRES or GMRES (see, e.g., Chapter 6).

8.2.1 ▪ Schur Complement Reduction Method

The **Schur complement reduction method** is based on a **block LU factorization** of the **generalized saddle-point matrix** A. Suppose that the matrix A is nonsingular. Then we see from (8.3) that

$$A = \begin{bmatrix} B & E \\ E^\mathsf{T} & -C \end{bmatrix} = \begin{bmatrix} I & 0 \\ E^\mathsf{T}B^{-1} & I \end{bmatrix}\begin{bmatrix} B & E \\ 0 & S \end{bmatrix},$$

where

$$S = -(C + E^\mathsf{T}B^{-1}E)$$

is the Schur complement. By rewriting the generalized saddle-point problem (8.1) as

$$\begin{bmatrix} B & E \\ 0 & S \end{bmatrix}\begin{bmatrix} x \\ y \end{bmatrix} = \begin{bmatrix} I & 0 \\ E^\mathsf{T}B^{-1} & I \end{bmatrix}^{-1}\begin{bmatrix} f \\ g \end{bmatrix}$$

$$= \begin{bmatrix} I & 0 \\ -E^\mathsf{T}B^{-1} & I \end{bmatrix}\begin{bmatrix} f \\ g \end{bmatrix}$$

$$= \begin{bmatrix} f \\ g - E^\mathsf{T}B^{-1}f \end{bmatrix},$$

we may first compute the sub-vector y and then compute the sub-vector x by solving the following reduced linear subsystems:

$$\begin{cases} Sy = g - E^{\mathsf{T}}B^{-1}f, \\ Bx = f - Ey. \end{cases}$$

These two linear subsystems can be solved either directly or iteratively. If the matrix B is symmetric positive definite and the Schur complement S is symmetric negative definite, then we can apply highly reliable numerical methods such as the Cholesky factorization or the CG method.

The Schur complement reduction approach is attractive if the block size m is small and the linear subsystem with the coefficient matrix B can be solved efficiently. However, the Schur complement S may be completely full, so that it is too expensive to compute or factorize in practical applications. Numerical instability, as well as loss of symmetricity and negative definiteness, may also be issues for explicitly forming the Schur complement S, especially when the matrix block B is very ill-conditioned.

8.2.2 ▪ Null Space Method

The **null space method** is designed only for solving the **standard saddle-point problem** (8.2). It is popular in optimization and is, usually, referred to as the **reduced Hessian method** there; see [95, 142, 159, 250]. In this setting, the matrix B is the **Hessian matrix** of the cost function to be minimized, and the matrix E describes the constraint equation $E^{\mathsf{T}}x = g$.

We rewrite the standard saddle-point problem (8.2) into the following blockwise form:

$$\begin{cases} Bx + Ey = f, \\ E^{\mathsf{T}}x = g. \end{cases} \tag{8.31}$$

Assume that the matrix E is of full rank and

$$\operatorname{Ker}(H_B) \cap \operatorname{Ker}(E^{\mathsf{T}}) = \{0\}, \quad \text{with} \quad H_B = \frac{1}{2}(B + B^{\mathsf{T}}).$$

Then the linear system (8.31) admits a unique solution; see Theorem 8.5.

In the null space method, we suppose that one particular solution $\tilde{x}$ of the constraint equation $E^{\mathsf{T}}x = g$ is available. Let $Z \in \mathbb{R}^{n \times (n-m)}$ be the matrix whose columns span the null space of the matrix E^{T}. Then, for any solution x_* of the constraint equation $E^{\mathsf{T}}x = g$, there exists a vector $v \in \mathbb{R}^{n-m}$ such that

$$x_* = \tilde{x} + Zv.$$

By substituting this expression into the first equation of (8.31) and multiplying it from the left with the matrix Z^{T}, we have

$$Z^{\mathsf{T}}BZv = Z^{\mathsf{T}}(f - B\tilde{x}). \tag{8.32}$$

Recall that under the condition

$$\operatorname{Ker}(H_B) \cap \operatorname{Ker}(E^{\mathsf{T}}) = \{0\},$$

the matrix $Z^{\mathsf{T}}BZ$ is nonsingular; see Exercise 8.7.

Once the solution vector v is obtained from solving the linear system (8.32), we have $x_* = \tilde{x} + Zv$. Then we can compute the solution sub-vector y_* by solving the linear system

$$E^{\mathsf{T}}Ey = E^{\mathsf{T}}(f - Bx_*),$$

Note that we have used x_* and y_* to denote the blockwise components of the exact solution z_* of the standard saddle-point problem (8.31).

It is interesting to observe that when the matrix B is invertible, the null space method is just the Schur complement reduction method applied to the **dual saddle-point problem**

$$\begin{bmatrix} B^{-1} & Z \\ Z^{\mathsf{T}} & 0 \end{bmatrix} \begin{bmatrix} w \\ v \end{bmatrix} = \begin{bmatrix} -\tilde{x} \\ -Z^{\mathsf{T}} f \end{bmatrix},$$

where $\tilde{x} \in \mathbb{R}^n$ is a particular solution of the constraint equation $E^{\mathsf{T}} x = g$.

One advantage of the null space method is that we do not need to compute the matrix B^{-1}. In fact, the method is applicable even when the matrix block B is singular, as long as the condition

$$\mathrm{Ker}(H_B) \cap \mathrm{Ker}(E^{\mathsf{T}}) = \{0\}$$

is satisfied. The null space method is often used in applications that require the solution of a sequence of standard saddle-point linear systems of the type

$$\begin{bmatrix} B_k & E \\ E^{\mathsf{T}} & 0 \end{bmatrix} \begin{bmatrix} x \\ y \end{bmatrix} = \begin{bmatrix} f_k \\ g_k \end{bmatrix}, \quad k = 1, 2, \ldots,$$

where the matrix block B_k changes with k while the matrix block E remains fixed. In this case, the basis matrix Z of the null space of the matrix E^{T} can be used repeatedly and needs to be computed only once.

We note that the particular solution for the constraint equation $E^{\mathsf{T}} x = g$ can be usually obtained as a by-product of the computation necessary to obtain the basis matrix Z. Hence, the main difficulty in the null space method is the computation of the basis matrix Z. Theoretically, there are a number of methods to this end; two of the possible ways are described in the following.

As $E \in \mathbb{R}^{n \times m}$ is of full column rank, there exists a **permutation matrix** P such that

$$PE = \begin{bmatrix} E_m \\ E_{n-m} \end{bmatrix},$$

where $E_m \in \mathbb{R}^{m \times m}$ is nonsingular. Then the columns of the matrix

$$Z = P^{\mathsf{T}} \begin{bmatrix} -\left(E_m^{\mathsf{T}}\right)^{-1} E_{n-m}^{\mathsf{T}} \\ I \end{bmatrix}$$

form a basis of the subspace $\mathrm{Ker}(E^{\mathsf{T}})$ [350].

Another way to compute an **orthonormal basis** of the subspace $\mathrm{Ker}(E^{\mathsf{T}})$ is to use the **QR factorization**. Let

$$E = Q \begin{bmatrix} R \\ 0 \end{bmatrix}, \quad \text{with} \quad Q \in \mathbb{R}^{n \times n} \quad \text{and} \quad R \in \mathbb{R}^{m \times m},$$

be the QR factorization of the matrix E. Then, the first m columns of the matrix Q form an orthonormal basis for the subspace $\mathrm{Ran}(E)$, and the remaining $n - m$ columns of the matrix Q form an orthonormal basis for the subspace $\mathrm{Ker}(E^{\mathsf{T}})$.

We remark again that the null space method cannot be applied to solve the generalized saddle-point problem (8.1), that is, the case $C \neq 0$.

8.3 · Stationary Iteration Methods

In this section, we selectively describe several stationary iteration methods that are based on structured splittings of the saddle-point matrices, and rigorously demonstrate their basic convergence properties. The convergence theories for some of these iteration methods are established only for the **standard saddle-point problem** (8.25), but are still open for the **generalized** saddle-point problem (8.24) so far, while those for the other iteration methods can be established completely for both standard and generalized saddle-point problems.

8.3.1 ▪ Uzawa Iteration

The **Uzawa iteration method** [320] is the simplest and one of the most widely used iteration methods for solving the standard saddle-point problems, especially for those arising from the (steady) Stokes problem [143, 160, 161, 315, 319]. It is a **stationary iteration scheme** consisting of simultaneous iterations for both block entries x and y of the solution vector $z = [x^\mathsf{T}, y^\mathsf{T}]^\mathsf{T}$.

Consider the **standard saddle-point problem** (8.25) with the matrix block B being symmetric positive definite. Then the **Uzawa iteration method** is defined as follows:

$$\begin{cases} Bx^{(k+1)} = f - Ey^{(k)}, \\ y^{(k+1)} = y^{(k)} + \tau(E^\mathsf{T}x^{(k+1)} - g), \end{cases} \quad k = 0, 1, 2, \dots, \tag{8.33}$$

where $\tau > 0$ is an **iteration parameter**.

As pointed out in [165], the iteration method (8.33) can be rewritten into a standard stationary iteration scheme of the form

$$z^{(k+1)} = \tilde{M}(\tau)^{-1}\tilde{N}(\tau)\, z^{(k)} + \tilde{M}(\tau)^{-1}\tilde{b},$$

where

$$\tilde{M}(\tau) = \begin{bmatrix} B & 0 \\ -E^\mathsf{T} & \dfrac{1}{\tau}I \end{bmatrix}, \quad \tilde{N}(\tau) = \begin{bmatrix} 0 & -E \\ 0 & \dfrac{1}{\tau}I \end{bmatrix}, \quad \text{and} \quad z^{(k)} = \begin{bmatrix} x^{(k)} \\ y^{(k)} \end{bmatrix}.$$

It is easy to verify that

$$\tilde{A} = \tilde{M}(\tau) - \tilde{N}(\tau)$$

is a splitting of the matrix $\tilde{A}$, and

$$\tilde{G}(\tau) \triangleq \tilde{M}(\tau)^{-1}\tilde{N}(\tau) = \begin{bmatrix} 0 & -B^{-1}E \\ 0 & I - \tau S \end{bmatrix} \tag{8.34}$$

is the corresponding **iteration matrix** of the Uzawa method, where

$$S = E^\mathsf{T}B^{-1}E$$

is the **Schur complement** of the matrix $\tilde{A}$. It follows that all eigenvalues of the iteration matrix $\tilde{G}(\tau)$ are either 0, or the eigenvalues of the matrix $I - \tau S$. Hence, the eigenvalues of the iteration matrix $\tilde{G}(\tau)$ are real, and at least n of them are exactly zero.

Note from (8.34) that

$$\begin{aligned} \rho(\tilde{G}(\tau)) &= \rho(I - \tau S) \\ &= \max_{\lambda \in \sigma(S)} |1 - \tau\lambda| \\ &= \max\left\{|1 - \tau\lambda_{\min}(S)|, |1 - \tau\lambda_{\max}(S)|\right\}, \end{aligned} \tag{8.35}$$

where $\lambda_{\max}(S)$ and $\lambda_{\min}(S)$ denote the largest and smallest eigenvalues of the Schur complement $S = E^\mathsf{T}B^{-1}E$, respectively. This fact then straightforwardly leads to the following convergence result.

Theorem 8.14. *For the standard saddle-point problem* (8.25) *with* $n \geq m$, *suppose that* $B \in \mathbb{R}^{n \times n}$ *is symmetric positive definite and* $E \in \mathbb{R}^{n \times m}$ *is of full column rank. Then the Uzawa iteration method* (8.33) *is convergent if and only if*

$$0 < \tau < \frac{2}{\lambda_{\max}(S)}, \tag{8.36}$$

where $S = E^{\mathsf{T}} B^{-1} E$ *is the Schur complement of the standard saddle-point matrix* $\tilde{A}$.

Moreover, the **asymptotic convergence factor** $\rho(\tilde{G}(\tau))$ *of the Uzawa iteration method attains the minimum at*

$$\tau_{opt} = \frac{2}{\lambda_{\max}(S) + \lambda_{\min}(S)},$$

with the corresponding **optimal asymptotic convergence factor** *being given by*

$$\varrho_{\mathrm{opt}} \triangleq \rho(\tilde{G}(\tau_{opt})) = \frac{\lambda_{\max}(S) - \lambda_{\min}(S)}{\lambda_{\max}(S) + \lambda_{\min}(S)}. \tag{8.37}$$

Proof. From (8.35) we know that the Uzawa iteration method (8.33) is convergent if and only if both inequalities

$$|1 - \tau \lambda_{\min}(S)| < 1 \quad \text{and} \quad |1 - \tau \lambda_{\max}(S)| < 1$$

hold true for any $\tau > 0$. Solving these two inequalities then straightforwardly results in the convergence condition in (8.36).

Besides, based on (8.35), by making use of the monotone property of the functions $|1 - \tau \lambda_{\min}(S)|$ and $|1 - \tau \lambda_{\max}(S)|$ with respect to τ we have

$$\begin{aligned}
\rho(\tilde{G}(\tau)) &= \max\left\{|1 - \tau \lambda_{\min}(S)|, \; |1 - \tau \lambda_{\max}(S)|\right\} \\
&= \begin{cases} 1 - \tau \lambda_{\min}(S), & \text{for} \quad 0 \leq \tau \leq \tau_{opt}, \\ \tau \lambda_{\max}(S) - 1, & \text{for} \quad \tau_{opt} < \tau \leq \tau_{\max}, \end{cases}
\end{aligned} \tag{8.38}$$

where

$$\tau_{\max} = \frac{2}{\lambda_{\max}(S)}.$$

It then follows from the monotone property of this piecewise linear function $\rho(\tilde{G}(\tau))$ with respect to the variable τ that the minimum of $\rho(\tilde{G}(\tau))$ is attained at the point $\tau = \tau_{opt}$. By substituting this optimal value of the iteration parameter τ into the formula (8.38) of $\rho(\tilde{G}(\tau))$, we can straightforwardly obtain the optimal convergence factor shown in (8.37). $\quad\square$

Let

$$\kappa(S) \triangleq \frac{\lambda_{\max}(S)}{\lambda_{\min}(S)}$$

be the **Euclidean condition number** of the Schur complement S. Then Theorem 8.14 shows that the **optimal asymptotic convergence factor** of the Uzawa iteration method can be alternatively formulated as

$$\varrho_{\mathrm{opt}} = \frac{\kappa(S) - 1}{\kappa(S) + 1}. \tag{8.39}$$

Hence, if the Schur complement S is well-conditioned, the Uzawa iteration method will exhibit a fast **convergence rate**.

In the Uzawa iteration method, we need to solve the linear subsystems with respect to the matrix B. These linear subsystems can be solved either by direct methods or by iterative methods. If the **Richardson iteration** with an **extrapolation parameter**, say, e.g., α, is used to solve the first equation in the Uzawa iteration method (8.33), we obtain the iteration scheme

$$\begin{cases} x^{(k+1)} = x^{(k)} + \alpha(f - Ey^{(k)} - Bx^{(k)}), \\ y^{(k+1)} = y^{(k)} + \tau(E^{\mathsf{T}}x^{(k+1)} - g), \end{cases} \quad k = 0, 1, 2, \ldots.$$

This is the **Arrow–Hurwicz iteration method** [5, 6], which can also be regarded as a stationary iteration scheme with respect to the matrix splitting

$$\tilde{A} = \tilde{M}(\alpha, \tau) - \tilde{N}(\alpha, \tau),$$

where

$$\tilde{M}(\alpha, \tau) = \begin{bmatrix} \frac{1}{\alpha}I & 0 \\ -E^{\mathsf{T}} & \frac{1}{\tau}I \end{bmatrix} \quad \text{and} \quad \tilde{N}(\alpha, \tau) = \begin{bmatrix} \frac{1}{\alpha}I - B & -E \\ 0 & \frac{1}{\tau}I \end{bmatrix}.$$

This iteration scheme includes two iteration parameters α and τ, and can be regarded as a special case of the ***generalized accelerated overrelaxation*** (GAOR) iteration method introduced and discussed in [49]. Its convergence conditions and **optimal iteration parameters** can be discussed in an analogous fashion to the Uzawa iteration method, and can also be obtained straightforwardly from those for the GAOR iteration method; see, for instance, [7, 49, 143, 278].

If the matrix B is symmetric positive semidefinite, even if the matrix E is of full column rank, the Uzawa iteration method is no longer well-defined because the matrix B is singular now.

However, if we further assume

$$\mathrm{Ker}(B) \cap \mathrm{Ker}(E^{\mathsf{T}}) = \{0\},$$

then the standard saddle-point matrix $\tilde{A}$ is nonsingular. For the blockwise form

$$\begin{cases} Bx + Ey = f, \\ -E^{\mathsf{T}}x = -g \end{cases}$$

corresponding to the standard saddle-point problem (8.25), by multiplying the second equation from the left with the matrix $-\gamma E$ and adding the resulting equation to the first equation side by side, respectively, we obtain

$$(B + \gamma EE^{\mathsf{T}})x + Ey = f + \gamma Eg.$$

As a result, the standard saddle-point problem (8.25) is equivalently reformulated into the augmented form

$$\begin{bmatrix} B + \gamma EE^{\mathsf{T}} & E \\ -E^{\mathsf{T}} & 0 \end{bmatrix} \begin{bmatrix} x \\ y \end{bmatrix} = \begin{bmatrix} f + \gamma Eg \\ -g \end{bmatrix}. \tag{8.40}$$

Suppose $\gamma > 0$. Then it follows from

$$\mathrm{Ker}(B) \cap \mathrm{Ker}(E^{\mathsf{T}}) = \{0\}$$

that the matrix $B + \gamma EE^{\mathsf{T}}$ is symmetric positive definite. Consequently, we can apply the Uzawa iteration method to solve the **augmented standard saddle-point problem** (8.40).

Now we go back to discuss the Uzawa iteration method. Alternatively, by eliminating $x^{(k+1)}$ in (8.33) we can obtain

$$
\begin{aligned}
y^{(k+1)} &= y^{(k)} + \tau \left[E^{\mathsf{T}} B^{-1}(f - E y^{(k)}) - g \right] \\
&= y^{(k)} + \tau \left(E^{\mathsf{T}} B^{-1} f - g - E^{\mathsf{T}} B^{-1} E y^{(k)} \right) \\
&= (I - \tau S) y^{(k)} + \tau (E^{\mathsf{T}} B^{-1} f - g),
\end{aligned}
\tag{8.41}
$$

which is equivalent to the **stationary Richardson iteration** applied to the **Schur complement system**

$$
S y = E^{\mathsf{T}} B^{-1} f - g.
\tag{8.42}
$$

The iteration scheme (8.41) converges if and only if the **spectral radius** of its iteration matrix $I - \tau S$ is less than 1, that is,

$$
\rho(I - \tau S) < 1.
$$

Therefore, this iteration scheme shares the same convergence condition, optimal iteration parameter, and optimal convergence factor as the Uzawa iteration method; see Theorem 8.14.

8.3.2 ▪ GSOR Iteration

The **generalized SOR** (GSOR) iteration method [49] is another kind of iteration method for efficiently solving the **standard saddle-point problem** (8.25).

For a given nonsingular symmetric matrix $Q \in \mathbb{R}^{m \times m}$, by splitting the coefficient matrix $\tilde{A}$ as

$$
\tilde{A} = \tilde{D} - \tilde{L} - \tilde{U},
$$

with

$$
\tilde{D} = \begin{bmatrix} B & 0 \\ 0 & Q \end{bmatrix}, \quad \tilde{L} = \begin{bmatrix} 0 & 0 \\ E^{\mathsf{T}} & 0 \end{bmatrix}, \quad \tilde{U} = \begin{bmatrix} 0 & -E \\ 0 & Q \end{bmatrix},
$$

we can obtain the following **GSOR iteration method**:

$$
\begin{bmatrix} x^{(k+1)} \\ y^{(k+1)} \end{bmatrix} = (\tilde{D} - \Omega \tilde{L})^{-1} [(I - \Omega) \tilde{D} + \Omega \tilde{U}] \begin{bmatrix} x^{(k)} \\ y^{(k)} \end{bmatrix} + (\tilde{D} - \Omega \tilde{L})^{-1} \Omega \begin{bmatrix} f \\ -g \end{bmatrix},
\tag{8.43}
$$

where

$$
\Omega = \begin{bmatrix} \omega I_n & 0 \\ 0 & \tau I_m \end{bmatrix}, \quad \text{with} \quad \omega \neq 0 \quad \text{and} \quad \tau \neq 0.
$$

This iteration scheme is a technical modification of the classical block SOR iteration scheme for solving the blockwise systems of linear equations.

The corresponding matrix splitting is given by

$$
\tilde{A} = \tilde{M}(\omega, \tau) - \tilde{N}(\omega, \tau),
$$

with

$$
\begin{aligned}
\tilde{M}(\omega, \tau) &= \Omega^{-1}(\tilde{D} - \Omega \tilde{L}) = \begin{bmatrix} \frac{1}{\omega} B & 0 \\ -E^{\mathsf{T}} & \frac{1}{\tau} Q \end{bmatrix}, \\
\tilde{N}(\omega, \tau) &= \Omega^{-1}[(I - \Omega)\tilde{D} + \Omega \tilde{U}] = \begin{bmatrix} (\frac{1}{\omega} - 1)B & -E \\ 0 & \frac{1}{\tau} Q \end{bmatrix},
\end{aligned}
\tag{8.44}
$$

and the **iteration matrix** is given by

$$\tilde{G}(\omega, \tau) = \tilde{M}(\omega, \tau)^{-1} \tilde{N}(\omega, \tau) = \begin{bmatrix} (1-\omega)I & -\omega B^{-1} \\ (1-\omega)\tau Q^{-1}E^\mathsf{T} & I - \omega\tau Q^{-1}S \end{bmatrix},$$

where

$$S = E^\mathsf{T} B^{-1} E$$

is the Schur complement of the standard saddle-point matrix $\tilde{A}$ in (8.25).

We remark that the **GSOR iteration scheme** (8.43) is equivalent to

$$\begin{cases} x^{(k+1)} = (1-\omega)x^{(k)} + \omega B^{-1}(f - Ey^{(k)}), \\ y^{(k+1)} = y^{(k)} + \tau Q^{-1}(E^\mathsf{T} x^{(k+1)} - g). \end{cases} \tag{8.45}$$

If we choose $\tau = \omega$, then the iteration scheme (8.45) is called the **SOR-like iteration method** [170]. When $\omega = 1$ and $Q = I$, the GSOR iteration method reduces to the **Uzawa iteration method**; and when $\tau = \omega = 1$, it gives the **preconditioned Uzawa iteration method** [121].

The GSOR iteration method is convergent if and only if its iteration matrix $\tilde{G}(\omega, \tau)$ is convergent, that is, $\rho(\tilde{G}(\omega, \tau)) < 1$.

Theorem 8.15. *Consider the standard saddle-point problem (8.25) with $n \geq m$. Suppose that $B \in \mathbb{R}^{n \times n}$ is symmetric positive definite, $Q \in \mathbb{R}^{m \times m}$ is either symmetric positive definite or symmetric negative definite, and $E \in \mathbb{R}^{n \times m}$ is of full column rank. Denote by $S = E^\mathsf{T} B^{-1} E$ the Schur complement of the matrix $\tilde{A}$, and by $\mu_{\min}$ and $\mu_{\max}$ the smallest and largest eigenvalues of the matrix $Q^{-1}S$, respectively. Then, the GSOR iteration method (8.43), or equivalently, (8.45), is convergent if the iteration parameters ω and τ satisfy either of the following two conditions:*

(i) *when the matrix Q is symmetric positive definite,*

$$0 < \omega < 2 \quad and \quad 0 < \tau < \frac{2(2-\omega)}{\omega\mu_{\max}};$$

(ii) *when the matrix Q is symmetric negative definite,*

$$0 < \omega < 2 \quad and \quad \frac{2(2-\omega)}{\omega\mu_{\min}} < \tau < 0.$$

Proof. We first demonstrate that the GSOR iteration method is convergent under the condition (i). Note that when the matrix Q is symmetric positive definite, all eigenvalues μ of the matrix $Q^{-1}S$ are real and nonzero, and it holds that $\mu_{\min} > 0$.

Let λ be a nonzero eigenvalue of the iteration matrix $\tilde{G}(\omega, \tau)$ and $[u^\mathsf{T}, v^\mathsf{T}]^\mathsf{T} \in \mathbb{C}^{n+m}$, with $u \in \mathbb{C}^n$ and $v \in \mathbb{C}^m$, be the corresponding eigenvector. Then we have

$$[(I - \Omega)\tilde{D} + \Omega\tilde{U}] \begin{bmatrix} u \\ v \end{bmatrix} = \lambda(\tilde{D} - \Omega\tilde{L}) \begin{bmatrix} u \\ v \end{bmatrix},$$

or equivalently,

$$\begin{bmatrix} (1-\omega)B & -\omega E \\ 0 & Q \end{bmatrix} \begin{bmatrix} u \\ v \end{bmatrix} = \lambda \begin{bmatrix} B & 0 \\ -\tau E^\mathsf{T} & Q \end{bmatrix} \begin{bmatrix} u \\ v \end{bmatrix}.$$

That is to say, it holds that

$$\begin{cases} (1-\omega)Bu - \omega Ev = \lambda Bu, \\ Qv = \lambda(-\tau E^\mathsf{T} u + Qv), \end{cases}$$

or equivalently,

$$\begin{cases} (1 - \omega - \lambda)Bu = \omega Ev, \\ (\lambda - 1)Qv = \lambda \tau E^{\mathsf{T}}u. \end{cases} \tag{8.46}$$

We first prove that $\lambda \neq 1$. Assume $\lambda = 1$. Then it holds that

$$E^{\mathsf{T}}u = 0 \quad \text{and} \quad Bu = -Ev.$$

By multiplying the last equation from the left with the vector u^* we have

$$u^*Bu = -u^*Ev = -(E^{\mathsf{T}}u)^*v = 0.$$

As the matrix B is symmetric positive definite, it follows that $u = 0$. Hence,

$$Ev = -Bu = 0.$$

Since the matrix E is of full column rank, we know that $v = 0$. This contradicts the fact that the vector $[u^{\mathsf{T}}, v^{\mathsf{T}}]^{\mathsf{T}}$ is an eigenvector of the GSOR iteration matrix $\tilde{G}(\omega, \tau)$ and is, thus, nonzero. Therefore, $\lambda \neq 1$.

If $\lambda = 1 - \omega$, then $|\lambda| < 1$ if and only if $0 < \omega < 2$.

Now, suppose $\lambda \neq 1 - \omega$. From the first equation in (8.46) we obtain

$$u = \frac{\omega}{1 - \omega - \lambda}B^{-1}Ev.$$

Substituting it into the second equation in (8.46) leads to

$$(1 - \omega - \lambda)(\lambda - 1)v = \lambda \tau \omega Q^{-1}Sv.$$

We conclude that $v \neq 0$. Otherwise, it follows from the first equation in (8.46) that $Bu = 0$ and, thus, $u = 0$, which leads to a contradiction. Therefore, the complex scalar

$$\frac{(1 - \omega - \lambda)(\lambda - 1)}{\lambda \tau \omega}$$

is an eigenvalue of the matrix $Q^{-1}S$, with the corresponding eigenvector being v. That is to say, there exists an eigenvalue μ of the matrix $Q^{-1}S$ such that

$$\mu = \frac{(1 - \omega - \lambda)(\lambda - 1)}{\lambda \tau \omega},$$

or equivalently,

$$\lambda^2 + (\tau\omega\mu + \omega - 2)\lambda + 1 - \omega = 0. \tag{8.47}$$

According to Exercise 8.9 (see also [358, page 171]), we know that $|\lambda| < 1$ if and only if

$$|1 - \omega| < 1 \quad \text{and} \quad |\tau\omega\mu + \omega - 2| < 2 - \omega.$$

By straightforwardly solving these two inequalities, we immediately obtain

$$0 < \omega < 2 \quad \text{and} \quad 0 < \tau < \frac{2(2 - \omega)}{\omega\mu}.$$

As the real function $\frac{2(2-\omega)}{\omega\mu}$ is monotone decreasing with respect to the variable $\mu > 0$, its minimum is achieved at $\mu_{\max}$.

In conclusion, if

$$0 < \omega < 2 \quad \text{and} \quad 0 < \tau < \frac{2(2 - \omega)}{\omega \mu_{\max}},$$

then $|\lambda| < 1$, which means that $\rho(\tilde{G}(\omega, \tau)) < 1$ and the GSOR iteration method is asymptotically convergent.

When the matrix Q is symmetric negative definite, all eigenvalues μ of the matrix $Q^{-1}S$ are also real and nonzero, and it holds that $\mu_{\max} < 0$. By letting $\tilde{\tau} := -\tau$ and $\tilde{\mu} := -\mu$, we then obtain the same problem as the case $\mu_{\min} > 0$ discussed in the above, but now with

$$\tilde{\mu}_{\min} \triangleq \min \left\{ -\mu \, : \, \mu \in \sigma(Q^{-1}S) \right\} = -\mu_{\max} \triangleq -\max \left\{ \mu \, : \, \mu \in \sigma(Q^{-1}S) \right\}$$

and

$$\tilde{\mu}_{\max} \triangleq \max \left\{ -\mu \, : \, \mu \in \sigma(Q^{-1}S) \right\} = -\mu_{\min} \triangleq -\min \left\{ \mu \, : \, \mu \in \sigma(Q^{-1}S) \right\}$$

satisfying

$$\tilde{\mu}_{\max} \geq \tilde{\mu}_{\min} > 0.$$

This shows that the GSOR iteration method is also convergent if ω and $\tilde{\tau}$ satisfy the conditions

$$0 < \omega < 2 \quad \text{and} \quad 0 < \tilde{\tau} < \frac{2(2 - \omega)}{\omega \tilde{\mu}_{\max}},$$

or equivalently, if the iteration parameters ω and τ satisfy Condition (ii).

As a matter of fact, this case is only a substitution of a symmetric negative definite matrix Q corresponding to a negative parameter τ.   □

Note that in the derivation of the **quadratic polynomial equation** (8.47), we only used the assumption that the matrix Q is symmetric and nonsingular, but did not require that the matrix Q is either positive definite or negative definite.

Moreover, from the quadratic polynomial equation (8.47), we can immediately obtain the following relationship between the eigenvalues of the GSOR iteration matrix $\tilde{G}(\omega, \tau)$ and those of the matrix $Q^{-1}S$.

Corollary 8.16. *Consider the standard saddle-point problem (8.25) with $n \geq m$. Let $B \in \mathbb{R}^{n \times n}$ be symmetric positive definite, and $E \in \mathbb{R}^{n \times m}$ be of full column rank. Suppose that $Q \in \mathbb{R}^{m \times m}$ is symmetric and nonsingular. If μ is an eigenvalue of the matrix $Q^{-1}S$, then the λ determined by the quadratic polynomial equation (8.47) is an eigenvalue of the GSOR iteration matrix $\tilde{G}(\omega, \tau)$. On the other hand, if λ is an eigenvalue of the GSOR iteration matrix $\tilde{G}(\omega, \tau)$, then the μ determined by the quadratic polynomial equation (8.47) is an eigenvalue of the matrix $Q^{-1}S$. Therefore, the nonzero eigenvalues of the GSOR iteration matrix $\tilde{G}(\omega, \tau)$ are given by*

$$\lambda = 1 - \omega, \quad \text{or} \quad \lambda = \frac{1}{2} \left(2 - \omega - \tau \omega \mu \pm \sqrt{(2 - \omega - \tau \omega \mu)^2 - 4(1 - \omega)} \right).$$

By careful manipulations, for the **optimal iteration parameters** and the corresponding **optimal convergence factor** of the GSOR iteration method, we can obtain the following result.

Theorem 8.17. [49] *Consider the standard saddle-point problem (8.25) with $n \geq m$. Suppose that $B \in \mathbb{R}^{n \times n}$ is symmetric positive definite, $Q \in \mathbb{R}^{m \times m}$ is either symmetric positive definite or symmetric negative definite, and $E \in \mathbb{R}^{n \times m}$ is of full column rank. Denote by $S = E^{\mathsf{T}} B^{-1} E$ the*

Schur complement of the matrix $\tilde{A}$, and by $\mu_{\min}$ and $\mu_{\max}$ the smallest and largest eigenvalues of the matrix $Q^{-1}S$, respectively. Then

(i) *when the matrix Q is symmetric positive definite, the optimal iteration parameters ω_{opt} and τ_{opt} are given by*

$$\omega_{\mathrm{opt}} = \frac{4\sqrt{\mu_{\min}\mu_{\max}}}{(\sqrt{\mu_{\min}} + \sqrt{\mu_{\max}})^2} \quad and \quad \tau_{\mathrm{opt}} = \frac{1}{\sqrt{\mu_{\min}\mu_{\max}}},$$

and the corresponding optimal convergence factor of the GSOR iteration method is given by

$$\varrho_{\mathrm{opt}} \triangleq \rho(\tilde{G}(\omega_{\mathrm{opt}}, \tau_{\mathrm{opt}})) = \frac{\sqrt{\mu_{\max}} - \sqrt{\mu_{\min}}}{\sqrt{\mu_{\max}} + \sqrt{\mu_{\min}}};$$

(ii) *when the matrix Q is symmetric negative definite, the optimal iteration parameters ω_{opt} and τ_{opt} are given by*

$$\omega_{\mathrm{opt}} = \frac{4\sqrt{\mu_{\min}\mu_{\max}}}{(\sqrt{|\mu_{\min}|} + \sqrt{|\mu_{\max}|})^2} \quad and \quad \tau_{\mathrm{opt}} = -\frac{1}{\sqrt{\mu_{\min}\mu_{\max}}},$$

and the corresponding optimal convergence factor of the GSOR iteration method is given by

$$\varrho_{\mathrm{opt}} \triangleq \rho(\tilde{G}(\omega_{\mathrm{opt}}, \tau_{\mathrm{opt}})) = \frac{\sqrt{|\mu_{\min}|} - \sqrt{|\mu_{\max}|}}{\sqrt{|\mu_{\min}|} + \sqrt{|\mu_{\max}|}}.$$

Proof. The proof of this theorem is relatively technical and more involved, so it is omitted. For the details, see [49]. □

Evidently, Theorem 8.17 implies that $\omega_{\mathrm{opt}} \leq 1$. This shows that **underrelaxation** with respect to the relaxation parameter ω (i.e., the case $0 < \omega \leq 1$) can produce GSOR iteration sequence of fast convergent rate. Moreover, by Theorem 8.17 (i) and (ii) we only need to take the matrix Q to be a symmetric positive definite matrix and consider the case that both iteration parameters τ and ω are positive reals. In this case, if we additionally let

$$\kappa(Q^{-1}S) \triangleq \frac{\lambda_{\max}(Q^{-1}S)}{\lambda_{\min}(Q^{-1}S)} = \frac{\mu_{\max}}{\mu_{\min}}$$

be the condition number of the **preconditioned Schur complement** $Q^{-1}S$, then Theorem 8.17 (i) shows that the **optimal convergence factor** of the GSOR iteration method can be alternatively reformulated as

$$\varrho_{\mathrm{opt}} = \frac{\sqrt{\kappa(Q^{-1}S)} - 1}{\sqrt{\kappa(Q^{-1}S)} + 1}.$$

Consequently, the **asymptotic convergence rate** of the **GSOR iteration method** is one order faster than that of the **Uzawa iteration method**; see (8.39). However, it is essentially the same as that of the conjugate gradient method preconditioned with the matrix Q and applied to the reduced Schur complement system in (8.42); see also Theorem 6.28 in Chapter 6.

8.3.3 ▪ HSS Iteration

We now turn to consider a class of **matrix splitting iteration methods** for solving the **generalized saddle-point problem** (8.24). To this end, we assume that $B \in \mathbb{R}^{n \times n}$ is symmetric positive definite, $C \in \mathbb{R}^{m \times m}$ is symmetric positive semidefinite, and $E \in \mathbb{R}^{n \times m}$ is such that

$$\text{Ker}(E) \cap \text{Ker}(C) = \{0\}.$$

Then from Theorem 8.4 we know that the **generalized saddle-point matrix** $\tilde{A}$ is nonsingular. As a result, the linear system (8.24) has a unique solution.

The symmetric and skew-symmetric parts of the matrix $\tilde{A}$ in (8.24) are given by

$$\tilde{H} = \frac{1}{2}(\tilde{A} + \tilde{A}^{\mathsf{T}}) = \begin{bmatrix} B & 0 \\ 0 & C \end{bmatrix}$$

and

$$\tilde{S} = \frac{1}{2}(\tilde{A} - \tilde{A}^{\mathsf{T}}) = \begin{bmatrix} 0 & E \\ -E^{\mathsf{T}} & 0 \end{bmatrix},$$

respectively. So, it holds that

$$\tilde{A} = \tilde{H} + \tilde{S}.$$

Recall that this is an **orthogonal decomposition** in the sense of the **matrix inner product**; see Theorem 1.42 in Chapter 1.

Consider the following two splittings of the matrix $\tilde{A}$:

$$\begin{aligned} \tilde{A} &= (\alpha I + \tilde{H}) - (\alpha I - \tilde{S}) \\ &= (\alpha I + \tilde{S}) - (\alpha I - \tilde{H}), \end{aligned} \tag{8.48}$$

where I is the identity matrix and $\alpha > 0$ is a prescribed **iteration parameter**. Following the convention, we still call this couple of splittings the ***Hermitian and skew-Hermitian splitting*** (HSS), rather than the symmetric and skew-symmetric splitting, of the generalized saddle-point matrix $\tilde{A}$.

With straightforward application of the HSS iteration technique in Section 5.5.1 of Chapter 5 to the **HS splitting** in (8.48), Benzi and Golub [65] discussed the following **HSS iteration method** for solving the **generalized saddle-point problem** (8.24):

$$\begin{cases} (\alpha I + \tilde{H})z^{(k+\frac{1}{2})} &= (\alpha I - \tilde{S})z^{(k)} + \tilde{b}, \\ (\alpha I + \tilde{S})z^{(k+1)} &= (\alpha I - \tilde{H})z^{(k+\frac{1}{2})} + \tilde{b}. \end{cases} \tag{8.49}$$

In blockwise elements, the first half-step of this iteration method necessitates the solution of two (uncoupled) linear subsystems of the form

$$\begin{cases} (\alpha I + B)x^{(k+\frac{1}{2})} &= \alpha x^{(k)} - Ey^{(k)} + f, \\ (\alpha I + C)y^{(k+\frac{1}{2})} &= E^{\mathsf{T}}x^{(k)} + \alpha y^{(k)} - g. \end{cases} \tag{8.50}$$

Both of these linear subsystems are symmetric positive definite, so they can be solved effectively by any sparse linear solver designed for the symmetric positive definite linear systems, for example, the **sparse Cholesky factorization** or the **preconditioned conjugate gradient scheme**. Note that the positive shift α introduces an additional term αI added to the main diagonals of the submatrices B and C, which leads to improvement on the condition numbers of these linear subsystems. This, in turn, tends to improve the rate of convergence of iterative methods applied to (8.50).

However, the second half-step of the iteration method (8.49) is less trivial. It requires the solution of two coupled linear subsystems of the form

$$\begin{cases} \alpha x^{(k+1)} + Ey^{(k+1)} &= (\alpha I - B)x^{(k+\frac{1}{2})} + f, \\ -E^{\mathsf{T}}x^{(k+1)} + \alpha y^{(k+1)} &= (\alpha I - C)y^{(k+\frac{1}{2})} - g. \end{cases} \tag{8.51}$$

In general, any **sparse LU factorization** or **linear iteration solver** could be used to solve this linear subsystem, if its size is not too large. Besides, as its coefficient matrix is a **normal matrix** of the form "identity-plus-skew-symmetric," the coupled linear subsystem (8.51) can also be solved by various **Lanczos-type methods** applicable to linear systems of this kind; see, e.g., [97, 166, 204, 207, 208, 346]. Note that many of these schemes can benefit from the fact that for even moderate values of α, the condition number of the matrix $\alpha I + \tilde{S}$ is often rather small.

In particular, the linear subsystem (8.51) may also be solved by making use of the **block Gaussian elimination**. For example, if m is smaller than n, we may eliminate $x^{(k+1)}$ from the second equation using the first one (**Schur complement reduction**), leading to a smaller (order m) linear system with respect to $y^{(k+1)}$ of the form

$$\left(\alpha I + \frac{1}{\alpha}E^{\mathsf{T}}E\right)y^{(k+1)} = \frac{1}{\alpha}E^{\mathsf{T}}\left[(\alpha I - B)x^{(k+\frac{1}{2})} + f\right] + (\alpha I - C)y^{(k+\frac{1}{2})} - g. \tag{8.52}$$

Once the solution $y^{(k+1)}$ has been computed from this linear system, the vector $x^{(k+1)}$ is given by

$$x^{(k+1)} = \frac{1}{\alpha}\left[(\alpha I - B)x^{(k+\frac{1}{2})} + f - Ey^{(k+1)}\right].$$

Alternatively, if n is smaller than m, we may eliminate $y^{(k+1)}$ from the first equation using the second one (**Schur complement reduction** too), leading to a smaller (order n) linear system with respect to $x^{(k+1)}$ of the form

$$\left(\alpha I + \frac{1}{\alpha}EE^{\mathsf{T}}\right)x^{(k+1)} = (\alpha I - B)x^{(k+\frac{1}{2})} + f - \frac{1}{\alpha}E\left[(\alpha I - C)y^{(k+\frac{1}{2})} - g\right]. \tag{8.53}$$

Once the solution $x^{(k+1)}$ has been computed from this linear system, the vector $y^{(k+1)}$ is given by

$$y^{(k+1)} = \frac{1}{\alpha}\left[E^{\mathsf{T}}x^{(k+1)} + (\alpha I - C)y^{(k+\frac{1}{2})} - g\right].$$

If the matrix $E^{\mathsf{T}}E$ or the matrix EE^{T} is sufficiently sparse, the linear subsystem in (8.52) or in (8.53) could be formed explicitly and solved by a **sparse Cholesky factorization**. Otherwise, they could be solved by the **preconditioned conjugate gradient scheme** with an appropriate preconditioner.

Note that the **generalized saddle-point matrix** $\tilde{A}$ in (8.24) is only positive semidefinite, as its symmetric part $\tilde{H}$ is symmetric positive semidefinite. Hence, the convergence theory, that is, Theorem 5.66 in Chapter 5 established for non-Hermitian positive definite linear systems, cannot guarantee the asymptotic convergence of the **HSS iteration method** in (8.49). However, due to the particular structure and concrete property of the matrix $\tilde{A}$, the HSS iteration method (8.49) is still convergent unconditionally to the exact solution of the **generalized saddle-point problem** (8.24).

In order to establish the convergence theory for the HSS iteration method (8.49), we eliminate the intermediate vector $z^{(k+\frac{1}{2})}$ and write this iteration as a **standard stationary iteration scheme** of the form

$$z^{(k+1)} = \tilde{G}(\alpha)\, z^{(k)} + \tilde{c}(\alpha), \tag{8.54}$$

where

$$\tilde{G}(\alpha) \triangleq (\alpha I + \tilde{S})^{-1}(\alpha I - \tilde{H})(\alpha I + \tilde{H})^{-1}(\alpha I - \tilde{S}) \tag{8.55}$$

is the HSS **iteration matrix**, and

$$\tilde{c}(\alpha) \triangleq 2\alpha(\alpha I + \tilde{S})^{-1}(\alpha I + \tilde{H})^{-1}\tilde{b}.$$

Indeed, by letting

$$\begin{cases} \tilde{M}(\alpha) & = & \frac{1}{2\alpha}(\alpha I + \tilde{H})(\alpha I + \tilde{S}), \\ \tilde{N}(\alpha) & = & \frac{1}{2\alpha}(\alpha I - \tilde{H})(\alpha I - \tilde{S}), \end{cases}$$

we have

$$\tilde{A} = \tilde{M}(\alpha) - \tilde{N}(\alpha) \tag{8.56}$$

and

$$\tilde{G}(\alpha) = \tilde{M}(\alpha)^{-1}\tilde{N}(\alpha), \quad \tilde{c}(\alpha) = \tilde{M}(\alpha)^{-1}\tilde{b}.$$

As a consequence, the **HSS iteration** (8.54) can also be regarded as a matrix splitting iteration induced by the splitting (8.56) of the generalized saddle-point matrix $\tilde{A}$.

Note that the fixed-point iteration scheme (8.54) converges for arbitrary initial guesses $z^{(0)} \in \mathbb{R}^{n+m}$ and right-hand sides $\tilde{b}$ to the exact solution $z_* = \tilde{A}^{-1}\tilde{b}$ if and only if the corresponding iteration matrix $\tilde{G}(\alpha)$ in (8.55) is convergent, that is, $\rho(\tilde{G}(\alpha)) < 1$, where $\rho(\tilde{G}(\alpha))$ denotes the **spectral radius** of the HSS iteration matrix $\tilde{G}(\alpha)$.

Theorem 8.18. [65] *Consider the generalized saddle-point problem* (8.24). *Suppose that* $B \in \mathbb{R}^{n \times n}$ *is symmetric positive definite,* $C \in \mathbb{R}^{m \times m}$ *is symmetric positive semidefinite, and* $E \in \mathbb{R}^{n \times m}$ *is such that* $\mathrm{Ker}(E) \cap \mathrm{Ker}(C) = \{0\}$. *Then, the HSS iteration method* (8.49) *is unconditionally convergent, that is,* $\rho(\tilde{G}(\alpha)) < 1$ *for all* $\alpha > 0$.

Proof. The HSS iteration matrix $\tilde{G}(\alpha)$ in (8.55) is similar to the matrix

$$\hat{G}(\alpha) = (\alpha I + \tilde{H})^{-1}(\alpha I - \tilde{H})(\alpha I + \tilde{S})^{-1}(\alpha I - \tilde{S}).$$

So, it holds that

$$\rho(\tilde{G}(\alpha)) = \rho(\hat{G}(\alpha)).$$

Let

$$\hat{R}(\alpha) = (\alpha I + \tilde{H})^{-1}(\alpha I - \tilde{H}) \quad \text{and} \quad \hat{Q}(\alpha) = (\alpha I + \tilde{S})^{-1}(\alpha I - \tilde{S}).$$

Then we have

$$\hat{G}(\alpha) = \hat{R}(\alpha)\,\hat{Q}(\alpha) \tag{8.57}$$

and

$$\hat{R}(\alpha) = \begin{bmatrix} (\alpha I + B)^{-1}(\alpha I - B) & 0 \\ 0 & (\alpha I + C)^{-1}(\alpha I - C) \end{bmatrix}. \tag{8.58}$$

As the matrix B is symmetric positive definite, the matrix C is symmetric positive semidefinite, and the iteration parameter α is positive, it holds that

$$\mu \triangleq \|(\alpha I + B)^{-1}(\alpha I - B)\|_2 < 1 \quad \text{and} \quad \nu \triangleq \|(\alpha I + C)^{-1}(\alpha I - C)\|_2 \le 1. \quad (8.59)$$

Hence, we know that

$$\begin{aligned}
\|\hat{R}(\alpha)\|_2 &= \max\left\{\|(\alpha I + B)^{-1}(\alpha I - B)\|_2,\ \|(\alpha I + C)^{-1}(\alpha I - C)\|_2\right\} \\
&= \max\{\mu,\ \nu\} \\
&\le 1.
\end{aligned}$$

In addition, we can straightforwardly verify that the matrix $\hat{Q}(\alpha)$ is a **Cayley transform** of the matrix $\tilde{S}$, so it is a unitary matrix and satisfies $\|\hat{Q}(\alpha)\|_2 = 1$. It then follows from (8.57) that

$$\|\hat{G}(\alpha)\|_2 \le \|\hat{R}(\alpha)\|_2\|\hat{Q}(\alpha)\|_2 \le 1,$$

which shows that

$$\rho(\hat{G}(\alpha)) \le \|\hat{G}(\alpha)\|_2 \le 1.$$

We further claim that it must hold that

$$\rho(\hat{G}(\alpha)) < 1, \quad \forall \alpha > 0,$$

so that the HSS iteration method (8.49) is unconditionally convergent.

In fact, if $\rho(\hat{G}(\alpha)) = 1$, then there is an eigenvalue λ of the matrix $\hat{G}(\alpha)$ such that $|\lambda| = 1$. Let $\hat{z}$ be a **normalized eigenvector** of the matrix $\hat{G}(\alpha)$ corresponding to this eigenvalue λ, that is, the vector $\hat{z}$ satisfies $\|\hat{z}\|_2 = 1$. Then from (8.57) we have

$$\hat{R}(\alpha)\,\hat{Q}(\alpha)\,\hat{z} = \lambda\hat{z},$$

which is equivalent to

$$\hat{R}(\alpha)\,z = \lambda\,\hat{Q}(\alpha)^{\mathsf{T}}\,z, \quad (8.60)$$

where

$$z = \hat{Q}(\alpha)\,\hat{z}.$$

Note that this vector z also satisfies $\|z\|_2 = 1$. Denote by $z = [x^{\mathsf{T}}, y^{\mathsf{T}}]^{\mathsf{T}}$ with $x \in \mathbb{C}^n$ and $y \in \mathbb{C}^m$. Then we see that

$$\|x\|_2^2 + \|y\|_2^2 = \|z\|_2^2 = 1.$$

From (8.60), by making use of (8.58) and (8.59), we can obtain

$$\begin{aligned}
1 = |\lambda|^2 = \|\lambda\,\hat{Q}(\alpha)^{\mathsf{T}}\,z\|_2^2 \\
&= \|\hat{R}(\alpha)\,z\|_2^2 \\
&= \|(\alpha I + B)^{-1}(\alpha I - B)x\|_2^2 + \|(\alpha I + C)^{-1}(\alpha I - C)y\|_2^2 \\
&\le \|(\alpha I + B)^{-1}(\alpha I - B)\|_2^2\,\|x\|_2^2 + \|(\alpha I + C)^{-1}(\alpha I - C)\|_2^2\,\|y\|_2^2 \\
&= \mu\|x\|_2^2 + \nu\|y\|_2^2 \\
&\le \|x\|_2^2 + \|y\|_2^2 = 1.
\end{aligned}$$

This implies that

$$\mu\|x\|_2^2 + \nu\|y\|_2^2 = \|x\|_2^2 + \|y\|_2^2,$$

or in other words,

$$(1 - \mu)\|x\|_2^2 + (1 - \nu)\|y\|_2^2 = 0,$$

which is only possible if $\|x\|_2 = 0$, and either $\|y\|_2 = 0$ or $\nu = 1$. Therefore, it holds that $x = 0$. With $x = 0$ and $\hat{Q}(\alpha)^\mathsf{T} = \hat{Q}(\alpha)^{-1}$, the equality (8.60) can be rewritten as

$$\begin{bmatrix} (\alpha I + B)^{-1}(\alpha I - B) & 0 \\ 0 & (\alpha I + C)^{-1}(\alpha I - C) \end{bmatrix} \begin{bmatrix} 0 \\ y \end{bmatrix} = \lambda \begin{bmatrix} \alpha I & -E \\ E^\mathsf{T} & \alpha I \end{bmatrix}^{-1} \begin{bmatrix} \alpha I & E \\ -E^\mathsf{T} & \alpha I \end{bmatrix} \begin{bmatrix} 0 \\ y \end{bmatrix},$$

or equivalently,

$$\begin{bmatrix} \alpha I & -E \\ E^\mathsf{T} & \alpha I \end{bmatrix} \begin{bmatrix} (\alpha I + B)^{-1}(\alpha I - B) & 0 \\ 0 & (\alpha I + C)^{-1}(\alpha I - C) \end{bmatrix} \begin{bmatrix} 0 \\ y \end{bmatrix} = \lambda \begin{bmatrix} \alpha I & E \\ -E^\mathsf{T} & \alpha I \end{bmatrix} \begin{bmatrix} 0 \\ y \end{bmatrix}.$$

That is to say, it holds that

$$-E(\alpha I + C)^{-1}(\alpha I - C)y = Ey \quad \text{and} \quad \alpha(\alpha I + C)^{-1}(\alpha I - C)y = \alpha y. \quad (8.61)$$

From the second equality in (8.61) we get

$$(\alpha I + C)^{-1}(\alpha I - C)y = y,$$

which is equivalent to

$$Cy = 0.$$

Using this fact, from the first equality in (8.61) we obtain

$$-Ey = Ey,$$

or $Ey = 0$. It then follows that

$$y \in \mathrm{Ker}(C) \cap \mathrm{Ker}(E),$$

so that $y = 0$.

Consequently, under the assumption $\rho(\hat{G}(\alpha)) = 1$ we have demonstrated that $z = 0$, which contradicts the fact that $\|z\|_2 = 1$. Thus, it must hold that $\rho(\hat{G}(\alpha)) < 1$. □

Theorem 8.18 only shows that the spectral radius of the HSS iteration matrix is less than 1. There is no discussion about other convergence properties such as estimates of the **contraction factor** and the **asymptotic convergence rate**, as well as the choice of the **optimal iteration parameter** in a certain sense. In fact, it is very difficult to analyze such properties for the HSS iteration method, as each eigenvalue of its iteration matrix depends not only on the iteration parameter and all eigenvalues of the Hermitian part of the coefficient matrix, but also on the eigenvectors corresponding to those eigenvalues; see [65] for more details.

8.3.4 ▪ AHSS Iteration

The *accelerated Hermitian and skew-Hermitian splitting* (AHSS) iteration method is a two-parameter acceleration of the **HSS iteration method** in (8.49). The **AHSS iteration method** was first proposed and discussed by Bai and Golub in [32] for the **standard saddle-point problem** (8.25), and later it was further developed and analyzed by Bai in [24] for the **generalized saddle-point problem** (8.24).

Let

$$\Theta = \left[\begin{array}{cc} \alpha I_n & 0 \\ 0 & \beta I_m \end{array} \right]$$

with α and β being two positive constants, and consider the following two splittings of the matrix $\tilde{A}$ in (8.24):

$$\tilde{A} = (\Theta + \tilde{H}) - (\Theta - \tilde{S})$$
$$= (\Theta + \tilde{S}) - (\Theta - \tilde{H}).$$

This couple of splittings is called the **accelerated Hermitian and skew-Hermitian splitting** of the **generalized saddle-point matrix** $\tilde{A}$. By alternatively iterating between these two splittings analogous in spirit to the HSS iteration, we obtain the following **AHSS iteration method** for solving the **generalized saddle-point problem** (8.24):

$$\begin{cases} (\Theta + \tilde{H})z^{(k+\frac{1}{2})} & = (\Theta - \tilde{S})z^{(k)} + \tilde{b}, \\ (\Theta + \tilde{S})z^{(k+1)} & = (\Theta - \tilde{H})z^{(k+\frac{1}{2})} + \tilde{b}. \end{cases} \quad (8.62)$$

In blockwise elements, the first half-step of this iteration method requires the solution of two (uncoupled) linear subsystems of the form

$$\begin{cases} (\alpha I + B)x^{(k+\frac{1}{2})} & = \alpha x^{(k)} - Ey^{(k)} + f, \\ (\beta I + C)y^{(k+\frac{1}{2})} & = E^\mathsf{T} x^{(k)} + \beta y^{(k)} - g, \end{cases} \quad (8.63)$$

while its second half-step needs the solution of two coupled linear subsystems of the form

$$\begin{cases} \alpha x^{(k+1)} + Ey^{(k+1)} & = (\alpha I - B)x^{(k+\frac{1}{2})} + f, \\ -E^\mathsf{T} x^{(k+1)} + \beta y^{(k+1)} & = (\beta I - C)y^{(k+\frac{1}{2})} - g. \end{cases} \quad (8.64)$$

In fact, the linear subsystems in (8.63) and (8.64) share the same structures and properties as those in (8.50) and (8.51), respectively, so that they can be solved efficiently by adopting the strategies and techniques suggested previously.

The AHSS iteration method is meaningful and practical from the viewpoint of both theory and applications, because, without introducing extra computational workload, it not only algorithmically generalizes the HSS iteration method to obtain a fast convergent iterative scheme, but also considerably decreases its numerical sensitivity with respect to the iteration parameters, especially when the two parameters involved are close to their optimal values.

Note that when $\alpha = \beta$, the AHSS iteration method naturally reduces to the HSS iteration method [65]; and when $\alpha \neq \beta$, different choices of α and β can yield various iteration methods for solving the generalized saddle-point problem (8.24).

After eliminating the intermediate vector $z^{(k+\frac{1}{2})}$, we can write the AHSS iteration method (8.62) as a **standard stationary iteration scheme** of the form

$$z^{(k+1)} = \tilde{G}(\alpha, \beta)\, z^{(k)} + \tilde{c}(\alpha, \beta), \quad (8.65)$$

where

$$\tilde{G}(\alpha, \beta) \equiv \tilde{G}(\Theta) \triangleq (\Theta + \tilde{S})^{-1}(\Theta - \tilde{H})(\Theta + \tilde{H})^{-1}(\Theta - \tilde{S}) \quad (8.66)$$

is the AHSS **iteration matrix**, and

$$\tilde{c}(\alpha, \beta) \equiv \tilde{c}(\Theta) \triangleq 2\Theta(\Theta + \tilde{S})^{-1}(\Theta + \tilde{H})^{-1}\tilde{b}.$$

In fact, by letting

$$\begin{cases} \tilde{M}(\Theta) &= \frac{1}{2}\Theta^{-1}(\Theta + \tilde{H})(\Theta + \tilde{S}), \\ \tilde{N}(\Theta) &= \frac{1}{2}\Theta^{-1}(\Theta - \tilde{H})(\Theta - \tilde{S}), \end{cases}$$

we have

$$\tilde{A} = \tilde{M}(\Theta) - \tilde{N}(\Theta) \tag{8.67}$$

and

$$\tilde{c}(\Theta) = \tilde{M}(\Theta)^{-1}\tilde{b}.$$

In addition, based on the commutative property of the matrices $\Theta - \tilde{H}$ and $(\Theta + \tilde{H})^{-1}$, we can obtain

$$\tilde{G}(\Theta) = \tilde{M}(\Theta)^{-1}\tilde{N}(\Theta).$$

As a consequence, the AHSS iteration (8.65) can also be regarded as a matrix splitting iteration induced by the splitting (8.67) of the generalized saddle-point matrix $\tilde{A}$. Thereby, the convergence theory for the AHSS iteration method can be demonstrated in an analogous fashion to that for the HSS iteration method (8.49).

Theorem 8.19. [24, 32] *Consider the generalized saddle-point problem* (8.24). *Suppose that* $B \in \mathbb{R}^{n \times n}$ *is symmetric positive definite,* $C \in \mathbb{R}^{m \times m}$ *is symmetric positive semidefinite, and* $E \in \mathbb{R}^{n \times m}$ *is such that* $\text{Ker}(E) \cap \text{Ker}(C) = \{0\}$. *Then, the AHSS iteration method* (8.62) *is unconditionally convergent, that is,* $\rho(\tilde{G}(\alpha, \beta)) < 1$ *for all* $\alpha, \beta > 0$, *where* $\tilde{G}(\alpha, \beta)$ *is the AHSS iteration matrix given in* (8.66).

Proof. Let

$$\Xi = \begin{bmatrix} \sqrt{\beta}I_n & 0 \\ 0 & \sqrt{\alpha}I_m \end{bmatrix}$$

and $\theta = \alpha\beta$. Then it holds that

$$\Xi\Theta\Xi = \theta I$$

and

$$\begin{aligned} \tilde{G}(\Theta) &= \Xi(\theta I + \hat{S})^{-1}(\theta I - \hat{H})(\theta I + \hat{H})^{-1}(\theta I - \hat{S})\Xi^{-1} \\ &\triangleq \Xi\hat{G}(\theta)\Xi^{-1}, \end{aligned}$$

where

$$\hat{H} = \Xi\tilde{H}\Xi = \begin{bmatrix} \beta B & 0 \\ 0 & \alpha C \end{bmatrix} \triangleq \begin{bmatrix} \hat{B} & 0 \\ 0 & \hat{C} \end{bmatrix},$$

$$\hat{S} = \Xi\tilde{S}\Xi = \begin{bmatrix} 0 & \sqrt{\alpha\beta}E \\ -\sqrt{\alpha\beta}E^{\mathsf{T}} & 0 \end{bmatrix} \triangleq \begin{bmatrix} 0 & \hat{E} \\ -\hat{E}^{\mathsf{T}} & 0 \end{bmatrix},$$

and

$$\hat{G}(\theta) = (\theta I + \hat{S})^{-1}(\theta I - \hat{H})(\theta I + \hat{H})^{-1}(\theta I - \hat{S}),$$

with

$$\hat{B} = \beta B, \quad \hat{C} = \alpha C, \quad \text{and} \quad \hat{E} = \sqrt{\alpha\beta}E.$$

It follows that $\hat{G}(\theta)$ is the HSS iteration matrix associated with the matrix

$$\hat{A} = \hat{H} + \hat{S} = \begin{bmatrix} \hat{B} & \hat{E} \\ -\hat{E}^{\mathsf{T}} & \hat{C} \end{bmatrix},$$

with the parameter being θ. As the matrix $\hat{B} \in \mathbb{R}^{n \times n}$ is symmetric positive definite, the matrix $\hat{C} \in \mathbb{R}^{m \times m}$ is symmetric positive semidefinite with $\mathrm{Ker}(\hat{C}) = \mathrm{Ker}(C)$, and the matrix $\hat{E} \in \mathbb{R}^{n \times m}$ is such that $\mathrm{Ker}(\hat{E}) = \mathrm{Ker}(E)$, we see that

$$\mathrm{Ker}(\hat{E}) \cap \mathrm{Ker}(\hat{C}) = \{0\}.$$

In accordance with Theorem 8.18, we know that the matrix $\hat{G}(\theta)$ is convergent unconditionally, that is, $\rho(\hat{G}(\theta)) < 1$ is valid for all $\theta > 0$.

According to the **similarity invariance** of the **matrix spectrum**, we immediately have

$$\rho(\tilde{G}(\alpha, \beta)) = \rho(\tilde{G}(\Theta)) = \rho(\hat{G}(\theta)) < 1, \quad \forall \alpha, \ \beta > 0,$$

which shows that the AHSS iteration method (8.62) is convergent unconditionally. □

8.3.5 ▪ Preconditioned HSS-Type Iterations

The convergence property of both HSS and AHSS iteration methods is strongly dependent on the conditioning of the **generalized saddle-point matrix** $\tilde{A}$ in (8.24). Hence, in order to further improve their convergence behavior, we may first symmetrically precondition the generalized saddle-point problem (8.24) and then employ the HSS or the AHSS iteration technique directly to the correspondingly **preconditioned linear system**, obtaining the **preconditioned HSS** and **AHSS iteration methods**; see [32, 33, 34, 38, 65].

To be more specific, we let $W \in \mathbb{R}^{n \times n}$ and $Z \in \mathbb{R}^{m \times m}$ be two nonsingular matrices, and write

$$R^{-1} = \begin{bmatrix} W & 0 \\ 0 & Z \end{bmatrix} \quad \text{and} \quad \hat{A} = R^{-\mathsf{T}}\tilde{A}R^{-1}.$$

Then we have

$$\begin{aligned}
\hat{A} &= \begin{bmatrix} W^{\mathsf{T}} & 0 \\ 0 & Z^{\mathsf{T}} \end{bmatrix} \begin{bmatrix} B & E \\ -E^{\mathsf{T}} & C \end{bmatrix} \begin{bmatrix} W & 0 \\ 0 & Z \end{bmatrix} \\
&= \begin{bmatrix} W^{\mathsf{T}}BW & W^{\mathsf{T}}EZ \\ -Z^{\mathsf{T}}E^{\mathsf{T}}W & Z^{\mathsf{T}}CZ \end{bmatrix} \\
&= \begin{bmatrix} \hat{B} & \hat{E} \\ -\hat{E}^{\mathsf{T}} & \hat{C} \end{bmatrix},
\end{aligned}$$

where

$$\hat{B} = W^{\mathsf{T}}BW, \quad \hat{C} = Z^{\mathsf{T}}CZ, \quad \text{and} \quad \hat{E} = W^{\mathsf{T}}EZ. \tag{8.68}$$

Hence, the **generalized saddle-point problem** (8.24) can be equivalently reformulated as

$$\begin{bmatrix} \hat{B} & \hat{E} \\ -\hat{E}^{\mathsf{T}} & \hat{C} \end{bmatrix} \begin{bmatrix} \hat{x} \\ \hat{y} \end{bmatrix} = \begin{bmatrix} \hat{f} \\ -\hat{g} \end{bmatrix}, \quad \text{or} \quad \hat{A}\hat{z} = \hat{b}, \tag{8.69}$$

with

$$\hat{z} = \begin{bmatrix} \hat{x} \\ \hat{y} \end{bmatrix} \triangleq Rz = \begin{bmatrix} W^{-1}x \\ Z^{-1}y \end{bmatrix} \quad \text{and} \quad \hat{b} = \begin{bmatrix} \hat{f} \\ -\hat{g} \end{bmatrix} \triangleq R^{-\mathsf{T}}\tilde{b} = \begin{bmatrix} W^{\mathsf{T}}f \\ -Z^{\mathsf{T}}g \end{bmatrix}. \tag{8.70}$$

So, instead of solving the original linear system (8.24), we can solve the **preconditioned linear system** (8.69) by any iterative method available.

For the **standard saddle-point problem** (8.25), that is, the special case of the **generalized saddle-point problem** (8.24) with $C = 0$, we may take the matrix W such that $W^{\mathsf{T}}BW = I_n$, for example, $W = B^{-\frac{1}{2}}$, or $W = L^{-1}$ with $B = L^{\mathsf{T}}L$ being the **Cholesky factorization** of the matrix block B, where L is a lower-triangular matrix; see [167, Chapter 4]. In addition, we may take the matrix Z to be some nonsingular matrix. Denote by $Q = Z^{-\mathsf{T}}Z^{-1}$. Then, the corresponding **preconditioned standard saddle-point matrix** is of the form

$$\hat{A} = \begin{bmatrix} I & \hat{E} \\ -\hat{E}^{\mathsf{T}} & 0 \end{bmatrix}, \tag{8.71}$$

with its symmetric and skew-symmetric parts being given by

$$\hat{H} = \frac{1}{2}(\hat{A} + \hat{A}^{\mathsf{T}}) = \begin{bmatrix} I & 0 \\ 0 & 0 \end{bmatrix}, \quad \hat{S} = \frac{1}{2}(\hat{A} - \hat{A}^{\mathsf{T}}) = \begin{bmatrix} 0 & \hat{E} \\ -\hat{E}^{\mathsf{T}} & 0 \end{bmatrix}.$$

Note that

$$\hat{A} = \hat{H} + \hat{S},$$

with the matrix $\hat{H}$ being Hermitian positive *semidefinite*.

Now, by first applying the AHSS iteration technique to the **preconditioned standard saddle-point problem** of the form (8.69), but with $\hat{B} = I$ and $\hat{C} = 0$ or with the coefficient matrix $\hat{A}$ being specified as in (8.71), and then transforming the obtained iteration scheme back to the original variables based on (8.68) and (8.70), we can obtain the following *preconditioned AHSS* (PAHSS) iteration method for solving the standard saddle-point problem (8.25); see [32, 34].

$$\begin{bmatrix} \alpha B & E \\ -E^{\mathsf{T}} & \beta Q \end{bmatrix} \begin{bmatrix} x^{(k+1)} \\ y^{(k+1)} \end{bmatrix} = \begin{bmatrix} \frac{\alpha(\alpha-1)}{\alpha+1}B & -\frac{\alpha-1}{\alpha+1}E \\ E^{\mathsf{T}} & \beta Q \end{bmatrix} \begin{bmatrix} x^{(k)} \\ y^{(k)} \end{bmatrix} + \begin{bmatrix} \frac{2\alpha}{\alpha+1}f \\ -2g \end{bmatrix}. \tag{8.72}$$

When $\alpha = \beta$, the **PAHSS iteration method** naturally reduces to the **PHSS iteration method** in [38]; see also [65].

From (8.72) we easily know that the PAHSS iteration method can be equivalently written as

$$\begin{bmatrix} x^{(k+1)} \\ y^{(k+1)} \end{bmatrix} = \tilde{G}(\alpha, \beta) \begin{bmatrix} x^{(k)} \\ y^{(k)} \end{bmatrix} + \tilde{F}(\alpha, \beta) \begin{bmatrix} f \\ -g \end{bmatrix}, \tag{8.73}$$

where

$$\tilde{G}(\alpha, \beta) = \begin{bmatrix} \alpha B & E \\ -E^{\mathsf{T}} & \beta Q \end{bmatrix}^{-1} \begin{bmatrix} \frac{\alpha(\alpha-1)}{\alpha+1}B & -\frac{\alpha-1}{\alpha+1}E \\ E^{\mathsf{T}} & \beta Q \end{bmatrix}$$

is the PAHSS **iteration matrix**, and

$$\tilde{F}(\alpha, \beta) = \begin{bmatrix} \alpha B & E \\ -E^{\mathsf{T}} & \beta Q \end{bmatrix}^{-1} \begin{bmatrix} \frac{2\alpha}{\alpha+1}I & 0 \\ 0 & 2I \end{bmatrix}.$$

In fact, the iteration scheme (8.73) may also result from the splitting

$$\tilde{A} = \tilde{M}(\alpha, \beta) - \tilde{N}(\alpha, \beta) \tag{8.74}$$

of the coefficient matrix $\tilde{A}$, with

$$\tilde{M}(\alpha,\beta) = \begin{bmatrix} \frac{\alpha+1}{2}B & \frac{\alpha+1}{2\alpha}E \\ -\frac{1}{2}E^{\mathsf{T}} & \frac{\beta}{2}Q \end{bmatrix}, \quad \tilde{N}(\alpha,\beta) = \begin{bmatrix} \frac{\alpha-1}{2}B & -\frac{\alpha-1}{2\alpha}E \\ \frac{1}{2}E^{\mathsf{T}} & \frac{\beta}{2}Q \end{bmatrix}.$$

In actual computations, at each iterate of the PAHSS iteration we need to solve a linear system with the coefficient matrix

$$\tilde{M}'(\alpha,\beta) = \begin{bmatrix} \alpha B & E \\ -E^{\mathsf{T}} & \beta Q \end{bmatrix}, \quad \text{or equivalently,} \quad \tilde{M}(\alpha,\beta). \tag{8.75}$$

Note that these matrices are real positive, or in other words, positive definite. Therefore, via the PAHSS iteration technique, the problem of solving a positive *semidefinite* linear system is transformed to the one of solving a sequence of positive *definite* linear systems; the latter may often possess better numerical properties than the former.

By making use of **block-triangular factorization** of the matrix $\tilde{M}'(\alpha,\beta)$ in (8.75), we can obtain the following computing version of the PAHSS iteration method.

Given an initial guess $z^{(0)} = \left[x^{(0)^{\mathsf{T}}}, y^{(0)^{\mathsf{T}}}\right]^{\mathsf{T}} \in \mathbb{R}^{n+m}$, and two positive constants α and β. For $k = 0, 1, 2, \dots$ until $\{z^{(k)}\}_{k=0}^{\infty} = \left\{\left[x^{(k)^{\mathsf{T}}}, y^{(k)^{\mathsf{T}}}\right]^{\mathsf{T}}\right\}_{k=0}^{\infty} \subset \mathbb{R}^{n+m}$ converges, compute the next iterate $z^{(k+1)} = \left[x^{(k+1)^{\mathsf{T}}}, y^{(k+1)^{\mathsf{T}}}\right]^{\mathsf{T}}$ according to the following procedure:

Step 1. Compute the current **residual vector** by

$$r^{(k)} = f - (Bx^{(k)} + Ey^{(k)}), \quad s^{(k)} = -g + E^{\mathsf{T}}x^{(k)};$$

Step 2. Compute the **auxiliary vectors** by

$$u^{(k)} = \frac{2}{\alpha+1}r^{(k)}, \quad v^{(k)} = E^{\mathsf{T}}B^{-1}u^{(k)} + 2s^{(k)};$$

Step 3. Compute the **update vectors** by solving the linear systems

$$\left(\beta Q + \frac{1}{\alpha}E^{\mathsf{T}}B^{-1}E\right)w^{(k)} = v^{(k)}, \quad Bt^{(k)} = u^{(k)} - Ew^{(k)};$$

Step 4. Form the next iterate according to

$$x^{(k+1)} = x^{(k)} + t^{(k)}, \quad y^{(k+1)} = y^{(k)} + w^{(k)}.$$

So, at each of the PAHSS iteration steps, we have to solve two subsystems of linear equations with the coefficient matrix B and one subsystem of linear equations with the coefficient matrix $\beta Q + \frac{1}{\alpha}E^{\mathsf{T}}B^{-1}E$, that is, the Schur complement of the matrix $\tilde{M}'(\alpha,\beta)$ defined in (8.75). This amount of computational cost is the same as the PCG [42, 49], and is comparable with those of the Uzawa and GSOR iteration methods [49, 66, 202, 203], which are used for solving the standard saddle-point problem (8.25).

It seems that solving linear systems of the form

$$\left(\beta Q + \frac{1}{\alpha}E^{\mathsf{T}}B^{-1}E\right)w = v \tag{8.76}$$

is costly and impractical in actual applications. However, by recalling that Q is an arbitrary symmetric positive definite matrix, we can choose it such that the matrix $\beta Q + \frac{1}{\alpha}E^{\mathsf{T}}B^{-1}E$

possesses a simple and easily invertible form (e.g., a (block) diagonal matrix, or a product of a (block) lower-triangular matrix with an (block) upper-triangular matrix), and, hence, these linear systems are cheaply solvable.

Theorems 8.18 and 8.19 have also demonstrated the unconditional convergence property of both PHSS and PAHSS iteration methods, as these two methods are special cases of the HSS and AHSS iteration methods applied to the **preconditioned linear system** (8.69)–(8.70), respectively. For the **optimal iteration parameters** that minimize the spectral radii of the PHSS and PAHSS iteration matrices, and for the corresponding **optimal asymptotic convergence factors**, we have the following result.

Theorem 8.20. *Consider the standard saddle-point problem (8.25) with* $n \geq m$. *Let* $B \in \mathbb{R}^{n \times n}$ *be symmetric positive definite,* $E \in \mathbb{R}^{n \times m}$ *be of full column rank, and* $\alpha, \beta > 0$ *be given constants. Assume that* $W \in \mathbb{R}^{n \times n}$ *and* $Z \in \mathbb{R}^{m \times m}$ *are nonsingular matrices such that* $W^{\mathsf{T}} B W = I_n$. *Denote by* $Q = Z^{-\mathsf{T}} Z^{-1}$, *and by* $\sigma_{\min}$ *and* $\sigma_{\max}$ *the smallest and largest singular values of the matrix* $W^{\mathsf{T}} E Z$. *Then the following statements hold true:*

(i) *for the PHSS iteration method, the optimal value of the iteration parameter* α *is given by*

$$\alpha_{\mathrm{opt}} = \sqrt{\sigma_{\min}\sigma_{\max}},$$

and, correspondingly, the optimal asymptotic convergence factor is given by

$$\varrho_{\mathrm{opt}} \triangleq \rho(\tilde{G}(\alpha_{\mathrm{opt}}))$$
$$= \left(\frac{\sigma_{\max} - \sigma_{\min}}{\sigma_{\max} + \sigma_{\min}}\right) \left(\frac{\sqrt{\sigma_{\min}\sigma_{\max}}}{\sqrt{\sigma_{\min}\sigma_{\max}} + 1} + \frac{\sqrt{(\sigma_{\max} + \sigma_{\min})^2 - 4\sigma_{\min}^2 \sigma_{\max}^2}}{(\sqrt{\sigma_{\min}\sigma_{\max}} + 1)(\sigma_{\max} - \sigma_{\min})}\right);$$

if $\sigma_{\min}\sigma_{\max} \leq \frac{1}{2}(\sigma_{\min} + \sigma_{\max})$, *and, otherwise, the optimal value of the iteration parameter* α *is given by*

$$\alpha_{\mathrm{opt}} = \frac{\sigma_{\max}}{\sqrt{2\sigma_{\max} - 1}},$$

and, correspondingly, the optimal asymptotic convergence factor is given by

$$\varrho_{\mathrm{opt}} \triangleq \rho(\tilde{G}(\alpha_{\mathrm{opt}})) = \frac{|\sigma_{\max} - 1|}{\sigma_{\max} + \sqrt{2\sigma_{\max} - 1}};$$

(ii) *for the PAHSS iteration method, the optimal values of the iteration parameters* α *and* β *are given by*

$$\alpha_{\mathrm{opt}} = \frac{\sigma_{\min} + \sigma_{\max}}{2\sqrt{\sigma_{\min}\sigma_{\max}}} \quad and \quad \beta_{\mathrm{opt}} = \frac{\sigma_{\min}\sigma_{\max}}{\alpha_{\mathrm{opt}}},$$

and, correspondingly, the optimal asymptotic convergence factor is given by

$$\varrho_{\mathrm{opt}} \triangleq \rho(\tilde{G}(\alpha_{\mathrm{opt}}, \beta_{\mathrm{opt}})) = \frac{\sqrt{\sigma_{\max}} - \sqrt{\sigma_{\min}}}{\sqrt{\sigma_{\max}} + \sqrt{\sigma_{\min}}}.$$

Proof. The proof of this theorem is relatively technical and more involved, so it is omitted. For the details, see [24, 31, 32, 33, 38]. □

We remark that the second case in (i) rarely appears in applications.

Let $S = E^{\mathsf{T}}B^{-1}E$ be the **Schur complement** of the **standard saddle-point matrix** $\tilde{A}$ in (8.25), and

$$\kappa(Q^{-1}S) \triangleq \frac{\lambda_{\max}(Q^{-1}S)}{\lambda_{\min}(Q^{-1}S)}$$

be the **condition number** of the **preconditioned Schur complement** $Q^{-1}S$. As

$$(W^{\mathsf{T}}EZ)^{\mathsf{T}}(W^{\mathsf{T}}EZ) = Z^{\mathsf{T}}E^{\mathsf{T}}WW^{\mathsf{T}}EZ = Z^{\mathsf{T}}E^{\mathsf{T}}B^{-1}EZ,$$

we see that

$$\lambda_{\min}(Q^{-1}S) = \sigma_{\min}^2 \quad \text{and} \quad \lambda_{\max}(Q^{-1}S) = \sigma_{\max}^2.$$

Then Theorem 8.20 shows that the principal part of the **optimal convergence factor** of the **PHSS iteration method** can be reformulated as

$$\varrho_{\mathrm{opt}} = \frac{\sqrt{\kappa(Q^{-1}S)} - 1}{\sqrt{\kappa(Q^{-1}S)} + 1},$$

and the optimal convergence factor of the **PAHSS iteration method** can be reformulated as

$$\varrho_{\mathrm{opt}} = \frac{\sqrt[4]{\kappa(Q^{-1}S)} - 1}{\sqrt[4]{\kappa(Q^{-1}S)} + 1}.$$

Consequently, the **asymptotic convergence rate** of the PHSS iteration method is essentially the same as those of the GSOR iteration method and the PCG method (incorporated with the preconditioner Q and applied to the reduced Schur complement system in (8.42)), while the asymptotic convergence rate of the PAHSS iteration method is exactly two orders faster than those of the PHSS, GSOR, and PCG iteration methods. Observing that both PHSS and PAHSS iteration methods have the same computational cost at each of their iteration steps, we can see that the PAHSS iteration method could be much more effective than the PCG, GSOR, and PHSS iteration methods in actual applications.

In addition, from Theorem 8.20 we also observe that the symmetric positive definite matrix $Q \in \mathbb{R}^{m \times m}$ should be chosen such that linear systems of the form (8.76) are easily solvable and the singular values of the matrix $W^{\mathsf{T}}EZ \in \mathbb{R}^{n \times m}$ are tightly clustered, or in other words, the matrix Q should be a good preconditioner for the Schur complement $S = E^{\mathsf{T}}B^{-1}E$.

8.4 ▪ Elementary Preconditioners

For saddle-point problems, the construction of high-quality preconditioners needs the exploitation of the block structure of the saddle-point matrices, together with detailed knowledge about the origin and structure of the involved various blocks. Because the latter varies greatly from application to application, there is no such thing as the "best" preconditioner for saddle-point problems. The choice of a preconditioner is strongly problem-dependent. For instance, techniques that give excellent results for the time-dependent Stokes problem may be completely inadequate for the steady-state case, or for the Oseen equations; and preconditioners that have been successfully used in optimization may be useless in fluid dynamics.

In the following, we introduce some elementary but popular preconditioners for the saddle-point problems.

8.4.1 ▪ HSS-Type Preconditioners

The matrix splittings in (8.56), (8.67), and (8.74) naturally induce the HSS, AHSS, and PAHSS preconditioning matrices for either the generalized or the standard saddle-point matrix $\tilde{A}$ in (8.24) or (8.25), respectively. Note that the **PHSS preconditioning matrix** is just a special case of the **PAHSS preconditioning matrix** when the two parameters involved are equal.

More specifically, these **HSS-type preconditioners** are of the following forms:

(i) the **HSS preconditioner**

$$\tilde{M}_{\mathrm{HSS}}(\alpha) = \frac{1}{2\alpha} \begin{bmatrix} \alpha I + B & 0 \\ 0 & \alpha I + C \end{bmatrix} \begin{bmatrix} \alpha I & E \\ -E^{\mathsf{T}} & \alpha I \end{bmatrix},$$

(ii) the **AHSS preconditioner**

$$\tilde{M}_{\mathrm{AHSS}}(\alpha, \beta) = \begin{bmatrix} \frac{1}{2\alpha} I & 0 \\ 0 & \frac{1}{2\beta} I \end{bmatrix} \begin{bmatrix} \alpha I + B & 0 \\ 0 & \beta I + C \end{bmatrix} \begin{bmatrix} \alpha I & E \\ -E^{\mathsf{T}} & \beta I \end{bmatrix},$$

(iii) the **PHSS preconditioner**

$$\tilde{M}_{\mathrm{PHSS}}(\alpha) = \begin{bmatrix} \frac{\alpha+1}{2} B & \frac{\alpha+1}{2\alpha} E \\ -\frac{1}{2} E^{\mathsf{T}} & \frac{\alpha}{2} Q \end{bmatrix},$$

(iv) the **PAHSS preconditioner**

$$\tilde{M}_{\mathrm{PAHSS}}(\alpha, \beta) = \begin{bmatrix} \frac{\alpha+1}{2} B & \frac{\alpha+1}{2\alpha} E \\ -\frac{1}{2} E^{\mathsf{T}} & \frac{\beta}{2} Q \end{bmatrix}.$$

Note that while the HSS and AHSS preconditioners can be applied to both generalized and standard saddle-point problems, the PHSS and PAHSS preconditioners can be applied only to the **standard saddle-point matrix**, in which the matrix Q is an arbitrary symmetric positive definite matrix.

Without causing any confusion, in the following we may represent these preconditioning matrices generically as $\tilde{M}$. The question then arises whether $\tilde{M}^{-1}\tilde{A}$ (or $\tilde{A}\tilde{M}^{-1}$) is positive real, for in this case the convergence of the **restarted GMRES iteration**, say, GMRES(ℓ), would be guaranteed for all restarts ℓ; see [120, 173, 288] and [289, p. 866].

More concretely, consider the **preconditioned linear system**

$$\tilde{\mathbf{A}}z = \tilde{\mathbf{b}}, \quad \text{with} \quad \tilde{\mathbf{A}} \triangleq \tilde{M}^{-1}\tilde{A} \text{ and } \tilde{\mathbf{b}} \triangleq \tilde{M}^{-1}\tilde{b}.$$

Assume that the coefficient matrix $\tilde{\mathbf{A}}$ is diagonalizable, i.e., there exist a nonsingular matrix $\tilde{\mathbf{X}} \in \mathbb{C}^{(n+m)\times(n+m)}$ and a diagonal matrix $\tilde{\mathbf{D}} \in \mathbb{C}^{(n+m)\times(n+m)}$ such that

$$\tilde{\mathbf{A}} = \tilde{\mathbf{X}}\tilde{\mathbf{D}}\tilde{\mathbf{X}}^{-1}.$$

Then it is well known from [289, Theorem 4] that the residual norm $\|\tilde{\mathbf{r}}^{(k)}\|_2$ at the k-th step of the **preconditioned GMRES** is bounded by

$$\|\tilde{\mathbf{r}}^{(k)}\|_2 \leq \kappa(\tilde{\mathbf{X}}) \, \epsilon^{(k)} \, \|\tilde{\mathbf{r}}^{(0)}\|_2,$$

where $\kappa(\tilde{\mathbf{X}})$ is the **Euclidean condition number** of the eigenvector matrix $\tilde{\mathbf{X}}$ and

$$\epsilon^{(k)} := \min_{p \in \mathcal{P}_k} \max_{\lambda_i \in \sigma(\tilde{\mathbf{A}})} |p(\lambda_i)|.$$

Here, $\mathcal{P}_k$ denotes the set of all polynomials $p(\lambda)$ of degree not greater than k such that $p(0) = 1$, and $\sigma(\tilde{\mathbf{A}})$ denotes the spectrum of the matrix $\tilde{\mathbf{A}}$. If all eigenvalues of the matrix $\tilde{\mathbf{A}}$ are contained in a circle with the radius ϱ on the right-half complex plane, then a special case of Theorem 5 in [289] implies that $\epsilon^{(k)} \leq \varrho^k$. Here, of course, we require that $\varrho < 1$, in order to guarantee the convergence.

If the coefficient matrix $\tilde{\mathbf{A}}$ is positive definite, then it is known from [120] and [289, p. 866] that the error bound

$$\|\tilde{\mathbf{r}}^{(k)}\|_2 \leq \left(1 - \frac{(\lambda_{\min}(\ddot{\mathbf{H}}))^2}{\lambda_{\max}(\tilde{\mathbf{A}}^{\mathsf{T}} \tilde{\mathbf{A}})} \right)^{\frac{k}{2}} \|\tilde{\mathbf{r}}^{(0)}\|_2$$

holds for the preconditioned GMRES, where $\ddot{\mathbf{H}}$ denotes the symmetric part of the matrix $\tilde{\mathbf{A}}$, and $\lambda_{\min}(\cdot)$ and $\lambda_{\max}(\cdot)$ denote, respectively, the smallest and the largest eigenvalues of the corresponding matrix. This gives a guarantee for the convergence of the restarted GMRES iteration, say again, GMRES(ℓ), for all ℓ when the matrix $\tilde{\mathbf{A}}$ is positive definite.

Unfortunately, the preconditioned matrices associated with the **HSS-type preconditioners** may be not positive real in general. However, when the matrix B is symmetric positive definite and the matrix $C = 0$, that is, for the **standard saddle-point matrix**, we can prove that these preconditioned matrices are positive real provided some further restrictions are imposed on the iteration parameters α and (or) β.

Theorem 8.21. [65] *Consider the standard saddle-point problem (8.25) with $n \geq m$. Let $B \in \mathbb{R}^{n \times n}$ be symmetric positive definite, $E \in \mathbb{R}^{n \times m}$ be of full column rank, and $\alpha, \beta > 0$ be given constants. Then*

(i) *for the HSS preconditioning, there exists a positive real α_o such that the matrix $\tilde{\mathbf{A}} = \tilde{M}_{\mathrm{HSS}}(\alpha)^{-1} \tilde{A}$ is positive definite for all $\alpha > \alpha_o$, and an analogous result holds for the **right-preconditioned matrix**, $\tilde{A} \tilde{M}_{\mathrm{HSS}}(\alpha)^{-1}$;*

(ii) *for the AHSS preconditioning, there exist positive reals α_o and β_o such that the matrix $\tilde{\mathbf{A}} = \tilde{M}_{\mathrm{AHSS}}(\alpha, \beta)^{-1} \tilde{A}$ is positive definite for all $\alpha > \alpha_o$ and $\beta > \beta_o$, and an analogous result holds for the right-preconditioned matrix, $\tilde{A} \tilde{M}_{\mathrm{AHSS}}(\alpha, \beta)^{-1}$.*

Proof. We only prove the result about the **HSS preconditioning**, as the result for the **AHSS preconditioning** can be demonstrated in an analogous fashion.

For brevity, we prove the positive definiteness of the **HSS-preconditioned matrix** only for the **left preconditioning**; the proof for the right-preconditioned matrix is similar.

The symmetric part of the HSS-preconditioned matrix $\tilde{\mathbf{A}} = \tilde{M}_{\mathrm{HSS}}(\alpha)^{-1} \tilde{A}$ is given by

$$\ddot{\mathbf{H}} \triangleq \frac{1}{2}(\tilde{\mathbf{A}} + \tilde{\mathbf{A}}^{\mathsf{T}}) = \frac{1}{2}(\tilde{M}_{\mathrm{HSS}}(\alpha)^{-1} \tilde{A} + \tilde{A}^{\mathsf{T}} \tilde{M}_{\mathrm{HSS}}(\alpha)^{-\mathsf{T}}).$$

This matrix is congruent to

$$\tilde{\mathbf{Z}} \triangleq \tilde{A} \tilde{M}_{\mathrm{HSS}}(\alpha)^{\mathsf{T}} + \tilde{M}_{\mathrm{HSS}}(\alpha) \tilde{A}^{\mathsf{T}}$$
$$= \frac{1}{2\alpha} \left[\tilde{A}(\alpha I - \tilde{S})(\alpha I + \tilde{H}) + (\alpha I + \tilde{H})(\alpha I + \tilde{S}) \tilde{A}^{\mathsf{T}} \right],$$

where we have used the fact that the matrix $\tilde{S}$ is skew-symmetric, so that $\tilde{S}^{\mathsf{T}} = -\tilde{S}$. A direct calculation shows that

$$\tilde{\mathbf{Z}} = \begin{bmatrix} Z(\alpha) & -BE \\ -E^{\mathsf{T}} B & E^{\mathsf{T}} E \end{bmatrix},$$

where

$$Z(\alpha) = B^2 + EE^{\mathsf{T}} + \alpha B + \frac{1}{2\alpha}(EE^{\mathsf{T}}B + BEE^{\mathsf{T}}).$$

We want to show that the matrix $\tilde{\mathbf{Z}}$ is symmetric positive definite for sufficiently large α. To this end, we observe that the matrix $\tilde{\mathbf{Z}}$ can be split as

$$\tilde{\mathbf{Z}} = \begin{bmatrix} B^2 & -BE \\ -E^{\mathsf{T}}B & E^{\mathsf{T}}E \end{bmatrix} + \begin{bmatrix} \tilde{Z}(\alpha) & 0 \\ 0 & 0 \end{bmatrix}, \tag{8.77}$$

where

$$\tilde{Z}(\alpha) = (\alpha B + EE^{\mathsf{T}}) + \frac{1}{2\alpha}(EE^{\mathsf{T}}B + BEE^{\mathsf{T}}).$$

The first matrix on the **right-hand side** of (8.77) is symmetric positive semidefinite, since

$$\begin{bmatrix} B^2 & -BE \\ -E^{\mathsf{T}}B & E^{\mathsf{T}}E \end{bmatrix} = \begin{bmatrix} B & 0 \\ -E^{\mathsf{T}} & I \end{bmatrix} \begin{bmatrix} I & 0 \\ 0 & 0 \end{bmatrix} \begin{bmatrix} B & -E \\ 0 & I \end{bmatrix}.$$

Next, we observe that the first part $\alpha B + EE^{\mathsf{T}}$ in the matrix $\tilde{Z}(\alpha)$ is symmetric positive definite for any $\alpha > 0$, but the second part $\frac{1}{2\alpha}(EE^{\mathsf{T}}B + BEE^{\mathsf{T}})$ is generally indefinite. The matrix $\tilde{Z}(\alpha)$ can be made symmetric positive definite by taking α sufficiently large, that is, there exists a positive real α_o such that the matrix $\tilde{Z}(\alpha)$ is symmetric positive definite for all $\alpha > \alpha_o$. Hence, for $\alpha > \alpha_o$ the matrix $\tilde{\mathbf{Z}}$ is the sum of two symmetric positive semidefinite matrices; therefore, it is itself symmetric positive semidefinite. Finally, the matrix $\tilde{\mathbf{Z}}$ must be nonsingular for all $\alpha > \alpha_o$ (and therefore positive definite). Indeed, it is clear from (8.77) that when $\tilde{Z}(\alpha)$ is symmetric positive definite, any null vector of the matrix $\tilde{\mathbf{Z}}$ must be of the form

$$\tilde{u} = \begin{bmatrix} 0 \\ \tilde{v} \end{bmatrix}, \quad \text{where} \quad \tilde{v} \in \mathbb{C}^m.$$

But then

$$\tilde{\mathbf{Z}}\tilde{u} = \begin{bmatrix} Z(\alpha) & -BE \\ -E^{\mathsf{T}}B & E^{\mathsf{T}}E \end{bmatrix} \begin{bmatrix} 0 \\ \tilde{v} \end{bmatrix} = \begin{bmatrix} -BE\tilde{v} \\ E^{\mathsf{T}}E\tilde{v} \end{bmatrix},$$

which cannot be zero unless $\tilde{v} = 0$, since the matrix E has full column rank and the matrix B is nonsingular. Hence, the matrix $\tilde{\mathbf{Z}}$ has no nontrivial null vector for $\alpha > \alpha_o$. This shows that the symmetric part of the HSS-preconditioned matrix $\tilde{M}_{\mathrm{HSS}}(\alpha)^{-1}\tilde{A}$ is symmetric positive definite for all $\alpha > \alpha_o$, since it is congruent to a matrix which is symmetric positive definite for all such values of α. Therefore, for $\alpha > \alpha_o$ the matrix $\tilde{M}_{\mathrm{HSS}}(\alpha)^{-1}\tilde{A}$ is positive definite. $\quad\square$

Theorem 8.22. *Consider the standard saddle-point problem (8.25) with $n \geq m$. Let $B \in \mathbb{R}^{n \times n}$ be symmetric positive definite, $E \in \mathbb{R}^{n \times m}$ be of full column rank, and α, β be two given positive constants. Assume that $Q \in \mathbb{R}^{m \times m}$ is a symmetric positive definite matrix. Then*

(i) *for the PHSS preconditioning, there exists a positive real α_o such that the matrix $\tilde{\mathbf{A}} = \tilde{M}_{\mathrm{PHSS}}(\alpha)^{-1}\tilde{A}$ is positive definite for any $\alpha \in (0, \alpha_o)$, and an analogous result holds for the right-preconditioned matrix, $\tilde{A}\tilde{M}_{\mathrm{PHSS}}(\alpha)^{-1}$;*

(ii) *for the PAHSS preconditioning, there exist positive reals α_o and β_o such that the matrix $\tilde{\mathbf{A}} = \tilde{M}_{\mathrm{PAHSS}}(\alpha, \beta)^{-1}\tilde{A}$ is positive definite for any $\alpha \in (0, \alpha_o)$ and $\beta \in (0, \beta_o)$, and an analogous result holds for the right-preconditioned matrix, $\tilde{A}\tilde{M}_{\mathrm{PAHSS}}(\alpha, \beta)^{-1}$.*

Proof. We only prove the result about the **PAHSS preconditioning**, as the result for the **PHSS preconditioning** can be obtained as a special case when $\alpha = \beta$.

For brevity, we prove the positive definiteness of the **PAHSS-preconditioned matrix** only for the **left preconditioning**; the proof for the **right-preconditioned matrix** is analogous.

Because the symmetric part of the PAHSS-preconditioned matrix $\tilde{\mathbf{A}} \triangleq \tilde{M}_{\text{PAHSS}}(\alpha, \beta)^{-1} \tilde{A}$ is given by

$$\tilde{\mathbf{H}} \triangleq \frac{1}{2}(\tilde{\mathbf{A}}^{\mathsf{T}} \mid \tilde{\mathbf{A}})$$
$$= \frac{1}{2}\left(\tilde{A}^{\mathsf{T}} \tilde{M}_{\text{PAHSS}}(\alpha, \beta)^{-\mathsf{T}} + \tilde{M}_{\text{PAHSS}}(\alpha, \beta)^{-1} \tilde{A}\right),$$

we can obtain

$$\hat{\mathbf{H}} \triangleq \tilde{M}_{\text{PAHSS}}(\alpha, \beta)\,\tilde{\mathbf{H}}\,(\tilde{M}_{\text{PAHSS}}(\alpha, \beta))^{\mathsf{T}}$$
$$= \frac{1}{2}\left(\tilde{M}_{\text{PAHSS}}(\alpha, \beta)\,\tilde{A}^{\mathsf{T}} + \tilde{A}\,(\tilde{M}_{\text{PAHSS}}(\alpha, \beta))^{\mathsf{T}}\right)$$
$$= \frac{1}{2}\left(\begin{bmatrix} \frac{\alpha+1}{2}B & \frac{\alpha+1}{2\alpha}E \\ -\frac{1}{2}E^{\mathsf{T}} & \frac{\beta}{2}Q \end{bmatrix}\begin{bmatrix} B & -E \\ E^{\mathsf{T}} & 0 \end{bmatrix} + \begin{bmatrix} B & E \\ -E^{\mathsf{T}} & 0 \end{bmatrix}\begin{bmatrix} \frac{\alpha+1}{2}B & -\frac{1}{2}E \\ \frac{\alpha+1}{2\alpha}E^{\mathsf{T}} & \frac{\beta}{2}Q \end{bmatrix}\right)$$
$$= \frac{1}{2}\begin{bmatrix} \frac{\alpha+1}{2}B^2 + \frac{\alpha+1}{2\alpha}EE^{\mathsf{T}} & -\frac{\alpha+1}{2}BE \\ -\frac{1}{2}E^{\mathsf{T}}B + \frac{\beta}{2}QE^{\mathsf{T}} & \frac{1}{2}E^{\mathsf{T}}E \end{bmatrix}$$
$$+ \frac{1}{2}\begin{bmatrix} \frac{\alpha+1}{2}B^2 + \frac{\alpha+1}{2\alpha}EE^{\mathsf{T}} & -\frac{1}{2}BE + \frac{\beta}{2}EQ \\ -\frac{\alpha+1}{2}E^{\mathsf{T}}B & \frac{1}{2}E^{\mathsf{T}}E \end{bmatrix}$$
$$= \frac{1}{2}\begin{bmatrix} (\alpha+1)B^2 + \frac{\alpha+1}{\alpha}EE^{\mathsf{T}} & -\frac{\alpha+2}{2}BE + \frac{\beta}{2}EQ \\ -\frac{\alpha+2}{2}E^{\mathsf{T}}B + \frac{\beta}{2}QE^{\mathsf{T}} & E^{\mathsf{T}}E \end{bmatrix}$$
$$\triangleq \hat{\mathbf{H}}_1 + \frac{1}{\alpha}\hat{\mathbf{H}}_2 + \alpha\hat{\mathbf{H}}_3 + \beta\hat{\mathbf{H}}_4,$$

where

$$\hat{\mathbf{H}}_1 = \frac{1}{2}\begin{bmatrix} B^2 + EE^{\mathsf{T}} & -BE \\ -E^{\mathsf{T}}B & E^{\mathsf{T}}E \end{bmatrix},$$
$$\hat{\mathbf{H}}_2 = \frac{1}{2}\begin{bmatrix} EE^{\mathsf{T}} & 0 \\ 0 & 0 \end{bmatrix},$$
$$\hat{\mathbf{H}}_3 = \frac{1}{4}\begin{bmatrix} 2B^2 & -BE \\ -E^{\mathsf{T}}B & 0 \end{bmatrix},$$
$$\hat{\mathbf{H}}_4 = \frac{1}{4}\begin{bmatrix} 0 & EQ \\ QE^{\mathsf{T}} & 0 \end{bmatrix}.$$

Let $\hat{\mathbf{H}}_1 = \hat{\mathbf{H}}_a + \hat{\mathbf{H}}_b$, with

$$\hat{\mathbf{H}}_a = \frac{1}{2}\begin{bmatrix} B^2 & -BE \\ -E^{\mathsf{T}}B & E^{\mathsf{T}}E \end{bmatrix}, \qquad \hat{\mathbf{H}}_b = \frac{1}{2}\begin{bmatrix} EE^{\mathsf{T}} & 0 \\ 0 & 0 \end{bmatrix}.$$

Then we easily see that the matrix $\hat{\mathbf{H}}_1$ is symmetric positive semidefinite, as both matrices $\hat{\mathbf{H}}_a$ and $\hat{\mathbf{H}}_b$ are symmetric positive semidefinite. Moreover, we can demonstrate that the matrix $\hat{\mathbf{H}}_1$ is nonsingular and, hence, is symmetric positive definite; see [31].

Now, let

$$\tilde{h}_1 = \lambda_{\min}(\hat{\mathbf{H}}_1), \quad \tilde{h}_2 = \lambda_{\min}(\hat{\mathbf{H}}_2), \quad \tilde{h}_3 = \|\hat{\mathbf{H}}_3\|_2, \quad \text{and} \quad \tilde{h}_4 = \|\hat{\mathbf{H}}_4\|_2.$$

Then we know that $\tilde{h}_1$ is a positive constant independent of both α and β, and $\tilde{h}_2 = 0$. By straightforward computations, we have

$$
\begin{aligned}
\lambda_{\min}(\hat{\mathbf{H}}) &= \min_{z \neq 0} \frac{z^{\mathsf{T}} \hat{\mathbf{H}} z}{z^{\mathsf{T}} z} \\
&\geq \min_{z \neq 0} \left\{ \frac{z^{\mathsf{T}} \hat{\mathbf{H}}_1 z}{z^{\mathsf{T}} z} + \frac{1}{\alpha} \frac{z^{\mathsf{T}} \hat{\mathbf{H}}_2 z}{z^{\mathsf{T}} z} - \alpha \left| \frac{z^{\mathsf{T}} \hat{\mathbf{H}}_3 z}{z^{\mathsf{T}} z} \right| - \beta \left| \frac{z^{\mathsf{T}} \hat{\mathbf{H}}_4 z}{z^{\mathsf{T}} z} \right| \right\} \\
&\geq \min_{z \neq 0} \frac{z^{\mathsf{T}} \hat{\mathbf{H}}_1 z}{z^{\mathsf{T}} z} + \frac{1}{\alpha} \cdot \min_{z \neq 0} \frac{z^{\mathsf{T}} \hat{\mathbf{H}}_2 z}{z^{\mathsf{T}} z} - \alpha \cdot \max_{z \neq 0} \left| \frac{z^{\mathsf{T}} \hat{\mathbf{H}}_3 z}{z^{\mathsf{T}} z} \right| - \beta \cdot \max_{z \neq 0} \left| \frac{z^{\mathsf{T}} \hat{\mathbf{H}}_4 z}{z^{\mathsf{T}} z} \right| \\
&\geq \lambda_{\min}(\hat{\mathbf{H}}_1) + \frac{1}{\alpha} \lambda_{\min}(\hat{\mathbf{H}}_2) - \alpha \|\hat{\mathbf{H}}_3\|_2 - \beta \|\hat{\mathbf{H}}_4\|_2 \\
&= \tilde{h}_1 - \alpha \tilde{h}_3 - \beta \tilde{h}_4.
\end{aligned}
$$

Therefore, there exist two positive reals α_o and β_o such that

$$
\tilde{h}_1 - \alpha \tilde{h}_3 - \beta \tilde{h}_4 > 0
$$

holds for all $\alpha \in (0, \alpha_o)$ and $\beta \in (0, \beta_o)$. This immediately shows that the matrix $\hat{\mathbf{H}}$ and, hence the matrix $\tilde{\mathbf{H}}$, is symmetric positive definite for all $\alpha \in (0, \alpha_o)$ and $\beta \in (0, \beta_o)$, so that for all such values of α and β the matrix $\tilde{M}_{\mathrm{PAHSS}}(\alpha, \beta)^{-1} \tilde{A}$ is positive definite. $\square$

For these **HSS-type preconditioned matrices**, as

$$
\tilde{\mathbf{A}} \triangleq \tilde{M}^{-1} \tilde{A} = I - \tilde{G},
$$

where

$$
\tilde{G} = \tilde{M}^{-1} \tilde{N}
$$

is the corresponding iteration matrices, with

$$
\tilde{N} = \tilde{M} - \tilde{A},
$$

and as these HSS-type iteration matrices are convergent, we see that all eigenvalues of the matrices $\tilde{\mathbf{A}}$ are located in a circle centered at the point $(1, 0)$ and having radius $\rho(\tilde{G})$ for all positive α and (or) β. As a result, these eigenvalues have positive real parts, so that the HSS-type preconditioned matrices $\tilde{\mathbf{A}}$ are positive stable.

In particular, for the PHSS- and PAHSS-preconditioned matrices, by making use of the results in Exercises 8.16 and 8.17 we can further verify that all of their eigenvalues are real and positive for all $\alpha \in (0, 1]$ and $\beta > 0$. This fact establishes the basis for further accelerating the PHSS and PAHSS iteration methods by the Chebyshev semi-iteration technique; see [329, Chapter 5].

More refined bounds and clustering results for the eigenvalues of the HSS-type preconditioned matrices can be found in [24,295]; and promising applications to constrained and weighted least-squares problems, as well as in the areas of image processing and fluid dynamics computations, etc., are discussed in [66,68,249,267,268,338].

8.4.2 ▪ Block Preconditioners

The **block preconditioners** include **block-diagonal** and **block-triangular preconditioners**, which are very popular in numerical optimization and computational fluid dynamics. These structured preconditioners have close relationships with the **Schur complement reduction**, in particular, with the **block-triangular factorizations** in (8.3) and (8.26). They can be described and analyzed more generally for arbitrary block two-by-two matrices even in the complex space, provided these matrices are nonsingular with, possibly, a nonsingular $(1, 1)$ or $(2, 2)$ block. However, for consistency here we only focus on the special cases of the **generalized saddle-point matrices**

$$A = \begin{bmatrix} B & E \\ E^\mathsf{T} & -C \end{bmatrix} \quad \text{and} \quad \tilde{A} = \begin{bmatrix} B & E \\ -E^\mathsf{T} & C \end{bmatrix} \tag{8.78}$$

defined in (8.1) and (8.24), as well as the **standard saddle-point matrices**

$$A = \begin{bmatrix} B & E \\ E^\mathsf{T} & 0 \end{bmatrix} \quad \text{and} \quad \tilde{A} = \begin{bmatrix} B & E \\ -E^\mathsf{T} & 0 \end{bmatrix} \tag{8.79}$$

defined in (8.2) and (8.25).

Throughout this section, we further relax the symmetric positive definiteness assumption imposed on the $(1, 1)$-block matrix B; and we only assume that $B \in \mathbb{R}^{n \times n}$ is nonsingular, and either the **Schur complement**

$$S = -(C + E^\mathsf{T} B^{-1} E)$$

of the **generalized saddle-point matrix** in **symmetric form**, i.e., the matrix A, or the Schur complement

$$\tilde{S} = C + E^\mathsf{T} B^{-1} E$$

of the **generalized saddle-point matrix** in **nonsymmetric form**, i.e., the matrix $\tilde{A}$, is nonsingular, so that both matrices A and $\tilde{A}$ are nonsingular.

Note that for the standard saddle-point matrices, i.e., the case $C = 0$, the assumption that the Schur complement is nonsingular can be replaced by the stronger assumptions that $n \geq m$, the matrix $B \in \mathbb{R}^{n \times n}$ is symmetric positive definite, and the matrix $E \in \mathbb{R}^{n \times m}$ is of full column rank.

8.4.2.1 ▪ Block-Diagonal Preconditioners

The **block-diagonal preconditioners** are defined by

$$P_D = \begin{bmatrix} B & 0 \\ 0 & S \end{bmatrix} \quad \text{and} \quad \tilde{P}_D = \begin{bmatrix} B & 0 \\ 0 & \tilde{S} \end{bmatrix}. \tag{8.80}$$

As $\tilde{S} = -S$, we can rewrite the matrix $\tilde{P}_D$ as

$$\tilde{P}_D = \begin{bmatrix} B & 0 \\ 0 & -S \end{bmatrix}.$$

Correspondingly, for the **left-preconditioned matrices** we have

$$T_+ \triangleq P_D^{-1} A = \begin{bmatrix} I & B^{-1}E \\ S^{-1}E^\mathsf{T} & S^{-1}C \end{bmatrix},$$

$$T_- \triangleq \tilde{P}_D^{-1} A = \begin{bmatrix} I & B^{-1}E \\ -S^{-1}E^\mathsf{T} & -S^{-1}C \end{bmatrix},$$

$$\tilde{T}_- \triangleq P_D^{-1} \tilde{A} = \begin{bmatrix} I & B^{-1}E \\ -S^{-1}E^\mathsf{T} & S^{-1}C \end{bmatrix},$$

$$\tilde{T}_+ \triangleq \tilde{P}_D^{-1} \tilde{A} = \begin{bmatrix} I & B^{-1}E \\ S^{-1}E^\mathsf{T} & -S^{-1}C \end{bmatrix}. \tag{8.81}$$

We remark that the **right-preconditioned matrices** can be formulated in an analogous fashion and are similar to their left-preconditioned counterparts, respectively.

It is difficult to analyze the eigenproperties about these **block-diagonal preconditioned matrices** for the **generalized saddle-point matrices** in (8.78). However, for the **standard saddle-point matrices** in (8.79), the eigenvalues of these **preconditioned matrices** are completely known.

Theorem 8.23. *For the standard saddle-point matrices A and $\tilde{A}$ in (8.79), let the block-diagonal preconditioners P_D and $\tilde{P}_D$ be defined as in (8.80). Assume that the matrix B is nonsingular and the matrix E is of full column rank such that both matrices A and $\tilde{A}$ are nonsingular. Then, for the corresponding preconditioned matrices T_+, T_-, $\tilde{T}_-$, and $\tilde{T}_+$ given in (8.81), it holds that*

(i) $\tilde{T}_+ = T_+$ and $\tilde{T}_- = T_-$;

(ii) $(T_+^3 + I)(T_+ - I) = 0$, so that the matrix T_+ has exactly four distinct eigenvalues

$$\pm 1, \quad \frac{1}{2}(1 \pm i\sqrt{3});$$

(iii) $(T_- - I)(T_-^2 - T_- - I) = 0$, so that the matrix T_- has exactly three distinct eigenvalues

$$1, \quad \frac{1}{2}(1 \pm \sqrt{5}).$$

(See [206, 245].)

Proof. The validity of (i) is obvious.

Note that for all cases we have

$$S = -E^{\mathsf{T}} B^{-1} E \quad \text{or} \quad S^{-1} E^{\mathsf{T}} B^{-1} E = -I.$$

In order to demonstrate (ii), with straightforward computations we have

$$T_+^2 = \begin{bmatrix} I + B^{-1} E S^{-1} E^{\mathsf{T}} & B^{-1} E \\ S^{-1} E^{\mathsf{T}} & -I \end{bmatrix},$$

$$T_+^3 = \begin{bmatrix} I + 2 B^{-1} E S^{-1} E^{\mathsf{T}} & 0 \\ 0 & -I \end{bmatrix},$$

$$T_+^4 = \begin{bmatrix} I + 2 B^{-1} E S^{-1} E^{\mathsf{T}} & -B^{-1} E \\ -S^{-1} E^{\mathsf{T}} & 0 \end{bmatrix}.$$

The equality in (ii) then follows directly from

$$T_+ + T_+^4 = \begin{bmatrix} 2(I + B^{-1} E S^{-1} E^{\mathsf{T}}) & 0 \\ 0 & 0 \end{bmatrix}$$

and

$$(T_+ + T_+^4) - T_+^3 = I.$$

We now turn to verify (iii). Also by straightforward computations we have

$$T_-^2 = \begin{bmatrix} I - B^{-1} E S^{-1} E^{\mathsf{T}} & B^{-1} E \\ -S^{-1} E^{\mathsf{T}} & I \end{bmatrix}.$$

Because

$$T_- - I = \begin{bmatrix} 0 & B^{-1}E \\ -S^{-1}E^\mathsf{T} & -I \end{bmatrix}$$

and

$$T_-^2 - T_- - I = \begin{bmatrix} -(I + B^{-1}ES^{-1}E^\mathsf{T}) & 0 \\ 0 & 0 \end{bmatrix},$$

it follows immediately that

$$(T_- - I)(T_-^2 - T_- - I) = 0. \qquad \square$$

In accordance with Theorem 8.23 we know that the block-diagonal preconditioned matrices are all diagonalizable, with the matrices T_+ and $\tilde{T}_+$ having four distinct nonzero eigenvalues, and the matrices T_- and $\tilde{T}_-$ having three distinct nonzero eigenvalues. Therefore, the dimensions of the Krylov subspaces with respect to them will be less than 4 and 3, respectively, which indicates that the **Krylov subspace iteration methods** of a certain **optimality property** (e.g., GMRES), when applied to the block-diagonal preconditioned standard saddle-point problems (8.2) and (8.25), will yield the exact solution after at most four or three steps in **exact arithmetic**.

8.4.2.2 ▪ Block-Triangular Preconditioners

If consideration of symmetry is not important, we can alternatively use the following **block-triangular preconditioners**:

$$P_T = \begin{bmatrix} B & E \\ 0 & S \end{bmatrix} \quad \text{and} \quad \tilde{P}_T = \begin{bmatrix} B & E \\ 0 & \tilde{S} \end{bmatrix}. \tag{8.82}$$

As $\tilde{S} = -S$, we can rewrite the matrix $\tilde{P}_T$ as

$$\tilde{P}_T = \begin{bmatrix} B & E \\ 0 & -S \end{bmatrix}.$$

Correspondingly, according to the **block-triangular factorizations** in (8.3) and (8.26), for the **right-preconditioned matrices** we have

$$T_+ \triangleq AP_T^{-1} = \begin{bmatrix} I & 0 \\ E^\mathsf{T}B^{-1} & I \end{bmatrix},$$

$$T_- \triangleq A\tilde{P}_T^{-1} = \begin{bmatrix} I & 0 \\ E^\mathsf{T}B^{-1} & -I \end{bmatrix},$$

$$\tilde{T}_- \triangleq \tilde{A}P_T^{-1} = \begin{bmatrix} I & 0 \\ -E^\mathsf{T}B^{-1} & I \end{bmatrix},$$

$$\tilde{T}_+ \triangleq \tilde{A}\tilde{P}_T^{-1} = \begin{bmatrix} I & 0 \\ -E^\mathsf{T}B^{-1} & -I \end{bmatrix}. \tag{8.83}$$

We remark that the **left-preconditioned matrices** can be formulated in an analogous fashion and are similar to their right-preconditioned counterparts, respectively.

Theorem 8.24. *For the generalized saddle-point matrices A and $\tilde{A}$ in (8.78), let the block-triangular preconditioners P_T and $\tilde{P}_T$ be defined as in (8.82). Assume that the $(1,1)$-block matrix B and the Schur complement S (or $\tilde{S}$) are nonsingular. Then, for the corresponding* *preconditioned matrices T_+, T_-, $\tilde{T}_-$, and $\tilde{T}_+$ given in (8.83), it holds that*

(i) *the matrices T_+ and $\tilde{T}_-$ have the minimal polynomial $(\lambda - 1)^2$;*

(ii) *the matrices T_- and $\tilde{T}_+$ have the minimal polynomial $(\lambda - 1)^2(\lambda + 1)^2$. (See [206, 245].)*

In accordance with Theorem 8.24 we know that the block-triangular preconditioned matrices are all diagonalizable, with the matrices T_+ and $\tilde{T}_-$ having one distinct nonzero eigenvalue, and the matrices T_- and $\tilde{T}_+$ having two distinct nonzero eigenvalues. Therefore, the dimensions of the Krylov subspaces with respect to them will be no more than 1 and 2, respectively, which indicates that the **Krylov subspace iteration methods** of certain **optimality property** (e.g., GMRES), when applied to the block-triangular preconditioned generalized saddle-point problems (8.1) and (8.24), will yield the exact solution after at most one or two steps in **exact arithmetic**.

We remark that instead of using the block upper-triangular preconditioners P_T and $\tilde{P}_T$ in (8.82), we can use the block lower-triangular preconditioners defined as follows:

$$P_T = \begin{bmatrix} B & 0 \\ E^\mathsf{T} & S \end{bmatrix} \quad \text{and} \quad \tilde{P}_T = \begin{bmatrix} B & 0 \\ -E^\mathsf{T} & \tilde{S} \end{bmatrix}.$$

These preconditioners possess analogous eigenproperties to those in (8.82).

In the implementations of the block-diagonal and block-triangular preconditioners, we need to solve linear subsystems involving the matrix B and the Schur complement S (or $\tilde{S}$) at each iteration step. Hence, the performance of such structured preconditioners depends on whether fast solvers for those linear subsystems are available. Or, one can use approximations to the matrices B^{-1} and S^{-1} (or $\tilde{S}^{-1}$). For discussions along this direction, see [23, 46, 232, 275].

In addition, we point out that the block lower-triangular preconditioner $\tilde{P}_T$ defined in the above can be considered as a special case resulting from the GSOR splitting matrix $\tilde{M}(\omega, \tau)$ in (8.44) with the specific choices $\omega = \tau = 1$ and $Q = \tilde{S}$.

8.4.3 · Constraint Preconditioners

For the **generalized saddle-point matrices** in (8.78), just as in Subsection 8.4.2, throughout this subsection, we also assume that the $(1, 1)$-block matrix $B \in \mathbb{R}^{n \times n}$ is nonsingular, and either of the Schur complements

$$S = -(C + E^\mathsf{T} B^{-1} E) \quad \text{and} \quad \tilde{S} = C + E^\mathsf{T} B^{-1} E$$

of the generalized saddle-point matrices in symmetric and nonsymmetric forms, i.e., the matrices A and $\tilde{A}$, is nonsingular, so that both matrices A and $\tilde{A}$ are nonsingular, too.

Again, note that for the **standard saddle-point matrices**, i.e., the case $C = 0$, a necessary condition for the Schur complement being nonsingular is that $n \geq m$, the matrix $B \in \mathbb{R}^{n \times n}$ is symmetric positive definite, and the matrix $E \in \mathbb{R}^{n \times m}$ is of full column rank.

The **constraint preconditioning matrices**

$$P = \begin{bmatrix} M & E \\ E^\mathsf{T} & -C \end{bmatrix} \quad \text{and} \quad \tilde{P} = \begin{bmatrix} M & E \\ -E^\mathsf{T} & C \end{bmatrix}$$

can be adopted to further improve the conditioning of the generalized saddle-point matrices A and $\tilde{A}$, respectively, so that the **Krylov subspace iteration methods**, when applied to the **generalized saddle-point problems** (8.1) and (8.24) incorporated with these preconditioners, can show significantly fast convergence speeds in actual computations; see [23, 109, 110, 111, 117, 171, 215, 232] and the references therein.

The **constraint preconditioners**, especially popular in areas such as numerical optimization and numerical partial differential equations, are closely related to the null space methods. Indeed, they originally stem from appropriate approximations to the target problems arising from optimization or discretized partial differential equations. Therefore, this kind of preconditioning is motivated and constructed on the problem level, rather than on the matrix level as usual.

Below we give an intuitive illustration about the above viewpoint by specifically focusing on the *equality constraint quadratic programming* (ECQP) problem:

$$\begin{cases} \min\limits_{x\in\mathbb{R}^n} \ \frac{1}{2}x^{\mathsf{T}}Bx - x^{\mathsf{T}}f, \\ \text{s.t. } E^{\mathsf{T}}x = g, \end{cases} \tag{8.84}$$

where $B \in \mathbb{R}^{n\times n}$ is a symmetric positive definite matrix, $E \in \mathbb{R}^{n\times m}$ is a full column-rank matrix, $f \in \mathbb{R}^n$ and $g \in \mathbb{R}^m$ are known vectors, and $x \in \mathbb{R}^n$ is an unknown vector, with $n \geq m$. By making use of the Lagrangian multiplier approach, we know that the *Karush–Kuhn–Tucker* (KKT) condition with respect to (8.84) is given by

$$\begin{cases} Bx + Ey = f, \\ E^{\mathsf{T}}x = g, \end{cases}$$

where $y \in \mathbb{R}^m$ is the **Lagrangian multiplier**. This block system of linear equations is exactly of the form of the standard saddle-point problem (8.2), which is also equivalent to the standard saddle-point problem (8.25).

For the ECQP problem (8.84), if the **cost function**

$$\frac{1}{2}x^{\mathsf{T}}Bx - x^{\mathsf{T}}f$$

is approximated by another function

$$\frac{1}{2}x^{\mathsf{T}}Mx - x^{\mathsf{T}}f$$

through an approximate matrix $M \in \mathbb{R}^{n\times n}$ to the **Hessian matrix** $B \in \mathbb{R}^{n\times n}$, but the constraints are kept exactly, then we obtain the following **ECQP problem**:

$$\begin{cases} \min\limits_{x\in\mathbb{R}^n} \ \frac{1}{2}x^{\mathsf{T}}Mx - x^{\mathsf{T}}f, \\ \text{s.t. } E^{\mathsf{T}}x = g, \end{cases} \tag{8.85}$$

which is an approximation to the ECQP problem (8.84). The **KKT condition** corresponding to (8.85) is given by

$$\begin{cases} Mx + Ey = f, \\ E^{\mathsf{T}}x = g, \end{cases}$$

or in matrix-vector form,

$$\begin{bmatrix} M & E \\ E^{\mathsf{T}} & 0 \end{bmatrix} \begin{bmatrix} x \\ y \end{bmatrix} = \begin{bmatrix} f \\ g \end{bmatrix}.$$

This approximate **KKT system** then naturally provides a preconditioning for the original KKT system. In other words, the matrices

$$P = \begin{bmatrix} M & E \\ E^{\mathsf{T}} & 0 \end{bmatrix} \quad \text{and} \quad \tilde{P} = \begin{bmatrix} M & E \\ -E^{\mathsf{T}} & 0 \end{bmatrix}$$

can serve as preconditioners for the standard saddle-point matrices

$$A = \begin{bmatrix} B & E \\ E^\mathsf{T} & 0 \end{bmatrix} \quad \text{and} \quad \tilde{A} = \begin{bmatrix} B & E \\ -E^\mathsf{T} & 0 \end{bmatrix}$$

in (8.79), respectively.

Now, let us go back to the generalized saddle-point matrices A and $\tilde{A}$. As

$$\begin{aligned} P^{-1}A &= \begin{bmatrix} M & E \\ E^\mathsf{T} & -C \end{bmatrix}^{-1} \begin{bmatrix} B & E \\ E^\mathsf{T} & -C \end{bmatrix} \\ &= \begin{bmatrix} M & E \\ -E^\mathsf{T} & C \end{bmatrix}^{-1} \begin{bmatrix} B & E \\ -E^\mathsf{T} & C \end{bmatrix} = \tilde{P}^{-1}\tilde{A}, \end{aligned}$$

the preconditioned matrix $\tilde{P}^{-1}\tilde{A}$ shares the same algebraic property as the preconditioned matrix $P^{-1}A$. Therefore, in the following we will conduct theoretical analysis for the matrix $P^{-1}A$ only.

Here we should remark that the numerical behavior of the Krylov subspace iteration methods incorporated with the preconditioners P and $\tilde{P}$, when used to solve the generalized saddle-point problems (8.1) and (8.24), respectively, could be drastically different in actual applications.

Let $E = QR$ be the **QR decomposition** of the matrix $E \in \mathbb{R}^{n \times m}$, with

$$Q = [Q_1, Q_2], \quad \text{where} \quad Q_1 \in \mathbb{R}^{n \times m} \quad \text{and} \quad Q_2 \in \mathbb{R}^{n \times (n-m)},$$

being an orthogonal matrix, and

$$R = \begin{bmatrix} R_1 \\ 0 \end{bmatrix}, \quad R_1 \in \mathbb{R}^{m \times m},$$

being an upper-triangular matrix. As

$$E^\mathsf{T}Q_1 = R^\mathsf{T}Q^\mathsf{T}Q_1 = [R_1^\mathsf{T}, \, 0] \begin{bmatrix} Q_1^\mathsf{T} \\ Q_2^\mathsf{T} \end{bmatrix} Q_1 = [R_1^\mathsf{T}, \, 0] \begin{bmatrix} I \\ 0 \end{bmatrix} = R_1^\mathsf{T},$$

$$E^\mathsf{T}Q_2 = R^\mathsf{T}Q^\mathsf{T}Q_2 = [R_1^\mathsf{T}, \, 0] \begin{bmatrix} Q_1^\mathsf{T} \\ Q_2^\mathsf{T} \end{bmatrix} Q_2 = [R_1^\mathsf{T}, \, 0] \begin{bmatrix} 0 \\ I \end{bmatrix} = 0,$$

we see that the columns of the matrix Q_1 form an **orthonormal basis** for the range space of the matrix E^T, and the columns of the matrix Q_2 form an orthonormal basis for the null space of the matrix E^T.

Denote by

$$U = \begin{bmatrix} Q & 0 \\ 0 & I_m \end{bmatrix} \quad \text{and} \quad J = \begin{bmatrix} 0 & 0 & I \\ 0 & I & 0 \\ I & 0 & 0 \end{bmatrix}.$$

Then the matrix $U \in \mathbb{R}^{(n+m) \times (n+m)}$ is orthogonal, and it holds that

$$\begin{aligned} U^\mathsf{T}AU &= \begin{bmatrix} Q^\mathsf{T}BQ & Q^\mathsf{T}E \\ E^\mathsf{T}Q & -C \end{bmatrix} \\ &= \begin{bmatrix} Q_1^\mathsf{T}BQ_1 & Q_1^\mathsf{T}BQ_2 & R_1 \\ Q_2^\mathsf{T}BQ_1 & Q_2^\mathsf{T}BQ_2 & 0 \\ R_1^\mathsf{T} & 0 & -C \end{bmatrix} \\ &= J \begin{bmatrix} R_1^\mathsf{T} & 0 & -C \\ Q_2^\mathsf{T}BQ_1 & Q_2^\mathsf{T}BQ_2 & 0 \\ Q_1^\mathsf{T}BQ_1 & Q_1^\mathsf{T}BQ_2 & R_1 \end{bmatrix} \triangleq J\hat{A}, \end{aligned}$$

where

$$\hat{A} = \begin{bmatrix} R_1^{\mathsf{T}} & 0 & -C \\ Q_2^{\mathsf{T}} B Q_1 & Q_2^{\mathsf{T}} B Q_2 & 0 \\ Q_1^{\mathsf{T}} B Q_1 & Q_1^{\mathsf{T}} B Q_2 & R_1 \end{bmatrix} \triangleq \begin{bmatrix} R_1^{\mathsf{T}} & 0 & -C \\ \hat{B}_{21} & \hat{B}_{22} & 0 \\ \hat{B}_{11} & \hat{B}_{12} & R_1 \end{bmatrix}, \qquad (8.86)$$

with

$$\hat{B}_{ij} = Q_i^{\mathsf{T}} B Q_j, \quad i, j = 1, 2. \qquad (8.87)$$

Analogously, we can obtain

$$\begin{aligned} U^{\mathsf{T}} P U &= \begin{bmatrix} Q^{\mathsf{T}} M Q & Q^{\mathsf{T}} E \\ E^{\mathsf{T}} Q & -C \end{bmatrix} \\ &= \begin{bmatrix} Q_1^{\mathsf{T}} M Q_1 & Q_1^{\mathsf{T}} M Q_2 & R_1 \\ Q_2^{\mathsf{T}} M Q_1 & Q_2^{\mathsf{T}} M Q_2 & 0 \\ R_1^{\mathsf{T}} & 0 & -C \end{bmatrix} \\ &= J \begin{bmatrix} R_1^{\mathsf{T}} & 0 & -C \\ Q_2^{\mathsf{T}} M Q_1 & Q_2^{\mathsf{T}} M Q_2 & 0 \\ Q_1^{\mathsf{T}} M Q_1 & Q_1^{\mathsf{T}} M Q_2 & R_1 \end{bmatrix} \triangleq J \hat{P}, \end{aligned}$$

where

$$\hat{P} = \begin{bmatrix} R_1^{\mathsf{T}} & 0 & -C \\ Q_2^{\mathsf{T}} M Q_1 & Q_2^{\mathsf{T}} M Q_2 & 0 \\ Q_1^{\mathsf{T}} M Q_1 & Q_1^{\mathsf{T}} M Q_2 & R_1 \end{bmatrix} \triangleq \begin{bmatrix} R_1^{\mathsf{T}} & 0 & -C \\ \hat{M}_{21} & \hat{M}_{22} & 0 \\ \hat{M}_{11} & \hat{M}_{12} & R_1 \end{bmatrix}, \qquad (8.88)$$

with

$$\hat{M}_{ij} = Q_i^{\mathsf{T}} M Q_j, \quad i, j = 1, 2. \qquad (8.89)$$

Evidently, we have

$$A = U J \hat{A} U^{\mathsf{T}} \quad \text{and} \quad P = U J \hat{P} U^{\mathsf{T}}. \qquad (8.90)$$

It then follows that the **preconditioned matrix** $P^{-1} A$, denoted as T, is given by

$$T = P^{-1} A = (U J \hat{P} U^{\mathsf{T}})^{-1} (U J \hat{A} U^{\mathsf{T}}) = U \hat{P}^{-1} \hat{A} U^{\mathsf{T}} \triangleq U \hat{T} U^{\mathsf{T}},$$

with

$$\hat{T} = \hat{P}^{-1} \hat{A}.$$

As the matrices T and $\hat{T}$ are orthogonally similar, they have the same eigenvalues. Moreover, if $\hat{z}$ is an eigenvector of the matrix $\hat{T}$, then $z = U\hat{z}$ is an eigenvector of the matrix T, and vice versa.

The above argument readily demonstrates the following conclusion.

Theorem 8.25. *For the standard saddle-point matrix A and the corresponding constraint pre-conditioning matrix P of the forms*

$$A = \begin{bmatrix} B & E \\ E^{\mathsf{T}} & 0 \end{bmatrix} \quad \text{and} \quad P = \begin{bmatrix} M & E \\ E^{\mathsf{T}} & 0 \end{bmatrix},$$

assume that $n \geq m$, and the $(1,1)$-block matrices $B, M \in \mathbb{R}^{n \times n}$ and the Schur complements

$-E^{\mathsf{T}}B^{-1}E, -E^{\mathsf{T}}M^{-1}E \in \mathbb{R}^{m \times m}$ *are nonsingular. Then*

(i) *the preconditioned matrix* $T = P^{-1}A$ *has an eigenvalue* 1 *with algebraic multiplicity* $2m$, *and* $n - m$ *non-unit eigenvalues which are those of the matrix* $\hat{T}_N \triangleq \hat{M}_{22}^{-1}\hat{B}_{22}$, *where* $\hat{B}_{22}$ *and* $\hat{M}_{22}$ *are defined in* (8.87) *and* (8.89);

(ii) *the preconditioned matrix* $T = P^{-1}A$ *has* $m + k + l$ *linearly independent eigenvectors, which are:*

   (i_1) m *eigenvectors of the form* $z = \begin{bmatrix} 0 \\ y \end{bmatrix}$, *with* $y \in \mathbb{R}^m$, *that correspond to the case* $\lambda = 1$,

   (i_2) k $(0 \le k \le n)$ *eigenvectors of the form* $z = \begin{bmatrix} x \\ y \end{bmatrix}$, *with* $x \in \mathbb{R}^n$ *and* $y \in \mathbb{R}^m$, *that correspond to the case* $\lambda = 1$, *for which all such vectors* $x \in \mathbb{R}^n$ *form a basis of the subspace* $\mathrm{Ker}(B - M)$,

   (i_3) l $(0 \le l \le n - m)$ *eigenvectors of the form* $z = \begin{bmatrix} x \\ y \end{bmatrix}$, *with* $x \in \mathbb{R}^n$ *and* $y \in \mathbb{C}^m$, *that correspond to the case* $\lambda \ne 1$.

Proof. Under the assumptions, we know that both matrices A and P are nonsingular, with their $(1, 2)$-block matrix $E \in \mathbb{R}^{n \times m}$ being of full column rank. Moreover, it follows from (8.90) that the matrices $\hat{A}$ and $\hat{P}$ defined in (8.86) and (8.88) are nonsingular, so that the matrix blocks R_1, $\hat{B}_{22}$ and $\hat{M}_{22}$ on their main diagonals are nonsingular, too.

Also from (8.86) and (8.88), by setting $C = 0$ we have

$$
\begin{aligned}
\hat{T} = \hat{P}^{-1}\hat{A} &= \begin{bmatrix} I & 0 & 0 \\ \hat{M}_{22}^{-1}\hat{M}_{21} & I & 0 \\ R_1^{-1}\hat{M}_{11} & R_1^{-1}\hat{M}_{12} & I \end{bmatrix}^{-1} \begin{bmatrix} R_1^{-\mathsf{T}} & 0 & 0 \\ 0 & \hat{M}_{22}^{-1} & 0 \\ 0 & 0 & R_1^{-1} \end{bmatrix} \begin{bmatrix} R_1^{\mathsf{T}} & 0 & 0 \\ \hat{B}_{21} & \hat{B}_{22} & 0 \\ \hat{B}_{11} & \hat{B}_{12} & R_1 \end{bmatrix} \\[2mm]
&= \begin{bmatrix} I & 0 & 0 \\ -\hat{M}_{22}^{-1}\hat{M}_{21} & I & 0 \\ -R_1^{-1}(\hat{M}_{11} - \hat{M}_{12}\hat{M}_{22}^{-1}\hat{M}_{21}) & -R_1^{-1}\hat{M}_{12} & I \end{bmatrix} \begin{bmatrix} I & 0 & 0 \\ \hat{M}_{22}^{-1}\hat{B}_{21} & \hat{M}_{22}^{-1}\hat{B}_{22} & 0 \\ R_1^{-1}\hat{B}_{11} & R_1^{-1}\hat{B}_{12} & I \end{bmatrix} \\[2mm]
&= \begin{bmatrix} I & 0 & 0 \\ \hat{M}_{22}^{-1}(\hat{B}_{21} - \hat{M}_{21}) & \hat{M}_{22}^{-1}\hat{B}_{22} & 0 \\ R_1^{-1}[\hat{B}_{11} - \hat{M}_{11} - \hat{M}_{12}\hat{M}_{22}^{-1}(\hat{B}_{21} - \hat{M}_{21})] & R_1^{-1}(\hat{B}_{12} - \hat{M}_{12}\hat{M}_{22}^{-1}\hat{B}_{22}) & I \end{bmatrix}.
\end{aligned}
$$

As the matrix $\hat{T}$ is orthogonally similar to the matrix T, the conclusion (i) then follows directly.

Now we turn to prove (ii). To this end, let λ be an eigenvalue of the matrix T and $z = [x^{\mathsf{T}}, y^{\mathsf{T}}]^{\mathsf{T}}$, with $x \in \mathbb{C}^n$ and $y \in \mathbb{C}^m$, be the corresponding eigenvector. Then from $Tz = \lambda z$ we know that

$$Az = \lambda Pz,$$

so that the vector z is an eigenvector of the matrix T if and only if it is nonzero and is in the null space of the matrix

$$\Psi(\lambda) \triangleq A - \lambda P = \begin{bmatrix} B - \lambda M & (1 - \lambda)E \\ (1 - \lambda)E^{\mathsf{T}} & 0 \end{bmatrix}. \tag{8.91}$$

When $\lambda = 1$, it holds that

$$\Psi(1) = \begin{bmatrix} B - M & 0 \\ 0 & 0 \end{bmatrix}.$$

Hence, the null space of the matrix $\Psi(1)$ includes vectors of the form

$$z = \begin{bmatrix} 0 \\ y \end{bmatrix}, \quad \forall y \in \mathbb{R}^m,$$

and can be spanned by the vectors of the form

$$z = \begin{bmatrix} x \\ y \end{bmatrix}, \quad \text{with} \quad x \in \text{Ker}(B - M), \ \forall\, y \in \mathbb{R}^m.$$

The number of such **linearly independent vectors** is no more than $m+k$, where $k \leq \dim(\text{Ker}(B - M))$.

When $\lambda \neq 1$, it follows from (8.91) that

$$\begin{cases} (B - \lambda M)x + (1 - \lambda)Ey = 0, \\ E^{\mathsf{T}}x = 0, \end{cases}$$

that is,

$$x \in \text{Ker}(E^{\mathsf{T}})$$

and

$$E^{\mathsf{T}}(B - \lambda M)x + (1 - \lambda)E^{\mathsf{T}}Ey = 0.$$

As a result, such eigenvectors z must satisfy the conditions

$$x \in \text{Ker}(E^{\mathsf{T}}) \quad \text{with} \quad y = \frac{1}{\lambda - 1}(E^{\mathsf{T}}E)^{-1}E^{\mathsf{T}}(B - \lambda M)x. \tag{8.92}$$

The number of such linearly independent vectors is no more than $n - m$, where we have noticed that $\dim(\text{Ker}(E^{\mathsf{T}})) = n - m$.

The above $m + k + l$ eigenvectors of the matrix T are linearly independent, because the eigenvectors corresponding to different eigenvalues are linearly independent and, with respect to each distinct eigenvalue, we can choose the linearly independent eigenvectors belonging to it only. □

From the proof process of Theorem 8.25 we see that for a non-unit real eigenvalue λ, the corresponding eigenvector $z = [x^{\mathsf{T}}, y^{\mathsf{T}}]^{\mathsf{T}}$ can be real, that is, $z \in \mathbb{R}^{n+m}$, as now both of its sub-vectors x and y are real; see (8.92).

In order to analyze the convergence property of the corresponding preconditioned Krylov subspace iteration methods, we need the following lemma.

Lemma 8.26. *For any positive integer k, let*

$$p_k(t) = \alpha_0 + \alpha_1 t + \cdots + \alpha_k t^k,$$

with $\alpha_k \neq 0$, be a polynomial of degree k. Then, for the block three-by-three matrix

$$W = \begin{bmatrix} 0 & 0 & 0 \\ W_{21} & V & 0 \\ W_{31} & W_{32} & 0 \end{bmatrix}$$

of square diagonal blocks, it holds that

$$p_k(W) = \begin{bmatrix} \alpha_0 I & 0 & 0 \\ \sum\limits_{j=1}^{k} \alpha_j V^{j-1} W_{21} & p_k(V) & 0 \\ \alpha_1 W_{31} + W_{32} \sum\limits_{j=2}^{k} \alpha_j V^{j-2} W_{21} & W_{32} \sum\limits_{j=1}^{k} \alpha_j V^{j-1} & \alpha_0 I \end{bmatrix},$$

$$W\, p_k(W) = \begin{bmatrix} 0 & 0 & 0 \\ p_k(V)\, W_{21} & V\, p_k(V) & 0 \\ \alpha_0 W_{31} + W_{32} \sum\limits_{j=1}^{k} \alpha_j V^{j-1} W_{21} & W_{32}\, p_k(V) & 0 \end{bmatrix},$$

and

$$W^2 p_k(W) = \begin{bmatrix} 0 & 0 & 0 \\ V\,p_k(V)\,W_{21} & V^2\,p_k(V) & 0 \\ W_{32}\,p_k(V)\,W_{21} & W_{32}\,V\,p_k(V) & 0 \end{bmatrix}.$$

Proof. For any positive integer $k \geq 1$, with straightforward computations we can obtain

$$W^{k+1} = \begin{bmatrix} 0 & 0 & 0 \\ V^k W_{21} & V^{k+1} & 0 \\ W_{32}V^{k-1}W_{21} & W_{32}V^k & 0 \end{bmatrix}.$$

It then follows that

$$p_k(W) = \alpha_0 I + \alpha_1 W + \sum_{j=2}^{k} \alpha_j W^j$$

$$= \alpha_0 I + \alpha_1 \begin{bmatrix} 0 & 0 & 0 \\ W_{21} & V & 0 \\ W_{31} & W_{32} & 0 \end{bmatrix} + \sum_{j=2}^{k} \alpha_j \begin{bmatrix} 0 & 0 & 0 \\ V^{j-1}W_{21} & V^j & 0 \\ W_{32}V^{j-2}W_{21} & W_{32}V^{j-1} & 0 \end{bmatrix}$$

$$= \begin{bmatrix} \alpha_0 I & 0 & 0 \\ \sum_{j=1}^{k} \alpha_j V^{j-1}W_{21} & \sum_{j=0}^{k} \alpha_j V^j & 0 \\ \alpha_1 W_{31} + W_{32}\sum_{j=2}^{k} \alpha_j V^{j-2}W_{21} & W_{32}\sum_{j=1}^{k} \alpha_j V^{j-1} & \alpha_0 I \end{bmatrix}$$

$$= \begin{bmatrix} \alpha_0 I & 0 & 0 \\ \sum_{j=1}^{k} \alpha_j V^{j-1}W_{21} & p_k(V) & 0 \\ \alpha_1 W_{31} + W_{32}\sum_{j=2}^{k} \alpha_j V^{j-2}W_{21} & W_{32}\sum_{j=1}^{k} \alpha_j V^{j-1} & \alpha_0 I \end{bmatrix}.$$

Based on the above expression of the polynomial matrix $p_k(W)$, we have

$$W\,p_k(W) = \begin{bmatrix} 0 & 0 & 0 \\ W_{21} & V & 0 \\ W_{31} & W_{32} & 0 \end{bmatrix} \begin{bmatrix} \alpha_0 I & 0 & 0 \\ \sum_{j=1}^{k} \alpha_j V^{j-1}W_{21} & p_k(V) & 0 \\ \alpha_1 W_{31} + W_{32}\sum_{j=2}^{k} \alpha_j V^{j-2}W_{21} & W_{32}\sum_{j=1}^{k} \alpha_j V^{j-1} & \alpha_0 I \end{bmatrix}$$

$$= \begin{bmatrix} 0 & 0 & 0 \\ \alpha_0 W_{21} + \sum_{j=1}^{k} \alpha_j V^j W_{21} & V\,p_k(V) & 0 \\ \alpha_0 W_{31} + W_{32}\sum_{j=1}^{k} \alpha_j V^{j-1}W_{21} & W_{32}\,p_k(V) & 0 \end{bmatrix}$$

$$= \begin{bmatrix} 0 & 0 & 0 \\ p_k(V)\,W_{21} & V\,p_k(V) & 0 \\ \alpha_0 W_{31} + W_{32}\sum_{j=1}^{k} \alpha_j V^{j-1}W_{21} & W_{32}\,p_k(V) & 0 \end{bmatrix}.$$

Moreover, by direct computations we know that

$$W^2 p_k(W) = W[W p_k(W)]$$

$$= \begin{bmatrix} 0 & 0 & 0 \\ W_{21} & V & 0 \\ W_{31} & W_{32} & 0 \end{bmatrix} \begin{bmatrix} 0 & 0 & 0 \\ p_k(V) W_{21} & V p_k(V) & 0 \\ \alpha_0 W_{31} + W_{32} \sum_{j=1}^{k} \alpha_j V^{j-1} W_{21} & W_{32} p_k(V) & 0 \end{bmatrix}$$

$$= \begin{bmatrix} 0 & 0 & 0 \\ V p_k(V) W_{21} & V^2 p_k(V) & 0 \\ W_{32} p_k(V) W_{21} & W_{32} V p_k(V) & 0 \end{bmatrix}. \qquad \square$$

Theorem 8.27. *For the standard saddle-point matrix A and the corresponding constraint preconditioning matrix P of the forms*

$$A = \begin{bmatrix} B & E \\ E^\mathsf{T} & 0 \end{bmatrix} \quad and \quad P = \begin{bmatrix} M & E \\ E^\mathsf{T} & 0 \end{bmatrix},$$

assume that $n \geq m$, and the $(1,1)$-block matrices $B, M \in \mathbb{R}^{n \times n}$ and the Schur complements $-E^\mathsf{T} B^{-1} E, -E^\mathsf{T} M^{-1} E \in \mathbb{R}^{m \times m}$ are nonsingular. If the degree of the minimal polynomial of the matrix

$$\hat{T}_N \triangleq \hat{M}_{22}^{-1} \hat{B}_{22}$$

is ν, then the degree of the minimal polynomial of the preconditioned matrix $T = P^{-1} A$ is at most $2 + \nu$, where the matrices $\hat{B}_{22}$ and $\hat{M}_{22}$ are defined in (8.87) and (8.89).

As a result, for any vector $v \in \mathbb{R}^{n+m}$, the Krylov subspace

$$\mathcal{K}(T, v) \triangleq \mathrm{span}\{v, Tv, T^2v, \dots\}$$

has dimension at most $2 + \nu$.

Proof. Note that the degrees of the minimal polynomials of the matrices $\hat{T}_N - I$ and $\hat{T}_N$ are exactly the same. Hence, we can let $p_\nu(t)$ be the **minimal polynomial** of the matrix $\hat{T}_N - I$. That is to say, it holds that $p_\nu(\hat{T}_N - I) = 0$. Now, in Lemma 8.26, by taking

$$k = \nu, \quad W = \hat{T} - I, \quad and \quad V = \hat{T}_N - I,$$

we immediately have

$$(\hat{T} - I)^2 p_\nu(\hat{T} - I) = 0,$$

that is, a polynomial of the degree $2 + \nu$ is an **annihilating polynomial** for the matrix $\hat{T} - I$. Equivalently, a polynomial of the degree $2 + \nu$ is an annihilating polynomial for the matrix $\hat{T}$ and, hence, for the matrix T as well, since the matrices $\hat{T}$ and T are orthogonally similar. Therefore, the degree of the minimal polynomial of the preconditioned matrix T is at most $2 + \nu$. $\qquad \square$

The results in Theorems 8.25 and 8.27 include those extended by Cao in [90] from the symmetric leading blocks to the more general case that the leading blocks B and M of the matrices A and P are both nonsymmetric.

For the **generalized saddle-point matrix** A and the corresponding **constraint preconditioning matrix** P, we now precisely describe the distribution of the eigenvalues and the characteristics of the eigenvectors of the **preconditioned matrix** $P^{-1}A$. These results are essential for assessing the convergence properties of the **Krylov subspace iteration methods**, incorporated with the preconditioner P, for solving the **generalized saddle-point problem** (8.1).

Theorem 8.28. [48] *For the generalized saddle-point matrix A and the corresponding constraint preconditioning matrix P of the forms*

$$A = \begin{bmatrix} B & E \\ E^\mathsf{T} & -C \end{bmatrix} \quad \text{and} \quad P = \begin{bmatrix} M & E \\ E^\mathsf{T} & -C \end{bmatrix},$$

assume that the $(1,1)$-block matrices $B, M \in \mathbb{R}^{n \times n}$ and the Schur complements $-(C + E^\mathsf{T}B^{-1}E)$, $-(C + E^\mathsf{T}M^{-1}E) \in \mathbb{R}^{m \times m}$ are nonsingular. Denote by $R = [E^\mathsf{T}, C] \in \mathbb{R}^{m \times (n+m)}$ and $Z = [X^\mathsf{T}, Y^\mathsf{T}]^\mathsf{T} \in \mathbb{R}^{(n+m) \times r}$, with $r \leq m$, where the columns of the matrix Z form a basis of the null space of the matrix R. Represent by k the dimension of the subspace $\mathrm{Ker}(B - M)$. Assume that the matrix $X \in \mathbb{R}^{n \times r}$ has rank $\ell \leq \min\{r, n\}$ and it is decomposed as $X = [X_f, X_o]$, with $X_f \in \mathbb{R}^{n \times \ell}$ having full column rank ℓ and $X_o \in \mathbb{R}^{n \times (r-\ell)}$. Then

(i) *the preconditioned matrix $T = P^{-1}A$ has an eigenvalue 1 with algebraic multiplicity at least $m + k$ and at most $n + m - \ell$, and at least ℓ non-unit eigenvalues which are defined by the* **generalized eigenvalue problem**

$$X_f^\mathsf{T}(B + EC^\dagger E^\mathsf{T})X_f u = \lambda X_f^\mathsf{T}(M + EC^\dagger E^\mathsf{T})X_f u, \quad \text{with} \quad u \in \mathbb{C}^\ell \setminus \{0\}, (8.93)$$

where $C^\dagger$ denotes the **Moore–Penrose generalized inverse** *of the matrix C;*

(ii) *the preconditioned matrix $T = P^{-1}A$ has $m + k + l$ linearly independent eigenvectors, which are:*

(i_1) *m eigenvectors of the form $z = \begin{bmatrix} 0 \\ y \end{bmatrix}$, with $y \in \mathbb{R}^m$, that correspond to the case $\lambda = 1$,*

(i_2) *k $(0 \leq k \leq n)$ eigenvectors of the form $z = \begin{bmatrix} x \\ y \end{bmatrix}$, with $x \in \mathbb{R}^n$ and $y \in \mathbb{R}^m$, that correspond to the case $\lambda = 1$, for which all such vectors $x \in \mathbb{R}^n$ form a basis of the subspace $\mathrm{Ker}(B - M)$,*

(i_3) *l $(0 \leq l \leq \ell)$ eigenvectors of the form $z = \begin{bmatrix} x \\ y \end{bmatrix}$, with $x \in \mathbb{C}^n$ and $y \in \mathbb{C}^m$, that correspond to the case $\lambda \neq 1$.*

Proof. Let λ be an eigenvalue of the matrix $T = P^{-1}A$, and

$$z = \begin{bmatrix} x \\ y \end{bmatrix}, \quad \text{with} \quad x \in \mathbb{C}^n \text{ and } y \in \mathbb{C}^m,$$

be the corresponding eigenvector. Clearly, it holds that

$$\begin{cases} Bx + Ey &= \lambda(Mx + Ey), \\ E^\mathsf{T}x - Cy &= \lambda(E^\mathsf{T}x - Cy). \end{cases} \tag{8.94}$$

From the second equation of (8.94) we obtain

$$(1 - \lambda)(E^\mathsf{T}x - Cy) = 0.$$

Hence, either $\lambda = 1$ or $E^\mathsf{T}x - Cy = 0$ holds true.

For $\lambda = 1$, from the first equation of (8.94) we immediately have $Bx = Mx$, or $x \in \text{Ker}(B - M)$. This shows that the corresponding eigenvectors are of the form $z = [0, y^\mathsf{T}]^\mathsf{T}$ or $z = [x^\mathsf{T}, y^\mathsf{T}]^\mathsf{T}$, with $x \in \mathbb{R}^n$ a basis vector of the subspace $\text{Ker}(B - M)$ and $y \in \mathbb{R}^m$. The number of the **linearly independent vectors** of such form is $m + k$. So, the algebraic multiplicity of the eigenvalue $\lambda = 1$ is at least $m + k$, too.

For $E^\mathsf{T} x - Cy = 0$, we know that

$$z := \begin{bmatrix} x \\ y \end{bmatrix} \in \text{Ker}(R).$$

Let the columns of the matrix

$$Z = \begin{bmatrix} X \\ Y \end{bmatrix}$$

form a basis of the subspace $\text{Ker}(R)$. Then we have $z = Z\hat{u}, \forall\, \hat{u} \in \mathbb{C}^r \setminus \{0\}$, such that $RZ = 0$, or in other words,

$$x = X\hat{u} \quad \text{and} \quad y = Y\hat{u}, \quad \forall \hat{u} \in \mathbb{C}^r \setminus \{0\},$$

such that

$$E^\mathsf{T} X - CY = 0,$$

where r is the dimension of $\text{Ker}(R)$. It then follows from the first equation of (8.94) again that

$$(BX + EY)\hat{u} = \lambda(MX + EY)\hat{u}. \tag{8.95}$$

From [102] and [108, 225, 226] we easily know that the matrix equation $CY = E^\mathsf{T} X$ is solvable if and only if

$$(I - CC^\dagger)E^\mathsf{T} X = 0. \tag{8.96}$$

Moreover, in this case, its general solution has the expression

$$Y = C^\dagger E^\mathsf{T} X + (I - C^\dagger C)W, \qquad \forall W \in \mathbb{R}^{m \times m}. \tag{8.97}$$

Now, the substitution of (8.97) into (8.95), followed by straightforward operations, can lead to the **generalized eigenvalue problem**

$$[(B + EC^\dagger E^\mathsf{T})X + E(I - C^\dagger C)W]\hat{u} = \lambda[(M + EC^\dagger E^\mathsf{T})X + E(I - C^\dagger C)W]\hat{u}. \tag{8.98}$$

Because $X = [X_f, X_o] \in \mathbb{R}^{n \times r}$ and $X_f \in \mathbb{R}^{n \times \ell}$ have the same rank ℓ, the columns of X_f form a basis of the range space of the matrix X. Let $T_f \in \mathbb{R}^{\ell \times (r - \ell)}$ be the **transformation matrix** such that $X_o = X_f T_f$. Conformably, we decompose the vector $\hat{u} \in \mathbb{C}^r$ as

$$\hat{u} = \begin{bmatrix} u_f \\ u_o \end{bmatrix}, \quad \text{with} \quad u_f \in \mathbb{C}^\ell \quad \text{and} \quad u_o \in \mathbb{C}^{r-\ell}.$$

It follows from $X_o = X_f T_f$ that

$$\begin{cases} \begin{aligned} (B + EC^\dagger E^\mathsf{T})X\hat{u} &= (B + EC^\dagger E^\mathsf{T})X_f u_f + (B + EC^\dagger E^\mathsf{T})X_o u_o \\ &= (B + EC^\dagger E^\mathsf{T})X_f(u_f + T_f u_o), \\ (M + EC^\dagger E^\mathsf{T})X\hat{u} &= (M + EC^\dagger E^\mathsf{T})X_f u_f + (M + EC^\dagger E^\mathsf{T})X_o u_o \\ &= (M + EC^\dagger E^\mathsf{T})X_f(u_f + T_f u_o). \end{aligned} \end{cases}$$

Therefore, the **generalized eigenvalue problem** (8.98) can be equivalently rewritten as

$$(B + EC^\dagger E^\mathsf{T})X_f u + E(I - C^\dagger C)W\hat{u} = \lambda[(M + EC^\dagger E^\mathsf{T})X_f u + E(I - C^\dagger C)W\hat{u}], \quad (8.99)$$

with $u = u_f + T_f u_o \in \mathbb{C}^\ell$.

Evidently, if $x = X_f u \notin \mathrm{Ker}(B - M)$, then $\lambda = 1$ can only occur when $u = 0$, or in other words, u_o is a solution of the linear system $T_f u_o = -u_f$. For this case, we have

$$x = X\hat{u} = X_f u_f + X_o u_o = X_f(u_f + T_f u_o) = X_f u = 0$$

and, hence, $x \in \mathrm{Ker}(B - M)$. This causes a contradiction.

Suppose $\lambda \neq 1$. Premultiplying (8.99) by X_f^T and then substituting $X_f^\mathsf{T} E = Y_f^\mathsf{T} C$ into the resulting equation, we obtain

$$X_f^\mathsf{T}(B + EC^\dagger E^\mathsf{T})X_f u = \lambda X_f^\mathsf{T}(M + EC^\dagger E^\mathsf{T})X_f u,$$

where $Y = [Y_f, Y_o] \in \mathbb{R}^{m \times r}$, with $Y_f \in \mathbb{R}^{m \times \ell}$ and $Y_o \in \mathbb{R}^{m \times (r-\ell)}$. Obviously, the number of all such kind of non-unit eigenvalues is at least ℓ.

This proves the validity of (i).

The conclusion (ii) follows straightforwardly from the basic fact in linear algebra that the eigenvectors corresponding to different eigenvalues of a matrix are linearly independent, and from the actual choices of the three groups of linearly independent eigenvectors of the matrix T.   □

In this theorem, we have used the notation $C^\dagger$, which is defined as the **Moore–Penrose generalized inverse** of the matrix $C \in \mathbb{R}^{m \times m}$ satisfying the following conditions:

(1) $CC^\dagger C = C$,
(2) $C^\dagger C C^\dagger = C^\dagger$,
(3) $(CC^\dagger)^\mathsf{T} = CC^\dagger$, and
(4) $(C^\dagger C)^\mathsf{T} = C^\dagger C$.

In particular, if the **singular value decomposition** of the matrix $C \in \mathbb{R}^{m \times m}$ is $C = U\Sigma V^\mathsf{T}$, where $U, V \in \mathbb{R}^{m \times m}$ are orthogonal matrices and $\Sigma = \mathrm{Diag}(\Sigma_C, 0) \in \mathbb{R}^{m \times m}$ is a block-diagonal matrix, with Σ_C being a diagonal matrix of positive diagonal entries, then

$$C^\dagger = V \mathrm{Diag}(\Sigma_C^{-1}, 0) U^\mathsf{T};$$

see, for example, [167].

Theorem 8.28 generalizes the result in Theorem 8.25; see [109, 215] and the references therein for more details and for different proofs.

If the matrix block $C \in \mathbb{R}^{m \times m}$ has a small 2-norm, $\|B\|_2 = \mathcal{O}(1)$ and $\|M\|_2 = \mathcal{O}(1)$, then the $X_f^\mathsf{T} EC^\dagger E^\mathsf{T} X_f$ terms will dominate the generalized eigenvalue problem (8.93) for $E^\mathsf{T} X_f u \notin \mathrm{Ker}(C)$ and, hence, there will be at least $\ell - \dim(\mathrm{Ker}(C))$ further eigenvalues clustered about 1 when $\|C\|_2 \ll 1$.

Of course, the preconditioned matrix $T = P^{-1}A$ may be generally not diagonalizable due to the total count of its eigenvectors described in Theorem 8.28 (ii). However, the eigenvectors corresponding to the unit eigenvalues of the preconditioned matrix T form an invariant subspace.

Remark 8.2. *From Bai and Ng [46] we know that the degree of the minimal polynomial of the preconditioned matrix $T = P^{-1}A$ is at most $\tilde{n} + 1$, where $\tilde{n}$ is the degree of the minimal polynomial of the matrix*

$$W = (I + M^{-1}ES_M^{-1}E^\mathsf{T})M^{-1}(B - M), \quad \text{with} \quad S_M = -(C + E^\mathsf{T}M^{-1}E).$$

Therefore, the dimension of the corresponding Krylov subspace

$$\mathcal{K}(T, v) \triangleq \mathrm{span}\{v, Tv, T^2 v, \ldots\}, \quad with \ v \in \mathbb{R}^{n+m},$$

is at most $\tilde{n} + 1$ and, in exact arithmetic, a Krylov subspace iteration method with an optimality property, e.g., GMRES, will terminate and achieve the exact solution of the generalized saddle-point problem (8.1) within at most $\tilde{n} + 1$ iteration steps. Note that it always holds that $\tilde{n} \leq n$; and $\tilde{n} < n$ can occur when $B - M \in \mathbb{R}^{n \times n}$ is a reduced low-rank matrix.

Remark 8.3. *When the generalized saddle-point matrix $A \in \mathbb{R}^{(n+m) \times (n+m)}$ and the corresponding constraint preconditioning matrix $P \in \mathbb{R}^{(n+m) \times (n+m)}$ are nonsingular, $B \in \mathbb{R}^{n \times n}$ is symmetric positive definite and $C \in \mathbb{R}^{m \times m}$ is symmetric, the generalized Schur complements $B + EC^\dagger E^\mathsf{T}$ and $M + EC^\dagger E^\mathsf{T}$ of the matrices A and P are symmetric and nonsingular. As $X_f \in \mathbb{R}^{n \times \ell}$ has full column rank, both $X_f^\mathsf{T}(B + EC^\dagger E^\mathsf{T})X_f$ and $X_f^\mathsf{T}(M + EC^\dagger E^\mathsf{T})X_f$ are symmetric and nonsingular matrices. Hence, it follows that the generalized eigenvalue problem (8.93) has only a finite number of nonzero eigenvalues. Moreover, when the matrices $X_f^\mathsf{T}(B + EC^\dagger E^\mathsf{T})X_f$ and $X_f^\mathsf{T}(M + EC^\dagger E^\mathsf{T})X_f$ are indefinite, the generalized eigenvalue problem (8.93) may have complex eigenvalues. If both of these matrices are positive/negative definite, then all eigenvalues of the generalized eigenvalue problem (8.93) are real. In particular, for the case that both of these matrices are symmetric positive definite, a projected preconditioned conjugate gradient method can be used to find the exact solution of the generalized saddle-point problem (8.1); see [109, 171].*

Remark 8.4. *If the matrix block $C \in \mathbb{R}^{m \times m}$ is symmetric and nonsingular, then $r = \ell$ and the generalized eigenvalue problem (8.93) can be equivalently expressed as*

$$X^\mathsf{T}(B + E^\mathsf{T} C^{-1} E)Xu = \lambda X^\mathsf{T}(M + E^\mathsf{T} C^{-1} E)Xu.$$

For this case, we can particularly let $X = [e_1, e_2, \ldots, e_r]$, with e_j, $j = 1, 2, \ldots, r$, being the j-th unit basis vector in $\mathbb{R}^n$, to further simplify this generalized eigenvalue problem.

Remark 8.5. *The actual application of Theorem 8.28 requires determination of the dimension of the null space $\mathrm{Ker}(B - M)$. The choice of the matrix block M may often stem from algebraic considerations that do not take the nullity of the matrix $B - M$ into account, which, in turn, may make it difficult to assess the geometric multiplicities of the eigenvalues of the preconditioned matrix and, hence, the convergence rate of the corresponding preconditioned iteration method may be difficult to estimate; see Remark 8.2.*

Analogously to Theorem 8.27, we can prove the following estimation about the dimension of the Krylov subspace:

$$\mathcal{K}(T, v) \triangleq \mathrm{span}\{v, Tv, T^2 v, \ldots\}, \quad with \ v \in \mathbb{R}^{n+m}. \tag{8.100}$$

Theorem 8.29. *Let the conditions of Theorem 8.28 be satisfied. Then the dimension of the Krylov subspace $\mathcal{K}(T, v)$ in (8.100) is at most $\tilde{n}_b + 1$, where*

$$\tilde{n}_b = \begin{cases} \min\{n - k + 1, n + m - 1\}, & for \quad n \leq k + \ell, \\ \min\{\ell + 1, n + m - 1\}, & for \quad n > k + \ell. \end{cases}$$

This theorem shows that in **exact arithmetic** a **Krylov subspace iteration method** with an **optimality property**, when incorporated with the **constraint preconditioner** P, will achieve the exact solution of the **generalized saddle-point problem** (8.1) within at most the number $\tilde{n}_b + 1$

of iteration steps. Since $\tilde{n}_b \leq n - k + 1$ and $\tilde{n} \leq n$, we easily see that the number of iteration steps of the preconditioned **Krylov subspace method** estimated in Theorem 8.29 may be smaller than that in Remark 8.2.

8.5 ▪ RPCG Methods

The **RPCG method**, introduced in Section 7.1.4 of Chapter 7, can be employed to effectively solve the standard and the generalized saddle-point linear systems, when we use specific choices of the restrictive matrices; see [23, 42, 56]. For convenience of the statements, in this section we focus on the standard saddle-point problem in symmetric form (8.2) and the generalized saddle-point problem in nonsymmetric form (8.24), as discussions for the generalized saddle-point problem in symmetric form (8.1) and the standard saddle-point problem in nonsymmetric form (8.25) are analogous. Then we also discuss about the RPCG method and its practical variants for solving the block two-by-two linear systems whose coefficient matrices are specifically assumed to be symmetric and positive definite.

8.5.1 ▪ RPCG for Saddle-Point Linear Systems

We recall that the **standard saddle-point problem** in **symmetric form** (8.2) is

$$\underbrace{\begin{bmatrix} B & E \\ E^{\mathsf{T}} & 0 \end{bmatrix}}_{A} \underbrace{\begin{bmatrix} x \\ y \end{bmatrix}}_{z} = \underbrace{\begin{bmatrix} f \\ g \end{bmatrix}}_{b}. \tag{8.101}$$

Here we assume that $A \in \mathbb{R}^{(n+m) \times (n+m)}$ is a nonsingular, symmetric, and indefinite matrix, and $f \in \mathbb{R}^n$ and $g \in \mathbb{R}^m$ are known vectors, with $n \geq m$. In particular, we suppose that the matrix $B \in \mathbb{R}^{n \times n}$ is symmetric positive definite, and the matrix $E \in \mathbb{R}^{n \times m}$ is of full column rank.

In accordance with (8.3), we know that the matrix $A \in \mathbb{R}^{(n+m) \times (n+m)}$ adopts the **block-triangular factorization**:

$$A = \underbrace{\begin{bmatrix} I & 0 \\ E^{\mathsf{T}} B^{-1} & -I \end{bmatrix}}_{P} \underbrace{\begin{bmatrix} B & 0 \\ 0 & S \end{bmatrix}}_{H} \underbrace{\begin{bmatrix} I & B^{-1}E \\ 0 & I \end{bmatrix}}_{Q},$$

where

$$S = E^{\mathsf{T}} B^{-1} E$$

is the negative Schur complement of the standard saddle-point matrix A. As the matrix $E \in \mathbb{R}^{n \times m}$ has full column rank, i.e., $\mathrm{rank}(E) = m$, the matrix $S \in \mathbb{R}^{m \times m}$ is symmetric positive definite. In addition, it holds that

$$W = Q^{-1} P^{\mathsf{T}} = \begin{bmatrix} I & -B^{-1}E \\ 0 & I \end{bmatrix} \begin{bmatrix} I & B^{-1}E \\ 0 & -I \end{bmatrix} = \begin{bmatrix} I & 2B^{-1}E \\ 0 & -I \end{bmatrix}.$$

Let $\widehat{S} \in \mathbb{R}^{m \times m}$ be a symmetric positive definite matrix such that it is an approximation to the matrix S. Then the block-diagonal matrix $G = \mathrm{Diag}(B, \widehat{S})$ is a reasonable preconditioner to the matrix $H = \mathrm{Diag}(B, S)$. If we take $M = PGQ$, then the **RPCG method** has the following special form for the standard saddle-point problem (8.101); see [42].

Algorithm 8.1: RPCG Method for Problem (8.101)

1: Choose $z^{(0)} \in \mathbb{R}^{n+m}$, $r_0 = b - Az^{(0)}$

2: let $r_0 = \left[r_0^{(1)^\mathsf{T}}, r_0^{(2)^\mathsf{T}} \right]^\mathsf{T}$

3: solve $Bt^{(1)} = r_0^{(1)}$

4: solve $\widehat{S}u_0^{(2)} = E^\mathsf{T}t^{(1)} - r_0^{(2)}$

5: solve $B\tilde{t}^{(1)} = Eu_0^{(2)}$

6: compute $u_0^{(1)} = t^{(1)} - \tilde{t}^{(1)}$

7: compute $v_0^{(1)} = u_0^{(1)} + 2\tilde{t}^{(1)}$

8: set $v_0^{(2)} = -u_0^{(2)}$

9: let $u_0 = \left[u_0^{(1)^\mathsf{T}}, u_0^{(2)^\mathsf{T}} \right]^\mathsf{T}$, $v_0 = \left[v_0^{(1)^\mathsf{T}}, v_0^{(2)^\mathsf{T}} \right]^\mathsf{T}$

10: set $p_0 = u_0$ and $q_0 = v_0$

11: **for** $k = 0, 1, 2, \ldots,$ **do**

12: $\qquad \alpha_k = -\dfrac{v_k^\mathsf{T} r_k}{q_k^\mathsf{T} A p_k}$

13: $\qquad z^{(k+1)} = z^{(k)} - \alpha_k p_k$

14: $\qquad r_{k+1} = r_k + \alpha_k A p_k$

15: $\qquad$ let $r_{k+1} = \left[r_{k+1}^{(1)^\mathsf{T}}, r_{k+1}^{(2)^\mathsf{T}} \right]^\mathsf{T}$

16: $\qquad$ solve $Bt^{(1)} = r_{k+1}^{(1)}$

17: $\qquad$ solve $\widehat{S}u_{k+1}^{(2)} = E^\mathsf{T}t^{(1)} - r_{k+1}^{(2)}$

18: $\qquad$ solve $B\tilde{t}^{(1)} = Eu_{k+1}^{(2)}$

19: $\qquad$ compute $u_{k+1}^{(1)} = t^{(1)} - \tilde{t}^{(1)}$

20: $\qquad$ compute $v_{k+1}^{(1)} = u_{k+1}^{(1)} + 2\tilde{t}^{(1)}$

21: $\qquad$ set $v_{k+1}^{(2)} = -u_{k+1}^{(2)}$

22: $\qquad$ let $u_{k+1} = \left[u_{k+1}^{(1)^\mathsf{T}}, u_{k+1}^{(2)^\mathsf{T}} \right]^\mathsf{T}$, $v_{k+1} = \left[v_{k+1}^{(1)^\mathsf{T}}, v_{k+1}^{(2)^\mathsf{T}} \right]^\mathsf{T}$

23: $\qquad \beta_k = \dfrac{v_{k+1}^\mathsf{T} r_{k+1}}{v_k^\mathsf{T} r_k}$

24: $\qquad p_{k+1} = u_{k+1} + \beta_k p_k$

25: $\qquad q_{k+1} = v_{k+1} + \beta_k q_k$

26: **end for**

One typical choice of the approximation matrix $\widehat{S}$ could be $\widehat{S} = E^\mathsf{T}KE$, with $K \in \mathbb{R}^{n \times n}$ being a sparse approximation to the matrix B^{-1}.

Because the matrix

$$P^{-1}Q^{-1} = \begin{bmatrix} I & B^{-1}E \\ E^\mathsf{T}B^{-1} & -I + E^\mathsf{T}B^{-2}E \end{bmatrix}$$

is symmetric but indefinite, we cannot find a symmetric positive definite matrix $G \in \mathbb{R}^{(n+m) \times (n+m)}$ such that $PGQ = I$. Therefore, for the standard saddle-point problem (8.101), the RPCG method (i.e., Algorithm 8.1) does not correspond to a no-preconditioned version RCG.

Noticing that for this problem,

$$AW = \begin{bmatrix} B & E \\ E^\mathsf{T} & C \end{bmatrix}, \quad \text{with} \quad C := 2E^\mathsf{T}B^{-1}E,$$

$$MW = \begin{bmatrix} B & E \\ E^\mathsf{T} & \widetilde{C} \end{bmatrix}, \quad \text{with} \quad \widetilde{C} := \widehat{S} + E^\mathsf{T}B^{-1}E,$$

we may transform the problem (8.101) into a block two-by-two linear system of symmetric positive definite coefficient matrix, and then use the classical PCG to compute an approximation to its exact solution.

The **generalized saddle-point problem** in **nonsymmetric form** (8.24) is

$$\underbrace{\begin{bmatrix} B & E \\ -E^\mathsf{T} & C \end{bmatrix}}_{\tilde{A}} \underbrace{\begin{bmatrix} x \\ y \end{bmatrix}}_{z} = \underbrace{\begin{bmatrix} f \\ -g \end{bmatrix}}_{\tilde{b}}, \tag{8.102}$$

where $\tilde{A} \in \mathbb{R}^{(n+m)\times(n+m)}$ is a nonsingular matrix, and $f \in \mathbb{R}^n$ and $g \in \mathbb{R}^m$ are known vectors. In particular, here we assume that the matrix $B \in \mathbb{R}^{n\times n}$ is symmetric positive definite, the matrix $C \in \mathbb{R}^{m\times m}$ is symmetric positive semidefinite, and the matrix $E \in \mathbb{R}^{n\times m}$, with $n \geq m$, such that $\text{Ker}(C) \cap \text{Ker}(E) = \{0\}$.

In accordance with (8.26), we know that the matrix $\tilde{A} \in \mathbb{R}^{(n+m)\times(n+m)}$ adopts the **block-triangular factorization**:

$$\tilde{A} = \underbrace{\begin{bmatrix} I & 0 \\ -E^\mathsf{T}B^{-1} & I \end{bmatrix}}_{P} \underbrace{\begin{bmatrix} B & 0 \\ 0 & S \end{bmatrix}}_{H} \underbrace{\begin{bmatrix} I & B^{-1}E \\ 0 & I \end{bmatrix}}_{Q},$$

where

$$S = C + E^\mathsf{T}B^{-1}E$$

is the Schur complement of the generalized saddle-point matrix $\tilde{A}$. Evidently, the matrix $S \in \mathbb{R}^{m\times m}$ is symmetric positive definite, and it holds that

$$W = Q^{-1}P^\mathsf{T} = \begin{bmatrix} I & -B^{-1}E \\ 0 & I \end{bmatrix} \begin{bmatrix} I & -B^{-1}E \\ 0 & I \end{bmatrix} = \begin{bmatrix} I & -2B^{-1}E \\ 0 & I \end{bmatrix}.$$

Let $\widehat{S} \in \mathbb{R}^{m\times m}$ be a symmetric positive definite matrix such that it is an approximation to the matrix S. Then the block-diagonal matrix $G = \text{Diag}(B, \widehat{S})$ is a reasonable preconditioner to the matrix $H = \text{Diag}(B, S)$. If we take $M = PGQ$, then the **RPCG method** has the following special form for the generalized saddle-point problem (8.102); see [42].

Algorithm 8.2: RPCG Method for Problem (8.102)

1: Choose $z^{(0)} \in \mathbb{R}^{n+m}$, $r_0 = \tilde{b} - \tilde{A}z^{(0)}$

2: let $r_0 = \left[r_0^{(1)^\mathsf{T}}, r_0^{(2)^\mathsf{T}} \right]^\mathsf{T}$

3: solve $Bt^{(1)} = r_0^{(1)}$

4: solve $\widehat{S}u_0^{(2)} = r_0^{(2)} + E^\mathsf{T}t^{(1)}$

5: solve $B\tilde{t}^{(1)} = Eu_0^{(2)}$

6: compute $u_0^{(1)} = t^{(1)} - \tilde{t}^{(1)}$

7: compute $v_0^{(1)} = u_0^{(1)} + 2\tilde{t}^{(1)}$

8: set $v_0^{(2)} = u_0^{(2)}$

9: let $u_0 = \left[u_0^{(1)^\mathsf{T}}, u_0^{(2)^\mathsf{T}} \right]^\mathsf{T}, v_0 = \left[v_0^{(1)^\mathsf{T}}, v_0^{(2)^\mathsf{T}} \right]^\mathsf{T}$

10: set $p_0 = u_0$ and $q_0 = v_0$

11: **for** $k = 0, 1, 2, \ldots,$ **do**

12: $\quad \alpha_k = -\dfrac{v_k^\mathsf{T} r_k}{q_k^\mathsf{T} \tilde{A} p_k}$

13: $\quad z^{(k+1)} = z^{(k)} - \alpha_k p_k$

14: $\quad r_{k+1} = r_k + \alpha_k \tilde{A} p_k$

15: $\quad$ let $r_{k+1} = \left[r_{k+1}^{(1)^\mathsf{T}}, r_{k+1}^{(2)^\mathsf{T}} \right]^\mathsf{T}$

16: $\quad$ solve $Bt^{(1)} = r_{k+1}^{(1)}$

17: $\quad$ solve $\widehat{S} u_{k+1}^{(2)} = r_{k+1}^{(2)} + E^\mathsf{T} t^{(1)}$

18: $\quad$ solve $B\tilde{t}^{(1)} = E u_{k+1}^{(2)}$

19: $\quad$ compute $u_{k+1}^{(1)} = t^{(1)} - \tilde{t}^{(1)}$

20: $\quad$ compute $v_{k+1}^{(1)} = u_{k+1}^{(1)} + 2\tilde{t}^{(1)}$

21: $\quad$ set $v_{k+1}^{(2)} = u_{k+1}^{(2)}$

22: $\quad$ let $u_{k+1} = \left[u_{k+1}^{(1)^\mathsf{T}}, u_{k+1}^{(2)^\mathsf{T}} \right]^\mathsf{T}, v_{k+1} = \left[v_{k+1}^{(1)^\mathsf{T}}, v_{k+1}^{(2)^\mathsf{T}} \right]^\mathsf{T}$

23: $\quad \beta_k = \dfrac{v_{k+1}^\mathsf{T} r_{k+1}}{v_k^\mathsf{T} r_k}$

24: $\quad p_{k+1} = u_{k+1} + \beta_k p_k$

25: $\quad q_{k+1} = v_{k+1} + \beta_k q_k$

26: **end for**

For this problem, two typical choices of the preconditioning matrix $M \in \mathbb{R}^{(n+m)\times(n+m)}$ to the coefficient matrix $\tilde{A} \in \mathbb{R}^{(n+m)\times(n+m)}$ can be obtained through the following two versions of the matrix $\widehat{S} \in \mathbb{R}^{m\times m}$:

(a) $\widehat{S} = C$, if the matrix $C \in \mathbb{R}^{m\times m}$ is symmetric positive definite;

(b) $\widehat{S} = \widehat{C} + \omega^2 E^\mathsf{T} K E$, where $\omega \in [0, 1]$ is a parameter, and $K \in \mathbb{R}^{n\times n}$ and $\widehat{C} \in \mathbb{R}^{m\times m}$ are sparse approximations to the matrices B^{-1} and C, respectively.

Correspondingly, we can obtain two versions of the RPCG method, i.e., RPCG(a) and RPCG(b).

We remark that in version (a) the restriction $n \geq m$ can be removed, so that it could be $n > m$, $n = m$, or $n < m$; and in version (b) the approximate matrices K and $\widehat{C}$ could be obtained through relaxation iterations or incomplete Cholesky factorizations of the matrices B and C, respectively.

Because the matrix

$$P^{-1}Q^{-1} = \begin{bmatrix} I & -B^{-1}E \\ E^\mathsf{T} B^{-1} & I - E^\mathsf{T} B^{-2} E \end{bmatrix}$$

is unsymmetric, we cannot find a symmetric positive definite matrix $G \in \mathbb{R}^{(n+m)\times(n+m)}$ such that $PGQ = I$. Therefore, for the generalized saddle-point problem (8.102), the RPCG method (i.e., Algorithm 8.2) does not correspond to a no-preconditioned version RCG either.

Noticing that for this problem,

$$\tilde{A}W = \begin{bmatrix} B & -E \\ -E^\mathsf{T} & C \end{bmatrix}, \quad \text{with} \quad C := C + 2E^\mathsf{T}B^{-1}E,$$

$$MW = \begin{bmatrix} B & -E \\ -E^\mathsf{T} & \widetilde{C} \end{bmatrix}, \quad \text{with} \quad \widetilde{C} := \widehat{S} + E^\mathsf{T}B^{-1}E,$$

we may transform the problem (8.102) into a block two-by-two linear system of symmetric positive definite coefficient matrix, and then use the classical PCG to compute an approximation to its exact solution.

8.5.2 ▪ RPCG for Block Two-by-Two SPD Linear Systems

We now discuss the RPCG method for the **block two-by-two linear systems** of the form

$$\underbrace{\begin{bmatrix} B & E \\ E^\mathsf{T} & C \end{bmatrix}}_{A} \underbrace{\begin{bmatrix} x \\ y \end{bmatrix}}_{z} = \underbrace{\begin{bmatrix} f \\ g \end{bmatrix}}_{b}. \tag{8.103}$$

Here we assume that $A \in \mathbb{R}^{(n+m)\times(n+m)}$ is a symmetric positive definite matrix, $B \in \mathbb{R}^{n\times n}$, $C \in \mathbb{R}^{m\times m}$, and $E \in \mathbb{R}^{n\times m}$, and $f \in \mathbb{R}^n$ and $g \in \mathbb{R}^m$ are known vectors.

Because $A \in \mathbb{R}^{(n+m)\times(n+m)}$ is symmetric positive definite, its diagonal blocks $B \in \mathbb{R}^{n\times n}$ and $C \in \mathbb{R}^{m\times m}$ are both symmetric positive definite too. By direct computations, we know that the matrix A adopts the following **block-triangular factorization**:

$$A = \underbrace{\begin{bmatrix} I & 0 \\ E^\mathsf{T}B^{-1} & I \end{bmatrix}}_{P} \underbrace{\begin{bmatrix} B & 0 \\ 0 & S \end{bmatrix}}_{H} \underbrace{\begin{bmatrix} I & B^{-1}E \\ 0 & I \end{bmatrix}}_{Q},$$

where

$$S = C - E^\mathsf{T}B^{-1}E$$

is the Schur complement of the matrix A. Evidently, the matrix $S \in \mathbb{R}^{m\times m}$ is also symmetric positive definite, and it holds that

$$W = Q^{-1}P^\mathsf{T} = \begin{bmatrix} I & -B^{-1}E \\ 0 & I \end{bmatrix}\begin{bmatrix} I & B^{-1}E \\ 0 & I \end{bmatrix} = I.$$

Let $\widehat{S} \in \mathbb{R}^{m\times m}$ be a symmetric positive definite matrix such that it is an approximation to the matrix S. Then the block-diagonal matrix $G = \text{Diag}(B, \widehat{S})$ is a reasonable preconditioner to the matrix $H = \text{Diag}(B, S)$. If we take $M = PGQ$, then the **RPCG method** has the following special form for the block two-by-two SPD problem (8.103); see [42].

Algorithm 8.3: RPCG Method for Problem (8.103)

1: Choose $z^{(0)} \in \mathbb{R}^{n+m}$, $r_0 = b - Az^{(0)}$

2: let $r_0 = \left[r_0^{(1)^\mathsf{T}}, r_0^{(2)^\mathsf{T}}\right]^\mathsf{T}$

3: solve $Bt^{(1)} = r_0^{(1)}$

4: solve $\widehat{S}u_0^{(2)} = r_0^{(2)} - E^\mathsf{T}t^{(1)}$

5: solve $B\tilde{t}^{(1)} = Eu_0^{(2)}$

6: compute $u_0^{(1)} = t^{(1)} - \tilde{t}^{(1)}$

7: let $u_0 = \left[u_0^{(1)^\mathsf{T}}, u_0^{(2)^\mathsf{T}}\right]^\mathsf{T}$

8: set $p_0 = u_0$

9: **for** $k = 0, 1, 2, \ldots,$ **do**

10: $\quad \alpha_k = -\dfrac{u_k^\mathsf{T} r_k}{p_k^\mathsf{T} A p_k}$

11: $\quad z^{(k+1)} = z^{(k)} - \alpha_k p_k$

12: $\quad r_{k+1} = r_k + \alpha_k A p_k$

13: $\quad$ let $r_{k+1} = \left[r_{k+1}^{(1)^\mathsf{T}}, r_{k+1}^{(2)^\mathsf{T}}\right]^\mathsf{T}$

14: $\quad$ solve $Bt^{(1)} = r_{k+1}^{(1)}$

15: $\quad$ solve $\widehat{S}u_{k+1}^{(2)} = r_{k+1}^{(2)} - E^\mathsf{T} t^{(1)}$

16: $\quad$ solve $B\tilde{t}^{(1)} = Eu_{k+1}^{(2)}$

17: $\quad$ compute $u_{k+1}^{(1)} = t^{(1)} - \tilde{t}^{(1)}$

18: $\quad$ let $u_{k+1} = \left[u_{k+1}^{(1)^\mathsf{T}}, u_{k+1}^{(2)^\mathsf{T}}\right]^\mathsf{T}$

19: $\quad \beta_k = \dfrac{u_{k+1}^\mathsf{T} r_{k+1}}{u_k^\mathsf{T} r_k}$

20: $\quad p_{k+1} = u_{k+1} + \beta_k p_k$

21: **end for**

For this problem, the above-described RPCG method is equivalent to the PCG method with a special type of preconditioner $M = PGQ$. Two typical choices of this preconditioner can be got through the following two versions of the matrix $\widehat{S} \in \mathbb{R}^{m \times m}$:

(a) $\widehat{S} = C$;

(b) $\widehat{S} = \widehat{C} - \omega^2 E^\mathsf{T} K E$, where $\omega \in [0,\, 1]$ is a parameter, and $K \in \mathbb{R}^{n \times n}$ and $\widehat{C} \in \mathbb{R}^{m \times m}$ are sparse approximations to the matrices B^{-1} and C, respectively.

Correspondingly, we can obtain two versions of the RPCG method, i.e., RPCG(a) and RPCG(b).

We remark that in version (b) the approximate matrices K and $\widehat{C}$ could be obtained through relaxation iterations or incomplete Cholesky factorizations of the matrices B and C, respectively.

8.5.3 ▪ Practical RPCG

For the block two-by-two SPD linear system (8.103), at each iteration step of the RPCG method, that is, Algorithm 8.3, we need to compute the exact solutions of two subsystems of linear equations with different right-hand side vectors but the same coefficient matrix $B \in \mathbb{R}^{n \times n}$; see also [42, Method 3.1]. This could be costly and impractical in actual applications, in particular, when the size of the matrix block B is very large.

In order to improve the computational efficiency of the RPCG method, we now present a practical strategy of constructing the transform matrices P and Q, as well as the approximation matrix G, and, consequently, obtain several practical and efficient iteration methods within the framework of RPCG; see [23, 56]. These practical RPCG methods can avoid exact inversions of the matrix blocks B and C, and they only require inexact solutions of the linear subsystems with the coefficient matrices B and C. Therefore, they are "inverse-free" variants of the RPCG method (i.e., Algorithm 8.3) for the block two-by-two SPD linear system (8.103); see also [42].

Because $A \in \mathbb{R}^{(n+m) \times (n+m)}$ is symmetric positive definite, its diagonal blocks $B \in \mathbb{R}^{n \times n}$ and $C \in \mathbb{R}^{m \times m}$ are symmetric positive definite too. Let $L_B \in \mathbb{R}^{n \times n}$ and $L_C \in \mathbb{R}^{m \times m}$ be nonsingular matrices such that

$$L_B^{-1} B L_B^{-\mathsf{T}} = J_B \quad \text{and} \quad L_C^{-1} C L_C^{-\mathsf{T}} = J_C. \tag{8.104}$$

Here we require that

$$J_B \approx I \quad \text{and} \quad J_C \approx I,$$

with I being the identity matrix whose dimension can be inferred from the context. Take

$$P = \begin{bmatrix} L_B & 0 \\ E^\mathsf{T} L_B^{-\mathsf{T}} & L_C \end{bmatrix} \quad \text{and} \quad Q = \begin{bmatrix} L_B^\mathsf{T} & L_B^{-1} E \\ 0 & L_C^\mathsf{T} \end{bmatrix} = P^\mathsf{T}. \tag{8.105}$$

Then, by direct computations, we have

$$A = PHQ = PHP^\mathsf{T},$$

where

$$H = \begin{bmatrix} J_B & (I - J_B)\widehat{E} \\ \widehat{E}^\mathsf{T}(I - J_B) & J_C - \widehat{E}^\mathsf{T}\widehat{E} - \widehat{E}^\mathsf{T}(I - J_B)\widehat{E} \end{bmatrix} \tag{8.106}$$

is a symmetric positive definite matrix,

$$\widehat{E} = L_B^{-1} E L_C^{-\mathsf{T}},$$

and

$$W = Q^{-1} P^\mathsf{T} = P^{-\mathsf{T}} P^\mathsf{T} = I.$$

Now, we can define the preconditioner as

$$M = PGP^\mathsf{T},$$

where

$$G \approx \widehat{G} := \begin{bmatrix} I & (I - J_B)\widehat{E} \\ \widehat{E}^\mathsf{T}(I - J_B) & \widehat{S} \end{bmatrix} \approx H \quad \text{and} \quad \widehat{S} = I - \widehat{E}^\mathsf{T}\widehat{E}. \tag{8.107}$$

Because

$$P^{-1} = \begin{bmatrix} L_B^{-1} & 0 \\ -L_C^{-1} E^\mathsf{T} L_B^{-\mathsf{T}} L_B^{-1} & L_C^{-1} \end{bmatrix},$$

by letting

$$t = \begin{bmatrix} t^{(1)} \\ t^{(2)} \end{bmatrix} \triangleq P^{-1} r = P^{-1} \begin{bmatrix} r^{(1)} \\ r^{(2)} \end{bmatrix}$$

and

$$\tilde{t} = \left[\begin{array}{c} \tilde{t}^{(1)} \\ \tilde{t}^{(2)} \end{array} \right] \triangleq P^{\mathsf{T}} u = P^{\mathsf{T}} \left[\begin{array}{c} u^{(1)} \\ u^{(2)} \end{array} \right],$$

with

$$r^{(1)}, u^{(1)}, t^{(1)}, \tilde{t}^{(1)} \in \mathbb{R}^n \quad \text{and} \quad r^{(2)}, u^{(2)}, t^{(2)}, \tilde{t}^{(2)} \in \mathbb{R}^m,$$

we can solve the generalized residual equation $Mu = r$ involved in Algorithm 7.7 through the formulas

- $L_B t^{(1)} = r^{(1)}, L_B^{\mathsf{T}} \hat{t}^{(1)} = t^{(1)}$;

- $L_C t^{(2)} = r^{(2)} - E^{\mathsf{T}} \hat{t}^{(1)}$;

- $G\tilde{t} = t$;

- $L_C^{\mathsf{T}} u^{(2)} = \tilde{t}^{(2)}$;

- $L_B \hat{t}^{(1)} = E u^{(2)}, L_B^{\mathsf{T}} u^{(1)} = \tilde{t}^{(1)} - \hat{t}^{(1)}$.

Consequently, we obtain the following practical variant of Algorithm 8.3, termed as the **practical RPCG method**, for solving the block two-by-two SPD linear system (8.103).

Algorithm 8.4: Practical RPCG Method for Problem (8.103)

1: Choose $z^{(0)} \in \mathbb{R}^{n+m}, r_0 = b - A z^{(0)}$

2: let $r_0 = \left[r_0^{(1)^{\mathsf{T}}}, r_0^{(2)^{\mathsf{T}}} \right]^{\mathsf{T}}$

3: solve $L_B t^{(1)} = r_0^{(1)}$ and $L_B^{\mathsf{T}} \hat{t}^{(1)} = t^{(1)}$

4: solve $L_C t^{(2)} = r_0^{(2)} - E^{\mathsf{T}} \hat{t}^{(1)}$

5: solve $G\tilde{t} = t$, with $t = \left[t^{(1)^{\mathsf{T}}}, t^{(2)^{\mathsf{T}}} \right]^{\mathsf{T}}$ and $\tilde{t} = \left[\tilde{t}^{(1)^{\mathsf{T}}}, \tilde{t}^{(2)^{\mathsf{T}}} \right]^{\mathsf{T}}$

6: solve $L_C^{\mathsf{T}} u_0^{(2)} = \tilde{t}^{(2)}$

7: solve $L_B \hat{t}^{(1)} = E u_0^{(2)}$ and $L_B^{\mathsf{T}} u_0^{(1)} = \tilde{t}^{(1)} - \hat{t}^{(1)}$

8: let $u_0 = \left[u_0^{(1)^{\mathsf{T}}}, u_0^{(2)^{\mathsf{T}}} \right]^{\mathsf{T}}$

9: set $p_0 = u_0$

10: **for** $k = 0, 1, 2, \ldots,$ **do**

11: $\quad \alpha_k = -\dfrac{u_k^{\mathsf{T}} r_k}{p_k^{\mathsf{T}} A p_k}$

12: $\quad z^{(k+1)} = z^{(k)} - \alpha_k p_k$

13: $\quad r_{k+1} = r_k + \alpha_k A p_k$

14: $\quad$ let $r_{k+1} = \left[r_{k+1}^{(1)^{\mathsf{T}}}, r_{k+1}^{(2)^{\mathsf{T}}} \right]^{\mathsf{T}}$

15: $\quad$ solve $L_B t^{(1)} = r_{k+1}^{(1)}$ and $L_B^{\mathsf{T}} \hat{t}^{(1)} = t^{(1)}$

16: $\quad$ solve $L_C t^{(2)} = r_{k+1}^{(2)} - E^{\mathsf{T}} \hat{t}^{(1)}$

17: $\quad$ solve $G\tilde{t} = t$, with $t = \left[t^{(1)^{\mathsf{T}}}, t^{(2)^{\mathsf{T}}} \right]^{\mathsf{T}}$ and $\tilde{t} = \left[\tilde{t}^{(1)^{\mathsf{T}}}, \tilde{t}^{(2)^{\mathsf{T}}} \right]^{\mathsf{T}}$

18: $\quad$ solve $L_C^{\mathsf{T}} u_{k+1}^{(2)} = \tilde{t}^{(2)}$

19:    solve $L_B \hat{t}^{(1)} = E u_{k+1}^{(2)}$ and $L_B^\mathsf{T} u_{k+1}^{(1)} = \tilde{t}^{(1)} - \hat{t}^{(1)}$

20:    let $u_{k+1} = \left[u_{k+1}^{(1)^\mathsf{T}}, u_{k+1}^{(2)^\mathsf{T}} \right]^\mathsf{T}$

21:    $\beta_k = \dfrac{u_{k+1}^\mathsf{T} r_{k+1}}{u_k^\mathsf{T} r_k}$

22:    $p_{k+1} = u_{k+1} + \beta_k p_k$
23: **end for**

According to the convergence of Algorithm 8.4, by making use of the convergence theorem about Algorithm 7.7 we can obtain the following result.

Theorem 8.30. *Let $A \in \mathbb{R}^{(n+m) \times (n+m)}$ be a symmetric positive definite matrix of the block two-by-two structure as in (8.103), and P and H be the matrices defined by (8.105) and (8.106) such that $A = PHP^\mathsf{T}$. Let $M = PGP^\mathsf{T}$, where $G \in \mathbb{R}^{(n+m) \times (n+m)}$ is a symmetric positive definite matrix approximating the matrix $\widehat{G} \in \mathbb{R}^{(n+m) \times (n+m)}$ defined by (8.107). Assume that*

$$x^\mathsf{T} J_B x \leq 1 \quad \text{and} \quad y^\mathsf{T} J_C y \leq 1 \tag{8.108}$$

hold for all normalized vectors $x \in \mathbb{R}^n$ and $y \in \mathbb{R}^m$, where J_B and J_C are the matrices defined in (8.104). Then

(i) *both matrices $\widehat{S}$ and $\widehat{G}$ defined in (8.107) are symmetric positive definite;*

(ii) *if there exist a nonnegative constant $\gamma \in [0, 1)$ such that*

$$|x^\mathsf{T} E y| \leq \gamma (x^\mathsf{T} B x)^{\frac{1}{2}} (y^\mathsf{T} C y)^{\frac{1}{2}}, \tag{8.109}$$

and two positive constants $\nu_B \in (0, 1)$ and $\nu_C \in (0, 1)$ such that

$$x^\mathsf{T} J_B x \geq 1 - \nu_B \quad \text{and} \quad y^\mathsf{T} J_C y \geq 1 - \nu_C \tag{8.110}$$

hold for all normalized vectors $x \in \mathbb{R}^n$ and $y \in \mathbb{R}^m$, the iteration sequence $\{z^{(k)}\}_{k=0}^\infty \subset \mathbb{R}^{n+m}$ generated by Algorithm 8.4 satisfies

$$\|z^{(k)} - z_*\|_A \leq 2 \left(\frac{\sqrt{\sigma(\nu, \gamma) \cdot \kappa(G^{-1} \widehat{G})} - 1}{\sqrt{\sigma(\nu, \gamma) \cdot \kappa(G^{-1} \widehat{G})} + 1} \right)^k \|z^{(0)} - z_*\|_A, \tag{8.111}$$

provided $\nu \in (0, 1)$ is such that $\gamma < \Gamma(\nu)$, where

$$\Gamma(\nu) = \frac{\sqrt{1 - \nu} \left(\sqrt{4 - 3\nu^2} - \nu \right)}{2(1 + \nu)} < \frac{1}{2} \sqrt{1 - \nu} \left(\sqrt{\nu^2 + 4} - \nu \right)$$

and

$$\nu = \max\{\nu_B, \nu_C\}, \quad \sigma(\nu, \gamma) = \frac{1 - \nu - \gamma \nu \sqrt{1 - \nu} - \gamma^2}{(1 - \nu)^2 - \gamma \nu \sqrt{1 - \nu} - (1 + \nu) \gamma^2},$$

$\kappa(G^{-1} \widehat{G})$ represents the Euclidean condition number of the matrix $G^{-1} \widehat{G}$, and $z_* = A^{-1} b$ is the exact solution of the system of linear equations (8.103).

Proof. We first prove (i). Because the matrix $A \in \mathbb{R}^{(n+m) \times (n+m)}$ is symmetric positive definite, we know that its Schur complement

$$S = C - E^{\mathsf{T}} B^{-1} E$$

is symmetric positive definite too. From (8.108) we can obtain the inequalities

$$x^{\mathsf{T}} B x \leq x^{\mathsf{T}} L_B L_B^{\mathsf{T}} x \quad \text{and} \quad y^{\mathsf{T}} C y \leq y^{\mathsf{T}} L_C L_C^{\mathsf{T}} y, \qquad \forall\, x \in \mathbb{R}^n, \ \forall\, y \in \mathbb{R}^m.$$

Therefore, it holds that

$$x^{\mathsf{T}} (L_B L_B^{\mathsf{T}})^{-1} x \leq x^{\mathsf{T}} B^{-1} x, \quad \forall\, x \in \mathbb{R}^n. \tag{8.112}$$

By straightforward computations we have

$$\begin{aligned}
\widehat{S} &= I - \widehat{E}^{\mathsf{T}} \widehat{E} \\
&= I - (L_C^{-1} E^{\mathsf{T}} L_B^{-\mathsf{T}})(L_B^{-1} E L_C^{-\mathsf{T}}) \\
&= L_C^{-1} \left[L_C L_C^{\mathsf{T}} - E^{\mathsf{T}} (L_B L_B^{\mathsf{T}})^{-1} E \right] L_C^{-\mathsf{T}}.
\end{aligned}$$

It then follows that, for any $y \in \mathbb{R}^m$,

$$\begin{aligned}
y^{\mathsf{T}} \widehat{S} y &= y^{\mathsf{T}} L_C^{-1} \left[L_C L_C^{\mathsf{T}} - E^{\mathsf{T}} (L_B L_B^{\mathsf{T}})^{-1} E \right] L_C^{-\mathsf{T}} y \\
&\geq y^{\mathsf{T}} L_C^{-1} \left[C - E^{\mathsf{T}} B^{-1} E \right] L_C^{-\mathsf{T}} y \\
&= y^{\mathsf{T}} L_C^{-1} S L_C^{-\mathsf{T}} y,
\end{aligned}$$

where the inequality is induced by (8.112). Hence, the matrix $\widehat{S}$ is symmetric positive definite.

Evidently, to demonstrate the symmetric positive definiteness of the matrix $\widehat{G}$ defined by (8.107), we only need to verify the symmetric positive definiteness of its Schur complement

$$S_{\widehat{G}} = \widehat{S} - \widehat{E}^{\mathsf{T}} (I - J_B)^2 \widehat{E}.$$

In fact, because, for all normalized vectors $x \in \mathbb{R}^n$, $x^{\mathsf{T}} J_B x \leq 1$ implies $1 \leq x^{\mathsf{T}} J_B^{-1} x$, we obtain for all $y \in \mathbb{R}^m$ that

$$\begin{aligned}
y^{\mathsf{T}} S_{\widehat{G}} y &\geq y^{\mathsf{T}} \left[\widehat{S} - \widehat{E}^{\mathsf{T}} (I - J_B) J_B^{-1} (I - J_B) \widehat{E} \right] y \\
&= y^{\mathsf{T}} \left(I - \widehat{E}^{\mathsf{T}} J_B^{-1} \widehat{E} \right) y + y^{\mathsf{T}} \widehat{E}^{\mathsf{T}} (I - J_B) \widehat{E} y \\
&\geq y^{\mathsf{T}} \left(I - \widehat{E}^{\mathsf{T}} J_B^{-1} \widehat{E} \right) y \\
&\geq y^{\mathsf{T}} L_C^{-1} S L_C^{-\mathsf{T}} y.
\end{aligned}$$

Hence, $S_{\widehat{G}}$ is a symmetric positive definite matrix.

We now turn to demonstrate the validity of (ii). Obviously, it holds that

$$\widehat{G} - H = \begin{bmatrix} I - J_B & 0 \\ 0 & I - J_C + \widehat{E}^{\mathsf{T}} (I - J_B) \widehat{E} \end{bmatrix}.$$

By (8.108) we immediately obtain the estimate

$$z^{\mathsf{T}} \widehat{G} z \geq z^{\mathsf{T}} H z, \quad \forall\, z \in \mathbb{R}^{n+m}.$$

On the other hand, as (i) implies for $y \in \mathbb{R}^m \setminus \{0\}$ that

$$0 < y^\mathsf{T} \widehat{S} y < y^\mathsf{T} y \quad \text{and} \quad y^\mathsf{T} \widehat{S}^{-1} y > y^\mathsf{T} y,$$

we know that

$$\|\widehat{D}^{-1}\|_2 = \max\left\{1, \ \max_{y \neq 0} \frac{y^\mathsf{T} \widehat{S}^{-1} y}{y^\mathsf{T} y}\right\} = \|\widehat{S}^{-1}\|_2,$$

where we have denoted by

$$\widehat{D} = \begin{bmatrix} I & 0 \\ 0 & \widehat{S} \end{bmatrix}$$

the symmetric positive definite block-diagonal matrix of the matrix $\widehat{G}$. Hence, by (8.107) it holds that

$$\|\widehat{D} - \widehat{G}\|_2 \le \|(I - J_B)\widehat{E}\|_2 \le \|\widehat{E}\|_2 \|I - J_B\|_2,$$

and when

$$\|\widehat{S}^{-1}\|_2 \|\widehat{E}\|_2 \|I - J_B\|_2 < 1,$$

it holds that

$$
\begin{aligned}
\|\widehat{G}^{-1}\|_2 &= \left\| \left[I - (I - \widehat{D}^{-1}\widehat{G}) \right]^{-1} \widehat{D}^{-1} \right\|_2 \\
&\le \frac{\|\widehat{D}^{-1}\|_2}{1 - \|\widehat{D}^{-1}\|_2 \|\widehat{D} - \widehat{G}\|_2} \\
&= \frac{\|\widehat{S}^{-1}\|_2}{1 - \|\widehat{S}^{-1}\|_2 \|\widehat{D} - \widehat{G}\|_2} \\
&\le \frac{\|\widehat{S}^{-1}\|_2}{1 - \|\widehat{S}^{-1}\|_2 \|\widehat{E}\|_2 \|I - J_B\|_2}.
\end{aligned}
\tag{8.113}
$$

It then follows that, for any $z = [x^\mathsf{T}, y^\mathsf{T}]^\mathsf{T} \in \mathbb{R}^{n+m} \setminus \{0\}$ with $x \in \mathbb{R}^n$ and $y \in \mathbb{R}^m$,

$$
\begin{aligned}
\frac{z^\mathsf{T} H z}{z^\mathsf{T} \widehat{G} z} &\ge 1 - \max_{z \neq 0} \left(1 - \frac{z^\mathsf{T} H z}{z^\mathsf{T} \widehat{G} z}\right) \\
&= 1 - \max_{z \neq 0} \frac{z^\mathsf{T} (\widehat{G} - H) z}{z^\mathsf{T} \widehat{G} z} \\
&\ge 1 - \|\widehat{G}^{-1}(\widehat{G} - H)\|_2 \\
&\ge 1 - \|\widehat{G}^{-1}\|_2 \|\widehat{G} - H\|_2 \\
&\ge 1 - \frac{\|\widehat{S}^{-1}\|_2}{1 - \|\widehat{S}^{-1}\|_2 \|\widehat{E}\|_2 \|I - J_B\|_2} \\
&\quad \cdot \max\left\{ \|I - J_B\|_2, \ \|I - J_C\|_2 + \|\widehat{E}\|_2^2 \|I - J_B\|_2 \right\} \\
&\ge 1 - \frac{\|\widehat{S}^{-1}\|_2 (1 + \|\widehat{E}\|_2^2)}{1 - \|\widehat{S}^{-1}\|_2 \|\widehat{E}\|_2 \|I - J_B\|_2} \cdot \max\left\{ \|I - J_B\|_2, \ \|I - J_C\|_2 \right\}.
\end{aligned}
$$

Because the inequality (8.109), together with (8.112) and (8.110), implies that

$$
\begin{aligned}
y^{\mathsf{T}}\widehat{E}^{\mathsf{T}}\widehat{E}y &= y^{\mathsf{T}}L_C^{-1}E^{\mathsf{T}}L_B^{-\mathsf{T}}L_B^{-1}EL_C^{-\mathsf{T}}y \\
&\le y^{\mathsf{T}}L_C^{-1}E^{\mathsf{T}}B^{-1}EL_C^{-\mathsf{T}}y \\
&\le \gamma\sqrt{(y^{\mathsf{T}}L_C^{-1}E^{\mathsf{T}}B^{-1})B(B^{-1}EL_C^{-\mathsf{T}}y)} \cdot \sqrt{y^{\mathsf{T}}L_C^{-1}CL_C^{-\mathsf{T}}y} \\
&= \gamma\sqrt{y^{\mathsf{T}}\widehat{E}^{\mathsf{T}}J_B^{-1}\widehat{E}y} \cdot \sqrt{y^{\mathsf{T}}L_C^{-1}CL_C^{-\mathsf{T}}y} \\
&\le \frac{\gamma}{\sqrt{1-\nu_B}} \cdot \sqrt{y^{\mathsf{T}}\widehat{E}^{\mathsf{T}}\widehat{E}y} \cdot \sqrt{y^{\mathsf{T}}L_C^{-1}CL_C^{-\mathsf{T}}y} \\
&\le \frac{\gamma}{\sqrt{1-\nu}} \cdot \sqrt{y^{\mathsf{T}}\widehat{E}^{\mathsf{T}}\widehat{E}y} \cdot \sqrt{y^{\mathsf{T}}L_C^{-1}CL_C^{-\mathsf{T}}y},
\end{aligned}
$$

by making use of (8.108) we can obtain

$$
y^{\mathsf{T}}\widehat{E}^{\mathsf{T}}\widehat{E}y \le \frac{\gamma^2}{1-\nu} \cdot y^{\mathsf{T}}L_C^{-1}CL_C^{-\mathsf{T}}y \le \frac{\gamma^2}{1-\nu} \cdot y^{\mathsf{T}}y
$$

and

$$
y^{\mathsf{T}}\widehat{S}y = y^{\mathsf{T}}(I - \widehat{E}^{\mathsf{T}}\widehat{E})y \ge \left(1 - \frac{\gamma^2}{1-\nu}\right)y^{\mathsf{T}}y,
$$

or equivalently,

$$
\|\widehat{E}\|_2 \le \frac{\gamma}{\sqrt{1-\nu}}, \quad \|\widehat{S}^{-1}\|_2 \le \frac{1-\nu}{1-\nu-\gamma^2}. \tag{8.114}
$$

In addition, noticing that (8.110) implies that

$$
\|I - J_B\|_2 \le \nu_B \le \nu \quad \text{and} \quad \|I - J_C\|_2 \le \nu_C \le \nu, \tag{8.115}
$$

and

$$
\gamma < \frac{1}{2}\sqrt{1-\nu}\left(\sqrt{\nu^2+4} - \nu\right)
$$

implies that

$$
\|\widehat{S}^{-1}\|_2\|\widehat{E}\|_2\|I - J_B\|_2 < 1,
$$

we therefore have

$$
\begin{aligned}
\frac{z^{\mathsf{T}}Hz}{z^{\mathsf{T}}\widehat{G}z} &\ge 1 - \frac{\frac{1-\nu}{1-\nu-\gamma^2} \cdot \left(1 + \frac{\gamma^2}{1-\nu}\right)}{1 - \frac{1-\nu}{1-\nu-\gamma^2} \cdot \frac{\gamma}{\sqrt{1-\nu}} \cdot \nu} \cdot \max\{\nu_B, \nu_C\} \\
&\ge 1 - \frac{(1-\nu+\gamma^2)\nu}{1-\nu-\gamma\nu\sqrt{1-\nu}-\gamma^2} \\
&> 0
\end{aligned}
$$

when $\nu \in (0, 1)$ satisfies $\gamma < \Gamma(\nu)$. Consequently,

$$
\kappa(\widehat{G}^{-1}H) \le \frac{1-\nu-\gamma\nu\sqrt{1-\nu}-\gamma^2}{(1-\nu)^2 - \gamma\nu\sqrt{1-\nu} - (1+\nu)\gamma^2} = \sigma(\nu,\gamma)
$$

and

$$
\kappa(M^{-1}A) = \kappa(G^{-1}H) \le \kappa(G^{-1}\widehat{G}) \cdot \kappa(\widehat{G}^{-1}H) \le \sigma(\nu,\gamma) \cdot \kappa(G^{-1}\widehat{G}).
$$

Now, from Theorem 7.4 (see also [42, Theorem 2.1]) we know that the iteration sequence $\{z^{(k)}\}_{k=0}^{\infty} \subset \mathbb{R}^{n+m}$ generated by the RPCG method satisfies

$$\|z^{(k)} - z_*\|_A \leq 2 \left(\frac{\sqrt{\kappa(M^{-1}A)} - 1}{\sqrt{\kappa(M^{-1}A)} + 1} \right)^k \|z^{(0)} - z_*\|_A$$

$$\leq 2 \left(\frac{\sqrt{\sigma(\nu, \gamma) \cdot \kappa(G^{-1}\widehat{G})} - 1}{\sqrt{\sigma(\nu, \gamma) \cdot \kappa(G^{-1}\widehat{G})} + 1} \right)^k \|z^{(0)} - z_*\|_A. \qquad \square$$

By particularly choosing the matrix $G \in \mathbb{R}^{(n+m) \times (n+m)}$ to be the **block Jacobi** (BJ) and the **block symmetric Gauss–Seidel** (BSGS) approximations of the matrix $\widehat{G} \in \mathbb{R}^{(n+m) \times (n+m)}$ in (8.107), we can obtain two special versions of the practical RPCG method defined as Algorithm 8.4. These two methods are called the **block Jacobi–type RPCG** (BJRPCG) method and the **block symmetric Gauss–Seidel–type RPCG** (BSGSRPCG) method, respectively, and are described precisely in the following.

8.5.3.1 ▪ BJRPCG Method

If the matrix $G \in \mathbb{R}^{(n+m) \times (n+m)}$ is taken to be the block Jacobi splitting matrix of the matrix $\widehat{G} \in \mathbb{R}^{(n+m) \times (n+m)}$ in (8.107), i.e.,

$$G = \begin{bmatrix} I & 0 \\ 0 & \widehat{S} \end{bmatrix}, \tag{8.116}$$

then from Algorithm 8.4 we can obtain the BJRPCG method for solving the block two-by-two SPD linear system (8.103).

Let

$$\widetilde{B} = L_B L_B^{\mathsf{T}} \approx B \quad \text{and} \quad \widetilde{S} = L_C \widehat{S} L_C^{\mathsf{T}} \approx S = C - E^{\mathsf{T}} B^{-1} E.$$

Then the **BJRPCG method** can be algorithmically described as follows.

Algorithm 8.5: BJRPCG Method for Problem (8.103)

1: Choose $z^{(0)} \in \mathbb{R}^{n+m}$, $r_0 = b - Az^{(0)}$

2: let $r_0 = \left[r_0^{(1)^{\mathsf{T}}}, r_0^{(2)^{\mathsf{T}}} \right]^{\mathsf{T}}$

3: solve $\widetilde{B} t^{(1)} = r_0^{(1)}$

4: solve $\widetilde{S} u_0^{(2)} = r_0^{(2)} - E^{\mathsf{T}} t^{(1)}$

5: solve $\widetilde{B} \tilde{t}^{(1)} = E u_0^{(2)}$

6: compute $u_0^{(1)} = t^{(1)} - \tilde{t}^{(1)}$

7: let $u_0 = \left[u_0^{(1)^{\mathsf{T}}}, u_0^{(2)^{\mathsf{T}}} \right]^{\mathsf{T}}$

8: set $p_0 = u_0$

9: **for** $k = 0, 1, 2, \ldots,$ **do**

10: $\qquad \alpha_k = -\dfrac{u_k^{\mathsf{T}} r_k}{p_k^{\mathsf{T}} A p_k}$

11: $\qquad z^{(k+1)} = z^{(k)} - \alpha_k p_k$

12:    $r_{k+1} = r_k + \alpha_k A p_k$

13:    let $r_{k+1} = \left[r_{k+1}^{(1)^{\mathsf{T}}}, r_{k+1}^{(2)^{\mathsf{T}}} \right]^{\mathsf{T}}$

14:    solve $\widetilde{B} t^{(1)} = r_{k+1}^{(1)}$

15:    solve $\widetilde{S} u_{k+1}^{(2)} = r_{k+1}^{(2)} - E^{\mathsf{T}} t^{(1)}$

16:    solve $\widetilde{B} \tilde{t}^{(1)} = E u_{k+1}^{(2)}$

17:    compute $u_{k+1}^{(1)} = t^{(1)} - \tilde{t}^{(1)}$

18:    let $u_{k+1} = \left[u_{k+1}^{(1)^{\mathsf{T}}}, u_{k+1}^{(2)^{\mathsf{T}}} \right]^{\mathsf{T}}$

19:    $\beta_k = \dfrac{u_{k+1}^{\mathsf{T}} r_{k+1}}{u_k^{\mathsf{T}} r_k}$

20:    $p_{k+1} = u_{k+1} + \beta_k p_k$
21: **end for**

Evidently, the only difference between Algorithm 8.5 and Algorithm 8.3 is that the former involves only an approximation matrix $\widetilde{B}$ of the matrix B, while the latter involves the matrix block B itself. Therefore, Algorithm 8.5 allows approximate inversion of the matrix block B at each iteration. Also, we note that, at each of its iteration steps, the BJRPCG method requires solutions of two subsystems of linear equations with the coefficient matrix $\widetilde{B} \in \mathbb{R}^{n \times n}$ and one subsystem of linear equations with the coefficient matrix $\widetilde{S} \in \mathbb{R}^{m \times m}$.

Based on Theorem 8.30, we can demonstrate the following convergence theorem for Algorithm 8.5.

Theorem 8.31. *Let the conditions of Theorem 8.30 be satisfied. Then the iteration sequence* $\{z^{(k)}\}_{k=0}^{\infty} \subset \mathbb{R}^{n+m}$ *generated by Algorithm 8.5 satisfies*

$$\| z^{(k)} - z_* \|_A \leq 2 \left(\frac{\sqrt{\delta(\nu, \gamma)} - 1}{\sqrt{\delta(\nu, \gamma)} + 1} \right)^k \| z^{(0)} - z_* \|_A,$$

provided $\nu \in (0, 1)$ *is such that* $\gamma < \Gamma(\nu)$, *where*

$$\Gamma(\nu) = \frac{\sqrt{1 - \nu} \left(\sqrt{4 - 3\nu^2} - \nu \right)}{2(1 + \nu)}$$

and

$$\delta(\nu, \gamma) = \frac{1 - \nu + \gamma\nu\sqrt{1 - \nu} - \gamma^2}{(1 - \nu)^2 - \gamma\nu\sqrt{1 - \nu} - (1 + \nu)\gamma^2}.$$

Proof. We first derive bounds for $\kappa(G^{-1}\widehat{G})$. From (8.107) we have

$$\widehat{G} = G + \begin{bmatrix} 0 & (I - J_B)\widehat{E} \\ \widehat{E}^{\mathsf{T}}(I - J_B) & 0 \end{bmatrix}$$

and, hence,

$$G^{-1}\widehat{G} = I + G^{-1} \begin{bmatrix} 0 & (I - J_B)\widehat{E} \\ \widehat{E}^{\mathsf{T}}(I - J_B) & 0 \end{bmatrix}.$$

It then follows that, for any $z \in \mathbb{R}^{n+m} \setminus \{0\}$,

$$
\begin{aligned}
\frac{z^{\mathsf{T}} \widehat{G} z}{z^{\mathsf{T}} G z} &\leq 1 + \|G^{-1}\|_2 \|(I - J_B) \widehat{E}\|_2 \\
&\leq 1 + \|\widehat{S}^{-1}\|_2 \|\widehat{E}\|_2 \|I - J_B\|_2 \\
&\leq 1 + \frac{\gamma \nu \sqrt{1 - \nu}}{1 - \nu - \gamma^2}
\end{aligned}
$$

and

$$
\begin{aligned}
\frac{z^{\mathsf{T}} \widehat{G} z}{z^{\mathsf{T}} G z} &\geq 1 - \|G^{-1}\|_2 \|(I - J_B) \widehat{E}\|_2 \\
&\geq 1 - \|\widehat{S}^{-1}\|_2 \|\widehat{E}\|_2 \|I - J_B\|_2 \\
&\geq 1 - \frac{\gamma \nu \sqrt{1 - \nu}}{1 - \nu - \gamma^2}.
\end{aligned}
$$

Here we have applied the estimates (8.114) and (8.115). Therefore, it holds that

$$
\kappa(G^{-1} \widehat{G}) \leq \frac{1 - \nu + \gamma \nu \sqrt{1 - \nu} - \gamma^2}{1 - \nu - \gamma \nu \sqrt{1 - \nu} - \gamma^2}.
$$

By substituting this estimate into the bound (8.111) in Theorem 8.30, we straightforwardly get the conclusion of Theorem 8.31.   □

8.5.3.2 ▪ BSGSRPCG Method

If the matrix $G \in \mathbb{R}^{(n+m) \times (n+m)}$ is taken to be the block symmetric Gauss–Seidel splitting matrix of the matrix $\widehat{G} \in \mathbb{R}^{(n+m) \times (n+m)}$ in (8.107), i.e.,

$$
G = \begin{bmatrix} I & (I - J_B)\widehat{E} \\ 0 & \widehat{S} \end{bmatrix} \begin{bmatrix} I & 0 \\ 0 & \widehat{S} \end{bmatrix}^{-1} \begin{bmatrix} I & 0 \\ \widehat{E}^{\mathsf{T}}(I - J_B) & \widehat{S} \end{bmatrix}, \tag{8.117}
$$

then from Algorithm 8.4 we can obtain the BSGSRPCG method for solving the block two-by-two SPD linear system (8.103).

Let

$$
\widetilde{B} = L_B L_B^{\mathsf{T}} \approx B \quad \text{and} \quad \widetilde{S} = L_C \widehat{S} L_C^{\mathsf{T}} \approx S = C - E^{\mathsf{T}} B^{-1} E.
$$

Then the **BSGSRPCG method** can be algorithmically described as follows.

Algorithm 8.6: BSGSRPCG Method for Problem (8.103)

1: Choose $z^{(0)} \in \mathbb{R}^{n+m}$, $r_0 = b - A z^{(0)}$

2: let $r_0 = \left[r_0^{(1)\mathsf{T}}, r_0^{(2)\mathsf{T}} \right]^{\mathsf{T}}$

3: solve $\widetilde{B} t^{(1)} = r_0^{(1)}$

4: solve $\widetilde{S} t^{(2)} = r_0^{(2)} - E^{\mathsf{T}} t^{(1)}$

5: solve $\widetilde{B} \widetilde{t}^{(1)} = E t^{(2)}$

6: solve $\widetilde{B} \widehat{t}^{(1)} = r_0^{(1)} + B \widetilde{t}^{(1)}$

7: compute $\widecheck{t}^{(1)} = \widehat{t}^{(1)} - \widetilde{t}^{(1)}$

8: solve $\widetilde{B} t^{(1)} = B \widecheck{t}^{(1)}$

9: solve $\widetilde{S}\tilde{t}^{(2)} = E^\mathsf{T}(\check{t}^{(1)} - t^{(1)})$

10: compute $u_0^{(2)} = t^{(2)} - \tilde{t}^{(2)}$

11: solve $\widetilde{B}\hat{t}^{(1)} = Eu_0^{(2)}$

12: compute $u_0^{(1)} = \check{t}^{(1)} - \hat{t}^{(1)}$

13: let $u_0 = \left[u_0^{(1)^\mathsf{T}}, u_0^{(2)^\mathsf{T}}\right]^\mathsf{T}$

14: set $p_0 = u_0$

15: **for** $k = 0, 1, 2, \ldots,$ **do**

16: $\quad \alpha_k = -\dfrac{u_k^\mathsf{T} r_k}{p_k^\mathsf{T} A p_k}$

17: $\quad z^{(k+1)} = z^{(k)} - \alpha_k p_k$

18: $\quad r_{k+1} = r_k + \alpha_k A p_k$

19: $\quad$ let $r_{k+1} = \left[r_{k+1}^{(1)^\mathsf{T}}, r_{k+1}^{(2)^\mathsf{T}}\right]^\mathsf{T}$

20: $\quad$ solve $\widetilde{B} t^{(1)} = r_{k+1}^{(1)}$

21: $\quad$ solve $\widetilde{S} t^{(2)} = r_{k+1}^{(2)} - E^\mathsf{T} t^{(1)}$

22: $\quad$ solve $\widetilde{B}\tilde{t}^{(1)} = E t^{(2)}$

23: $\quad$ solve $\widetilde{B}\hat{t}^{(1)} = r_{k+1}^{(1)} + B\tilde{t}^{(1)}$

24: $\quad$ compute $\check{t}^{(1)} = \hat{t}^{(1)} - \tilde{t}^{(1)}$

25: $\quad$ solve $\widetilde{B} t^{(1)} = B\check{t}^{(1)}$

26: $\quad$ solve $\widetilde{S}\tilde{t}^{(2)} = E^\mathsf{T}(\check{t}^{(1)} - t^{(1)})$

27: $\quad$ compute $u_{k+1}^{(2)} = t^{(2)} - \tilde{t}^{(2)}$

28: $\quad$ solve $\widetilde{B}\hat{t}^{(1)} = Eu_{k+1}^{(2)}$

29: $\quad$ compute $u_{k+1}^{(1)} = \check{t}^{(1)} - \hat{t}^{(1)}$

30: $\quad$ let $u_{k+1} = \left[u_{k+1}^{(1)^\mathsf{T}}, u_{k+1}^{(2)^\mathsf{T}}\right]^\mathsf{T}$

31: $\quad \beta_k = \dfrac{u_{k+1}^\mathsf{T} r_{k+1}}{u_k^\mathsf{T} r_k}$

32: $\quad p_{k+1} = u_{k+1} + \beta_k p_k$

33: **end for**

Clearly, at each of its iteration steps, the BSGSRPCG method requires solutions of five subsystems of linear equations with the coefficient matrix $\widetilde{B} \in \mathbb{R}^{n \times n}$ and two subsystems of linear equations with the coefficient matrix $\widetilde{S} \in \mathbb{R}^{m \times m}$. Therefore, its computing cost is about twice that of the BJRPCG method. However, from the convergence theorem established below we can see that the BSGSRPCG method is indeed faster than the BJRPCG method in terms of the upper bound of the convergence factor.

Theorem 8.32. *Let the conditions of Theorem 8.30 be satisfied. Then the iteration sequence* $\{z^{(k)}\}_{k=0}^\infty \subset \mathbb{R}^{n+m}$ *generated by Algorithm 8.6 satisfies*

$$\|z^{(k)} - z_*\|_A \leq 2\left(\frac{\sqrt{\delta(\nu, \gamma)} - 1}{\sqrt{\delta(\nu, \gamma)} + 1}\right)^k \|z^{(k)} - z_*\|_A,$$

provided $\nu \in (0, 1)$ *is such that* $\gamma < \Gamma(\nu)$, *where*

$$\Gamma(\nu) = \frac{\sqrt{1 - \nu}\left(\sqrt{4 - 3\nu^2} - \nu\right)}{2(1 + \nu)}.$$

and

$$\delta(\nu, \gamma) = \frac{(1-\nu)\nu^2\gamma^2 + (1-\nu-\gamma^2)\left(1-\nu-\gamma\nu\sqrt{1-\nu}-\gamma^2\right)}{\left[(1-\nu)^2 - \gamma\nu\sqrt{1-\nu} - (1+\nu)\gamma^2\right](1-\nu-\gamma^2)}.$$

Proof. We first derive bounds for $\kappa(G^{-1}\widehat{G})$. From (8.107) we have

$$G = \widehat{G} + \left[\begin{array}{cc} (I-J_B)\widehat{E}\widehat{S}^{-1}\widehat{E}^{\mathsf{T}}(I-J_B) & 0 \\ 0 & 0 \end{array}\right].$$

Hence, by making use of (8.108) and Theorem 8.30 (i) we can immediately obtain that, for all $z \in \mathbb{R}^{n+m}$,

$$z^{\mathsf{T}}Gz \geq z^{\mathsf{T}}\widehat{G}z,$$

or equivalently,

$$\frac{z^{\mathsf{T}}\widehat{G}z}{z^{\mathsf{T}}Gz} \leq 1, \quad \forall\, z \in \mathbb{R}^{n+m} \setminus \{0\}.$$

In addition, it holds that, for any $z \in \mathbb{R}^{n+m} \setminus \{0\}$,

$$\begin{aligned}
\frac{z^{\mathsf{T}}Gz}{z^{\mathsf{T}}\widehat{G}z} &\leq \max_{z\neq 0} \frac{z^{\mathsf{T}}Gz}{z^{\mathsf{T}}\widehat{G}z} \leq \|\widehat{G}^{-1}G\|_2 \\
&\leq 1 + \|\widehat{G}^{-1}\|_2\|(I-J_B)\widehat{E}\widehat{S}^{-1}\widehat{E}^{\mathsf{T}}(I-J_B)\|_2 \\
&\leq 1 + \|\widehat{G}^{-1}\|_2\|\widehat{E}\|_2^2\|\widehat{S}^{-1}\|_2\|I-J_B\|_2^2.
\end{aligned}$$

By applying the estimates (8.113), (8.114), and (8.115) to this inequality, we can further obtain

$$\begin{aligned}
\frac{z^{\mathsf{T}}Gz}{z^{\mathsf{T}}\widehat{G}z} &\leq 1 + \frac{\|\widehat{S}^{-1}\|_2^2\|\widehat{E}\|_2^2\|I-J_B\|_2^2}{1 - \|\widehat{S}^{-1}\|_2\|\widehat{E}\|_2\|I-J_B\|_2} \\
&\leq 1 + \frac{(1-\nu)\nu^2\gamma^2}{(1-\nu-\gamma^2)(1-\nu-\gamma\nu\sqrt{1-\nu}-\gamma^2)}.
\end{aligned}$$

Therefore, it holds that

$$\kappa(G^{-1}\widehat{G}) \leq \frac{(1-\nu)\nu^2\gamma^2 + (1-\nu-\gamma^2)(1-\nu-\gamma\nu\sqrt{1-\nu}-\gamma^2)}{(1-\nu-\gamma^2)(1-\nu-\gamma\nu\sqrt{1-\nu}-\gamma^2)}.$$

By substituting this estimate into the bound (8.111) in Theorem 8.30, we straightforwardly get the conclusion of Theorem 8.32.   □

Theorems 8.31 and 8.32 show that the effectiveness of the BJRPCG and BSGSRPCG methods depends on the property of the original problem and the quality of the approximation matrix as well. Therefore, which of these two methods is more effective in actual applications needs to be further examined by numerical experiments for the target problems.

Instead of the block Jacobi and the block symmetric Gauss–Seidel splitting matrices defined in (8.116) and (8.117), we can approximate the matrix $\widehat{G}$ in (8.107) by the modified block Jacobi and the modified block symmetric Gauss–Seidel splitting matrices and obtain the approximation matrix G, i.e., we can take G to be of the same form as (8.116) or (8.117) but replace $\widehat{S}$ by its approximation (for simplicity of notation, it is still denoted by $\widehat{S}$). This therefore leads to variants of the BJRPCG method and the BSGSRPCG method, which allow more flexible choices of the approximate Schur complement $\widetilde{S}$. Convergence theorems of these two variants can be easily established similarly to Theorems 8.31 and 8.32.

Now, we turn to discuss typical choices of the matrices L_B and L_C, or in other words, the matrices $\widetilde{B}$, $\widetilde{C}$, and $\widetilde{S}$, where $\widetilde{C} = L_C L_C^\mathsf{T} \approx C$.

Recalling that we have represented

$$\widetilde{B} = L_B L_B^\mathsf{T} \approx B, \quad \widetilde{S} = (\text{ or } \approx) L_C \widehat{S} L_C^\mathsf{T} \approx S = C - E^\mathsf{T} B^{-1} E,$$

let $M_B \in \mathbb{R}^{n \times n}$ be a symmetric positive definite matrix obtained possibly through *incomplete Cholesky* (IC) factorizations, splitting iterations (e.g., Jacobi, *symmetric Gauss–Seidel* (SGS), or *symmetric successive overrelaxation* (SSOR), etc.), or multigrid/multilevel approximations, etc., of the matrix block $B \in \mathbb{R}^{n \times n}$. Without loss of generality, we assume that Condition (8.108) is automatically satisfied, i.e.,

$$\frac{x^\mathsf{T} B x}{x^\mathsf{T} M_B x} \leq 1, \quad \forall\, x \in \mathbb{R}^n \setminus \{0\}.$$

Otherwise, we can turn to consider the shifted matrix

$$M_B := M_B + \beta I, \quad \text{with } \beta > 0 \text{ a constant,}$$

instead; see, e.g., [9]. In addition, we assume that the matrix splitting

$$B = M_B - N_B, \quad \text{with} \quad N_B = M_B - B,$$

is convergent, i.e., the spectral radius of the matrix $M_B^{-1} N_B$, denoted by $\rho(M_B^{-1} N_B)$, is less than 1. If such a matrix M_B further satisfies Condition (8.110), i.e.,

$$\min_{x \neq 0} \frac{x^\mathsf{T} B x}{x^\mathsf{T} M_B x} \geq 1 - \nu,$$

for a $\nu \in (0, 1)$ such that $\gamma < \Gamma(\nu)$, then we can take $\widetilde{B} = M_B$. Otherwise, we take

$$\widetilde{B} = B \left[I - \left(M_B^{-1} N_B \right)^{k_B} \right]^{-1} = M_B \left[\sum_{j=0}^{k_B - 1} \left(M_B^{-1} N_B \right)^j \right]^{-1},$$

where k_B is a positive integer such that

$$k_B > \frac{\ln(\nu)}{\ln\left(\rho(M_B^{-1} N_B) \right)}.$$

Such a matrix $\widetilde{B}$ will be symmetric positive definite and satisfy

$$\min_{x \neq 0} \frac{x^\mathsf{T} B x}{x^\mathsf{T} \widetilde{B} x} \geq 1 - \nu, \tag{8.118}$$

or Condition (8.110).

In fact, $\widetilde{B}$ is evidently symmetric, since

$$\widetilde{B}^\mathsf{T} = \left[\sum_{j=0}^{k_B - 1} \left(N_B M_B^{-1} \right)^j \right]^{-1} M_B = M_B \left[\sum_{j=0}^{k_B - 1} \left(M_B^{-1} N_B \right)^j \right]^{-1} = \widetilde{B}.$$

It is also positive definite, since the smallest eigenvalue of the matrix

$$
M_B^{-\frac{1}{2}} \widetilde{B} M_B^{-\frac{1}{2}} = M_B^{\frac{1}{2}} \left[\sum_{j=0}^{k_B-1} \left(M_B^{-1} N_B \right)^j \right]^{-1} M_B^{-\frac{1}{2}}
$$

$$
= \left(I - M_B^{-\frac{1}{2}} N_B M_B^{-\frac{1}{2}} \right) \left[I - \left(M_B^{-\frac{1}{2}} N_B M_B^{-\frac{1}{2}} \right)^{k_B} \right]^{-1}
$$

is bounded from below by the positive constant $\dfrac{1 - \rho(M_B^{-1} N_B)}{1 - [\rho(M_B^{-1} N_B)]^{k_B}}$. Moreover, $\widetilde{B}$ satisfies (8.118), since

$$
\max_{x \neq 0} \frac{x^{\mathsf{T}} \widetilde{B} x}{x^{\mathsf{T}} B x} = \rho(B^{-1} \widetilde{B}) = \rho([I - (M_B^{-1} N_B)^{k_B}]^{-1})
$$

$$
\leq \left[1 - \rho(M_B^{-1} N_B)^{k_B} \right]^{-1} := (1 - \nu)^{-1},
$$

with

$$
\nu = \rho(M_B^{-1} N_B)^{k_B}.
$$

The choice of the matrix $\widetilde{C}$ can be discussed in an analogous fashion.

According to the matrix $\widetilde{S} \in \mathbb{R}^{m \times m}$, we therefore have the following two typical choices:

(a) $\widetilde{S} = \widetilde{C}$;

(b) $\widetilde{S} = \widetilde{C} - E^{\mathsf{T}} \widetilde{K} E$, and $\widetilde{K} \in \mathbb{R}^{n \times n}$ is a sparse approximation to the matrix $\widetilde{B}^{-1}$.

Correspondingly, we obtain two practical versions of the BJRPCG method and the BSGSR-PCG method, denoted, respectively, by BJRPCG(a), BJRPCG(b) and BSGSRPCG(a), BSGSR-PCG(b).

8.6 ▪ Exercises

8.1. Let $B \in \mathbb{C}^{n \times n}, E \in \mathbb{C}^{n \times m}, F \in \mathbb{C}^{m \times n}$, and $C \in \mathbb{C}^{m \times m}$. Assume that the matrices B and C are nonsingular. Show that

$$
\begin{bmatrix} B & E \\ 0 & C \end{bmatrix}^{-1} = \begin{bmatrix} B^{-1} & -B^{-1} E C^{-1} \\ 0 & C^{-1} \end{bmatrix},
$$

$$
\begin{bmatrix} B & 0 \\ F & C \end{bmatrix}^{-1} = \begin{bmatrix} B^{-1} & 0 \\ -C^{-1} F B^{-1} & C^{-1} \end{bmatrix},
$$

$$
\begin{bmatrix} 0 & B \\ C & F \end{bmatrix}^{-1} = \begin{bmatrix} -C^{-1} F B^{-1} & C^{-1} \\ B^{-1} & 0 \end{bmatrix},
$$

$$
\begin{bmatrix} E & B \\ C & 0 \end{bmatrix}^{-1} = \begin{bmatrix} 0 & C^{-1} \\ B^{-1} & -B^{-1} E C^{-1} \end{bmatrix}.
$$

8.2. Prove the matrix equality (8.5).

8.3. Prove Theorem 8.5.

8.4. Prove the matrix equality (8.7).

8.5. Prove Theorems 8.12 and 8.13.

8.6. For $\alpha, \beta \in \mathbb{C}$, consider the matrices

$$A_{\alpha,\beta}^{+} = \begin{bmatrix} \alpha I & E \\ E^* & \beta I \end{bmatrix} \quad \text{and} \quad A_{\alpha,\beta}^{-} = \begin{bmatrix} \alpha I & E \\ -E^* & \beta I \end{bmatrix},$$

where $E \in \mathbb{C}^{n \times m}$. Give the analytic formulas, counting the multiplicity if there is any, for all eigenvalues of these two matrices.

(Hint: use the singular value decomposition of the matrix E.)

8.7. Let

$$A = \begin{bmatrix} B & E \\ E^{\mathsf{T}} & 0 \end{bmatrix} \quad \text{and} \quad H_B = \frac{1}{2}(B + B^{\mathsf{T}}).$$

Denote by Z the matrix whose columns span the null space of the matrix E^{T}. Then the matrix $Z^{\mathsf{T}} B Z$ is nonsingular if $\mathrm{Ker}(H_B) \cap \mathrm{Ker}(E^{\mathsf{T}}) = \{0\}$.

8.8. For the generalized saddle-point matrix

$$\tilde{A} = \begin{bmatrix} B & E \\ -E^{\mathsf{T}} & C \end{bmatrix},$$

let $S = C + E^{\mathsf{T}} B^{-1} E$ be its Schur complement. If the submatrix $B \in \mathbb{R}^{n \times n}$ is nonsingular, then it holds that

$$\begin{aligned} \tilde{A} &= \begin{bmatrix} B & 0 \\ -E^{\mathsf{T}} & S \end{bmatrix} \begin{bmatrix} I & B^{-1}E \\ 0 & I \end{bmatrix} \\ &= \begin{bmatrix} I & 0 \\ -E^{\mathsf{T}}B^{-1} & I \end{bmatrix} \begin{bmatrix} B & E \\ 0 & S \end{bmatrix} \\ &= \begin{bmatrix} I & 0 \\ -E^{\mathsf{T}}B^{-1} & I \end{bmatrix} \begin{bmatrix} B & 0 \\ 0 & S \end{bmatrix} \begin{bmatrix} I & B^{-1}E \\ 0 & I \end{bmatrix}. \end{aligned}$$

8.9. Prove the following conclusion; see [53, 57]. Let ζ and η be two complex constants. Then all roots of the complex **quadratic polynomial equation**

$$\lambda^2 + \zeta\lambda + \eta = 0$$

have modulus less than 1 if and only if

$$|\zeta - \bar{\zeta}\eta| + |\eta|^2 < 1. \tag{8.119}$$

In particular, if both ζ and η are real constants, then the condition (8.119) reduces to

$$|\eta| < 1 \quad \text{and} \quad |\zeta| < 1 + \eta.$$

(Hint: use the property of the **Schur polynomial**; see [54].)

8.10. Prove the following conclusion; see [54]. Let ζ, η, and ϵ be three complex constants. Then all roots of the complex **cubic polynomial equation**

$$\lambda^3 + \zeta\lambda^2 + \eta\lambda + \epsilon = 0$$

have modulus less than 1 if and only if

$$|\epsilon| < 1 \tag{8.120}$$

and

$$\left| (1 - |\epsilon|^2)(\zeta - \epsilon\bar{\eta}) - (\bar{\zeta} - \bar{\epsilon}\eta)(\eta - \epsilon\bar{\zeta}) \right| + \left| \eta - \epsilon\bar{\zeta} \right|^2 < (1 - |\epsilon|^2)^2. \tag{8.121}$$

In particular, if ζ, η, and ϵ are real constants, then the conditions (8.120) and (8.121) reduce to

$$|\epsilon| < 1, \quad |\zeta + \epsilon| < 1 + \eta \quad \text{and} \quad 1 - \eta + (\zeta - \epsilon)\epsilon > 0.$$

See [54].

(Hint: use the property of the **Schur polynomial**; see [54].)

8.11. Let

$$M = \begin{bmatrix} D & E^\mathsf{T} \\ E & -C \end{bmatrix}, \quad \text{with} \quad D \in \mathbb{R}^{n \times n}, \ C \in \mathbb{R}^{m \times m},$$

where D is a symmetric positive definite matrix. Denote by

$$M^{-1} = \begin{bmatrix} X & Y^\mathsf{T} \\ Y & Z \end{bmatrix}, \quad \text{with} \quad X \in \mathbb{R}^{n \times n}, \ Z \in \mathbb{R}^{m \times m}.$$

If λ is an eigenvalue of the matrix $D^{\frac{1}{2}} X D^{\frac{1}{2}}$, then $\lambda \in [0, 1]$.

(Hint: see [169].)

8.12. Let $\alpha, \beta \in \mathbb{R}$, and $S \in \mathbb{R}^{n \times n}$ be a skew-symmetric matrix. Prove the following statements:

(1) the matrix $\alpha I + \beta S$ is normal, and $\|\alpha I + \beta S\|_2 = \rho(\alpha I + \beta S)$.

(2) If n is even, the eigenvalues of the matrix $\alpha I + \beta S$ are $\alpha \pm \mathrm{i}\beta\theta_j$, $j = 1, 2, \ldots, \frac{n}{2}$, where $\pm\mathrm{i}\theta_j$, $j = 1, 2, \ldots, \frac{n}{2}$, are the eigenvalues of the matrix S; if n is odd, there is an additional eigenvalue α corresponding to the zero eigenvalue of the matrix S.

(3) If $D \in \mathbb{R}^{n \times n}$ is a diagonal matrix with entries $d_i \in (0, 1]$, $i = 1, 2, \ldots, n$, the eigenvalues $\xi + \mathrm{i}\,\eta$ of the matrix $D(\alpha I + \beta S)$ satisfy $\xi \in (0, \alpha]$ for $\alpha > 0$, $\xi \in [\alpha, 0)$ for $\alpha < 0$; and $|\eta| \le |\beta| |\lambda_{\max}(S)|$.

(Hint: see [169].)

8.13. Let α, β be two positive parameters and

$$\mathcal{Q}(\alpha, \beta) = (\Theta + S)^{-1}(\Theta - S),$$

where

$$\Theta = \begin{bmatrix} \alpha I_n & 0 \\ 0 & \beta I_m \end{bmatrix} \quad \text{and} \quad S = \begin{bmatrix} 0 & E \\ -E^* & 0 \end{bmatrix},$$

with $E \in \mathbb{C}^{n \times m}$. Prove the following statements:

(1) the matrix $\mathcal{Q}(\alpha, \beta)$ is a **Cayley transform** if and only if $\alpha = \beta$;
(Hint: consider the matrix equation $\mathcal{Q}(\alpha, \beta)^* \mathcal{Q}(\alpha, \beta) = I$.)

(2) $\|\mathcal{Q}(\alpha, \beta)\|_2 = \sqrt{1 + 2\delta \left(\delta + \sqrt{1 + \delta^2} \right)}$, where

$$\delta = \frac{|\alpha - \beta|}{\alpha\beta + \sigma_{\min}^2},$$

with $\sigma_{\min}$ being the smallest positive singular value of the matrix E;

(3) the **Cayley transform** $\mathcal{Q}(\alpha) := \mathcal{Q}(\alpha, \alpha)$ is the solution of the minimization problem

$$\min_{\alpha, \beta > 0} \|\mathcal{Q}(\alpha, \beta)\|_2.$$

8.14. Prove that the block two-by-two matrix $\tilde{M}'(\alpha, \beta)$ in (8.75) is positive definite.

8.15. Prove Statement (ii) in Theorem 8.21.

8.16. Let

$$\hat{A} = \begin{bmatrix} I & \hat{E} \\ -\hat{E}^* & 0 \end{bmatrix} \in \mathbb{C}^{(n+m) \times (n+m)},$$

where $\hat{E} \in \mathbb{C}^{n \times m}$ is of full column rank. Let $\hat{W} \in \mathbb{C}^{n \times n}$ and $\hat{Z} \in \mathbb{C}^{m \times m}$ be nonsingular matrices such that $\hat{W}^* \hat{W} = I_n$, and indicate by $\hat{\sigma}_1, \hat{\sigma}_2, \ldots, \hat{\sigma}_m$ the singular values of the matrix $\hat{W}^* \hat{E} \hat{Z}$. Denote by $\hat{G}(\alpha)$ the PHSS iteration matrix corresponding to the standard saddle-point matrix $\hat{A}$, with the iteration parameter being $\alpha > 0$. Prove the following statements:

(i) the eigenvalues of the PHSS iteration matrix $\hat{G}(\alpha)$ are $\frac{\alpha-1}{\alpha+1}$ with multiplicity $n-m$, and

$$\frac{1}{(\alpha+1)(\alpha^2+\hat{\sigma}_k^2)} \left(\alpha(\alpha^2 - \hat{\sigma}_k^2) \pm \sqrt{(\alpha^2+\hat{\sigma}_k^2)^2 - 4\alpha^4\hat{\sigma}_k^2} \right), \quad k = 1, 2, \ldots, m;$$

(ii) if λ is an eigenvalue of the PHSS iteration matrix $\hat{G}(\alpha)$, then, for $k = 1, 2, \ldots, m$, it holds that

$$|\lambda| = \begin{cases} \frac{|\alpha-1|}{\alpha+1}, & \text{or} \\ \sqrt{\frac{\alpha-1}{\alpha+1}}, & \text{for } \alpha^2 + \hat{\sigma}_k^2 \leq 2\alpha^2\hat{\sigma}_k, \quad \text{or} \\ \frac{\alpha}{\alpha+1} \left| \frac{|\alpha^2-\hat{\sigma}_k^2|}{\alpha^2+\hat{\sigma}_k^2} \pm \sqrt{\frac{1}{\alpha^2} - \frac{4\alpha^2\hat{\sigma}_k^2}{(\alpha^2+\hat{\sigma}_k^2)^2}} \right|, & \text{for } \alpha^2 + \hat{\sigma}_k^2 > 2\alpha^2\hat{\sigma}_k; \end{cases}$$

(iii) $\rho(\hat{G}(\alpha)) < 1, \forall \alpha > 0$.

8.17. Let

$$\hat{A} = \begin{bmatrix} I & \hat{E} \\ -\hat{E}^* & 0 \end{bmatrix} \in \mathbb{C}^{(n+m) \times (n+m)},$$

where $\hat{E} \in \mathbb{C}^{n \times m}$ is of full column rank. Let $\hat{W} \in \mathbb{C}^{n \times n}$ and $\hat{Z} \in \mathbb{C}^{m \times m}$ be nonsingular matrices such that $\hat{W}^* \hat{W} = I_n$, and indicate by $\hat{\sigma}_1, \hat{\sigma}_2, \ldots, \hat{\sigma}_m$ the singular values of the matrix $\hat{W}^* \hat{E} \hat{Z}$. Denote by $\hat{G}(\alpha, \beta)$ the PAHSS iteration matrix corresponding to the standard saddle-point matrix $\hat{A}$, with the iteration parameters being $\alpha, \beta > 0$. Prove the following statements:

(i) the eigenvalues of the PAHSS iteration matrix $\hat{G}(\alpha, \beta)$ are $\frac{\alpha-1}{\alpha+1}$ with multiplicity $n - m$, and

$$\frac{1}{(\alpha+1)(\alpha\beta+\hat{\sigma}_k^2)} \left(\alpha(\alpha\beta - \hat{\sigma}_k^2) \pm \sqrt{(\alpha\beta+\hat{\sigma}_k^2)^2 - 4\alpha^3\beta\hat{\sigma}_k^2} \right), \quad k = 1, 2, \ldots, m;$$

(ii) if λ is an eigenvalue of the PAHSS iteration matrix $\hat{G}(\alpha, \beta)$, then, for $k = 1, 2, \ldots,$ m, it holds that

$$|\lambda| = \begin{cases} \dfrac{|\alpha-1|}{\alpha+1}, & \text{or} \\[2mm] \sqrt{\dfrac{\alpha-1}{\alpha+1}}, & \text{for } \alpha\beta + \hat{\sigma}_k^2 \le 2\alpha\sqrt{\alpha\beta}\hat{\sigma}_k, \quad \text{or} \\[2mm] \dfrac{\alpha}{\alpha+1}\left| \dfrac{|\alpha\beta - \hat{\sigma}_k^2|}{\alpha\beta + \hat{\sigma}_k^2} \pm \sqrt{\dfrac{1}{\alpha^2} - \dfrac{4\alpha\beta\hat{\sigma}_k^2}{(\alpha\beta+\hat{\sigma}_k^2)^2}} \right|, & \text{for } \alpha\beta + \hat{\sigma}_k^2 > 2\alpha\sqrt{\alpha\beta}\hat{\sigma}_k; \end{cases}$$

(iii) $\rho(\hat{G}(\alpha, \beta)) < 1, \forall\, \alpha, \beta > 0$.

8.18. For $B \in \mathbb{C}^{n \times n}$ and $E \in \mathbb{C}^{n \times m}$, let

$$A = \begin{bmatrix} B & E \\ E^* & 0 \end{bmatrix}, \quad P_T = \begin{bmatrix} B & E \\ 0 & -S \end{bmatrix}, \quad \tilde{P}_T = \begin{bmatrix} B & E \\ 0 & S \end{bmatrix},$$

where $S = -E^* B^{-1} E$. Prove the following statements:

(i) $(P_T^{-1} A)^2 = I$, so the matrix $P_T^{-1} A$ is diagonalizable and has two distinct nonzero eigenvalues $\lambda = \pm 1$;

(ii) $(\tilde{P}_T^{-1} A - I)^2 = 0$, so the matrix $\tilde{P}_T^{-1} A$ is diagonalizable and has only one distinct eigenvalue $\lambda = 1$.

8.19. For $B \in \mathbb{C}^{n \times n}$ and $E \in \mathbb{C}^{n \times m}$, let

$$\tilde{A} = \begin{bmatrix} B & E \\ -E^* & 0 \end{bmatrix}, \quad P_T = \begin{bmatrix} B & E \\ 0 & -S \end{bmatrix}, \quad \tilde{P}_T = \begin{bmatrix} B & E \\ 0 & S \end{bmatrix},$$

where $S = E^* B^{-1} E$. Derive the minimal polynomials for the matrices $P_T^{-1}\tilde{A}$ and $\tilde{P}_T^{-1}\tilde{A}$.

8.20. For any positive integer k and complex numbers $c_1, c_2, \ldots, c_k$, let

$$p_k(t) = (t - c_k)\, p_{k-1}(t) = (t - c_k)(t - c_{k-1}) \cdots (t - c_1)$$

be a monic polynomial of degree k. Then, for the block three-by-three matrix

$$T = \begin{bmatrix} I & 0 & 0 \\ T_{21} & T_{22} & 0 \\ T_{31} & T_{32} & I \end{bmatrix}$$

of square diagonal blocks, it holds that

$$(T - I)\, p_k(T) = \begin{bmatrix} 0 & 0 & 0 \\ p_k(T_{22})\, T_{21} & (T_{22} - I)\, p_k(T_{22}) & 0 \\ T_{31}^{(k)} & T_{32}\, p_k(T_{22}) & 0 \end{bmatrix}$$

and

$$(T - I)^2\, p_k(T) = \begin{bmatrix} 0 & 0 & 0 \\ (T_{22} - I)\, p_k(T_{22})\, T_{21} & (T_{22} - I)^2\, p_k(T_{22}) & 0 \\ T_{32}\, p_k(T_{22})\, T_{21} & T_{32}(T_{22} - I)\, p_k(T_{22}) & 0 \end{bmatrix},$$

where

$$T_{31}^{(1)} = (1 - c_1) T_{31} + T_{32} T_{21},$$

and, for $k \ge 2$,

$$T_{31}^{(k)} = (1 - c_k) T_{31}^{(k-1)} + T_{32}\, p_{k-1}(T_{22})\, T_{21}.$$

(Hint: use induction on the positive integer k; see [90].)

8.21. For the block three-by-three matrix

$$T = \begin{bmatrix} I & 0 & 0 \\ T_{21} & I & 0 \\ T_{31} & T_{32} & I \end{bmatrix},$$

prove that

$$T^{-1} = \begin{bmatrix} I & 0 & 0 \\ -T_{21} & I & 0 \\ T_{32}T_{21} - T_{31} & -T_{32} & I \end{bmatrix}.$$

More generally, for the block m-by-m unit lower-triangular matrix

$$T = \begin{bmatrix} I & 0 & \cdots & 0 \\ T_{21} & I & \cdots & 0 \\ \vdots & \vdots & \ddots & \vdots \\ T_{m1} & T_{m2} & \cdots & I \end{bmatrix},$$

what is its inverse?

8.22. Under the assumptions of Theorem 8.28, can the matrix equality in (8.96) be satisfied automatically? If it cannot, under what additional conditions it is satisfied?

Appendix A
Software for Matrix Computations

Software is an important weapon that can allow computational methods to reach their full power in real-world applications, just like a gun for bullets and a cannon for cannonballs. In this part, we briefly introduce several commonly used **softwares** that are closely related to the main content of this book, including **BLAS** (Basic Linear Algebra Subprograms), **LAPACK** (Linear Algebra PACKage), **MATLAB** (MATrix LABoratory), and **IFISS** (Incompressible Flow and Iterative Solver Software).

A.1 ▪ BLAS

The BLAS consists of routines that provide standard **building blocks** for performing basic vector and matrix operations. BLAS has three levels: Level-1 BLAS performs scalar, vector, and vector-vector operations, Level-2 BLAS performs matrix-vector operations, and Level-3 BLAS performs matrix-matrix operations; see [113, 220].

The specification and implementation of Level-1 BLAS are the result of a collaborative project during the period from 1973 to 1977, and the specifications of Level-2 BLAS and Level-3 BLAS were drawn up during 1984–1986 and 1987–1988; see [113] for more details. As the BLAS pays great attention to making full use of the memory hierarchy of modern computers, it is commonly used in the development of high-quality linear algebra software, for example, LAPACK.

The BLAS represents fairly simple linear algebra kernels, and its reference source codes in **Fortran** are freely available at

- http://www.netlib.org/blas

The latest version of BLAS is also included in LAPACK. However, this is a reference implementation and is not optimized. Machine-specific optimized BLAS libraries are available and provided by the computer vendors (AMD, CRAY, HP, IBM, Intel, SUN, etc.). The recommended way to obtain an efficient BLAS is to use vendor BLAS libraries. In addition, the following two platform-independent and free-library alternatives are available:

- **ATLAS** (Automatically Tuned Linear Algebra Software) can automatically generate an **optimized BLAS library** for different computer architectures [345]. It is available at

  - http://math-atlas.sourceforge.net

- **OpenBLAS** is a free open-source alternative to the vendor BLAS implementations, whose speed is decent and fairly competitive with Vendor BLAS (e.g., MKL). It is available at

  - http://www.openblas.net/

Table A.1: Prefixes for Data Types

S — Real	C — Complex
D — Double Precision	Z — Double Complex

Table A.2: Prefixes for Matrix Types

GE — GEneral	GB — General Band	
SY — SYmmetric	SB — Symmetric Band	SP — Symmetric Packed
HE — HErmitian	HB — Hermitian Band	HP — Hermitian Packed
TR — TRiangular	TB — Triangular Band	TP — Triangular Packed

Table A.3: Level-1 BLAS Routines

Level-1 BLAS	Prefixes
xROTG - setup Givens rotation	S, D, C, Z
xROTMG - setup modified Givens rotation	S, D
xROT - apply Givens rotation	S, D
xSROT - apply Givens rotation	C
xDROTF - apply Givens rotation	Z
xROTM - apply modified Givens rotation	S, D
xSWAP - swap x and y	S, D, C, Z
xSCAL - perform $x \leftarrow \alpha x$	S, D, C, Z
xSSCAL - perform $x \leftarrow \alpha x$	C
xDSCAL - perform $x \leftarrow \alpha x$	Z
xCOPY - copy x into y	S, D, C, Z
xAXPY - perform $y \leftarrow \alpha x + y$	S, D, C, Z
xDOT - dot product $x^\mathsf{T} y$	S, D
xDOTU - dot product $x^\mathsf{T} y$	C, Z
xDOTC - dot product $x^* y$, conjugating the first vector	C, Z
xSDOT - dot product with extended precision accumulation $\alpha + x^\mathsf{T} y$	SD, D
xNRM2 - Euclidean norm of real vector	S, D
xCNRM2 - Euclidean norm of complex vector	S, D
xASUM - sum of absolute values	S, D
xASUM - sum of absolute values	SC, DZ
IxAMAX - index of maximum absolute value	S, D, C, Z

Multithreaded BLAS library is also available for most modern high-performance computers with shared memory. To obtain the BLAS technical forum standard [112] and an up-to-date list of available optimized BLAS, see the BLAS FAQ (Frequently Asked Questions) at

- http://www.netlib.org/blas

In the name of a BLAS routine, there are **prefixes** that indicate the data type on which it operates; see Table A.1.

Table A.4: Level-2 BLAS Routines

Level-2 BLAS	Prefixes
xGEMV - matrix-vector multiply	
$\qquad y \leftarrow \alpha A x + \beta y,\, y \leftarrow \alpha A^\mathsf{T} x + \beta y,\, y \leftarrow \alpha A^* x + \beta y$	S, D, C, Z
xGBMV - banded matrix-vector multiply	
$\qquad y \leftarrow \alpha A x + \beta y,\, y \leftarrow \alpha A^\mathsf{T} x + \beta y,\, y \leftarrow \alpha A^* x + \beta y$	S, D, C, Z
xSYMV - symmetric matrix-vector multiply $y \leftarrow \alpha A x + \beta y$	S, D
xSBMV - symmetric banded matrix-vector multiply $y \leftarrow \alpha A x + \beta y$	S, D
xSPMV - symmetric packed matrix-vector multiply $y \leftarrow \alpha A x + \beta y$	S, D
xHEMV - Hermitian matrix-vector multiply $y \leftarrow \alpha A x + \beta y$	C, Z
xHBMV - Hermitian banded matrix-vector multiply $y \leftarrow \alpha A x + \beta y$	C, Z
xHPMV - Hermitian packed matrix-vector multiply $y \leftarrow \alpha A x + \beta y$	C, Z
xTRMV - triangular matrix-vector multiply $x \leftarrow A x,\, x \leftarrow A^\mathsf{T} x,\, x \leftarrow A^* x$	S, D, C, Z
xTBMV - triangular banded matrix-vector multiply $x \leftarrow A x,\, x \leftarrow A^\mathsf{T} x,\, x \leftarrow A^* x$	S, D, C, Z
xTPMV - triangular packed matrix-vector multiply $x \leftarrow A x,\, x \leftarrow A^\mathsf{T} x,\, x \leftarrow A^* x$	S, D, C, Z
xTRSV - solving triangular matrix problems	
$\qquad x \leftarrow A^{-1} x,\, x \leftarrow A^{-\mathsf{T}} x,\, x \leftarrow A^{-*} x$	S, D, C, Z
xTBSV - solving triangular banded matrix problems	
$\qquad x \leftarrow A^{-1} x,\, x \leftarrow A^{-\mathsf{T}} x,\, x \leftarrow A^{-*} x$	S, D, C, Z
xTPSV - solving triangular packed matrix problems	
$\qquad x \leftarrow A^{-1} x,\, x \leftarrow A^{-\mathsf{T}} x,\, x \leftarrow A^{-*} x$	S, D, C, Z
xGER - rank-1 operation $A \leftarrow \alpha x y^\mathsf{T} + A$	S, D
xGERU - rank-1 operation $A \leftarrow \alpha x y^\mathsf{T} + A$	C, Z
xGER - rank-1 operation $A \leftarrow \alpha x y^* + A$	C, Z
xSYR - symmetric rank-1 operation $A \leftarrow \alpha x x^\mathsf{T} + A$	S, D
xSPR - symmetric packed rank-1 operation $A \leftarrow \alpha x x^\mathsf{T} + A$	S, D
xSYR2 - symmetric rank-2 operation $A \leftarrow \alpha x y^\mathsf{T} + \alpha y x^\mathsf{T} + A$	S, D
xSPR2 - symmetric packed rank-2 operation $A \leftarrow \alpha x y^\mathsf{T} + \alpha y x^\mathsf{T} + A$	S, D
xHER - Hermitian rank-1 operation $A \leftarrow \alpha x x^* + A$	C, Z
xHPR - Hermitian packed rank-1 operation $A \leftarrow \alpha x x^* + A$	C, Z
xHER2 - Hermitian rank-2 operation $A \leftarrow \alpha x y^\mathsf{T} + y(\alpha x)^* + A$	C, Z
xHPR2 - Hermitian packed rank-2 operation $A \leftarrow \alpha x y^* + y(\alpha x)^* + A$	C, Z

For Level-2 and Level-3 BLAS routines, besides the above four **prefixes** there are some other prefixes that indicate the matrix types; see Table A.2.

The packed format is relevant for symmetric, Hermitian, or triangular matrices. Half of the matrices (either the lower-triangular part or the upper-triangular part) is stored in a one-dimensional array. For example, the lower-triangular part of a 3-by-3 symmetric matrix

$$A = [a_{ij}] = \begin{bmatrix} a_{11} & a_{12} & a_{13} \\ a_{21} & a_{22} & a_{23} \\ a_{31} & a_{32} & a_{33} \end{bmatrix}$$

can be stored in the vector

$$\begin{bmatrix} a_{11}, a_{21}, a_{31}, a_{22}, a_{32}, a_{33} \end{bmatrix}.$$

Tables A.3–A.5 provide a quick reference to the BLAS, where "x" in the names of the routines denotes the prefix of a data type.

Table A.5: Level-3 BLAS Routines

Level-3 BLAS	Prefixes
xGEMM - matrix-matrix multiply	
$\quad C \leftarrow \alpha \operatorname{op}(A) \operatorname{op}(B) + \beta C, \operatorname{op}(X) = X, X^{\mathsf{T}}, X^{*}$	S, D, C, Z
xSYMM - symmetric matrix-matrix multiply	
$\quad C \leftarrow \alpha AB + \beta C, C \leftarrow \alpha BA + \beta C, A$ is symmetric	S, D, C, Z
xHEMM - Hermitian matrix-matrix multiply	
$\quad C \leftarrow \alpha AB + \beta C, C \leftarrow \alpha BA + \beta C, A$ is Hermitian	C, Z
xSYRK - symmetric rank-k update to a matrix	
$\quad C \leftarrow \alpha AA^{\mathsf{T}} + \beta C, C \leftarrow \alpha A^{\mathsf{T}}A + \beta C$	S, D, C, Z
xSYR2K - symmetric rank-$2k$ update to a matrix	
$\quad C \leftarrow \alpha AB^{\mathsf{T}} + \overline{\alpha} BA^{\mathsf{T}} + \beta C, C \leftarrow \alpha A^{\mathsf{T}}B + \overline{\alpha} B^{\mathsf{T}}A + \beta C$	S, D, C, Z
xHERK - Hermitian rank-k update to a matrix	
$\quad C \leftarrow \alpha AA^{*} + \beta C, C \leftarrow \alpha A^{*}A + \beta C$	C, Z
xHER2K - Hermitian rank-$2k$ update to a matrix	
$\quad C \leftarrow \alpha AB^{*} + \overline{\alpha} BA^{*} + \beta C, C \leftarrow \alpha A^{*}B + \overline{\alpha} B^{*}A + \beta C$	C, Z
xTRMM - triangular matrix-matrix multiply	
$\quad B \leftarrow \alpha \operatorname{op}(A) B, B \leftarrow \alpha B \operatorname{op}(A), \operatorname{op}(X) = X, X^{\mathsf{T}}, X^{*}$	S, D, C, Z
xTRSM - solving triangular linear systems with multiple right-hand side	
$\quad B \leftarrow \alpha \operatorname{op}(A^{-1}) B, B \leftarrow \alpha B \operatorname{op}(A^{-1}), \operatorname{op}(X) = X, X^{\mathsf{T}}, X^{*}$	S, D, C, Z

A.2 ▪ LAPACK

LAPACK, a library of Fortran subroutines [2], is an open-source software package for solving the most commonly occurring problems in numerical linear algebra, including systems of linear equations, linear least-squares problems, and eigenvalue and singular value problems. It is available at

- http://www.netlib.org/lapack

More specifically, LAPACK is designed to deal with the dense and banded matrix problems, and provides the most popular matrix factorizations like LU, Cholesky, QR, SVD, Schur, and generalized Schur. In all areas, similar functionality is provided for real and complex matrices, in both single and double precisions.

LAPACK is designed to achieve high efficiency on diverse modern machines with multi-layered memory hierarchies by reorganizing the algorithms to use block matrix operations, such as matrix multiplication, in the innermost loops. LAPACK routines are written so that as much of the computation as possible is performed by the highly efficient machine-specific implementations of the BLAS.

There have been a number of extensions of LAPACK:

- **CLAPACK** is the C version of LAPACK, which is built using a Fortran to C conversion utility called f2c. It is available at

  - http://www.netlib.org/clapack

- **ScaLAPACK** is a distributed-memory implementation of LAPACK for parallel distributed computing. It is available at

  - http://www.netlib.org/scalapack

- **PLASMA** (Parallel Linear Algebra for Scalable Multicore Architectures) aims to create a software framework that enables programmers to simplify the process of developing appli-

Table A.6: LAPACK Routines for System of Linear Equations

Type of Matrix	Routine Name		Prefixes
	Simple	Expert	
General dense	xGESV	xGESVX	S, D, C, Z
General band	xGBSV	xGBSVX	S, D
General tridiagonal	xGTSV	xGTSVX	S, D, C, Z
Symmetric positive definite	xPOSV	xPOSVX	S, D, C, Z
Symmetric positive definite (packed storage)	xPPSV	xPPSVX	S, D, C, Z
Hermitian positive definite	xPOSV	xPOSVX	C, Z
Hermitian positive definite (packed storage)	xPPSV	xPPSVX	C, Z
Banded symmetric positive definite	xPBSV	xPBSVX	S, D, C, Z
Tridiagonal symmetric positive definite	xPTSV	xPTSVX	S, D, C, Z
Symmetric indefinite	xSYSV	xSYSVX	S, D
Symmetric indefinite (packed storage)	xSPSV	xSPSVX	S, D
Hermitian indefinite	xHESV	xHESVX	C, Z
Hermitian indefinite (packed storage)	xHPSV	xHPSVX	C, Z
Complex symmetric	xSYSV	xSYSVX	C, Z

Table A.7: LAPACK Routines for Linear Least-Squares Problems

Type of Problem	Algorithm	Routine Name	Prefixes
		Simple	
General dense	QR or LQ factorization	xGELS	S, C
Equality-constrained	Generalized QR factorization	xGGLSE	S, C
General linear model problem	Generalized QR factorization	xGGGLM	S, C
		Expert	
General dense	Complete orthogonal factorization	xGELSY	S, C
General dense	SVD	xGELSS	S, C
General dense	Divide-and-conquer SVD	xGELSD	S, C

* *Linear least-squares* (LLS) problem: $\min_{x \in \mathbb{R}^n} \|b - Ax\|_2$, where $A \in \mathbb{R}^{m \times n}$ and $b \in \mathbb{R}^m$;

* Equality-constrained LLS problem: $\min_{x \in \mathbb{R}^n} \|c - Ax\|_2$ subject to $Bx = d$, where $A \in \mathbb{R}^{m \times n}$, $B \in \mathbb{R}^{p \times n}$, $c \in \mathbb{R}^m$ and $d \in \mathbb{R}^p$; and

* General linear model problem: $\min_{x \in \mathbb{R}^n, \, y \in \mathbb{R}^p} \|y\|_2$ subject to $Ax + By = d$, where $A \in \mathbb{R}^{m \times n}$, $B \in \mathbb{R}^{m \times p}$ and $d \in \mathbb{R}^m$.

cations such that these applications can achieve both high performance and good portability across a range of new multicore architectures. It is available at

- http://icl.cs.utk.edu/plasma

- **MAGMA** (Matrix Algebra on GPU and Multicore Architectures) aims to develop dense linear algebra libraries similar to LAPACK but for heterogeneous/hybrid "Multicore+GPU" architectures. It is available at

- http://icl.cs.utk.edu/magma

Table A.8: LAPACK Routines for Symmetric Eigenvalue Problems

Type of Problem	Routine Name	Prefixes
	Simple	
General symmetric	xSYEV	S, D, C, Z
General symmetric (packed storage)	xSPEV	S, D, C, Z
Banded matrix	xSBEV	S, D, C, Z
Tridiagonal matrix	xSTEV	S, D, C, Z
	Divide-and-Conquer	
General symmetric	xSYEVD	S, D, C, Z
General symmetric (packed storage)	xSPEVD	S, D, C, Z
Banded matrix	xSBEVD	S, D, C, Z
Tridiagonal matrix	xSTEVD	S, D, C, Z
	Expert	
General symmetric	xSYEVX	S, D, C, Z
General symmetric (packed storage)	xSPEVX	S, D, C, Z
Banded matrix	xSBEVX	S, D, C, Z
Tridiagonal matrix	xSTEVX	S, D, C, Z
	Relative Robust Representation	
General symmetric	xSYEVR	S, D, C, Z
Tridiagonal matrix	xSTEVR	S, D, C, Z

The **LAPACK** routines are divided into two types: simple driver routines and expert driver routines. The expert driver routines provide some more features such as allowing a matrix A to be replaced by its transpose A^{T} or its conjugate transpose A^*. They also provide error bounds, condition number estimate, scaling, and solution refinement. Each of these types of drivers has different implementations that take advantage of the special properties or storage schemes of the matrix A. In Tables A.6–A.8, we briefly introduce the LAPACK routines based on different types of numerical linear algebra problems [14].

There are four types of driver routines for solving the symmetric/Hermitian eigenvalue problems. The simple driver computes all eigenvalues and (optional) eigenvectors. The expert driver computes all or a selected subset of the eigenvalues and (optional) eigenvectors. The divide-and-conquer driver has the same functionality as, yet outperforms, the simple driver, but it requires more workspace. The *relative robust representation* (RRR) driver computes all or a subset of the eigenvalues and (optional) eigenvectors and is, generally, faster than any other type of driver routine and uses the least amount of workspace.

A.3 ▪ MATLAB

MATLAB is a commercial-oriented software, and it is also a kind of high-level programming language. It is provided by The MathWorks Company. MATLAB was originally developed in the 1970s by the numerical analyst Cleve B. Moler as an interactive system for calculations involving linear algebra problems. It is written in **FORTRAN** with matrix routines based on **LINPACK** and **EISPACK** [114, 157, 298], which are the most famous numerical linear algebra libraries at that time and now superseded by **LAPACK**; see, for example,

- http://www.netlib.org/linpack/
- http://www.netlib.org/eispack/

After decades of development, MATLAB has advanced significantly and has acquired a remarkable number of new features as well as a lot of practical toolboxes such as signal processing, optimization, symbolic mathematics, image processing, numerical simulations, data acquisition, machine learning, and artificial intelligence. Nowadays, MATLAB is generally recognized as the leading software for scientific computations and is prominent in both academic research and industrial applications.

MATLAB has a large number of high-quality built-in functions. Compared with other numerical-oriented languages such as Fortran, C, and C++, MATLAB is usually found to be much easier to use.

A beginner on learning MATLAB in scientific computing can refer to [153, 154].

A.4 ▪ IFISS

IFISS is an open-source software package for numerical study of incompressible flow problems, which can be run under **MATLAB** or **OCTAVE** [122]. It was developed by David J. Silvester, Howard C. Elman, and Alison Ramage. The IFISS package focuses on four specific partial differential equations: the Poisson equation, the convection-diffusion equation, the Stokes equation, and the Navier–Stokes equation. The package offers test model problems for each of these equations. In the latest version (i.e., version 3.5) [293], the Poisson equation constraint optimization problems are also included.

This software package concerns two features: the finite-element discretization and the iterative solution of the corresponding discrete systems of linear equations [123]. Frequently, these discrete linear systems can be equivalently reformulated into the forms of the standard and the generalized saddle-point problems. The preconditioned Krylov subspace methods are chosen to match the underlying problem. The package offers a range of efficient preconditioners, including algebraic methods such as incomplete LU factorizations, as well as the more sophisticated and state-of-the-art iterative methods, designed to take advantage of the structure of the discretized and linearized Navier–Stokes equations, such as the multigrid methods [311]. The software also offers a platform to generate new model problems by specifying new boundary conditions and introducing new problem domains.

The mathematical analysis of the numerical solution associated with this software package can be found in [124].

For a detailed introduction about **IFISS**, see

- http://www.cs.umd.edu/~elman/ifiss/
- http://www.cs.umd.edu/~elman/ifiss3.5/index.html

And for more information about **OCTAVE**, see

- http://www.gnu.org/software/octave/

Afterword

Writing a book is really a huge project, requiring a skillful and technical combination of science, engineering, art, and even more. The plan of writing this book can be dated back to the autumn of 2009, when I had only worked out an outline and some details for its content. With continuous hard work over many years, I completed a draft by the spring of 2020. After many corrections, modifications, supplements, and rewritings, this book was finally ready for publication. However, even now I think that this editing process is only locally semi-convergent, but far from globally convergent. In fact, each time I edit the book, I can always find many typos, errors, unsatisfactory sentences, or even inappropriate paragraphs. I then have to make a significant and thorough revision by editing the text once more.

Hence, even though this book has been formally published, I believe that there is still room to further improve its quality. Due to this, I really expect and welcome all kinds of comments and suggestions, which will be seriously considered in a second edition, should that come to pass.

Zhong-Zhi Bai
Zhong-Guan-Cun, Beijing, China
February 28, 2021

References

[1] G. Alexander, *Kronecker Products and Matrix Calculus: With Applications*, Ellis Horwood Limited, Chichester, 1981. (Cited on p. 37)

[2] E. Anderson, Z. Bai, C. Bischof, L. S. Blackford, J. Demmel, J. Dongarra, J. Du Croz, A. Greenbaum, S. Hammarling, A. McKenney, and D. Sorensen, *LAPACK Users' Guide*, The Third Edition, SIAM, Philadelphia, 1999. (Cited on p. 450)

[3] M. Arioli, V. Pták, and Z. Strakoš, Krylov sequences of maximal length and convergence of GMRES, *BIT*, 38 (1998), 636–643. (Cited on p. 287)

[4] W. E. Arnoldi, The principle of minimized iterations in the solution of the matrix eigenvalue problem, *Quarterly of Applied Mathematics*, 9 (1951), 17–29. (Cited on p. 249)

[5] K. J. Arrow and L. Hurwicz, Gradient method for concave programming. I: Local results, in *Studies in Linear and Non-linear Programming*, K. J. Arrow, L. Hurwicz, and H. Uzawa (Editors), Stanford University Press, Stanford, CA, 1958, pp. 117–126. (Cited on p. 384)

[6] K. J. Arrow and R. M. Solow, Gradient methods for constrained maxima, with weakened assumptions, in *Studies in Linear and Non-linear Programming*, K. J. Arrow, L. Hurwicz, and H. Uzawa (Editors), Stanford University Press, Stanford, CA, 1958, pp. 166–176. (Cited on p. 384)

[7] G. P. Astrakhantsev, Analysis of algorithms of the Arrow-Hurwicz type, *Computational Mathematics and Mathematical Physics*, 41 (2001), 15–26. (Cited on p. 384)

[8] O. Axelsson, *Iterative Solution Methods*, Cambridge University Press, Cambridge, 1994. (Cited on pp. 13, 27, 77, 80, 150, 176, 191, 200, 307, 335)

[9] O. Axelsson, Z.-Z. Bai, and S.-X. Qiu, A class of nested iteration schemes for linear systems with a coefficient matrix with a dominant positive definite symmetric part, *Numerical Algorithms*, 35 (2004), 351–372. (Cited on pp. 211, 439)

[10] O. Axelsson and M. G. Neytcheva, Eigenvalue estimates for preconditioned saddle point matrices, *Numerical Linear Algebra with Applications*, 13 (2006), 339–360. (Cited on p. 375)

[11] O. Axelsson and P. S. Vassilevski, Algebraic multilevel preconditioning methods. I, *Numerische Mathematik*, 56 (1989), 157–177. (Cited on pp. 26, 27)

[12] O. Axelsson and P. S. Vassilevski, Algebraic multilevel preconditioning methods. II, *SIAM Journal on Numerical Analysis*, 27 (1990), 1569–1590. (Cited on pp. 26, 27)

[13] Z.-J. Bai and J. W. Demmel, Computing the generalized singular value decomposition, *SIAM Journal on Scientific Computing*, 14 (1993), 1464–1486. (Cited on p. 72)

[14] Z. Bai, J. Demmel, J. Dongarra, J. Langou, and J. Wang, LAPACK, The Second Edition, in *Handbook of Linear Algebra*, L. Hogben (Editor), Chapman and Hall/CRC Press, New York, 2014, pp. 93-1–93-24. (Cited on p. 452)

[15] Z.-J. Bai and H.-Y. Zha, A new preprocessing algorithm for the computation of the generalized singular value decomposition, *SIAM Journal on Scientific Computing*, 14 (1993), 1007–1012. (Cited on p. 72)

[16] Z.-Z. Bai, *Parallel Iterative Methods for Large-Scale Systems of Algebraic Equations*, Ph.D. Thesis, Shanghai University of Science and Technology, Shanghai, 1993. (Cited on pp. 27, 181, 195)

[17] Z.-Z. Bai, The generalized Stein-Rosenberg type theorem for the PDAOR-method, *Mathematica Numerica Sinica*, 19 (1997), 329–335. (In Chinese) (Cited on p. 181)

[18] Z.-Z. Bai, A class of parallel decomposition-type relaxation methods for large sparse systems of linear equations, *Linear Algebra and Its Applications*, 282 (1998), 1–24. (Cited on p. 181)

[19] Z.-Z. Bai, On the convergence of the multisplitting methods for the linear complementarity problem, *SIAM Journal on Matrix Analysis and Applications*, 21 (1999), 67–78. (Cited on pp. 155, 332)

[20] Z.-Z. Bai, Sharp error bounds of some Krylov subspace methods for non-Hermitian linear systems, *Applied Mathematics and Computation*, 109 (2000), 273–285. (Cited on pp. 281, 288, 307, 309)

[21] Z.-Z. Bai, On the convergence of additive and multiplicative splitting iterations for systems of linear equations, *Journal of Computational and Applied Mathematics*, 154 (2003), 195–214. (Cited on pp. 155, 179)

[22] Z.-Z. Bai, An algebraic convergence theorem for the multiplicative Schwarz iteration, *Numerical Mathematics, A Journal of Chinese Universities (English Series)*, 12 (2003), 179–182. (Cited on p. 155)

[23] Z.-Z. Bai, Structured preconditioners for nonsingular matrices of block two-by-two structures, *Mathematics of Computation*, 75 (2006), 791–815. (Cited on pp. 410, 422, 427)

[24] Z.-Z. Bai, Optimal parameters in the HSS-like methods for saddle-point problems, *Numerical Linear Algebra with Applications*, 16 (2009), 447–479. (Cited on pp. 179, 214, 394, 396, 400, 406)

[25] Z.-Z. Bai, Eigenvalue estimates for saddle point matrices of Hermitian and indefinite leading blocks, *Journal of Computational and Applied Mathematics*, 237 (2013), 295–306. (Cited on p. 375)

[26] Z.-Z. Bai, Motivations and realizations of Krylov subspace methods for large sparse linear systems, *Journal of Computational and Applied Mathematics*, 283 (2015), 71–78. (Cited on pp. 172, 173, 248, 305, 307, 309, 376)

[27] Z.-Z. Bai, R. H. Chan, and Z.-R. Ren, On sinc discretization and banded preconditioning for linear third-order ordinary differential equations, *Numerical Linear Algebra with Applications*, 18 (2011), 471–497. (Cited on p. 31)

[28] Z.-Z. Bai, R. H. Chan, and Z.-R. Ren, On order-reducible sinc discretizations and block-diagonal preconditioning methods for linear third-order ordinary differential equations, *Numerical Linear Algebra with Applications*, 21 (2014), 108–135. (Cited on p. 31)

[29] Z.-Z. Bai, I. S. Duff, and A. J. Wathen, A class of incomplete orthogonal factorization methods. I: Methods and theories, *BIT*, 41 (2001), 53–70. (Cited on pp. 336, 339, 343, 349, 353)

[30] Z.-Z. Bai, I. S. Duff, and J.-F. Yin, Numerical study on incomplete orthogonal factorization preconditioners, *Journal of Computational and Applied Mathematics*, 226 (2009), 22–41. (Cited on pp. 349, 352)

[31] Z.-Z. Bai and G. H. Golub, Generalized preconditioned Hermitian and skew-Hermitian splitting iteration methods for saddle-point problems, *Technical Report SCCM-04-07*, Scientific Computing and Computational Mathematics Program, Department of Computer Science, Stanford University, 2002. Available on line at http://www-sccm.stanford.edu/. (Cited on pp. 214, 400, 405)

[32] Z.-Z. Bai and G. H. Golub, Accelerated Hermitian and skew-Hermitian splitting iteration methods for saddle-point problems, *IMA Journal of Numerical Analysis*, 27 (2007), 1–23. (Cited on pp. 214, 223, 394, 396, 397, 398, 400)

[33] Z.-Z. Bai, G. H. Golub, and C.-K. Li, Optimal parameter in Hermitian and skew-Hermitian splitting method for certain two-by-two block matrices, *SIAM Journal on Scientific Computing*, 28 (2006), 583–603. (Cited on pp. 214, 223, 397, 400)

[34] Z.-Z. Bai, G. H. Golub, and C.-K. Li, Convergence properties of preconditioned Hermitian and skew-Hermitian splitting methods for non-Hermitian positive semidefinite matrices, *Mathematics of Computation*, 76 (2007), 287–298. (Cited on pp. 214, 223, 397, 398)

[35] Z.-Z. Bai, G. H. Golub, L.-Z. Lu, and J.-F. Yin, Block triangular and skew-Hermitian splitting methods for positive-definite linear systems, *SIAM Journal on Scientific Computing*, 26 (2005), 844–863. (Cited on pp. 218, 219, 223)

[36] Z.-Z. Bai, G. H. Golub, and M. K. Ng, Hermitian and skew-Hermitian splitting methods for non-Hermitian positive definite linear systems, *SIAM Journal on Matrix Analysis and Applications*, 24 (2003), 603–626. (Cited on pp. 211, 212, 213)

[37] Z.-Z. Bai, G. H. Golub, and M. K. Ng, On successive-overrelaxation acceleration of the Hermitian and skew-Hermitian splitting iterations, *Numerical Linear Algebra with Applications*, 14 (2007), 319–335. (Cited on pp. 214, 215)

[38] Z.-Z. Bai, G. H. Golub, and J.-Y. Pan, Preconditioned Hermitian and skew-Hermitian splitting methods for non-Hermitian positive semidefinite linear systems, *Numerische Mathematik*, 98 (2004), 1–32. (Cited on pp. 214, 223, 397, 398, 400)

[39] Z.-Z. Bai and A. Hadjidimos, Optimization of extrapolated Cayley transform with non-Hermitian positive definite matrix, *Linear Algebra and Its Applications*, 463 (2014), 322–339. (Cited on p. 220)

[40] Z.-Z. Bai, Y.-M. Huang, and M. K. Ng, On preconditioned iterative methods for Burgers equations, *SIAM Journal on Scientific Computing*, 29 (2007), 415–439. (Cited on p. 31)

[41] Z.-Z. Bai, Y.-M. Huang, and M. K. Ng, On preconditioned iterative methods for certain time-dependent partial differential equations, *SIAM Journal on Numerical Analysis*, 47 (2009), 1019–1037. (Cited on p. 31)

[42] Z.-Z. Bai and G.-Q. Li, Restrictively preconditioned conjugate gradient methods for systems of linear equations, *IMA Journal of Numerical Analysis*, 23 (2003), 561–580. (Cited on pp. 319, 399, 422, 424, 426, 427, 428, 434)

[43] Z.-Z. Bai, G.-Q. Li, and L.-Z. Lu, Combinative preconditioners of modified incomplete Cholesky factorization and Sherman-Morrison-Woodbury update for self-adjoint elliptic Dirichlet-periodic boundary value problems, *Journal of Computational Mathematics*, 22 (2004), 833–856. (Cited on pp. 327, 335)

[44] Z.-Z. Bai and R. Nabben, Some properties of the block matrices in the parallel decomposition-type relaxation methods, *Applied Numerical Mathematics*, 29 (1999), 167–170. (Cited on p. 181)

[45] Z.-Z. Bai and M. K. Ng, Preconditioners for nonsymmetric block Toeplitz-like-plus-diagonal linear systems, *Numerische Mathematik*, 96 (2003), 197–220. (Cited on p. 30)

[46] Z.-Z. Bai and M. K. Ng, On inexact preconditioners for nonsymmetric matrices, *SIAM Journal on Scientific Computing*, 26 (2005), 1710–1724. (Cited on pp. 410, 420)

[47] Z.-Z. Bai and M. K. Ng, Erratum, *Numerical Linear Algebra with Applications*, 19 (2012), 891. (Cited on p. 215)

[48] Z.-Z. Bai, M. K. Ng, and Z.-Q. Wang, Constraint preconditioners for symmetric indefinite matrices, *SIAM Journal on Matrix Analysis and Applications*, 31 (2009), 410–433. (Cited on pp. 371, 375, 418)

[49] Z.-Z. Bai, B. N. Parlett, and Z.-Q. Wang, On generalized successive overrelaxation methods for augmented linear systems, *Numerische Mathematik*, 102 (2005), 1–38. (Cited on pp. 384, 385, 388, 389, 399)

[50] Z.-Z. Bai and M. Rozložník, On the numerical behavior of matrix splitting iteration methods for solving linear systems, *SIAM Journal on Numerical Analysis*, 53 (2015), 1716–1737. (Cited on p. 176)

[51] Z.-Z. Bai and Y.-F. Su, On the convergence of a class of parallel decomposition-type relaxation methods, *Applied Mathematics and Computation*, 81 (1997), 1–21. (Cited on p. 181)

[52] Z.-Z. Bai, J.-C. Sun, and D.-R. Wang, A unified framework for the construction of various matrix multisplitting iterative methods for large sparse system of linear equations, *Computers and Mathematics with Applications*, 32 (1996), 51–76. (Cited on p. 181)

[53] Z.-Z. Bai and M. Tao, Rigorous convergence analysis of alternating variable minimization with multiplier methods for quadratic programming problems with equality constraints, *BIT Numerical Mathematics*, 56 (2016), 399–422. (Cited on p. 441)

[54] Z.-Z. Bai and M. Tao, On preconditioned and relaxed AVMM methods for quadratic programming problems with equality constraints, *Linear Algebra and Its Applications*, 516 (2017), 264–285. (Cited on pp. 441, 442)

[55] Z.-Z. Bai and D.-R. Wang, Generalized matrix multisplitting relaxation methods and their convergence, *Numerical Mathematics, A Journal of Chinese Universities (English Series)*, 2 (1993), 87–100. (Cited on p. 181)

[56] Z.-Z. Bai and Z.-Q. Wang, Restrictive preconditioners for conjugate gradient methods for symmetric positive definite linear systems, *Journal of Computational and Applied Mathematics*, 187 (2006), 202–226. (Cited on pp. 422, 427)

[57] Z.-Z. Bai and Z.-Q. Wang, On parameterized inexact Uzawa methods for generalized saddle point problems, *Linear Algebra and Its Applications*, 428 (2008), 2900–2932. (Cited on p. 441)

[58] Z.-Z. Bai and W.-T. Wu, On refinement of the generalized Bendixson theorem, *Applied Numerical Mathematics*, 164 (2021), 125–138. (Cited on p. 31)

[59] Z.-Z. Bai and J.-F. Yin, Modified incomplete orthogonal factorization methods using Givens rotations, *Computing*, 86 (2009), 53–69. (Cited on pp. 349, 350, 352)

[60] R. Beauwens, Factorization iterative methods, M-operators and H-operators, *Numerische Mathematik*, 31 (1979), 335–357. (Cited on pp. 196, 201)

[61] B. Beckermann and A. B. J. Kuijlaars, Superlinear convergence of conjugate gradients, *SIAM Journal on Numerical Analysis*, 39 (2001), 300–329. (Cited on p. 284)

[62] B. Beckermann and A. B. J. Kuijlaars, Superlinear CG convergence for special right-hand sides, *Electronic Transactions on Numerical Analysis*, 14 (2002), 1–19. (Cited on p. 284)

[63] M. Benzi, Preconditioning techniques for large linear systems: A survey, *Journal of Computational Physics*, 182 (2002), 418–477. (Cited on pp. 307, 308, 360)

[64] M. Benzi, M. J. Gander, and G. H. Golub, Optimization of the Hermitian and skew-Hermitian splitting iteration for saddle-point problems, *BIT*, 43 (2003), 881–900. (Cited on p. 214)

[65] M. Benzi and G. H. Golub, A preconditioner for generalized saddle point problems, *SIAM Journal on Matrix Analysis and Applications*, 26 (2004), 20–41. (Cited on pp. 214, 223, 390, 392, 394, 395, 397, 398, 403)

[66] M. Benzi, G. H. Golub, and J. Liesen, Numerical solution of saddle point problems, *Acta Numerica*, 14 (2005), 1–137. (Cited on pp. 363, 375, 399, 406)

[67] M. Benzi, C. D. Meyer, and M. Tůma, A sparse approximate inverse preconditioner for the conjugate gradient method, *SIAM Journal on Scientific Computing*, 17 (1996), 1135–1149. (Cited on p. 360)

[68] M. Benzi and M. K. Ng, Preconditioned iterative methods for weighted Toeplitz least squares problems, *SIAM Journal on Matrix Analysis and Applications*, 27 (2006), 1106–1124. (Cited on pp. 214, 406)

[69] M. Benzi and V. Simoncini, On the eigenvalues of a class of saddle point matrices, *Numerische Mathematik*, 103 (2006), 173–196. (Cited on p. 377)

[70] M. Benzi and M. Tůma, A sparse approximate inverse preconditioner for nonsymmetric linear systems, *SIAM Journal on Scientific Computing*, 19 (1998), 968–994. (Cited on p. 360)

[71] M. Benzi and M. Tůma, A comparative study of sparse approximate inverse preconditioners, *Applied Numerical Mathematics*, 30 (1999), 305–340. (Cited on pp. 358, 360)

[72] A. Berman and R. J. Plemmons, *Nonnegative Matrices in the Mathematical Sciences*, SIAM, Philadelphia, 1994. (Cited on pp. 19, 160, 196, 207)

[73] D. S. Bernstein, *Matrix Mathematics: Theory, Facts, and Formulas with Application to Linear Systems Theory*, Princeton University Press, Princeton, NJ, 2005. (Cited on p. 74)

[74] D. Bertaccini, G. H. Golub, S. Serra-Capizzano, and C. T. Possio, Preconditioned HSS methods for the solution of non-Hermitian positive definite linear systems and applications to the discrete convection-diffusion equation, *Numerische Mathematik*, 99 (2005), 441–484. (Cited on pp. 214, 223)

[75] G. Birkhoff and S. Mac Lane, *A Survey of Modern Algebra*, The Revised Version, The MacMillan Company, New York, 1953. (Cited on p. 234)

[76] Å. Björck, *Numerical Methods for Least Squares Problems*, SIAM, Philadelphia, 1996. (Cited on pp. 56, 72)

[77] A. E. Brandt, Multi-level adaptive solutions to boundary-value problems, *Mathematics of Computation*, 31 (1977), 333–390. (Cited on p. 323)

[78] A. E. Brandt, S. F. McCormick, and J. W. Ruge, Algebraic multigrid (AMG) for automatic multigrid solution with application to geodetic computations, Institute for Computational Studies, P.O. Box 1852, Fort Collins, Colorado, 1982. (Cited on p. 323)

[79] A. T. Brauer, Limits for the characteristic roots of a matrix, *Duke Mathematical Journal*, 13 (1946), 387–395. (Cited on p. 152)

[80] C. Brezinski, M. Redivo-Zaglia, and H. Sadok, A breakdown-free Lanczos type algorithm for solving linear systems, *Numerische Mathematik*, 63 (1992), 29–38. (Cited on p. 291)

[81] C. Brezinski, M. Redivo-Zaglia, and H. Sadok, Breakdowns in the implementation of the Lánczos method for solving linear systems, *Computers and Mathematics with Applications*, 33 (1997), 31–44. (Cited on p. 291)

[82] C. Brezinski, M. Redivo-Zaglia, and H. Sadok, New look-ahead Lanczos-type algorithms for linear systems, *Numerische Mathematik*, 83 (1999), 53–85. (Cited on p. 291)

[83] F. Brezzi and M. Fortin, *Mixed and Hybrid Finite Element Methods*, Springer-Verlag, New York, 1991. (Cited on p. 363)

[84] E. T. Browne, Limits to the characteristic roots of a matrix, *The American Mathematical Monthly*, 46 (1939), 252–265. (Cited on p. 42)

[85] R. A. Brualdi and S. Mellendorf, Regions in the complex plane containing the eigenvalues of a matrix, *The American Mathematical Monthly*, 101 (1994), 975–985. (Cited on p. 152)

[86] A. M. Bruaset, *A Survey of Preconditioned Iterative Methods*, Longman Scientific & Technical, Harlow, UK, 1995. (Cited on pp. 307, 308)

[87] N. I. Buleev, A numerical method for solving two-dimensional diffusion equations, *Atomic Energy*, 6 (1960), 222–224. (In Russian) (Cited on p. 325)

[88] N. I. Buleev, A numerical method for solving two- and three-dimensional diffusion equations, *Matematicheskii Sbornik*, 51 (1960), 227–238. (In Russian) (Cited on p. 325)

[89] Z.-H. Cao, A note on P-regular splitting of Hermitian matrix, *SIAM Journal on Matrix Analysis and Applications*, 21 (2000), 1392–1393. (Cited on p. 209)

[90] Z.-H. Cao, A note on constraint preconditioning for nonsymmetric indefinite matrices, *SIAM Journal on Matrix Analysis and Applications*, 24 (2002), 121–125. (Cited on pp. 417, 444)

[91] Z.-H. Cao, *Variational Iterative Methods*, Science Press, Beijing, 2005. (In Chinese) (Cited on pp. 18, 29, 42)

[92] T. F. Chan and H. A. van der Vorst, Approximate and incomplete factorizations, in *Parallel Numerical Algorithms*, D. E. Keyes, A. Sameh, and V. Venkatakrishnan (Editors), ICASE/LaRC Interdisciplinary Series in Science and Engineering, Kluwer Academic, Dordrecht, 4 (1997), pp. 167–202. (Cited on p. 308)

[93] S. Chandra Sekhara Rao, Existence and uniqueness of WZ factorization, *Parallel Computing*, 23 (1997), 1129–1139. (Cited on p. 54)

[94] X.-S. Chen, W. Li, and W.-W. Sun, Some new perturbation bounds for the generalized polar decomposition, *BIT Numerical Mathematics*, 44 (2004), 237–244. (Cited on p. 73)

[95] T. F. Coleman, *Large Sparse Numerical Optimization*, Springer, Berlin, 1984. (Cited on p. 380)

[96] L. Collatz, Aufgaben monotoner Art, *Archiv der Mathematik*, 3 (1952), 366–376. (Cited on p. 161)

[97] P. Concus and G. H. Golub, A generalized conjugate gradient method for nonsymmetric systems of linear equations, in *Computing Methods in Applied Sciences and Engineering*, R. Glowinski and J. L. Lions (Editors), Lecture Notes in Economics and Mathematical Systems, Springer-Verlag, Berlin, 134 (1976), pp. 56–65. (Cited on pp. 211, 284, 391)

[98] R. Courant, Über die Eigenwerte bei den Differentialgleichungen der mathematischen Physik, *Mathematische Zeitschrift*, 7 (1920), 1–57. (Cited on p. 21)

[99] G. Cramer, Intr. à l'analyse de lignes courbes algébriques, *Geneva: Europeana*, (1750), 657–659. (Cited on p. 171)

[100] G. Csordas and R. S. Varga, Comparisons of regular splittings of matrices, *Numerische Mathematik*, 44 (1984), 23–35. (Cited on p. 199)

[101] J. J. M. Cuppen, A divide and conquer method for the symmetric tridiagonal eigenproblem, *Numerische Mathematik*, 36 (1981), 177–195. (Cited on p. 56)

[102] H. Dai, *Matrix Theory*, Science Press, Beijing, 2001. (In Chinese) (Cited on p. 419)

[103] J. W. Daniel, W. B. Gragg, L. Kaufman, and G. W. Stewart, Reorthogonalization and stable algorithms for updating the Gram-Schmidt QR factorization, *Mathematics of Computation*, 30 (1976), 772–795. (Cited on pp. 251, 338)

[104] B. Danloy, On the choice of signs for Householder's matrices, *Journal of Computational and Applied Mathematics*, 2 (1976), 67–69. (Cited on p. 48)

[105] J. W. Demmel, *Applied Numerical Linear Algebra*, SIAM, Philadelphia, 1997. (Cited on pp. 169, 174)

[106] B. L. R. De Moor and G. H. Golub, Generalized singular value decompositions: A proposal for a standardized nomenclature, *Numerical Analysis Project*, Computer Science Department, Stanford University, Stanford, CA, 1989. (Cited on pp. 71, 72)

[107] B. L. R. De Moor and H.-Y. Zha, A tree of generalizations of the ordinary singular value decomposition, *Linear Algebra and Its Applications*, 147 (1991), 469–500. (Cited on p. 72)

[108] Y.-B. Deng, Z.-Z. Bai, and Y.-H. Gao, Iterative orthogonal direction methods for Hermitian minimum norm solutions of two consistent matrix equations, *Numerical Linear Algebra with Applications*, 13 (2006), 801–823. (Cited on p. 419)

[109] H. S. Dollar, Constraint-style preconditioners for regularized saddle point problems, *SIAM Journal on Matrix Analysis and Applications*, 29 (2007), 672–684. (Cited on pp. 410, 420, 421)

[110] H. S. Dollar, N. I. M. Gould, W. H. A. Schilders, and A. J. Wathen, Implicit-factorization preconditioning and iterative solvers for regularized saddle-point systems, *SIAM Journal on Matrix Analysis and Applications*, 28 (2006), 170–189. (Cited on p. 410)

[111] H. S. Dollar and A. J. Wathen, Approximate factorization constraint preconditioners for saddle-point matrices, *SIAM Journal on Scientific Computing*, 27 (2006), 1555–1572. (Cited on p. 410)

[112] J. Dongarra, Basic linear algebra subprograms technical (BLAST) forum standard, *The International Journal of High Performance Computing Applications*, 16 (2002), 1–111. (Cited on p. 448)

[113] J. Dongarra, V. Eijkhout, and J. Langou, BLAS, The Second Edition, in *Handbook of Linear Algebra*, L. Hogben (Editor), Chapman and Hall/CRC Press, New York, 2014, pp. 92-1–92-8. (Cited on p. 447)

[114] J. J. Dongarra, C. B. Moler, J. R. Bunch, and G.W. Stewart, *LINPACK Users' Guide*, SIAM, Philadelphia, 1979. (Cited on p. 452)

[115] J. Douglas, Jr., Alternating direction methods for three space variables, *Numerische Mathematik*, 4 (1962), 41–63. (Cited on p. 211)

[116] I. S. Duff, A. M. Erisman, C. W. Gear, and J. K. Reid, Sparsity structure and Gaussian elimination, *ACM SIGNUM Newsletter*, 23 (1988), 2–8. (Cited on p. 325)

[117] C. Durazzi and V. Ruggiero, Indefinitely preconditioned conjugate gradient method for large sparse equality and inequality constrained quadratic problems, *Numerical Linear Algebra with Applications*, 10 (2003), 673–688. (Cited on p. 410)

[118] M. Eiermann, W. Niethammer, and R. S. Varga, Acceleration of relaxation methods for non-Hermitian linear systems, *SIAM Journal on Matrix Analysis and Applications*, 13 (1992), 979–991. (Cited on p. 211)

[119] S. C. Eisenstat, Efficient implementation of a class of preconditioned conjugate gradient methods, *SIAM Journal on Scientific and Statistical Computing*, 2 (1981), 1–4. (Cited on p. 327)

[120] S. C. Eisenstat, H. C. Elman, and M. H. Schultz, Variational iterative methods for nonsymmetric systems of linear equations, *SIAM Journal on Numerical Analysis*, 20 (1983), 345–357. (Cited on pp. 402, 403)

[121] H. C. Elman and G. H. Golub, Inexact and preconditioned Uzawa algorithms for saddle point problems, *SIAM Journal on Numerical Analysis*, 31 (1994), 1645–1661. (Cited on p. 386)

[122] H. C. Elman, A. Ramage, and D. J. Silvester, Algorithm 866: IFISS, A MATLAB toolbox for modelling incompressible flow, *ACM Transactions on Mathematical Software*, 33 (2007), 1–18. (Cited on p. 453)

[123] H. C. Elman, A. Ramage, and D. J. Silvester, IFISS: A computational laboratory for investigating incompressible flow problems, *SIAM Review*, 56 (2014), 261–273. (Cited on p. 453)

[124] H. C. Elman, D. J. Silvester, and A. J. Wathen, *Finite Elements and Fast Iterative Solvers: With Applications in Incompressible Fluid Dynamics*, The Second Edition, Oxford University Press, Oxford, 2014. (Cited on pp. 363, 453)

[125] D. J. Evans, The use of pre-conditioning in iterative methods for solving linear equations with symmetric positive definite matrices, *Journal of the Institute of Mathematics and its Applications*, 4 (1968), 295–314. (Cited on p. 307)

[126] D. J. Evans and M. Barulli, BSP linear solvers for dense matrices, *Parallel Computing*, 24 (1998), 777–795. (Cited on p. 54)

[127] D. J. Evans and M. Hatzopoulos, A parallel linear system solver, *International Journal of Computer Mathematics*, 7 (1979), 227–238. (Cited on p. 54)

[128] L. M. Ewerbring and F. T. Luk, Canonical correlations and generalized SVD: Applications and new algorithms, *Journal of Computational and Applied Mathematics*, 27 (1989), 37–52. (Cited on p. 72)

[129] V. Faber, W. D. Joubert, E. Knill, and T. A. Manteuffel, Minimal residual method stronger than polynomial preconditioning, *SIAM Journal on Matrix Analysis and Applications*, 17 (1996), 707–729. (Cited on p. 288)

[130] V. Faber and T. A. Manteuffel, Necessary and sufficient conditions for the existence of a conjugate gradient method, *SIAM Journal on Numerical Analysis*, 21 (1984), 352–362. (Cited on p. 288)

[131] D. K. Faddeev and V. N. Faddeeva, *Computational Methods of Linear Algebra*, W. H. Freeman and Company, San Francisco-London, 1963. (Cited on p. 301)

[132] K. Fan, Topological proofs for certain theorems on matrices with non-negative elements, *Monatshefte für Mathematik*, 62 (1958), 219–237. (Cited on p. 169)

[133] K. Fan, Note on M-matrices, *The Quarterly Journal of Mathematics*, Oxford Second Series, 11 (1960), 43–49. (Cited on p. 329)

[134] M. Fiedler, *Special Matrices and Their Applications in Numerical Mathematics*, Martinus Nijhoff Publishers, Dordrecht, 1986. (Cited on pp. 24, 25, 39)

[135] B. Fischer, *Über komplexe Tschebyscheff-Approximationsprobleme, die bei Iterationsverfahren zur Lösung linearer Gleichungssysteme entstehen*, Dissertation, Universität Hamburg, Hamburg, 1987. (Cited on p. 232)

[136] B. Fischer, *Polynomial Based Iteration Methods for Symmetric Linear Systems*, Wiley-Teubner Series Advances in Numerical Mathematics, John Wiley & Sons Limited, Chichester, 1996. (Cited on p. 285)

[137] E. Fischer, Über quadratische Formen mit reellen Koeffizienten, *Monatshefte für Mathematik und Physik*, 16 (1905), 234–249. (Cited on p. 21)

[138] B. Fischer and R. W. Freund, On the constrained Chebyshev approximation problem on ellipses, *Journal of Approximation Theory*, 62 (1990), 297–315. (Cited on pp. 230, 232)

[139] B. Fischer and R. W. Freund, Chebyshev polynomials are not always optimal, *Journal of Approximation Theory*, 65 (1991), 261–272. (Cited on pp. 230, 231)

[140] B. Fischer, A. Ramage, D. J. Silvester, and A. J. Wathen, Minimum residual methods for augmented systems, *BIT*, 38 (1998), 527–543. (Cited on pp. 378, 379)

[141] R. Fletcher, Conjugate gradient methods for indefinite systems, in "Proceeding of the Dundee Conference on Numerical Analysis 1975", G. A. Watson (Editor), Lecture Notes in Mathematics, Springer-Verlag, Berlin, 506 (1976), pp. 73–89. (Cited on pp. 281, 292)

[142] R. Fletcher, *Practical Methods of Optimization*, The Second Edition, John Wiley & Sons Limited, Chichester, UK, 1987. (Cited on p. 380)

[143] M. Fortin and R. Glowinski, *Augmented Lagrangian Methods: Applications to the Numerical Solution of Boundary Value Problems*, Vol. 15 of Studies in Mathematics and its Applications, North-Holland Publishing Company, Amsterdam, 1983. Translated from the French by B. Hunt and D. C. Spicer. (Cited on pp. 363, 382, 384)

[144] S. P. Frankel, Convergence rates of iterative treatments of partial differential equations, *Mathematical Tables and Other Aids to Computation*, 4 (1950), 65–75. (Cited on p. 178)

[145] R. W. Freund, M. H. Gutknecht, and N. M. Nachtigal, An implementation of the look-ahead Lanczos algorithm for non-Hermitian matrices, *SIAM Journal on Scientific Computing*, 14 (1993), 137–158. (Cited on p. 291)

[146] R. W. Freund and N. M. Nachtigal, QMR: A quasi-minimal residual method for non-Hermitian linear systems, *Numerische Mathematik*, 60 (1991), 315–339. (Cited on pp. 293, 294)

[147] R. W. Freund and N. M. Nachtigal, An implementation of the QMR method based on coupled two-term recurrences, Technical Report 92.15, RIACS, NASA Ames Research Center, CA, 1992. (Cited on p. 294)

[148] R. W. Freund and S. Ruscheweyh, On a class of Chebyshev approximation problems which arise in connection with a conjugate gradient type method, *Numerische Mathematik*, 48 (1986), 525–542. (Cited on p. 232)

[149] V. M. Fridman, The method of minimal iterations with minimal errors for a system of linear algebraic equations with symmetric matrix, *Zhurnal Vychislitel' noĭ Matematiki i Matematichskoĭ Fiziki*, 2 (1962), 341–342. (In Russian). English Translation in *USSR Computational Mathematics and Mathematical Physics*, 2 (1963), 362–363. (Cited on p. 281)

[150] G. F. Frobenius, *Über matrizen aus nicht negativen Elementen*, Sitzungsberichte der Königlich Preussischen Akademie der Wissenschaften, Berlin, 1912, 456–477. (Cited on pp. 134, 138, 147)

[151] A. Frommer and G. Mayer, Convergence of relaxed parallel multisplitting methods, *Linear Algebra and Its Applications*, 119 (1989), 141–152. (Cited on p. 201)

[152] A. Frommer and D. B. Szyld, H-splittings and two-stage iterative methods, *Numerische Mathematik*, 63 (1992), 345–356. (Cited on p. 201)

[153] W. Gander, *Learning MATLAB – A Problem Solving Approach*, Springer, Cham, 2015. (Cited on p. 453)

[154] W. Gander, M. J. Gander, and F. Kwok, *Scientific Computing – An Introduction Using Maple and MATLAB*, Texts in Computational Science and Engineering, Vol. 11, Springer, Cham, 2014. (Cited on p. 453)

[155] W. N. Gansterer, J. Schneid, and C. W. Ueberhuber, Mathematical properties of equilibrium systems, Technical Report AURORA TR2003-13, University of Vienna and Vienna University of Technology, 2003. (Cited on p. 367)

[156] F. R. Gantmacher, *The Theory of Matrices*, Vol. II, Chelsea Publishing Company, New York, 1959. (Cited on p. 33)

[157] B. S. Garbow, J. M. Boyle, J. J. Dongarra, and C. B. Moler, *Matrix Eigensystem Routines – EISPACK Guide Extension*, Lecture Notes in Computer Science, Vol. 51, Springer-Verlag, Berlin, 1977. (Cited on p. 452)

[158] S. Geršgorin, Ueber die Abgrenzung der Eigenwerte einer Matrix, *Izvestiya Akademii Nauk SSSR Seriya Matematicheskaya*, 1 (1931), 749–754. (Cited on pp. 148, 149)

[159] P. E. Gill, W. Murray, and M. H. Wright, *Practical Optimization*, Academic Press, London, 1981. (Cited on p. 380)

[160] R. Glowinski, *Numerical Methods for Nonlinear Variational Problems*, Springer Series in Computational Physics, Springer, New York, 1984. (Cited on p. 382)

[161] R. Glowinski, *Finite Element Methods for Incompressible Viscous Flow*, Vol. IX of Handbook of Numerical Analysis, Part 3: Numerical Methods for Fluids, North-Holland, Amsterdam, 2003. (Cited on p. 382)

[162] M. Goldberg and E. G. Straus, Elementary inclusion relations for generalized numerical ranges, *Linear Algebra and Its Applications*, 18 (1977), 1–24. (Cited on p. 109)

[163] M. Goldberg and E. Tadmor, On the numerical radius and its applications, *Linear Algebra and Its Applications*, 42 (1982), 263–284. (Cited on p. 82)

[164] G. H. Golub and W. M. Kahan, Calculating the singular values and pseudo-inverse of a matrix, *SIAM Journal on Numerical Analysis*, 2 (1965), 205–224. (Cited on p. 303)

[165] G. H. Golub and M. L. Overton, The convergence of inexact Chebyshev and Richardson iterative methods for solving linear systems, *Numerische Mathematik*, 53 (1988), 571-593. (Cited on p. 382)

[166] G. H. Golub and D. Vanderstraeten, On the preconditioning of matrices with skew-symmetric splittings, *Numerical Algorithms*, 25 (2000), 223–239. (Cited on pp. 211, 391)

[167] G. H. Golub and C. F. Van Loan, *Matrix Computations*, The Third Edition, Johns Hopkins University Press, Baltimore, MD, 1996. (Cited on pp. 7, 40, 46, 47, 48, 50, 60, 61, 63, 64, 66, 68, 174, 307, 321, 322, 398, 420)

[168] G. H. Golub and R. S. Varga, Chebyshev semi-iterative methods, successive overrelaxation iterative methods, and second order Richardson iterative methods, *Numerische Mathematik*, 3 (1961), 147–168. (Cited on p. 225)

[169] G. H. Golub and A. J. Wathen, An iteration for indefinite systems and its application to the Navier-Stokes equations, *SIAM Journal on Scientific Computing*, 19 (1998), 530–539. (Cited on pp. 211, 442)

[170] G. H. Golub, X. Wu, and J.-Y. Yuan, SOR-like methods for augmented systems, *BIT*, 41 (2001), 71–85. (Cited on p. 386)

[171] N. I. M. Gould, M. E. Hribar, and J. Nocedal, On the solution of equality constrained quadratic programming problems arising in optimization, *SIAM Journal on Scientific Computing*, 23 (2001), 1376–1395. (Cited on pp. 410, 421)

[172] A. Greenbaum, Comparison of splittings used with the conjugate gradient algorithm, *Numerische Mathematik*, 33 (1979), 181–193. (Cited on p. 283)

[173] A. Greenbaum, *Iterative Methods for Solving Linear Systems*, SIAM, Philadelphia, 1997. (Cited on pp. 357, 402)

[174] A. Greenbaum and L. Gurvits, Max-min properties of matrix factor norms, *SIAM Journal on Scientific Computing*, 15 (1994), 348–358. (Cited on pp. 285, 288)

[175] A. Greenbaum, V. Pták, and Z. Strakoš, Any nonincreasing convergence curve is possible for GMRES, *SIAM Journal on Matrix Analysis and Applications*, 17 (1996), 465–469. (Cited on p. 287)

[176] A. Greenbaum and Z. Strakoš, Matrices that generate the same Krylov residual spaces, in *Recent Advances in Iterative Methods*, Vol. 60 of The IMA Volumes in Mathematics and its Applications, Springer, New York, 1994, pp. 95–118. (Cited on p. 287)

[177] A. Greenbaum and L. N. Trefethen, GMRES/CR and Arnoldi/Lanczos as matrix approximation problems, *SIAM Journal on Scientific Computing*, 15 (1994), 359–368. (Cited on p. 288)

[178] M. Gu and S. C. Eisenstat, A stable and efficient algorithm for the rank-one modification of the symmetric eigenproblem, *SIAM Journal on Matrix Analysis and Applications*, 15 (1994), 1266–1276. (Cited on p. 56)

[179] M. Gu and S. C. Eisenstat, A divide-and-conquer algorithm for the symmetric tridiagonal eigenproblem, *SIAM Journal on Matrix Analysis and Applications*, 16 (1995), 172–191. (Cited on p. 56)

[180] I. Gustafsson, A class of first order factorization methods, *BIT*, 18 (1978), 142–156. (Cited on p. 327)

[181] K. E. Gustafson and D. K. M. Rao, *Numerical Range: The Field of Values of Linear Operators and Matrices*, Springer-Verlag, New York, 1997. (Cited on pp. 78, 80, 85, 98, 104)

[182] M. H. Gutknecht, A completed theory of the unsymmetric Lanczos process and related algorithms. Part I, *SIAM Journal on Matrix Analysis and Applications*, 13 (1992), 594–639. (Cited on p. 291)

[183] M. H. Gutknecht, A completed theory of the unsymmetric Lanczos process and related algorithms. Part II, *SIAM Journal on Matrix Analysis and Applications*, 15 (1994), 15–58. (Cited on p. 291)

[184] M. H. Gutknecht, Lanczos-type solvers for nonsymmetric linear systems of equations, *Acta Numerica*, 6 (1997), 271–397. (Cited on p. 291)

[185] M. H. Gutknecht and Z. Strakoš, Accuracy of two three-term and three two-term recurrences for Krylov space solvers, *SIAM Journal on Matrix Analysis and Applications*, 22 (2000), 213–229. (Cited on p. 293)

[186] W. Hackbusch, *Iterative Solution of Large Sparse Systems of Equations*, Springer-Verlag, New York, 1994. (Cited on p. 176)

[187] A. Hadjidimos, Accelerated overrelaxation method, *Mathematics of Computation*, 32 (1978), 149–157. (Cited on p. 180)

[188] G. F. Hadley, *Nonlinear and Dynamic Programming*, Addison-Wesley, Reading, MA, 1964. (Cited on p. 365)

[189] L. A. Hagemen and D. M. Young, *Applied Iterative Methods*, Academic Press, New York, 1981. (Cited on pp. 238, 239)

[190] P. R. Halmos, *A Hilbert Space Problem Book*, D. Van Nostrand, New York, 1967; The Second Edition, Springer-Verlag, New York, 1982. (Cited on pp. 80, 104, 105)

[191] V. Hari and K. Veselić, On Jacobi methods for singular value decompositions, *SIAM Journal on Scientific and Statistical Computing*, 8 (1987), 741–754. (Cited on p. 72)

[192] J. W. Harris and H. Stöcker, Hyperbolic Functions, in *Handbook of Mathematics and Computational Science*, Springer-Verlag, New York, 1998, pp. 245–262. (Cited on p. 226)

[193] I. N. Herstein, A note on primitive matrices, *The American Mathematical Monthly*, 61 (1954), 18–20. (Cited on p. 145)

[194] M. R. Hestenes, Multiplier and gradient methods, *Journal of Optimization Theory and Applications*, 4 (1969), 303–320. (Cited on p. 363)

[195] M. R. Hestenes and E. L. Stiefel, Methods of conjugate gradients for solving linear systems, *Journal of Research of the National Bureau of Standards*, 49 (1952), 409–436. (Cited on pp. 263, 268, 321)

[196] N. J. Higham, *Accuracy and Stability of Numerical Algorithms*, The Second Edition, SIAM, Philadelphia, 2002. (Cited on p. 61)

[197] M.-K. Ho and M. K. Ng, Splitting iterations for circulant-plus-diagonal systems, *Numerical Linear Algebra with Applications*, 12 (2005), 779–792. (Cited on p. 218)

[198] R. M. Holland, A. J. Wathen, and G. J. Shaw, Sparse approximate inverses and target matrices, *SIAM Journal on Scientific Computing*, 26 (2005), 1000–1011. (Cited on p. 359)

[199] R. A. Horn and C. R. Johnson, *Matrix Analysis*, Cambridge University Press, New York, 1985. (Cited on pp. 12, 13, 14, 17, 18, 21, 22, 24, 31, 32, 51, 52, 56, 66, 94, 125, 128, 141, 142, 148)

[200] R. A. Horn and C. R. Johnson, *Topics in Matrix Analysis*, Cambridge University Press, New York, 1991. (Cited on pp. 37, 38, 77, 80, 94, 101, 104)

[201] J.-G. Hu, *Iterative Methods for Systems of Linear Algebraic Equations*, Science Press, Beijing, 1991. (In Chinese) (Cited on pp. 164, 166)

[202] Q.-Y. Hu and J. Zou, Two new variants of nonlinear inexact Uzawa algorithms for saddle-point problems, *Numerische Mathematik*, 93 (2002), 333–359. (Cited on p. 399)

[203] Q.-Y. Hu and J. Zou, Nonlinear inexact Uzawa algorithms for linear and nonlinear saddle-point problems, *SIAM Journal on Optimization*, 16 (2006), 798–825. (Cited on p. 399)

[204] M. Huhtanen, A Hermitian Lanczos method for normal matrices, *SIAM Journal on Matrix Analysis and Applications*, 23 (2002), 1092–1108. (Cited on p. 391)

[205] V. P. Il'in, *Iterative Incomplete Factorization Methods*, World Scientific, Singapore, 1992. (Cited on p. 325)

[206] I. C. F. Ipsen, A note on preconditioning nonsymmetric matrices, *SIAM Journal on Scientific Computing*, 23 (2001), 1050–1051. (Cited on pp. 408, 410)

[207] E.-X. Jiang, Algorithm for solving shifted skew-symmetric linear system, *Frontiers of Mathematics in China*, 2 (2007), 227–242. (Cited on p. 391)

[208] E.-X. Jiang, *Matrix Computations*, Science Press, Beijing, 2008. (In Chinese) (Cited on p. 391)

[209] C. R. Johnson, Numerical determination of the field of values of a general complex matrix, *SIAM Journal on Numerical Analysis*, 15 (1978), 595–602. (Cited on p. 80)

[210] M. T. Jones and P. E. Plassmann, An improved incomplete Cholesky factorization, *ACM Transactions on Mathematical Software*, 21 (1995), 5–17. (Cited on p. 334)

[211] M. T. Jones and P. E. Plassmann, Algorithm 740: Fortran subroutines to compute improved incomplete Cholesky factorizations, *ACM Transactions on Mathematical Software*, 21 (1995), 18–19. (Cited on p. 334)

[212] W. D. Joubert, A robust GMRES-based adaptive polynomial preconditioning algorithm for nonsymmetric linear systems, *SIAM Journal on Scientific Computing*, 15 (1994), 427–439. (Cited on pp. 285, 288)

[213] B. Kågström, The generalized singular value decomposition and the general $(A - \lambda B)$-problem, *BIT*, 24 (1984), 568–583. (Cited on p. 72)

[214] W. M. Kahan, *Gauss-Seidel Methods of Solving Large Systems of Linear Equations*, Doctoral Thesis, University of Toronto, 1958. (Cited on p. 187)

[215] C. Keller, N. I. M. Gould, and A. J. Wathen, Constraint preconditioning for indefinite linear systems, *SIAM Journal on Matrix Analysis and Applications*, 21 (2000), 1300–1317. (Cited on pp. 410, 420)

[216] L. Yu. Kolotilina and A. Yu. Yeremin, Factorized sparse approximate inverse preconditionings. I: Theory, *SIAM Journal on Matrix Analysis and Applications*, 14 (1993), 45–58. (Cited on p. 360)

[217] D. Kressner, *Numerical Methods for General and Structured Eigenvalue Problems*, Springer-Verlag, Berlin, 2005. (Cited on p. 56)

[218] Y. A. Kuznetsov, Matrix iterative methods in subspaces, *Proceeding of the International Congress of Mathematicians*, Warszawa, 2 (1983), 1509–1521. (Cited on pp. 209, 242)

[219] C. Lanczos, Solution of systems of linear equations by minimized iterations, *Journal of Research of the National Bureau of Standards*, 49 (1952), 33–53. (Cited on pp. 288, 292)

[220] C. L. Lawson, R. J. Hanson, D. R. Kincaid, and F. T. Krogh, Basic linear algebra subprograms for FORTRAN usage, *ACM Transactions on Mathematical Software*, 5 (1979), 308–323. (Cited on p. 447)

[221] R. B. Lehoucq, *Analysis and Implementation of an Implicitly Restarted Arnoldi Iteration*, Ph.D. Thesis, Rice University, Houston, TX, 1995. (Cited on pp. 260, 262, 291)

[222] C.-K. Li, The C-convex matrices, *Linear and Multilinear Algebra*, 21 (1987), 303–312. (Cited on p. 114)

[223] C.-K. Li, C-numerical ranges and C-numerical radii, *Linear and Multilinear Algebra*, 37 (1994), 51–82. (Cited on pp. 105, 108, 110, 111, 112, 114, 115)

[224] C.-K. Li, T.-Y. Tam, and N.-K. Tsing, The generalized spectral radius, numerical radius and spectral norm, *Linear and Multilinear Algebra*, 16 (1984), 215–237. (Cited on p. 113)

[225] A.-P. Liao and Z.-Z. Bai, Least-squares solution of $AXB = D$ over symmetric positive semidefinite matrices X, *Journal of Computational Mathematics*, 21 (2003), 175–182. (Cited on p. 419)

[226] A.-P. Liao, Z.-Z. Bai, and Y. Lei, Best approximate solution of matrix equation $AXB + CYD = E$, *SIAM Journal on Matrix Analysis and Applications*, 27 (2005), 675–688. (Cited on p. 419)

[227] J. Liesen, Computable convergence bounds for GMRES, *SIAM Journal on Matrix Analysis and Applications*, 21 (2000), 882–903. (Cited on p. 287)

[228] J. Liesen and P. Tichý, Convergence analysis of Krylov subspace methods, *GAMM-Mitteilungen*, 27 (2004), 153–173. (Cited on pp. 281, 287, 288)

[229] J. Liesen and P. Tichý, Behavior of CG and MINRES for symmetric tridiagonal Toeplitz matrices, Preprint 34-2004, Institute of Mathematics, Technical University of Berlin, 2004. (Cited on p. 284)

[230] C.-J. Lin and J. J. Moré, Incomplete Cholesky factorizations with limited memory, *SIAM Journal on Scientific Computing*, 21 (1999), 24–45. (Cited on p. 334)

[231] D. G. Luenberger, *Linear and Nonlinear Programming*, Addison-Wesley, Reading, MA, 1984. (Cited on p. 365)

[232] L. Lukšan and J. Vlček, Indefinitely preconditioned inexact Newton method for large sparse equality constrained non-linear programming problems, *Numerical Linear Algebra with Applications*, 5 (1998), 219–247. (Cited on p. 410)

[233] M. E. Lundquist and W. W. Barrett, Rank inequalities for positive semidefinite matrices, *Linear Algebra and Its Applications*, 248 (1996), 91–100. (Cited on p. 25)

[234] T. A. Manteuffel, An incomplete factorization technique for positive definite linear systems, *Mathematics of Computation*, 34 (1980), 473–497. (Cited on p. 332)

[235] M. D. Marcus and I. Filippenko, Nondifferentiable boundary points of the higher numerical range, *Linear Algebra and Its Applications*, 21 (1978), 217–232. (Cited on p. 105)

[236] M. D. Marcus and H. Minc, *A Survey of Matrix Theory and Matrix Inequalities*, Allyn and Bacon, Boston, 1964. (Cited on p. 153)

[237] M. D. Marcus, B. N. Moyls, and I. Filippenko, Normality and the higher numerical range, *Canadian Journal of Mathematics*, 30 (1978), 419–430. (Cited on p. 111)

[238] T. P. A. Mathew, *Domain Decomposition Methods for the Numerical Solution of Partial Differential Equations*, Springer-Verlag, Berlin, 2008. (Cited on p. 323)

[239] G. Mayer, Comparison theorems for iterative methods based on strong splittings, *SIAM Journal on Numerical Analysis*, 24 (1987), 215–227. (Cited on p. 201)

[240] J. A. Meijerink and H. A. van der Vorst, An iterative solution method for linear systems of which the coefficient matrix is a symmetric M-matrix, *Mathematics of Computation*, 31 (1977), 148–162. (Cited on pp. 321, 325, 327, 330, 332)

[241] G. Meinardus, *Approximation of Functions: Theory and Numerical Methods*, Springer-Verlag, New York, 1967. (Cited on p. 230)

[242] G. A. Meurant, *Computer Solution of Large Linear Systems*, Studies in Mathematics and Its Applications, Vol. 28, North-Holland, Amsterdam, 1999. (Cited on p. 335)

[243] J. J. Modi, *Parallel Algorithms and Matrix Computation*, Clarendon Press, Oxford, 1988. (Cited on pp. 54, 195)

[244] C. B. Moler and G. W. Stewart, An algorithm for generalized matrix eigenvalue problems, *SIAM Journal on Numerical Analysis*, 10 (1973), 241–256. (Cited on p. 64)

[245] M. F. Murphy, G. H. Golub, and A. J. Wathen, A note on preconditioning for indefinite linear systems, *SIAM Journal on Scientific Computing*, 21 (2000), 1969–1972. (Cited on pp. 408, 410)

[246] A. Neumaier, New techniques for the analysis of linear interval equations, *Linear Algebra and Its Applications*, 58 (1984), 273–325. (Cited on p. 201)

[247] A. Neumaier, On the comparison of H-matrices with M-matrices, *Linear Algebra and Its Applications*, 83 (1986), 135–141. (Cited on p. 201)

[248] A. Neumaier, *Interval Methods for Systems of Equations*, Cambridge University Press, Cambridge, New York, 1990. (Cited on p. 201)

[249] M. K. Ng, Circulant and skew-circulant splitting methods for Toeplitz systems, *Journal of Computational and Applied Mathematics*, 159 (2003), 101–108. (Cited on pp. 218, 406)

[250] J. M. Nocedal and S. J. Wright, *Numerical Optimization*, The Second Edition, Springer Series in Operations Research and Financial Engineering, Springer, New York, 2006. (Cited on pp. 363, 380)

[251] R. Oldenburger, Infinite powers of matrices and characteristic roots, *Duke Mathematical Journal*, 6 (1940), 357–361. (Cited on p. 19)

[252] D. P. O'Leary and R. E. White, Multi-splittings of matrices and parallel solution of linear systems, *SIAM Journal on Algebraic Discrete Methods*, 6 (1985), 630–640. (Cited on p. 181)

[253] G. Opfer and G. E. Schober, Richardson's iteration for nonsymmetric matrices, *Linear Algebra and Its Applications*, 58 (1984), 343–361. (Cited on p. 232)

[254] J. M. Ortega, *Numerical Analysis, A Second Course*, Academic Press, New York, 1972. (Cited on p. 207)

[255] J. M. Ortega, *Introduction to Parallel and Vector Solution of Linear Systems*, Plenum Press, New York, 1988. (Cited on pp. 195, 210)

[256] J. M. Ortega and R. J. Plemmons, Extensions of the Ostrowski-Reich theorem for SOR iterations, *Linear Algebra and Its Applications*, 28 (1979), 177–191. (Cited on p. 207)

[257] J. M. Ortega and W. C. Rheinboldt, *Iterative Solution of Nonlinear Equations in Several Variables*, Academic Press, New York, London, 1970. (Cited on pp. 2, 176, 196)

[258] A. M. Ostrowski, On the linear iteration procedures for symmetric matrices, *Rendiconti di Matematica e delle sue Applicazioni*, 14 (1954), 140–163. (Cited on pp. 191, 208)

[259] C. C. Paige, Bidiagonalization of matrices and solution of linear equations, *SIAM Journal on Numerical Analysis*, 11 (1974), 197–209. (Cited on p. 301)

[260] C. C. Paige, Computing the generalized singular value decomposition, *SIAM Journal on Scientific and Statistical Computing*, 7 (1986), 1126–1146. (Cited on p. 72)

[261] C. C. Paige, B. N. Parlett, and H. A. van der Vorst, Approximate solutions and eigenvalue bounds from Krylov subspaces, *Numerical Linear Algebra with Applications*, 2 (1995), 115–133. (Cited on pp. 269, 275)

[262] C. C. Paige, M. Rozložník, and Z. Strakoš, Modified Gram–Schmidt (MGS), least squares, and backward stability of MGS-GMRES, *SIAM Journal on Matrix Analysis and Applications*, 28 (2006), 264–284. (Cited on p. 251)

[263] C. C. Paige and M. A. Saunders, Solution of sparse indefinite systems of linear equations, *SIAM Journal on Numerical Analysis*, 12 (1975), 617–629. (Cited on pp. 269, 274, 275, 276)

[264] C. C. Paige and M. A. Saunders, Towards a generalized singular value decomposition, *SIAM Journal on Numerical Analysis*, 18 (1981), 398–405. (Cited on pp. 70, 71)

[265] C. C. Paige and M. A. Saunders, LSQR: An algorithm for sparse linear equations and sparse least squares, *ACM Transactions on Mathematical Software*, 8 (1982), 43–71. (Cited on pp. 301, 302)

[266] C. C. Paige and M.-S. Wei, History and generality of the CS decomposition, *Linear Algebra and Its Applications*, 208/209 (1994), 303–326. (Cited on p. 70)

[267] J.-Y. Pan, Z.-Z. Bai, and M. K. Ng, Two-step waveform relaxation methods for implicit linear initial value problems, *Numerical Linear Algebra with Applications*, 12 (2005), 293–304. (Cited on pp. 214, 406)

[268] J.-Y. Pan, M. K. Ng, and Z.-Z. Bai, New preconditioners for saddle point problems, *Applied Mathematics and Computation*, 172 (2006), 762–771. (Cited on pp. 214, 223, 406)

[269] A. T. Papadopoulos, I. S. Duff, and A. J. Wathen, A class of incomplete orthogonal factorization methods. II: Implementation and results, *BIT Numerical Mathematics*, 45 (2005), 159–179. (Cited on p. 349)

[270] B. N. Parlett, Analysis of algorithms for reflections in bisectors, *SIAM Review*, 13 (1971), 197–208. (Cited on p. 48)

[271] B. N. Parlett, *The Symmetric Eigenvalue Problem*, The Second Edition, Corrected Reprint of the 1980 Original, SIAM, Philadelphia, 1998. (Cited on pp. 21, 48, 56, 263)

[272] B. N. Parlett, D. R. Taylor, and Z.-A. Liu, A look-ahead Lanczos algorithm for unsymmetric matrices, *Mathematics of Computation*, 44 (1985), 105–124. (Cited on p. 291)

[273] D. W. Peaceman and H. H. Rachford, Jr., The numerical solution of parabolic and elliptic differential equations, *Journal of the Society for Industrial and Applied Mathematics*, 3 (1955), 28–41. (Cited on p. 211)

[274] O. Perron, Zur Theorie der Matrices, *Mathematische Annalen*, 64 (1907), 248–263. (Cited on pp. 128, 138, 145)

[275] I. Perugia and V. Simoncini, Block-diagonal and indefinite symmetric preconditioners for mixed finite element formulations, *Numerical Linear Algebra with Applications*, 7 (2000), 585–616. (Cited on p. 410)

[276] M. J. D. Powell, A method for nonlinear constraints in minimization problems, in *Optimization*, R. Fletcher (Editor), Academic Press, London, 1969, pp. 283–298. (Cited on p. 363)

[277] A. Quarteroni and A. Valli, *Domain Decomposition Methods for Partial Differential Equations*, Oxford Science Publications, Oxford, 1999. (Cited on p. 323)

[278] W. Queck, The convergence factor of preconditioned algorithms of the Arrow–Hurwicz type, *SIAM Journal on Numerical Analysis*, 26 (1989), 1016–1030. (Cited on p. 384)

[279] E. Reich, On the convergence of the classical iterative method of solving linear simultaneous equations, *The Annals of Mathematical Statistics*, 20 (1949), 448–451. (Cited on pp. 191, 209)

[280] L. F. Richardson, The approximate arithmetical solution by finite differences of physical problems involving differential equations with an application to the stresses to a masonry dam, *Philosophical Transactions of the Royal Society of London, Series A*, 210 (1911), 307–357. (Cited on p. 223)

[281] T. J. Rivlin, *Chebyshev Polynomials: From Approximation Theory to Algebra and Number Theory*, John Wiley & Sons, New York, 1990. (Cited on p. 231)

[282] Y. Robert, Regular incomplete factorizations of real positive definite matrices, *Linear Algebra and Its Applications*, 48 (1982), 105–117. (Cited on p. 332)

[283] T. Rusten and R. Winther, A preconditioned iterative method for saddlepoint problems, *SIAM Journal on Matrix Analysis and Applications*, 13 (1992), 887–904. (Cited on p. 367)

[284] Y. Saad, Preconditioning techniques for nonsymmetric and indefinite linear systems, *Journal of Computational and Applied Mathematics*, 24 (1988), 89–105. (Cited on pp. 335, 336, 337, 338, 349)

[285] Y. Saad, *Numerical Methods for Large Eigenvalue Problems*, Manchester University Press, Manchester, UK, 1992. (Cited on p. 56)

[286] Y. Saad, A flexible inner-outer preconditioned GMRES algorithm, *SIAM Journal on Scientific Computing*, 14 (1993), 461–469. (Cited on p. 315)

[287] Y. Saad, ILUT: A dual threshold incomplete LU factorization, *Numerical Linear Algebra with Applications*, 1 (1994), 387–402. (Cited on pp. 333, 346)

[288] Y. Saad, *Iterative Methods for Sparse Linear Systems*, The Second Edition, SIAM, Philadelphia, 2003. (Cited on pp. 15, 20, 32, 226, 229, 232, 247, 252, 301, 307, 308, 309, 318, 321, 322, 323, 327, 328, 335, 346, 357, 360, 402)

[289] Y. Saad and M. H. Schultz, GMRES: A generalized minimal residual algorithm for solving nonsymmetric linear systems, *SIAM Journal on Scientific and Statistical Computing*, 7 (1986), 856–869. (Cited on pp. 287, 309, 357, 402, 403)

[290] Y. Saad and H. A. van der Vorst, Iterative solution of linear systems in the 20th century, *Journal of Computational and Applied Mathematics*, 123 (2000), 1–33. (Cited on p. 284)

[291] I. Schur, Über die characteristischen wurzeln einer linearen substitution mit einer anwendung auf die theorie der integralgleichungen, *Mathematische Annalen*, 66 (1909), 488–510. (Cited on p. 62)

[292] Y. Shapira, *Matrix-Based Multigrid: Theory and Applications*, The Second Edition, Springer, New York, 2008. (Cited on p. 323)

[293] D. J. Silvester, H. C. Elman, and A. Ramage, Incompressible Flow and Iterative Solver Software: An Open-Source Software Package, Version 3.5, September, 2016. Available online at http://www.cs.umd.edu/~elman/ifiss3.5.html. (Cited on p. 453)

[294] D. J. Silvester and A. J. Wathen, Fast iterative solution of stabilised Stokes systems. Part II: Using general block preconditioners, *SIAM Journal on Numerical Analysis*, 31 (1994), 1352–1367. (Cited on pp. 367, 369, 375)

[295] V. Simoncini and M. Benzi, Spectral properties of the Hermitian and skew-Hermitian splitting preconditioner for saddle point problems, *SIAM Journal on Matrix Analysis and Applications*, 26 (2004), 377–389. (Cited on pp. 214, 223, 406)

[296] V. Simoncini and D. B. Szyld, On the occurrence of superlinear convergence of exact and inexact Krylov subspace methods, *SIAM Review*, 47 (2005), 247–272. (Cited on p. 284)

[297] G. L. G. Sleijpen, H. A. van der Vorst, and J. Modersitzki, Differences in the effects of rounding errors in Krylov solvers for symmetric indefinite linear systems, *SIAM Journal on Matrix Analysis and Applications*, 22 (2000), 726–751. (Cited on p. 275)

[298] B. T. Smith, J. M. Boyle, J. J. Dongarra, B. S. Garbow, Y. Ikebe, V. C. Klema, and C. B. Moler, *Matrix Eigensystem Routines – EISPACK Guide*, The Second Edition, Lecture Notes in Computer Science, Vol. 6, Springer-Verlag, Berlin, 1976. (Cited on p. 452)

[299] V. N. Solov'ëv, A generalization of Geršgorin's theorem, *Mathematics of the USSR-Izvestiya*, 23 (1984), 545–560. (Cited on p. 152)

[300] Y.-Z. Song, Comparisons of nonnegative splittings of matrices, *Linear Algebra and Its Applications*, 154-156 (1991), 433–455. (Cited on pp. 196, 201)

[301] P. Sonneveld, CGS: A fast Lanczos-type solver for nonsymmetric linear systems, *SIAM Journal on Scientific and Statistical Computing*, 10 (1989), 36–52. (Cited on pp. 296, 297)

[302] D. C. Sorensen, Implicit application of polynomial filters in a k-step Arnoldi method, *SIAM Journal on Matrix Analysis and Applications*, 13 (1992), 357–385. (Cited on pp. 260, 262, 291)

[303] P. Stein, Some general theorems on iterants, *Journal of Research of the National Bureau of Standards*, 48 (1952), 82–83. (Cited on pp. 28, 39)

[304] G. W. Stewart, On the sensitivity of the eigenvalue problem $Ax = \lambda Bx$, *SIAM Journal on Numerical Analysis*, 9 (1972), 669–686. (Cited on p. 64)

[305] G. W. Stewart, *Introduction to Matrix Computations*, Academic Press, New York, 1973. (Cited on p. 21)

[306] G. W. Stewart, On the perturbation of pseudo-inverses, projections and linear least squares problems, *SIAM Review*, 19 (1977), 634–662. (Cited on p. 70)

[307] G. W. Stewart, Computing the CS decomposition of a partitioned orthonormal matrix, *Numerische Mathematik*, 40 (1982), 297–306. (Cited on p. 72)

[308] G. W. Stewart, *Matrix Algorithms, Vol I: Basic Decompositions*, SIAM, Philadelphia, 1998. (Cited on pp. 67, 68)

[309] J. Stoer and R. Bulirsch, *Introduction to Numerical Analysis*, The Second Edition, Springer-Verlag, New York, 1993. (Cited on p. 30)

[310] G. Strang, *Linear Algebra and Its Applications*, Academic Press, New York, 1980. (Cited on p. 33)

[311] K. Stüben, Algebraic multigrid (AMG): Experiences and comparisons, *Applied Mathematics and Computation*, 13 (1983), 419–451. (Cited on pp. 323, 453)

[312] O. Taussky, A generalization of a theorem of Lyapunov, *Journal of the Society for Industrial and Applied Mathematics*, 9 (1961), 640–643. (Cited on p. 39)

[313] O. Taussky, Bounds for the characteristic roots of matrices, *Duke Mathematical Journal*, 15 (1948), 1043–1044. (Cited on p. 151)

[314] D. R. Taylor, *Analysis of the Look Ahead Lanczos Algorithm*, Ph.D. Thesis, Department of Mathematics, University of California, Berkeley, CA, 1982. (Cited on p. 291)

[315] R. M. Temam, *Navier-Stokes Equations: Theory and Numerical Analysis*, Vol. 2 of Studies in Mathematics and Its Applications, The Third Edition, North-Holland, Amsterdam, 1984. (Cited on p. 382)

[316] A. Toselli and O. B. Widlund, *Domain Decomposition Methods – Algorithms and Theory*, Springer-Verlag, Berlin, 2005. (Cited on p. 323)

[317] L. N. Trefethen and D. Bau, III, *Numerical Linear Algebra*, SIAM, Philadelphia, 1997. (Cited on pp. 66, 307)

[318] U. Trottenberg, C. W. Oosterlee, and A. Schüller, *Multigrid*, Academic Press, San Diego, CA, 2001. (Cited on p. 323)

[319] S. Turek, *Efficient Solvers for Incompressible Flow Problems: An Algorithmic and Computational Approach*, Vol. 6 of Lecture Notes in Computational Science and Engineering, Springer, Berlin, 1999. (Cited on p. 382)

[320] H. Uzawa, Iterative methods for concave programming, in *Studies in Linear and Nonlinear Programming*, K. J. Arrow, L. Hurwicz, and H. Uzawa (Editors), Stanford University Press, Stanford, CA, 1958, pp. 154–165. (Cited on p. 382)

[321] A. van der Sluis and H. A. van der Vorst, The rate of convergence of conjugate gradients, *Numerische Mathematik*, 48 (1986), 543–560. (Cited on p. 284)

[322] H. A. van der Vorst, Bi-CGSTAB: A fast and smoothly converging variant of Bi-CG for the solution of nonsymmetric linear systems, *SIAM Journal on Scientific and Statistical Computing*, 13 (1992), 631–644. (Cited on p. 297)

[323] H. A. van der Vorst, *Iterative Krylov Methods for Large Linear Systems*, Cambridge University Press, Cambridge, UK, 2003. (Cited on pp. 294, 357)

[324] S. Van Huffel and J. P. Vandewalle, *The Total Least Squares Problem: Computational Aspects and Analysis*, SIAM, Philadelphia, 1991. (Cited on p. 56)

[325] C. F. Van Loan, Generalizing the singular value decomposition, *SIAM Journal on Numerical Analysis*, 13 (1976), 76–83. (Cited on p. 71)

[326] C. F. Van Loan, Computing the CS and the generalized singular value decompositions, *Numerische Mathematik*, 46 (1985), 479–491. (Cited on p. 72)

[327] C. F. Van Loan, On the method of weighting for equality-constrained least-squares problems, *SIAM Journal on Numerical Analysis*, 22 (1985), 851–864. (Cited on p. 363)

[328] R. S. Varga, Factorization and normalized iterative methods, in *Boundary Problems in Differential Equations*, R. E. Langer (Editor), University Wisconsin Press, Madison, 1960, pp. 121–142. (Cited on p. 325)

[329] R. S. Varga, *Matrix Iterative Analysis*, Prentice-Hall, Englewood Cliffs, NJ, 1962. The Second Edition, Springer-Verlag, Berlin, 2000. (Cited on pp. 134, 141, 142, 156, 162, 191, 196, 199, 224, 225, 233, 242, 406)

[330] R. S. Varga, *Geršgorin and His Circles*, Springer-Verlag, Berlin, 2004. (Cited on p. 154)

[331] R. S. Varga, E. B. Saff, and V. Mehrmann, Incomplete factorizations of matrices and connections with H-matrices, *SIAM Journal on Numerical Analysis*, 17 (1980), 787–793. (Cited on p. 332)

[332] P. S. Vassilevski, *Multilevel Block Factorization Preconditioners: Matrix-Based Analysis and Algorithms for Solving Finite Element Equations*, Springer, New York, 2008. (Cited on p. 323)

[333] V. V. Voevodin, The question of non-self-adjoint extension of the conjugate gradient method is closed, *U.S.S.R. Computational Mathematics and Mathematical Physics*, 23 (1983), 143–144. (Cited on p. 288)

[334] H. F. Walker, Implementation of the GMRES method using Householder transformations, *SIAM Journal on Scientific and Statistical Computing*, 9 (1988), 152–163. (Cited on pp. 251, 259)

[335] C.-L. Wang and Z.-Z. Bai, Sufficient conditions for the convergent splittings of non-Hermitian positive definite matrices, *Linear Algebra and Its Applications*, 330 (2001), 215–218. (Cited on pp. 210, 211)

[336] L. Wang and Z.-Z. Bai, Convergence conditions for splitting iteration methods for non-Hermitian linear systems, *Linear Algebra and Its Applications*, 428 (2008), 453–468. (Cited on pp. 210, 211)

[337] X.-G. Wang, K. A. Gallivan, and R. B. Bramley, CIMGS: An incomplete orthogonal factorization preconditioner, *SIAM Journal on Scientific Computing*, 18 (1997), 516–536. (Cited on pp. 335, 338, 349)

[338] A. J. Wathen, Preconditioning, *Acta Numerica*, 24 (2015), 329–376. (Cited on pp. 307, 308, 406)

[339] D. S. Watkins, *Fundamentals of Matrix Computations*, The Second Edition, John Wiley & Sons, New York, 2002. (Cited on p. 46)

[340] J. W. Watts III, A conjugate gradient-truncated direct method for the iterative solution of the reservoir simulation pressure equation, *Society of Petroleum Engineers Journal*, 21 (1981), 345–353. (Cited on p. 327)

[341] M.-S. Wei, *Theories and Computations of Generalized Least-Squares Problems*, Science Press, Beijing, 2006. (In Chinese) (Cited on pp. 56, 70, 72)

[342] F. B. Weissler, Some remarks concerning iterative methods for linear systems, *SIAM Journal on Matrix Analysis and Applications*, 16 (1995), 448–461. (Cited on p. 207)

[343] R. Westwick, A theorem on numerical range, *Linear and Multilinear Algebra*, 2 (1975), 311–315. (Cited on p. 108)

[344] H. Weyl, Das asymptotische Verteilungsgesetz der Eigenwerte linearer partieller Differentialgleichungen (mit einer Anwendung auf die Theorie der Hohlraumstrahlung), *Mathematische Annalen*, 71 (1912), 441–479. (Cited on p. 22)

[345] R. C. Whaley, A. Petitet, and J. J. Dongarra, Automated empirical optimizations of software and the ATLAS project, *Parallel Computing*, 27 (2001), 3–35. (Cited on p. 447)

[346] O. B. Widlund, A Lanczos method for a class of nonsymmetric systems of linear equations, *SIAM Journal on Numerical Analysis*, 15 (1978), 801–812. (Cited on pp. 211, 391)

[347] H. W. Wielandt, Unzerlegbare, nicht negative Matrizen, *Mathematische Zeitschrift*, 52 (1950), 642–648. (Cited on p. 141)

[348] J. H. Wilkinson, *The Algebraic Eigenvalue Problem*, Clarendon Press, Oxford University, Oxford, 1965. (Cited on p. 61)

[349] R. Winther, Some superlinear convergence results for the conjugate gradient method, *SIAM Journal on Numerical Analysis*, 17 (1980), 14–17. (Cited on p. 284)

[350] P. Wolfe, The Reduced Gradient Method, Technical Report, The RAND Corporation, Santa Monica, CA, 1962. (Cited on p. 381)

[351] Z. I. Woźnicki, *Two-sweep iterative methods for solving large linear systems and their application to the numerical solution of multi-group, multi-dimensional neutron diffusion equation*, Doctoral Dissertation, Report Number 1447-CYFRONET-PM-A, Institute of Nuclear Research, SwierkOtwock, Poland, 1973. (Cited on p. 199)

[352] Z. I. Woźnicki, Nonnegative splitting theory, *Japan Journal of Industrial and Applied Mathematics*, 11 (1994), 289–342. (Cited on p. 201)

[353] M. H. Wright, Interior methods for constrained optimization, *Acta Numerica*, 1 (1992), 341–407. (Cited on p. 363)

[354] S. J. Wright, *Primal-Dual Interior-Point Methods*, SIAM, Philadelphia, 1997. (Cited on p. 363)

[355] S.-F. Xu, *Theory and Methods for Matrix Computations*, Peking University Press, Beijing, 1995. (In Chinese) (Cited on p. 207)

[356] P. Y. Yalamov and D. J. Evans, The WZ matrix factorisation method, *Parallel Computing*, 21 (1995), 1111–1120. (Cited on p. 54)

[357] D. M. Young, *Iterative Methods for Solving Partial Difference Equations of Elliptic Type*, Ph.D. Thesis, Harvard University, 1950. (Cited on p. 178)

[358] D. M. Young, *Iterative Solution of Large Linear Systems*, Academic Press, New York, 1971. (Cited on pp. 176, 191, 192, 193, 387)

[359] H.-Y. Zha, A numerical algorithm for computing the restricted singular value decomposition of matrix triplets, *Linear Algebra and Its Applications*, 168 (1992), 1–25. (Cited on p. 72)

[360] C.-Y. Zhang and M. Benzi, P-regular splitting iterative methods for non-Hermitian positive definite linear systems, *Electronic Transactions on Numerical Analysis*, 36 (2009/10), 39–53. (Cited on p. 210)

Subject Index